M

Buildings and Health

THE ROSEHAUGH GUIDE

To the Design, Construction, Use and
Management of Buildings

Buildings and Health

THE ROSEHAUGH GUIDE

To the Design, Construction, Use and
Management of Buildings

Editors

**Steve Curwell, Chris March
and Roger Venables**

RIBA Publications

© Rosehaugh Environmental (Technical Services) Ltd 1990

Published by
RIBA Publications Ltd
Finsbury Mission, 39 Moreland Street, London EC1V 8BB

ISBN 0 947877 78 9

Technical and coordinating editor: Roger Venables
Publishing editor: Alaine Hamilton

Book design: Penny Mills
Typeset by Tony Mills

Printed by Richard Clay Ltd, Bungay

FOREWORD

Godfrey Bradman
Chairman, Rosehaugh plc

It is currently impossible to pick up a newspaper without seeing some reference to environmental problems and the steps being taken by Governments, companies and individuals to address them.

Often the problems appear intractable and yet there is a growing determination that they must be effectively tackled if we are not to pass on to succeeding generations a world more heavily polluted and with greater environmental problems than those which we inherited.

For all those involved in shaping the built environment, the environmental challenge has never been more pressing. The threats to health caused by leaded paintwork, old leaded pipes and asbestos have been apparent for some time and alternative materials are now routinely used. But the past decade has brought to light a whole series of new environmental and health problems directly related to the buildings in which we live and work. Sick building syndrome, Legionnaires' disease and the widespread use of CFCs in building materials are the most well known of these recently identified threats.

As a contribution towards a better understanding of the health risks posed by some building materials and the alternatives which were available to them, I commissioned in 1985 a book which brought together accumulated knowledge across a range of professional disciplines. *Hazardous Building Materials: A Guide to the Selection of Alternatives* generated a surprisingly large response and it became obvious that not only was my concern widely shared, but that the subject itself was a much bigger one than had previously been imagined.

The recent introduction of the Control of Substances Hazardous to Health (COSHH) regulations has given a new urgency to a fuller understanding on the part of manufacturers and specifiers of the potential health risks of all products used in buildings. The five years since the publication of *Hazardous Building Materials* have also seen the emergence of new health risks and of materials and operating practices which can minimise them. It was therefore timely to produce a new book which updates and expands on that initial publication. This is what *Buildings and Health* attempts to do. By bringing together the latest

information from a range of experts in respect of the major
environmental concerns affecting the building industry, it should provide
both a major step forward in our understanding of the issues and a
practical guide for action and, I hope, stimulate the serious debate which
must take place.

Our environment is to a significant extent affected by the buildings in
which we live and work. I hope that this book will make a positive
contribution towards ensuring that sound environmental decisions are
taken at all stages of the building process.

All those involved in the commissioning, design and maintenance of
property bear a heavy responsibility to act in an environmentally
responsible way.

FOREWORD

Maxwell Hutchinson
President of the Royal Institute of British Architects

As the country's largest industry and largest employer of manpower, the construction industry has a particular responsibility for the quality of the nation's buildings and infrastructure. As Godfrey Bradman argues, all those in the construction and property industries have a special responsibility for promoting and preserving the quality of the built environment.

The widely publicised global environmental hazards are now coming home to roost, and those with the responsibility for designing and commissioning buildings must harden their determination to take the lead by instituting and carrying through standards of practice that will diminish health threats to us all as individuals, and start to make up lost ground in the world as a whole.

At least a start has been made. Global warming is now a global issue. It is recognised that one country's power stations are another's acid rain. At national and international level the task of setting out new regulations and prescribing tough standards for a sustainable environment has been tackled with enthusiasm and commitment, but the wheels inevitably grind slowly and time is not on our side.

Rosehaugh's initiative in commissioning this book must be applauded by us all. It demonstrates that a considerable body of knowledge is beginning to develop; it shows us that technology is starting to put into our hands the means of confronting our environmental problems and eventually controlling them.

Although the process of damage and deterioration has only started its about-turn, we must all use our influence to make sure that the construction industry, at every level and throughout all its disciplines, uses its strength to make sure that the right choices are made at the drawing board, in specifications, and on site.

The Royal Institute of British Architects has made its position and commitment clear. At the end of 1989 it published its Environmental Policy Statement − a green mandate to all architects obliging them to seek their clients' specific instructions on all matters to do with environmentally-sensitive design. But will others in the construction industry follow suit? They cannot afford not to – so much is at stake. This important book spells out the reasons why, and the practical steps which can be taken to guard our health, our environment, and the longevity of the planet itself.

Maxwell Hutchinson

CONTENTS

CONTRIBUTORS

John Addison BSc is Head of the Mineralogy Section in the Chemistry and Mineralogy Group at the Institute of Occupational Medicine Ltd (IOM), Edinburgh. He was educated in Stirling and received a BSc Honours degree in Geology from the University of Glasgow. He joined IOM in 1978 after research work at the Hunterian Museum in Glasgow. At IOM he is responsible, among other things, for the identification and quantification of minerals in airborne dusts and bulk samples using a wide range of analytical techniques. His research has involved extensive studies of coal-mine dusts, asbestos minerals, toxicity of asbestos and other minerals, analysis of asbestos in autopsy cases and oil-shale studies. He is closely involved in a number of IOM Instruction Courses, has acted as a consultant mineralogist in a number of cases, and is author of over 25 scientific publications.

Paul Appleby BSc(Hons) CEng MCIBSE MASHRAE is Managing Director of Building Health Consultants Ltd, a London-based company which specialises in the diagnosis, prevention and alleviation of building-related illnesses and indoor environmental problems. He also runs a consultancy practice based in Norwich, offering a range of expert services to the construction and manufacturing industries. He has over 20 years' experience in the building services industry, in consultancy and contracting, research and lecturing. He is an internationally recognised expert on building-related health problems, air-conditioning, ventilation and room air movement, having published widely in these and other areas. Much of his consultancy has concerned the investigation and solution of problems associated with buildings and their services. He is actively involved in writing, conferences and committee work for the Chartered Institution of Building Services Engineers and the British Occupational Hygiene Society, making important contributions to professional guidance and standards.

Mike Bailey MSc CBiol MIBiol is a Director of, and Occupational Safety Consultant to Building Health Consultants Ltd. He is a biologist with a special interest in occupational health. He has been acting as a consultant to property developers, building managers, property service managers and to General Managers in the Health Service for the past five years. He has extensive experience of buildings and building water systems and has written guidance and many articles on the prevention of Legionnaires' Disease.

Peter Bateman FIPR FAIE FRES MCIM MSOFHT MCAM is Director of Public Relations for Rentokil Ltd, and a past President of the British Pest Control Association. He has also completed five years on the Council of the Society of Food Hygiene Technology and is a former advisor to the College for the Distributive Trades. Author of 'Household Pests', he also lectures, writes and broadcasts regularly on matters relating to the working environment, including public health and pest control, and the maintenance of a range of building services in commercial and industrial premises, from treatment of air-conditioning and water systems to the provision of specialist washroom services. After eight years' commercial experience with Unilever, he has spent the past 28 years advising on subjects as diverse as dry rot and insulation to electrostatic air filters and the value of green foliage plants indoors. His work on the BPCA's legislation working party led to joint consultations with Government on recent pest control regulations and food hygiene law, and contributed to the lifting of Crown Immunity.

Peter Bodsworth BSc DipOccHyg MRSC MIOH is a Senior Occupational Hygienist at the Institute of Occupational Medicine which he joined in 1978. His previous experience was with Thomas Ness Coal Products' Technical Service. He has been involved in projects both underground and on the surface of mines. As well as being fully underground-trained, he also has substantial experience in measuring environmental conditions in collieries, including dust and fumes. He has been responsible for managing underground teams carrying out research in respirable dust and quartz exposures from men working in mines. His expertise also includes the measurement and control of diesel fumes, dust formation and control measures for a variety of mining machines including face machines, ripping machines, and roof supports. His non-mining work includes respirable dust and quartz measurements in quarries, acting as an expert witness in litigation cases involving asbestos, surveys of welding fume and its control, surveys of the thermal environment and implementing control measures and carrying out noise surveys for both occupational health and community-related reasons. He is a Member of the Council of the Institute of Occupational Hygienists and a qualified National Measurement Accreditation Service (NAMAS) asbestos assessor.

Alan Bradley DipOccHyg MIOH MIOSH is Director of Occupational Hygiene at the Institute of Occupational Medicine Ltd (IOM) based on the Edinburgh Headquarters and three out-stations. He joined the National Coal Board in 1955 and worked for five years as a laboratory technician and underground as a dust control engineer. In 1960 he joined the Pneumoconiosis Field Research Unit where he took part in underground environment surveys and analysis of samples. On the formation of the IOM in 1970, he became the Regional Investigator responsible for the IOM's field operations in the north of England and Scotland. During this period he took a one-year sabbatical at Newcastle University to study occupational hygiene and subsequently qualified as a professional occupational hygienist. The Occupational Hygiene Service at IOM carries out environmental management, survey work, environmental control and litigation consultancies on an international basis. Mr Bradley has also acted as project leader on many major research projects notably in the field of dust monitoring strategies and dust control.

Stephen Curwell BSc MSc RIBA is an architect and Principal Lecturer and Course Leader for the BA Honours Degree in Architecture at Leeds Polytechnic. He lectured to the honours degree courses in Quantity Surveying, Building Surveying and Environmental Science at the University of Salford from 1979 to 1986. His architectural education was undertaken at Queens University of Belfast where he graduated in 1973. In addition to his work in the field of buildings and health, he has completed a range of building technology research and consultancy projects including buildability, housing quality, computer-aided design, and building defects. He is co-author and editor of *Hazardous Building Materials: A Guide to the Selection of Alternatives*, co-author of *CFCs in Buildings* and has published numerous papers in the field of health and buildings. Mr Curwell is a member of the Royal Institute of British Architects' Environment and Energy Group and is convenor of that committee's Hazardous Materials and Environmental Quality Working Party.

Jim Dodgson BSc DipEd FIOH was Head of the Environmental Branch at the Institute of Occupational Medicine, Edinburgh, from 1977 to 1988 and President of the British Occupational Hygiene Society from 1981 to 1982. He is now a consultant in occupational hygiene. He has considerable experience in environmental research, having published over 50 research papers in this field, including several on asbestos and man-made mineral fibres. He led the environmental studies of conditions in the European man-made mineral fibre industry as part of the collaborative epidemiological investigations by several European Institutes which was organized by the Joint European Medical Research Board. He has also been responsible for the organization of the British Occupational Hygiene Society's quinquennial international symposia on inhaled particles, either as organizing secretary or chairman, since 1975.

Kenneth Fletcher BA(Cantab) PhD DipRCPath has been an independent consultant since 1983. He obtained a BA in biochemistry at Cambridge University in 1951 and a PhD at London University. He worked for the Medical Research Council for 13 years studying thyroid hormone at University College Hospital and Hammersmith Hospital and infantile malnutrition in Jamaica. In 1965 he joined ICI as joint manager of the toxicology laboratory with a main responsibility for pesticides. In 1976 he was seconded for two years as a consultant to the Health and Safety Executive. He has served as UK representative to OECD expert toxicology groups.

Christopher Forster BSc PhD FiChemE FIWEM is a Senior Lecturer in the School of Civil Engineering at the University of Birmingham. He obtained a BSc degree at the University of Hull in 1960 and a PhD at the University of Wales in 1971. He is the author of some 90 research papers and seven books in the area of wastewater treatment.

Professor Morris Greenberg MB FRCP FFOM is currently Visiting Professor, Division of Environmental and Occupational Medicine, Department of Community Health, Mount Sinai School of Medicine, City University, New York. He is a graduate of University College, London and University College Hospital Medical School, London University. His previous positions include Senior Medical Officer in the Division of Toxicology and Environmental Health, Department of Health, HM Medical Inspector of Factories, and Occupational Physician at Philips Industries. He has been an Honorary Lecturer at the Cardiothoracic Institute, London and Consultant to the World Health Organization, the International Labour Organization and the Commission of the European Communities. He has served on various BSI committees and learned societies, as well as Medical Secretary to various independent government committees. Publications include *Occupational morbidity and mortality studies.*

Roy Harrison BSc PhD FRSC FRMetSoc is the Director of the Institute of Aerosol Science, University of Essex. He obtained a BSc Honours degree in chemistry (1969), a PhD degree in organic chemistry (1972) and DSc in environmental chemistry (1989) at the University of Birmingham. His main interests are aerosol science, environmental chemistry, pollution control and environmental technology. He is a member or former member of a number of national committees and is World Health Organization Consultant on air pollution. He is on the editorial boards of several technical journals and is the author/co-author of about 150 publications.

Robin Howie DipOccHyg is a Senior Occupational Hygienist at the Institute of Occupational Medicine Ltd. He has been involved in most aspects of occupational hygiene since 1974, with particular emphasis upon Respiratory Protective Equipment (RPE) and the measurement and evaluation of the consequences of occupational exposure to noise. He has been responsible for all testing of RPE carried out by IOM and involved in field evaluation of wearability, in the preparation of British Standard Specifications and in the development of new devices. He has been particularly involved in all aspects of occupational noise including both measurement of exposure and evaluation of the effects of noise exposure on hearing ability.

John Hume BSc PhD is Senior Research Manager with Warrington Fire Research (London). He has over 16 years' experience in the chemistry of uncontrolled fires having taken part in many full-scale tests in that time. This work includes collaborative projects with the Department of the Environment on the mechanism of smoke formation and with the European Space Agency and the Ministry of Defence on the problems of plastics off-gassing. He was responsible for gas analysis during the Ronan Point fire test conducted by the Fire Research Station. The results of his work have been presented at various international conferences and in the scientific literature. Most recently he has been responsible for the development of the United Kingdom's first Cone Calorimeter and its use as a predictive tool for full scale heat release, smoke and toxic gas yields. He has a PhD in Chemistry and has specialised in Analytical Chemistry with particular emphasis on analysis of airborne hazards from both industrial processes and accidental fires using combinations of Mass and Infra-red Spectroscopy with Gas Chromatography.

Robert Lowe MA PhD is a Lecturer at Leeds Polytechnic Department of Architecture and Landscape. He lectured in the Department of Building Science at Sheffield University from 1984 to 1986. He studied Physics at Cambridge and graduated in 1977. He was a post-graduate student and research fellow (1982–1984) at the Energy Research Group of the Open University. In 1983 he completed a Doctoral Thesis in Generation of Electricity from Wind Power. During the period 1982–1984, he managed the largest field trial of highly insulated and passive solar houses in the United Kingdom. He is author of numerous papers in journals and conferences on subjects of wind power, low energy housing, combined heat and power, and energy and the environment.

Chris March BSc(Tech) MCIOB is Senior Lecturer and Course Director for the BSc degree in Construction Management at the University of Salford. He has also had experience in industry as production controller with John Laing Construction Ltd, and then as production manager and factory manager at John Laing Concrete Ltd. He is co-author and editor of *Hazardous Building Materials: A Guide to the Selection of Alternatives* and co-author of *CFCs in Buildings*. He has also published a number of papers in the field of health and buildings.

Jon Miles BA MSc is head of a group at the National Radiological Protection Board (NRPB) carrying out surveys of occupational and domestic exposure to radon, investigating the behaviour of radon and its decay products, and developing measurement techniques and radon preventive measures. He has worked at the NRPB for the past 15 years, initially on neutron dosimetry and then on radon. He has been involved in the development of standards for the measurement of radon and radon decay products, and has organized four international intercomparisons of measurement techniques for the Commission of the European Communities. His BA in Physics at Lancaster University was followed by an MSc at Manchester by thesis on development of a transfer instrument for neutron dosimetry.

Andrew Nicholl BSc MPhil CertOccHyg is a Senior Occupational Hygienist at the Institute of Occupational Medicine Ltd in Edinburgh. He has a wide range of experience in ergonomics and occupational hygiene, having worked in these areas for British Steel Corporation, Ergolab AB of Sweden and the National Coal Board before joining IOM. Specific studies have included the ergonomic factors of wearing ear protectors, the interaction effects of heat and noise in industrial tasks, thermal conditions in mining, active man-cooling, and dust formation at face ends.

John Rees BSc PhD FRSA is currently Director of John F. Rees Environmental Consulting, and was recently Director and General Manager of Biotreatment Limited and a Director of Biotal Limited. He obtained a BSc Honours degree in biological sciences and chemistry from Leicester University in 1971 and a PhD at the University of London in 1974. He was elected FRSA in 1988. After working at the Harwell Laboratory and at the United States EPA he became a founder director of Biotal Limited in 1984. Dr. Rees has considerable technical background in landfill processes and contaminated land both with regard to assessment and resolution of problems. He has played the major role in directing and developing Biotal/Biotreatment's environmental business which encompasses treatment of toxic waste, landfill and land reclamation. He has published numerous scientific papers and has been a member of the organising committee of many national and international conferences on landfill and contaminated land.

Alastair Robertson BSc PhD is Director of Chemistry and Mineralogy at the Institute of Occupational Medicine Ltd. He graduated with a BSc Honours degree in chemistry in 1971 and completed his PhD in chemistry in 1976. For the past 10 years, he has been in charge of the Institute's extensive analytical chemistry laboratory which provides analyses of fibres, minerals, gases, vapours, metals and other dusts for research studies and consultancy in occupational health and related fields. In addition, he has been closely associated with research into gas and vapour health effects associated with exposure to oxides of nitrogen in coal-mines, the mineralogy of coal-mine dusts and their harmfulness to health, diesel fume exposure in coal mines and studies of exposure to quarry dusts. He is responsible for the contract analytical sampling service and related consultancy for third parties covering different types of industry. In parallel with these activities he has been an active member of a number of national and international committees involved in setting criteria levels for various substances. He has published 18 papers and reports on occupational hygiene matters.

Eddie Salter is managing director of SKC Ltd (Dorset) which is involved in air sampling for the environment. He has experience on gas chromatographic techniques, and has been involved in environmental analysis and monitoring of the atmosphere for many years. He has presented seminars in India and number of Scandinavian and European countries.

EurIng. David Shillito CEng FIChemE FRMetS is the Senior Technical Director of Cremer & Warner Ltd, based in their London office. He joined the firm in 1969 from a background in the chemical process industries and he specialised in environmental protection, safety and accident investigation. His consultancy practice is diverse, ranging from odour and dust nuisances to major accident investigations such as the Kings Cross Underground Station fire where he led the Cremer & Warner team as Consultants to the Court of Inquiry. The common theme through his consultancy work is that of interdisciplinary trouble-shooting, working with specialists from other disciplines. He is actively involved with the Institution of Chemical Engineers and is a Council Member of the Academy of British Experts.

Frank Smith BSc MIFireE MSFSE is a Senior Fire Consultant at Warrington Fire Research Consultants, where he is particularly involved in the fire safety design of buildings. He began his career in fire safety as a Technical Officer with the Fire Protection Association (FPA) where he answered queries and produced technical publications on fire safety matters. For a while he was editor of the FPA's journal 'Fire Prevention' before joining consulting engineers Ewbank Preece Ltd as a fire engineer. He is a member of the Society of Fire Safety Engineers and a member by examination of the Institution of Fire Engineers.

Paul Tomlinson BSc MSc MPhil MRTPI is a Senior Environmental Planner with Ove Arup & Partners' Environmental Group. He was educated at Sunderland Polytechnic, Imperial College and Newcastle University and gained a BSc in Environmental Studies, a MSc in Environmental Technology and a MPhil in Town and Country Planning. Since 1980 he has been working in Environmental Assessment having been employed by the University of Aberdeen in the research unit for Project Appraisal for Development Control which has subsequently become the Centre for Environmental Management and Planning Ltd (CEMP). In 1983 he worked for the Environment and Groundwater Water Research Institute in the University of Oklahoma before returning to CEMP. During 1987 he was employed by the South Lakeland District Council where he was responsible for economic development and countryside management policies. Since joining Ove Arup &

Partners in 1988, he has undertaken environmental assessments of numerous projects, including power stations, highways, new settlements and waste disposal schemes. He has overseas experience in environmental assessment, working for clients such as the World Health Organisation, the United Nations Economic Commission for Europe and others involving work in the People's Republic of China, India and other South-east Asian countries.

David Tong MSc is a Director of Building Use Studies Ltd and heads their research and consultancy team who work on health hazards in buildings. He is a psychologist by training but has always worked with architects and engineers. Previously he worked at the University of Surrey, investigating human factors in building design and management.

Mark Tyler MA(Oxon) LLM(Lond) is a solicitor with McKenna & Co in London. He is a member of the firm's Environmental Law Group which has an extensive practice embracing all aspects of English and European environmental law including planning law, construction, health and safety, and product liability. He advises major companies from the UK, Europe and North America on regulatory matters and liability, and has extensive experience of representing clients involved in prosecutions and claims for damages. He has published articles and presented seminars on liability and safety-related issues, and is co-author of the bi-monthly *McKenna & Co Environmental Law Bulletin.*

Roger Venables BSc(Eng) DipM CEng MICE MBIM MCIM ACGI is a Director of Venables Consultancy Services Ltd, which provides business development, computing, training, technical development and editorial services to the construction and offshore/underwater engineering industries. A civil engineering graduate of Imperial College, he worked for a major contractor on site and in the design office before gaining his membership of the Institution of Civil Engineers in 1973. His main professional experience at this time was on civil engineering projects for the oil industry. He then spent fifteen years with CIRIA, the Construction Industry Research & Information Association, including ten as a Research Manager and then General Manager of UEG, CIRIA's offshore engineering group. He gained substantial experience in the promotion and management of collaborative R&D, feasibility studies, market assessment studies, and the editing and preparation for publication of R&D results to practitioners in industry. The technical areas covered were wide-ranging, and included many aspects of offshore and underwater engineering, marine technology, civil engineering and building.

Ian Viney BSc is currently a business development manager and has been closely involved in the study and resolution of contaminated land problems since 1981. Whilst in the Environmental Safety Group, AERE he was involved in the study of the environmental problems associated with the landfilling of wastes and the factors influencing the production and control of landfill gas. Having graduated with a BSc Honours degree in environmental science from Swansea University in 1984 he joined Biotreatment Limited becoming responsible for assessment programmes on a wide range of former industrial sites and landfills. He has been involved in the development of innovative land decontamination techniques and has more recently played a significant role in the development of Biotreatment's environmental business.

Sheena Wilson BSc(Hons) practises as an independent consultant to developers and occupiers in the area of office buildings and user requirements, with emphasis on planning for office moves and health issues. She was a founder member and Director of Building Use Studies, a research and consultancy firm specialising in the preparation of design guidelines and briefing information on all types of buildings, but particularly offices. In 1985, she headed a nationwide statistical study of the incidence of sick building syndrome published as 'The Office Environment Survey'. Since then she has carried out a number of diagnostic studies of particular buildings. In 1988, she joined Jones Lang Wootton where much of her work involved advising on user requirements at the design stage of new office developments and on precautions against the risk of building-related illness. In addition to the Office Environment Survey, she has been the author of several major research studies such as 'Premises of Excellence' which documented methods of building management in large corporations. She is a frequent writer in a number of journals and an experienced public speaker.

UNITS USED IN THE TEXT

The following symbols for units have been used through the book. In some circumstances where it is considered that the use of symbols is unusual or could be misleading (for example 1 s^{-1} per person) the unit has been given in full in English (litres per second per person).

bq m^{-3} = becquerels per cubic metre (of air)

kg m^{-3} = kilograms per cubic metre

km = kilometre

kw = kilowatt

kwht = kilowatt hour thermal

m = metre

m^3 = cubic metres

mg = milligram

mg l^{-1} = milligrams per litre

mm = millimetre

mg m^{-3} = milligrams (of substance) per cubic metre (normally of air or earth)

µg dl^{-1} = micrograms per decilitre (100 millilitres)

µg l^{-1} = micrograms per litre

µm = micron, or 1×10^{-6} metres

ppb = parts per billion

ppbv = parts per billion by volume

ppm = parts per million

ppmv = parts per million by volume

Section A

Introduction/General Considerations

CHAPTER A1

INTRODUCTION / HOW TO USE THE GUIDE

Steve Curwell, Chris March and Roger Venables

Leeds Polytechnic, University of Salford, and
Venables Consultancy Services Ltd

OBJECTIVES – WHY A BOOK ON BUILDINGS AND HEALTH?

It is generally accepted that the quality of life and health of the majority of citizens of affluent Western countries has never been better. people are living longer, and have more 'creature comforts' and greater mobility than ever before. However, over recent years, it has also become clear that there has been a price to be paid for this progress through a wide range of environmental effects, many of them adverse. These effects are sometimes at the level of the individual, for example, the poisoning of a child who consumes old leaded paint, at the community level, such as river pollution from a leak at a chemical plant, at a national scale, such as acid rain damage to forests, or even at a global scale, such as the recently discovered problem of depletion of the ozone layer.

The construction industry plays a leading role in our development of environmental quality. All involved in commissioning, designing and constructing buildings and other aspects of our infrastructure will continue to shape the form of our human settlements. The quality of the built environment affects its inhabitants in fundamental ways, and is dependent not only on the architectural form and specification, but on the quality and nature of the materials used, the care taken in construction, the quality of the building services design and components, the timely and effective maintenance of the building fabric and support systems, and the energy efficiency of the design and operation of the finished building. In addition, complex interactions between these factors often make ideal solutions to different problems mutually incompatible. For example, combining the highest quality air-conditioning systems, the flexibility for occupiers of opening windows, and the highest-possible level of energy efficiency cannot be achieved. Difficult compromise decisions often have to be made.

Public attitudes to environmental issues, health and risk are developing fast, but they remain inconsistent. The public are prepared to tolerate far greater hazards, statistically speaking, such as those associated with motor transport, than those encountered in buildings (Royal Commission on Environmental Pollution, 1984). It seems that a lack of individual control over the environment and the decision-making process for the construction of a building greatly affects what people perceive as acceptable hazards.

Developments in science and medicine continue to improve our understanding of the effects of materials, industrial processes, and man's own actions on the environment and human beings. The experience with asbestos shows clearly that indications today that a material is harmless to humans do not mean discovery of a hazard in the future will never occur.

It was to address these issues that this book was first conceived. An earlier book on hazardous building materials (Curwell and March, 1986) drew together for the first time 'accumulated knowledge in different disciplines to help in the selection and evaluation of more safe and suitable building materials'. This book extends much of the earlier work to design and construction, to the indoor and external environments, and to the wider environmental issues now so much at the forefront of individual and political concern. The specific aims have been:

- to draw attention to the increasing concern about the built environment;
- to describe the hazards to health which occur during the construction, use, maintenance, refurbishment and demolition of buildings;
- to give guidance to all those involved in the construction process (clients, developers, specifiers, designers, surveyors, contractors, maintenance teams, and demolition contractors) about how they can influence specific hazards and health issues they may face in their work – how they could design and build safer buildings;
- to highlight the balances that have to be struck between competing pressures (such as between energy conservation and the desire for air-conditioning);
- to describe the legislative framework in which building development and construction takes place;
- to highlight the impact of building developments on the wider environmental issues such as ozone depletion and global warming, and the measures the building industry can take to reduce that impact;
- to contribute to and stimulate the continuing debate about these issues and to indicate how some of them can be resolved.

The Guide is intended to be of use and interest to everyone connected with the construction industry, but it is aimed primarily at those who design and specify buildings, and their related materials, equipment and components, those who manage and maintain buildings, and those who use and occupy them. It is therefore of direct interest and concern to construction professionals, namely architects, structural engineers, building services engineers, interior designers, surveyors, contractors, as well as to those who commission buildings in both the public and private sectors.

A HISTORICAL PERSPECTIVE

It is now very difficult for us to imagine the period before the advent of modern medicine, when epidemics of fatal or crippling disease were common and major industrial diseases were accepted as a necessary byproduct of the way that certain people earned their living, and so it is easy to lose sight of the reasoning behind regulations both at the workplace and for the design and construction of buildings.

Some of the major steps in environmental and health improvements of the past, which were usually associated with advances of medical understanding, illustrate the interrelationship between the built environment, health, and living and working conditions.

Although the need for good sanitation was understood long before the Romans, its importance was rediscovered in the early Victorian period. Epidemics of typhoid fever in the squalid overcrowded conditions prevalent in the burgeoning industrial towns brought home the close link between poor housing, water supply, inadequate sanitation and disease. The construction of reservoirs and distribution systems together with effective drainage and sewage treatment brought about major improvements in public health. Regulatory developments of this period provide the basis for the present building regulations and practice on the spacing of buildings and for sanitation. Thus a major assumption of this book is that effective sanitation is provided by compliance with regulations, and the subject is not covered further.

The development of steam technology from the 1840s onwards combined with the continuing exploitation of coal reserves for heating led to major air pollution in towns and cities. In the 1940s and early 1950s, London 'smog' every autumn may have been the subject of music hall jokes, but this was lost on those who suffered serious respiratory complaints as a result of it. The Clean Air Act of 1956 had the effect of limiting the burning of untreated coal and effected a major change in fuel use. Unfortunately, the improvements in the external air quality in the majority of UK cities brought about by this legislation have been largely negated by the pollution caused by the rapid expansion of motor transport.

Deaths from mesothelioma, a tumour of the chest cavity caused by occupational exposure to asbestos dust many years before, brought the realisation that work could literally be the 'death of you'. However, serious industrial diseases had long been recognized and accepted as part of the job, e.g. miners' 'black lung', and impaired hearing in the textile industries. As a result of the development of occupational medicine and epidemiology and the general advance of science, the causes of many illnesses were found to be associated with the workplace. As working people became more affluent, the trade unions more powerful, and as expectations about the quality of life increased, workers and the population in general became less tolerant of circumstances that created such diseases. Improved working conditions followed regulations to control specific industrial diseases, which were eventually superseded by the Health and Safety at Work etc Act in 1974. This placed a duty of care on all employers to protect their workers and also, significantly, on the worker to protect himself by using the safety procedures and equipment recommended. The Act led to a much greater understanding of the effect on health of a wide range of materials, and to this day research work undertaken to assess risks to workers in a range of differing situations provides the basic data from which the 'control limits' for exposure of the general population are extrapolated.

General environmental contamination or hazard can also result from incorrect or irresponsible disposal of hazardous materials, and this is now controlled by regulation. Asbestos and radioactive materials are obvious examples. However, the 150 years of industrialization, from the Industrial Revolution to today, have left a legacy of contamination which is only just beginning to be appreciated as we redevelop derelict industrial areas.

ENSURING ADEQUATE HEALTH 'QUALITY'

Medical provision in the United Kingdom costs billions of pounds each year. It is aimed primarily at curing and preventing disease, and so a definition of good health must include the absence of disease. However, the World Health Organization's definition given in 1961 (Mant and Muir Gray, 1986) is broader, going beyond the absence of disease or infirmity to the provision of a state of complete physical, mental and social well-being. As the living and working environment will have a major influence on an individual's sense of well-being, this broader concept of health overlaps the aims and objectives of building design considerably. The concept of comfort, one of the primary aims of buildings after the provision of shelter and security, is synonymous with 'well-being'. Studies of 'sick buildings' have drawn a connection between poor comfort conditions and symptoms of ill health in the users.

The attributes of healthy life have been defined by Mitchell (1984) as:

- a clean and safe environment;
- time for rest and recreation;
- a reasonable living standard;
- freedom from chronic worry;
- hope for the future;
- an adequate level of self-confidence and autonomy;
- having a worthwhile and fulfilling job.

Clearly the majority of these are influenced by society as a whole, but they give an insight into the influences that affect an individual's sense of well-being.

Most of the building- and environment-related problems described in this Guide are concerned with measures to control serious ill-health, but many also relate to materials or methods of building that may cause the worker or user to suffer minor irritation or ailments. Thus the broader definition of health is taken as the basis for a number of the recommendations. However, an individual's concept of a 'clean and safe environment' will be influenced, as mentioned earlier, by his or her perception of the risk involved.

The health effects of chronic low level exposure to many materials remains very difficult to assess. The reasons for this are numerous, but an understanding of the way that science and medicine attempt to establish the hazards may be helpful. The two main methods are toxicology and epidemiology. Toxicological research provides early indication of the possible health effects of new materials, e.g. by means of experimental work on laboratory animals and/or tissue samples, but the relationship of such work to health effects in man and true environmental conditions is always difficult to interpret. Epidemiological research of necessity lags behind material developments, which inevitably means that the population's health may be at risk in the intervening period. Large-scale trials are usually undertaken which attempt to eliminate or consider the effects of other environmental factors beyond those under investigation. This is extremely difficult, as it is almost impossible in the normal situation to identify the dose of, or exposure to, any contaminant that an individual might receive in buildings. Factors such as the form of the material (solid or gas), its location in the building, the probable ventilation rate, the possibility of wear or erosion of the material, periods of occupation, maintenance requirements etc. all play a part.

ISSUES OF CONCERN IN CONSTRUCTION PROJECTS

Some of the issues of concern for those involved in construction projects are set out below in relation to the stages in the development cycle.

Overall project design
- the scale of the development in relation to its surroundings, its occupants and the local ecology;
- overall strategy for selection of materials;
- overall ventilation and energy strategies;
- building form, provision of atria and other amenity areas, and their effect on the comfort of occupants;
- treatment of, and designing to take account of, contaminated land;
- environmental assessment.

Planning and land use
- location of developments in relation to transport and other infrastructure;
- energy use and conservation in the construction and use of buildings;
- the presence of naturally occurring hazards such as radon;
- identification and treatment of contaminated land.

Demolition
- identification of contaminants and their safe treatment or disposal;
- controlled disposal of asbestos and other fibrous materials;
- control of dusts and fumes;
- control of pests in a building to be demolished which may remain on site to affect any new development.

Detailed building design
- detailed strategy for selection of materials;
- detailed ventilation and energy strategies, and their interaction;
- specific actions aimed at reducing the likelihood of sick building syndrome occurring;
- actions to take account of natural hazards such as radon and pests.

Construction phase
- protective measures for handling hazardous materials;
- control of dusts, fumes, solvents and gases;
- control of materials purchasing to ensure unspecified substitute materials are not used;
- adherence to the Control of Substances Hazardous to Health Regulations;
- secure storage of materials before use;
- control of noise, both on and off site;

- control of pests;
- control of site drainage.

Building occupancy and maintenance
- lingering odours and/or contaminants from the construction phase;
- adequate indoor air quality;
- management action to avoid sick building syndrome;
- management action to avoid Legionnaires' Disease;
- allergic response to building material components;
- timely and effective maintenance;
- selection of materials for maintenance work;
- pest control.

Refurbishment
- identification of contaminants and their safe treatment or disposal;
- controlled disposal of asbestos and other fibrous materials;
- control of dusts and fumes;
- pest control.

Wider environmental issues
- selection and efficient use of materials;
- reduction of use of CFC-containing materials;
- use of timber from sustainable supplies;
- energy conservation/energy strategy for building design, construction and operation;
- the balances to be struck between competing demands, for example the interaction between energy and ventilation strategies;
- the next 'safe' material discovered to be hazardous after all.

ABOUT THE GUIDE

The Guide is in five sections:

✳ Section A chapters set the book in the context of the stages in the development cycle, current concerns about buildings and health, and the developing environmental debate, introduce the process of assessment of risk and the legislative framework in which building development and construction now take place.

✳ Section B on Materials and the Building Structure, and Section C on the Internal and External Environments provide information and guidance on a number of materials, building services, systems and

Figure A1.1 The relationship of the book chapters to stages in the building development cycle

Stage in the development cycle Chapter	A1	A2	A3	B1	B2	B3	B4	B5
Overall project design	√	√	√		√		√	
Planning and land use	√	√	√		√			
Demolition	√	√	√	√	√	√	√	√
Detailed building design	√	√	√		√		√	√
Construction phase	√	√	√	√	√		√	
Building occupancy and maintenance	√	√	√	√	√	√	√	√
Refurbishment	√	√	√	√	√	√	√	√
Wider environmental issues	√	√	√		√			√

environmental matters, and the hazards associated with them, with (wherever possible) practical guidance on action that can be taken by construction professionals to reduce the identified hazards.

✴ Section D on the Wider Environmental Impact provides guidance on the environmental assessment of building projects, and the impact of building projects and the actions of their designers on two of today's major environmental concerns – reduction of emission and use of CFCs, and energy consumption and the 'greenhouse effect'.

✴ Section E provides some overall conclusions, like this introduction related to the stages in the development cycle, and sets an agenda and questions for the continuing debate on buildings and health.

Figure A1.1 relates the structure and individual chapters to the same stages in the development cycle used above and in the Overall Conclusions.

The book has been written by a group of invited specialist authors, each given a broad brief to provide their contribution to the need for guidance and the continuing debate about how buildings affect individuals' health. Two commissioning editors, who had prepared the earlier book on hazardous building materials and with considerable expertise in this area, selected the subject titles and authors, and provided a number of chapters themselves. Finally, an independent consultant with a construction, technical development and publishing background has been overall editor and prepared this Introduction and the Overall Conclusions in conjunction with his colleagues on the project.

B6	B7	B8	C1	C2	C3	C4	C5	C6	C7	C8	C9	D1	D2	D3	E
√	√	√	√	√	√	√	√				√	√	√	√	√
	√					√					√	√		√	√
√	√				√		√	√			√				√
√	√	√	√	√	√	√	√	√	√	√		√	√	√	
√	√						√			√					√
√		√	√	√	√	√	√	√	√				√	√	
√	√	√	√	√	√		√	√			√	√	√	√	√
	√				√				√		√	√	√	√	√

REFERENCES

Curwell, S.R. & March, C.G., *Hazardous Building Materials: A Guide to the Selection of Alternatives*, E. & F.N. Spon, London, 1986

Mant, D.C. and Muir Gray, J.A. (1986), *Building Regulation and Health*, BRE Report, Building Research Establishment, Garston.

Mitchell, J. (1984), *What is to be Done about Illness and Health?*, Penguin, Harmondsworth.

Royal Commission on Environmental Pollution (1984), *Tenth Report, Tackling Pollution — Experience and Prospects*, HM Stationery Office, London, p. 16.

THE ASSESSMENT OF RISK

David Shillito

Cremer & Warner Ltd

INTRODUCTION

The assessment of risk is a relatively simple process involving three stages:

- *Hazard identification*, which involves awareness of the existence of the hazard, and then identifying what the hazard actually is;
- *Risk analysis*, which involves analysis of the hazard, the chances of it occurring, and the range of consequences which can result if the hazard should occur;
- *Risk handling*, which concerns what to do about the risk, and can involve avoidance, prevention, protection, insurance, or just accepting it.

There is nothing new about this process. It is used consciously and subconsciously by all people in dealing with everyday risks, such as crossing a road or negotiating a winding staircase and by decision-makers from all walks of life, the punter on the race course, the city financier, the innovator or entrepreneur, and the technician servicing the evaporative cooling tower.

The term 'risk assessment' has become associated with the process of safe design of high hazard installations in industries such as nuclear power generation, chemical processing, and liquid and gaseous fuel processing, storage and distribution. This still relatively new technology has its own jargon, numerical methods and criteria of acceptability (or tolerability). As the technology has grown it has specialised, and developed a focus on the consequential risk of death or serious injuries both at the installation and in the local community (termed societal risk). It has also tended to drift away from the problems of everyday life.

Even with highly automated process plants, human error can play a substantial part in risk analysis. Failure rates of say electrical or mechanical components are much more easily quantified than 'human factors'. Human error, and the production of 'unforgiving mistakes', is a function of management systems and corporate psychology or sociology.

However, Quantitative Risk Assessment (QRA) has added substantially to the fund of knowledge of design. The most notable lessons from it are:

- There are substantial benefits in relation to the quality of the final product in bringing together the developer, designer and user at the outset.
- The use of numbers in the quantification of risks has improved the quality of the arguments being used, and this can have a radical influence on the quality of the decisions.
- Quantification also aids the translation of technological or scientific problems into a financial context.
- On detailed analysis, hazards and consequences are found to be highly interactive. Problem solving has to be a highly inter-disciplinary process.
- Detailed, inter-disciplinary analysis usually yields many more options than were thought to be available in the first place.
- The process often results in simple, practicable solutions.

Risk assessment is no more than a tool in the management tool box. The tool box itself can be called a wide variety of names, an appropriate name might be Total Quality Management, because the objective of the exercise is to enhance performance and ensure freedom from deficiencies

BUILDINGS & HEALTH

We spend 80 to 90% of our life in the built environment, so that environment is bound to have a profound effect on our health. The Constitution of the World Health Organisation states that 'Health is a state of complete physical, mental and social well-being, and not merely the absence of disease or infirmity'. To be healthy, our buildings must be comfortable enough to sustain the state of well-being, and they must be safe. It may be difficult to visualise conditions where social well-being and safety are not closely related; however, it must be remembered that both buildings and machines, once built, have to be used, serviced, maintained and modified. The building is important to the environment in which it stands. Buildings influence their physical environment, the access arrangements, roads, lighting, the wind field and water balance, and also the sociology of area. The sociology of the locality also has a considerable influence on the building use, and this too can reflect back on social well-being.

In the second half of the 1980s the changes in public attitudes to mass residential block housing can perhaps be attributed to the influence of Alice Coleman's book Utopia on Trial. Published in 1985, the book reported a study of 4099 blocks of flats in inner London and measured the association between each block's 'design disadvantagement scale' and indices of environmental degradation (litter, graffiti, vandal damage, excrement). There now appears to be a consensus view that building design has had a marked influence on social degradation in city life. There is a growing feeling that crime and safety cannot be disassociated from the design of the 'built environment'.

While the authorities and their planners may hope they can control the uses of an area and perhaps its sociology, power to influence these issues is concentrated in the hands of developers. If a developer can also 'improve' the locality through his project, then his financial risk will be well assured.

CONCEPT OF RISK

The concept of risk is usually associated with events which occur suddenly and consequences which are quickly apparent. A common accident in the home such as a fall on the stairs, with a heavy landing against a wall, might produce concussion, or injury to the person's back. However, chronic discomfort could influence that person's health for many years to come.

Similarly, events such as fires can produce psychological scars which can take many years to heal, if ever, particularly when people are badly burnt. For such people to feel comfortable in buildings, extraordinary precautions in design and style may be necessary. These 'extras' are necessary to enable the person to cope with his or her disability.

Health risks frequently result from prolonged exposure to environmental conditions. Often we are not conscious of these risks: either the consequences may appear to be too remote to be important, or their chance of occurrence is perceived to be too low to be real.

Asbestos, radon, legionella, sick building syndrome etc. all appear to have gone through cycles of 'notoriety', and no doubt these cycles will recur under different names and disguises. Each health scare has its own special impact by producing reactions in healthy communities and, in most cases, the reactions are beneficial, but sometimes they are excessive. Much stress has been caused over the perceived need for emergency remedial work – for example to remove asbestos from schools during term time. The over-reaction to any stimulus often produces more serious risks than those that provoked the reaction.

HOW ARE HAZARDS IDENTIFIED?

Engineers, architects or building users are bombarded with information about health risks. It comes in newspapers and television programmes, publications, textbooks, codes of practice and guidance. How is it used – proactively or only reactively?

Most professionals in handling a tricky problem will 'work to the book'. An architect commissioned to examine and report on an existing building may suspect problems with the heating and ventilation systems. The building services engineer may also produce a report. Those responsible for the building will use these opinions together with information about the costs of remedial action and then decide on the action to be taken. Solutions will often reflect the minimum acceptable standards of the design codes.

What about the users of the building? The office manager may be in the best position to recognise the existence of a problem with, say, the ventilation system. The personnel department may hold the staff sickness records, the accident records, and complaints made by individual workers. Will the office manager or personnel manager be consulted? Not often enough. An office worker suffering persistent health problems at work will usually take them to his or her general practitioner rather than to the company doctor even if there is one. How then does the company doctor learn about them? Many occupational health problems remain hidden because the information system of the building user is either ineffective or remains untapped.

The usual processes for the identification of a problem either at home or at work are reactive. The problem has to develop to a stage of being so major that, either due to importunity or fear of legal consequences, then 'something has to be done about it'. It usually takes this level of problem development before the users of buildings and the technical specialists are brought together. It is only at this level of development that the existence of the 'problem' can be formally accepted. Unfortunately, the first indications of incipient problems are from lack of comfort or loss of good health for the occupants. Similarly, the first symptoms of a lack of safety is an elevated level of small accidents. Often both occur together and are usually invisible to the management systems.

The risks may be there for all to see but it requires the combination of information from different sources to see them. All accident investigators have experienced the extreme clarity of hindsight.

The processes of designing, constructing and modifying buildings to improve standards of health will require closer and closer communications between designers, users and health specialists. This communication will involve the constructive development of ideas and concepts for the future as well as sorting out the problems of today.

HAZARDS

Buildings, like roads, are dangerous places, Tables A2.1 and A2.2, taken from the RoSPA Annual Report of 1988/9, clearly show the high level of accidents in the home is close to that on the roads. Most would agree that this situation is unacceptable, but perhaps the more dramatic finding is that accidents in the home produce six times the number of hospital cases than occur from road accidents. And by far the greatest cause of

Table A2.1 Accidents in the United Kingdom

	DEATHS	HOSPITAL CASES
Road	5,600	400,000
Home	5,100	2,400,000
Work	650	1,200,000
Sport/Leisure	400	1,000,000
Other Transport	250	
Other Falls	1,000	2,000,000
Others	1,000	
TOTAL	14,000	7,000,000

Table A2.2 Fatal Home Accidents in Great Britain 1987

Falls	2,957
Fires	744
Poisonings	492
Suffocation/choking	338
Others	449
TOTAL	4,980

fatal home accidents in Great Britain in 1987 were falls. Fires, perhaps surprisingly, are very much in second place.

Much international research has been undertaken on accidents in the home involving falls, and it appears to be accepted that, as an architectural element, stairs are the major cause. As with most other causes of accidents, the consensus view is that there is a strong need for improving the design of stairs to mitigate accidents, in particular, in preventing the occurrence of falls, and preventing injury as a result of the fall.

In looking at the design of a staircase, it is important to remember the conditions in which it will be used. The home staircase has to be safe not only for the elderly but also for teenagers and children. The emergency fire escape should be suitable for mass occupancy in stressful conditions. The modern office staircase may have only one hand rail and it is frequently closely bounded by glass windows, low walls and sharp edged radiators in the crash zone. Further impedimenta are provided; hose reels, fire extinguishers and large pot plants. A simple fall can thus result in serious injuries. How often does the safety officer pass by these hazards in order to inspect the hose reels?

Similar problems have been presented to the designers of cars. Impact with the front windscreen, the dashboard and steering wheel have been major causes of injury in head-on collisions. Primary protection has been provided in the seat belt (and the air bag). These devices have prevented injuries. Further safety measures have been added to the design; the use of padded surfaces, tighter glass specifications, collapsible steering wheels and crumple zones.

Higher standards of design safety are required to ensure that the conventional home and office staircase provides adequate protection to minimise injury from falls.

The main exposure to structural hazards in and around buildings is controlled by statutory regulations, codes of practice and by the ethical considerations of designers. This is amply demonstrated by the differences in fatalities resulting from the recent earthquakes of relatively similar magnitudes in California and Iran. But it must be remembered that, even in the UK, unusually intense storms such as those in October 1987 and February 1990 can cause immense damage. Where a storm produces flooding such as in Towyn in Wales in 1990, much of the damage is caused by contamination resulting from the sewerage system. It is necessary to review hazards from the wider natural environmental standpoint as well as the specific agents of the built environment.

Table A2.3 presents in summary form a list of hazards which should be considered in the design and use of buildings.

THE PROCESS OF RISK ASSESSMENT

The three processes involved are hazard identification, hazard analysis, and risk handling. The identification of hazards is the most important because it comes first. The other two processes follow on naturally from identification.

In the chemical process industries the assessment of risks has developed within the context of loss prevention. There, loss prevention applies to financial loss, a connection which has provided a vehicle for the development of 'safety engineering'. Loss prevention in the process industries is achieved by maintaining the unity of vision in the development of the project from conception to the progressive modification of the in-service plant.

Phases of Development and Risk Reviews

When risk assessment is used as a tool throughout the progressive phases of design and implementation of a project, it is normally used in 6 phases:

- Conceptual Design
- Preliminary Design
- Detailed Design
- Construction
- Commissioning
- Progressive in-use modification

Table A2.3 Possible Hazards for Buildings

ENVIRONMENT	MAIN BUILDING	INTERNAL SERVICES
Earthquake	Protection of service entry point to building	Ventilation:
Subsidence & heave		• rates for occupancy
Flooding by incursion, by rain & deluge	Axillary fuel storage	• comfort/environmental criteria
Frost	Fire safety design	• system reliability
	Fire escapes & evacuation	• removal of vapours
Snow		• area to area carry over
Hail	Air inlet location	• system hygiene
Lightning	Exhaust air location	Drinking water system
Wind by structural load, by projectiles, and effects on people	Internal water leakage	Services water system
	Drains	Hygiene systems
	Access to service systems	Foul sewerage
Light:	Cooling systems	Fire:
• too much		• prevention
• not enough	Pedestrian access	• protection
Water table change	Car parking: security, ventilation & fire proofing	• training
Contaminated land		Staircase safety
Radon	Materials of construction, eg mineral fibre insulation; wood treatments	Slippery floors
Social environment; vandalism, crime, terrorism		Window fall safety
		Pool & bath safety
Disease, vectors	Lifts & escalators	Electrical and gas systems
Legionella	Access for roof repairs	Stability of furniture
Gaseous effluents	Access for cleaning	Cleanability
Dust and fibre emissions	Tree roots & foundations	Lighting
Water system integrity	External lighting	Window cleaning safety
Sewage system integrity	Special facilities for the disabled, food preparation	Internal noise insulation
Vibration		Electrostatics
Noise	Security of money, computer power back-up, clean rooms, document security, storage of flammable & hazardous materials	Pest infestation control
Acid rain		Harmonic vibration
Global warming and ozone depletion		Colour harmony
Energy efficiency		Storage for hazardous chemicals

The phases may well overlap but the thorough assessment of risks at the initial stages is more important than in the latter stages because changes and improvements can be achieved more quickly and cheaply than later on. Indeed changes may not be possible at the later stages. However, early on, necessary project information is less readily available.

Planning is an essential element in any development and requires leadership and discipline. Where a formal structure of risk analysis is built into all stages of the development plan, the perceived impact of criticism can be made more acceptable by formalising a design review process.

Design Reviews

The central feature of the design review process is that it must involve every discipline involved with the design as a whole. A building is not just an external shell to house any particular use; it provides an enclosed working floor area with a specific controlled environment.

Conceptual design reviews are usually non-quantitative. The design review team should be carefully structured with members from each professional discipline and the representatives of the owner and, if possible, the user. The objective of the design, the design intention, is tabled. The role of the review team is communication between the disciplines to establish the details of the design policy and the way in which it can be implemented. This can involve materials, methods, programme, services, utilities, external/internal environment, and safety compliance with existing and future regulations. Much of the work may appear unnecessary and routine. It is only by reviewing the process that the unusual component can be recognised as it slowly becomes 'visible'.

Review meetings need not be long but they need to be formalised with a chairman and a secretary; the course of the discussion has to be planned. The product of these meetings is usually an acceptance of the need to cover certain areas of the preliminary design with greater care, and the need for more information on other areas such as materials and design.

The *Preliminary design review* is a similar but more detailed process. One factor at this stage might be the commissioning of separate studies, not only to fulfil statutory requirements, but also for other reasons such as 'peace of mind' or 'public relations'. For example, independent consultants might be used for an environmental assessment, or a fire safety assessment covering fire protection, safe evacuation and minimisation of financial loss. This would be the time to examine the design for tripping and falling safety, ventilation, the water system and other services.

The preliminary design stage reviews can prove invaluable in the production of the specification for the main contracts. Unless the harmony of the design intention can be built into the main contracts there is little hope of achieving the desired end product.

Detail design reviews involve assessment of the interaction of detail design work which may have been done by different teams or organisations. It is at this stage where the quantum of detail has become so large that it is usually difficult to find more than a few people who can retain the necessary unity of vision. At this stage too the cost of the project is starting to increase rapidly. Time schedules and budgets may be causing concern. Unless the principles of the earlier design review have been fully accepted and integrated within the design, deviations will start being justified on financial grounds. Detail design is completed with the signing-off of designs for construction.

Construction Phase Reviews

At this stage, the Project reviews should fall within the implementation of quality assurance plans formalised in the various contracts. By this stage, much of the inter-disciplinary work should have been completed and the results should be starting to be evident. The co-ordination role between the disciplines should become less stressful.

Commissioning and In-use Modification Reviews

These are usually undertaken with the preparation of 'punch lists', the building-up of checklists of items to be completed and interfaced. Preparation and evaluation of documentation becomes a further major task at this stage.

Commissioning can slide gently into 'in-use modification'. Where the final user of the building has not been involved in design, construction and perhaps not the commissioning, major re-working is the rule rather than the exception. This highlights one of the major elements of the commissioning stages which is the existence and validity of the project documentation. Even simple things can eventually become major headaches like the 'as built' drawings showing the location of the gas, electricity, water and sewage lines, the treatment and maintenance schedules for the cooling tower, the lifts etc.

The Functions of Design Review

Like risk assessment as a whole, design reviews have three functions:

- to identify hazards;
- to analyze the hazards and their consequences to produce an analysis of risk;
- to work out methods by which the risks can be handled.

These three functions can be combined into the overlying requirement of relating the design to its final use. It is the job of the design review team to ensure that the intentions of the design are translated effectively into buildings that are efficient and safe to use, so that the users can operate within them with complete health and safety. This introduces the concept of 'operation': the designers must consider the 'operations' within the installation which is the end product of their design.

While the designers may not be able to foresee all the operations which could be undertaken within their buildings, they should be capable of examining in detail the operations intended in the design concept. For example, in designing a facility to be used by large numbers of people, perhaps a football stadium, or a religious centre, the safe use of the public access ways is an architectural feature which must be given detailed attention. Fire safety in underground facilities places special requirements on 'area isolation', 'ventilation' and special consideration must be given to the ways materials behave in fires. Emergencies can occur in any building. Provision of facilities for handling such emergencies can be designed-in at little extra cost when the need is identified early on.

Buildings have to be cleaned, maintained, the equipment serviced. The limited space so frequently allocated for building services often places operational restraints on maintenance. This might be made more acceptable if high reliability equipment were specified. Again, facilities for monitoring the services can be essential to the user.

Hazard Identification requires a formal, structured meeting of minds from the different disciplines. The design is analyzed element by element in relation to its use. The hazards are identified as a result of consideration of the uses of the design and its operation. This is often called an Operability Study. Where Hazard Identification is a central purpose, the review is often called a 'Hazard and Operability Study' frequently abbreviated to HAZOP. This method is now used in the design concepts for nearly all high hazard industries. The food industries have developed a similar methodology known as Hazard Analysis and Critical Control Point Studies (HACCP).

A full HAZOP study involves the structured assessment of a design, line by line. A set of key words is used to consider the perturbations of operation to which the design must respond safely eg. temperature too high, pressure too low, flow too low etc.

Under the control of the Chairman, the HAZOP team 'as a single mind' assess the design. The Secretary records the findings on a spreadsheet. The team may analyze both the hazard and its consequences. They recommend modifications, or they may leave the risk assessment stage to other specialists in that field. It is usual for a HAZOP team to make recommendations for:

- small design improvements;
- further hazard analysis studies to refine the optimum solution to a problem;
- recommendations for problems to be solved by other means than changes in the design.

The HAZOP study is thus the design review methodology for the Detailed Design Stage. However, it can also be used in a more simple format for the analysis of the Preliminary Design or even the Conceptional Design. In these phases, where less information is available, the methodology is modified, and the result is often known as a First Stage Hazop or Coarse Hazop.

A note of caution is necessary at this stage. The HAZOP is not a simple cure-all. It is lengthy, time consuming, often boring and usually expensive. The Coarse Hazop, if properly performed by a good team, can be highly effective and can also be an interesting educative experience. In the wrong hands it can lack all these virtues.

Risk Assessment in high hazard industries usually involves probabilistic risk assessment methods. Fault tree methodology is frequently used for study of the development of the consequences.

A fault tree is a graphical representation of the logical relations between a particular 'top event', an accident or incident, and the primary causal events of the initiating circumstances. The state of the system is defined in terms of events and the variables. The two main elements of the trees are thus the 'event definitions' and the 'logic gates' which connect them. Logic gates are usually of two types: 'AND' or 'OR'. The AND gate exists only if all the inputs exist. To produce a gas explosion in the boiler room (the top event) requires a gas leak AND accumulation forming a flammable atmosphere AND a source of ignition. The OR gate exists where only one of the inputs is needed. Either the pilot light OR the electrical switch could provide the source of ignition.

The top event is developed down the branches of the tree to the intermediate fault events which are in turn developed to the primary failures. The fault tree is thus a simplified representation of the whole system. The probability of occurrence for each event can then be systematically combined to give the probability of the top event.

The event tree is similar. Whereas the fault tree starts from the top event, such as a gas explosion, and then works down, the Event Tree begins with a particular initial event and works from the bottom up.

In this way the consequences of an initial event, for example a temporary heavy ground load adjacent to the building walls, could be traced onwards: through the cracking of the gas pipe, the leakage of gas into the building, ignition at the light switch, to the top event of the gas explosion.

Such an quantitative assessment might reveal that the probability of occurrence of an accident is so low that no remedial measures can be justified. However, quantitative risk assessment is more often used to compare one design option with another. In this situation risk assessment can be used in conceptual design long before there are plans available for a HAZOP study.

Risk Handling can be, in general, accomplished in five ways. In logical order these are:

- Avoidance
- Prevention
- Protection
- Transfer (usually insurance)
- Acceptance.

These ideas are best illustrated by examples and Table A2.4 shows examples (which are not intended to be comprehensive) of how these principles can be applied to four of the hazards in British buildings.

CONCLUSION

✳ The assessment of risk is not a new concept: what is advocated here is the importance of being aware of the consequences which designs can produce. Good management practice requires awareness of what is likely to happen as a result of the actions of individual people. Once that awareness has been gained, the situation should be accepted and appropriate action taken.

✳ The identification, assessment and handling of risks should be placed in the right context. They are component parts in the processes of design, planning, implementation and usage. Most safety professionals may agree that most, if not all buildings can be modified to improve the health, safety and comfort of its occupants. This would suggest that something has gone wrong in the design and usage of buildings in the past. Designers, constructors and users of buildings have not 'got their act together'.

✳ Most designers are obsessed with their own professional preoccupations. The chief hazard facing the designer today is 'obsession'; obsession with external visual appearance, with value for money as in cost/unit floor area, with capital cost, ease of maintenance, interior design, building services, even with ease of access or car parking arrangements. Placing undue importance on any of these at the expense of the other uses of the building as a whole

Table A2.4 Examples of Risk Handling

	FALLING ON STAIRS	FIRES	LEGIONELLA	WOOD PRESERVATIVE
Avoidance	Live in a bungalow. Use efficient lifts and escalators.	Not really possible as people are flammable.	Use indirect cooling systems rather than evaporative cooling towers.	Use wood in design which does not require treatment (not very satisfactory).
Prevention	Avoid uneven risers or gradient, winders, deep pile carpets, provide two hand rails, avoid steep long narrow stair cases.	Avoid flammable materials have a no-smoking policy, good electrical design.	Use modular systems. Design for reliable water temperature control. Design for for cleanability.	Use substances which offer least risk (eg those with permethrin or boron as active ingredients).
Protection	Padding in crash zone, no glass, radiators, fire or pot plants to fall on to.	Sprinklers, fire extinguishers hose reels, training, protection of structural steel.	Ensure correct biocide usage – commission independent audit facility.	Operatives to wear effective personal protection. Make provision for bake-out of a building before occupancy.
Transfer	I　　N　　S　　U　　R　　A　　N　　C　　E			
Accept	Monitor performance to ensure that the risk is still acceptable.			

will lead to a lack of balance. This will affect the health, safety and comfort the building will provide.

* The message of the chapter is that design is an interdisciplinary process, and that everything is important even if some aspects must have priority at certain points in the programme. If possible, the approach to the risk assessment must be 'quantify-everything'; even if the numbers are at best only approximate, the process will still improve the quality of arguments in the assessment.

* Questions of health and comfort have the superficial appearance of being quite remote from safety and financial loss prevention: in fact they are closely associated. Densely populated, badly ventilated buildings are not likely to be cost-efficient. Sickness records, absenteeism, accident rates, error rates, time spent in restoration of production quality show this clearly. A single accident on a staircase can cost an employer much more than the simple modifications required to avoid serious injury. Surely such action must be a good investment.

* With larger accidents, the cost of modifications to in-use buildings together with the other consequential costs can produce a severe dip in the overall financial performance of a large company. Few organisations can afford the financial risks of large accidents. Few companies can dispense with the assessment of their risks in the design or use of their buildings.

* The only way in which risks to health can be treated is through effective communication between all those involved: designers, builders, users and researchers into health, safety and welfare. If a mission statement were required for the assessment of risk, it should perhaps be structured around the concept of assuring the efficient communication and cooperation between professionals to enable the product of their work to be 'fit-for-the-purposes' for which they were designed. This is design for improvement of the quality of life.

REFERENCES AND FURTHER READING

A Guide to hazard and operability studies, Chemical Industries Association, London, 1987

Coleman, A , with Brown, F , Cottle, I., Marshall, P., Redknap, C., and Sex. R., *Utopia on Trial*, Hilary Shipman, London, 1985

Dickson, G.C.A., *Risk Analysis*, Institute of Risk Management, 1987

Institution of Chemical Engineers, *HAZOP and HAZAN*, IChemE, Rugby 1986

Institution of Chemical Engineers, *Risk assessment in the process industries*, IChemE Publications, Rugby, 1985

Quantified Risk Assessment: Its Input to Decision Making, Health and Safety Executive, 1989

Royal Society for the Prevention of Accidents, *Annual Report 1988/9*, RoSPA, London

Royal Society of London, *Assessment and perception of risk*, 1981

Sime, J.D. (Editor) *Safety in the Built Environment*, E. & F. N. Spon, 1988

World Health Organisation, *Constitution*, WHO, Geneva, May 1976

LEGISLATIVE AND REGULATORY ISSUES

Mark Tyler

McKenna & Co

INTRODUCTION

Over the last two decades the law governing material and pollutants that do harm to man and the environment has developed at a rate which few could have imagined, reflecting not only the influence of the European Community but also the resolve of the United Kingdom's own legislators to take effective action as the extent of the harm being done begins to be better understood. This chapter:

- reviews the ways in which national and European legislation imposes regulatory controls over the use of land and building materials;
- considers some of the legislation which may be expected in these areas in the future;
- examines the role of the planning system in reducing hazards;
- outlines the disparate area of law relating to product safety and the provision of information about hazards;
- considers a number of other areas which can affect occupants of finished buildings – the dangers inherent in construction and demolition processes, and the less well-understood health problems[1].

PLANNING, SITE PREPARATION AND DEALING WITH HAZARDS ON LAND

Planning Applications

Town and Country Planning Acts 1971 and 1990 (TCPA)

The UK has relied to a considerable extent on the planning system for land use to address the broad environmental issues associated with developments. By requiring permission to carry out development, the planning authority can exercise indirect control over pollution emissions and potential risks to persons in the locality. Under the provisions of the TCPA and its Scottish counterpart, any development, unless falling within the range of exemptions defined as 'permitted development', requires permission from the local planning authority. The local planning authority in determining the application must have regard to all 'material' planning considerations. Whilst there is a presumption in favour of granting planning permission for development the local planning authority can nevertheless refuse consent if demonstrable harm will result and, in this context, pollution and public health concerns are considered to be material. In practice, objections can often be overcome by authorities imposing suitable conditions on a planning consent or by special contracts ('Section 52 Agreements' in the 1971 Act, or 'Section 106 Agreements' under the consolidating legislation of the 1990 Act) with developers in ways prescribed by the legislation. The effectiveness of such control does however depend on the extent to which local planning authorities are able to insist on proper investigations of potential problems with developments, and the enhancement of planning powers is regarded by many as essential for ensuring that adequate steps will be taken in the future to deal with environmental hazards and in particular contaminated land — see Chapter C9.

European Directive on Environmental Assessment

The importance of environmental considerations for the planning system has been recognised by the European community which in 1985 adopted the Directive on The Assessment of the Effects of Certain Public and Private Projects on the Environment[2]. (The effect of European Directives is not to introduce new law directly into Member States; instead, they are addressed to the Governments of the Member States whose obligation is to introduce national legislation within a specified time-scale). For developments made subject to the controls, there has to be express consideration (at the planning stage) of the direct and indirect effects of a project on factors described in the Directive as:

- human beings, fauna and flora;
- soil, water, air, climate and the landscape;
- the interaction between the factors mentioned in the first and second indents;
- material assets and the cultural heritage.

Developers are therefore required to supply a statement containing a description of their project, measures to avoid or reduce any adverse

effects and data on the impact on the environment such as the type and
quality of emissions of pollutants.

Town and Country Planning (Assessment of Environmental Effects) Regulations 1988

These regulations implement the principles of the Directive in the
United Kingdom[3]. (Certain types of projects other than buildings, eg
motorways, pipelines and land drainage are covered by separate
regulations)[4-10]. The 1988 Regulations specify the building developments
for which an Environmental Assessment will now be required; a separate
authorisation is not required in addition to planning permission but the
result of the formalised assessment process must be considered prior to
the grant of planning consent and various other statutory bodies may
have to be consulted by the local authority. Wider scrutiny may follow
by virtue of the requirement that the Assessment be made available for
public inspection by the local authority. A DoE Circular[11] provides a
detailed explanation of how the assessment procedure operates. Chapter
D1 deals in detail with environmental assessment.

There are two categories of developments for which an Environmental
Assessment may be required. Developments in the first category are
subject to mandatory assessment requirements – exceptionally hazardous
types of installations such as oil refineries and hazardous waste disposal
facilities. The second (and larger) category of developments require
environmental assessment only if (in the view of the local planning
authority in first instance) they would be likely to have an effect on the
environment by virtue of fact such as their nature, size or location. These
developments could include facilities for the manufacture of pesticides,
infrastructure projects such as an industrial estate development, an urban
development project, a holiday village or a hotel complex. (For details of
the development categories to which the Regulations may apply, see the
Schedules to the Regulations). If the applicability of the Regulations is
uncertain, it is possible to apply to the planning authority prior to
submission of a planning application for an opinion whether or not the
environmental assessment process applies, and there is provision made for
appeals to the Secretary of State.

In many ways, Environmental Assessment in the UK represents a
formalisation of procedures which were already followed by local
planning authorities when dealing with contentious or environmentally
sensitive projects and it may not therefore represent a major development
in practice as it does in some other Member States with less sophisticated
systems for examining developments individually. Initial indications since
the introduction of the regulations in 1988 suggest that Environmental
Impact Assessments are prepared for approximately 150 projects annually.

The DoE circular warns local planning authorities against requesting assessments unless they are required under the terms of the Directive and it is, therefore, possible that the scope for formal assessment of environmental effects of smaller projects generally is more narrowly confined than it was before. The Circular also points out however that local planning authorities still have general powers to call for further and better information from applicants and that requirements for formal assessment of certain types of project do not lessen their responsibilities to look at the environmental implication of all projects for which planning permission is sought. As planning officers become more accustomed to working with the regulations, it seems probable that levels of consciousness about the environmental consequences of developments generally will be raised. Already there is growing pressure for there to be assessments of smaller developments, and developers are receiving informal indications that a voluntary assessment would assist in obtaining planning permission[12].

Responsibilities for Contaminated Land

There are a number of legal obligations to consider when land under development has been contaminated with substances deposited on the site, often long before the developer acquired ownership. Of immediate concern is the possible risk to persons working on the site. In order to comply with obligations under health and safety legislation, and the Occupiers Liability Act 1957 which requires care to be taken for the safety of visitors to premises, land owners and their design teams need to investigate possible ground contamination or gas emissions in order to warn contractors about the condition of the land before work commences. In addition, the Building Regulations 1985[13] contain provisions relating to site preparation and contaminants, including the requirement that 'precautions should be taken to avoid danger to health caused by substances found on or in the ground covered by the building'. This requirement is elaborated upon in Approved Document C to the Regulations although, as with all the Approved Documents, the guidance it contains does not have statutory force.

Another concern may be information about possible contamination requested by the local planning authority when the planning application is made, if this is not already being provided under the requirements for an Environmental Assessment. There are numerous practical difficulties for land owners in this area, and as yet legislation has not made a significant impact on these: there is for instance no registration system in the UK identifying the location and extent of contaminated land. The House of Commons Environment Committee, in its report on contaminated land[14], proposed that such registers should be introduced. A requirement for district councils to compile and maintain these registers is being incorporated into the Environmental Protection Bill. Another problem identified by the Environment Committee in this area is the *caveat emptor* principle which applies to sales of land, whereby the seller is under no obligation to disclose the existence of contamination to the purchaser. The Committee called for the principle to be abolished and replaced with a new positive duty to give full disclosure of known contamination. The Law Commission, however, has advised against the abolition of *caveat emptor* and it seems likely to remain part of English law for some time to come[15].

In spite of the present limitations there are however a number of existing legislative provisions which create sources for information concerning contamination of land. Where it has not been possible to obtain reliable reports from the previous owners, a number of authorities and information sources may be able to help:

- the planning authority, who may be familiar with the history of the site from their records;
- other statutory bodies may have relevant information by virtue of reporting requirements under regulations applying to sites where significant quantities of hazardous substances are used or stored;
- such information may be available from the Health and Safety Executive because it is one of the requirements of the Reporting of Injuries, Diseases and Dangerous Occurrences Regulations 1985[16] that accidental releases of any substance in circumstances which might pose a risk to health are notified;
- the National Rivers Authority (NRA) may have details of contamination on land from its monitoring of ground water and river quality;
- and data may be available from waste disposal authorities responsible for licensing the deposit of controlled wastes and other pollution legislation;
- surveys carried out for the purposes of identifying sites under the Derelict Land Act 1982 and Derelict Land Grants may also contain relevant information.

A further practical difficulty in dealing with contaminated land is the absence of legal criteria to determine when the site is deemed to be sufficiently clean. Some guidance, albeit limited, can be found in Approved Document C to the Building Regulations. Current recommendations on clean-up standards is presently found in guidance notes issued by the Inter-Departmental Committee on the Redevelopment of Contaminated Land (ICRCL) which is an advisory body to local authorities. These recommendations have no statutory force but they might be made legally binding by being incorporated into an agreement between the local planning authority and the developer under the TCPA or a contract with a clean-up contractor engaged by the developer. The House of Commons Environment Committee has called for legislation to make a system for standards for soil quality apply to all sites, irrespective of whether they are undergoing development or already in use.

Contaminated land is covered in detail in Chapter C9.

Landfill and Gases

Landfill gases generated by disposal of putrescible waste can be a particular problem for development in areas to which landfill gas may migrate. There is no specific planning legislation or other regulatory code relating to landfill gases but the Department of the Environment has recently provided guidance to local planning authorities in the form of a DoE Circular[17] which deals with development on landfills. The Circular should be read in conjunction with Waste Management Papers[18] numbers 4, 26 and 27 relating to various aspects of landfill operations. The Circular discusses provisions for new and existing landfill sites, notes that powers of control over gas emissions from closed landfills may be limited, but that there is an obligation on occupiers to ensure the safety of persons on or near their land under the Occupiers Liability Act 1957. The Circular notes the statutory provisions applicable and the possibility of a common law action for nuisance, and suggests that planning decisions made in accordance with its guidance should ensure that the risk of migration of landfill gas is taken into account.

There is no prohibition on development near landfills, but treatment of landfill gas can be a material consideration in determining if permission should be granted and gas mitigation measures may be secured by planning conditions or agreements between the local planning authority and the developer.

Enforcement action in respect of hazards

Where hazards are identified at the planning and site preparation stage the legislative controls outlined above can often be used to require effective remedial action or at least precautionary steps to be taken. If the hazards do not become apparent until after the work has begun, other legislation has to be considered. In the case of contaminated land, in practice there may be very little prospect of clean-up obligations arising unless an off-site medium such as ground-water is found to be adversely affected; UK policy has been broadly aimed at responding to specific contamination situations, unlike for example United States legislation[19-24] which reflects a political commitment actively to seek out and deal with contamination, backed up with vigorous reporting requirements for historical contamination.

The Water Act 1989 and The Control of Pollution Act 1974

The Water Act 1989 empowers the National Rivers Authority (NRA) to take steps to prevent the pollution of water or to clean-up existing pollution. The costs of these operations can be recovered from the persons who made the discharges in question or, if it was action to prevent an anticipated discharge, from any person who caused or knowingly permitted the matter in question to be present at the place from which it was likely to enter the relevant waters. Specified works and operations could be carried out by the NRA if it appears that any poisonous noxious or polluting matter or any solid waste matter is likely to enter 'controlled' waters. The NRA would be entitled to recover its expenses reasonably incurred in carrying out those operations from any person who caused or knowingly permitted the matter in question to be present at the place from which it was likely to enter any controlled waters or caused or knowingly permitted the matter in question to be present in controlled waters.

Section 16 of the Control of Pollution Act 1974 (which will be replaced in due course by provisions contained in the Environmental Protection Bill) empowers a waste disposal authority to serve a notice on the occupier of land where waste has been deposited requiring its removal and/or the taking of steps with a view to eliminating or reducing the consequences of the deposit of the waste. Failure to comply with a notice is an offence and in addition to the imposition of a fine the authority may do what the person on whom the notice was served failed to do, and may recover its expenses from him.

The powers under these two Acts are extensive but are not commonly exercised. However, where the hazards pose a tangible and immediate risk to human health, enforcement measures are considerably more likely to be used. Moreover, local authorities are under an obligation pursuant to public health legislation to inspect their districts for the protection of 'statutory nuisances' and to bring about their abatement. These nuisances are defined by legislation[25] and include among other things accumulations and deposits of materials which are prejudicial to health or a nuisance, and dust and effluvia from trade or business premises which may be injurious to the public or a nuisance. Local authorities have the power to serve an abatement notice for such nuisances but under current provisions this needs to be supported with a Court order before it becomes enforceable. The

Environmental Protection Bill would alter the position so that abatement notices would have direct effect without an order having to be obtained from the Court. The Bill also makes provision for local authorities to take preventative action in anticipation of statutory nuisances (which will be redefined by the Bill with more clarity) before they actually arise. It seems however that statutory nuisances will remain focused upon interference with human health and comfort rather than the protection of the environment from pollutants. The House of Commons Environment Committee Report referred to above recommended that statutory nuisances should be clarified so as to include protection of the environment.

Other Provisions

Certain other statutory provisions may be used in appropriate cases to deal with buildings posing particular risks to the environment generally or to human health. The TCPA enables local planning authorities to require proper maintenance of land where the amenity of the area is adversely affected. Section 76 of the Building Act 1984 also gives local authorities powers to intervene and carry out remedial works at the expense of the owner where, in certain circumstances, they have been remiss in complying with directions to deal with premises deemed to be prejudicial to health or a nuisance. There are even powers under the TCPA for local authorities to order the discontinuance of use of buildings or land, or to impose conditions on their continued use, although this may give rise to rights of compensation for the owner. In practice these powers would only be exercised in extreme cases. Finally, certain public health or environmental issues are addressed by their own specific legislation. Infestation with pests for example may be dealt with by local authorities under the Prevention of Damage by Pests Act 1949; litter and waste problems may be subject to the Refuse and Disposal (Amenity) Act 1978 and the Litter Act 1983. Provisions with regard to litter will also be strengthened with the passage of the Environmental Protection Bill.

Enforcement powers where there is an immediate risk to safety or health tend to be used more frequently than the public health measures described above, which are weaker in comparison because of the requirement to prove the existence of a nuisance which can be difficult in many cases. The principal statute in this area is the Health and Safety at Work etc Act 1974 (HSWA) under which enforcing authorities (which are, depending on the type of premises concerned, the Health and Safety Executive, Her Majesty's Inspectorate of Pollution or local authorities) have formidable powers to suspend operations or prohibit work altogether until the risk to persons working in an area or to the public at large have been dealt with.

LEGISLATIVE INFLUENCES ON CHOICE OF BUILDING MATERIALS

In spite of the growing awareness of the properties of materials put into buildings and the interest shown in energy efficiency and other measures to protect the environment, there are surprisingly few products which are prohibited from use by law, notwithstanding the existence of powers to effect bans which exist under various statutes. Among the few notable exceptions are asbestos, which has been banned in most of its forms by a series of regulations introduced during the 1980s[26-28], and polychlorinated biphenyls (PCBs) and polychlorinated terphenyls (PCTs), the supply and use of which is now forbidden under pollution legislation[29]. (Somewhat ironically, attention is now beginning to focus on regulating the use of asbestos and PCB or PCT *substitutes* which also now appear to pose their own risks[30].) After the adoption of the Montreal Protocol on protecting the ozone layer, European Community Member States have also restricted the use of chlorofluorocarbons (CFCs) by a Community Regulation requiring manufacturers to halve production from 1986 levels by the year 2000[31]; importation of CFCs from outside the Community has also now been regulated. An international conference in London in June 1990 reached agreement for CFCs (and certain other ozone-depleting gases) to be phased out altogether by the end of the century. More general legal restrictions on materials and energy uses may be introduced in future UK environmental legislation which is planned to address the problem of the 'Greenhouse Effect'. See Chapters D2 and D3.

Legislative Controls

Regulation 7 of the Building Regulations 1985 requires that 'any building work shall be carried out with proper materials and in a workmanlike manner', and work has to be carried out in accordance with the requirements in Schedule 1 of the Regulations which include, with regard to toxic substances, precautions in connection with cavity insulation and other obligations concerning hygiene and sanitation. The Approved Document on Regulation 7 discusses material-quality and workmanship in terms of both health and safety of persons and energy conservation and reference is made to methods of establishing fitness with aids such a British Standards, Agrément Certificates, testing and certification and quality assurance schemes. However, the only area in which the Building Regulations presently have a direct impact on material specification with regard to human health is toxic fumes from cavity insulation where specific provision is made in Approved Document D in relation to urea-formaldehyde foam. Approved Document L, concerning conservation of fuel and power, compares the thermal conductivity of some common building materials but contains no specific provisions about the choice of products. The generality of legal requirements contained in the Building Regulations limits their effect in compelling the use of safer building materials.

An alternative to prohibiting products altogether is to allow their use subject to a system of approval and licensing as occurs in some other regulated areas, notably medicines. The administrative costs and bureaucracy of such schemes tend to discourage their use but one such system exists under the Control of Pesticides Regulations 1986[32] in relation to a broad range of substances used as herbicides, fungicides, insecticides, wood preservatives, biocides and chemicals for sterilising soil. This legislation prevents the advertising, sale, supply, storage and use of pesticides unless they have been granted official 'Approval' after the submission of safety data and they meet the general requirements set out in formal 'Consents' published under the regulations. Pesticides when sold must also meet strict labelling requirements.

The approval system for pesticides, although intended to be self financing, has highlighted the inherent difficulties with this legislative technique. Firstly, many existing products have been manufactured for long periods and data acceptable by modern standards has not been produced. Secondly, obtaining and verifying data on new products requires the commitment of substantial resources. Because of these difficulties, regulatory systems in the future are likely to be aimed at laying down detailed criteria of safety which products must meet, and the licensing of materials is unlikely to become significantly more widespread.

There is however a variety of more general legal requirements which serve to discourage the use of harmful substances and dangerous products and these provisions are reinforced by obligations imposed on manufacturers and suppliers of goods to investigate and warn about their potential for harm. This is an area of law in which the European Community is becoming particularly active.

Design responsibilities

In the absence of generally applicable legal restrictions on the choice of materials, there are theoretically no controls over products which may be used in a building. In practice this is not the case, to a large extent because of the use of non-mandatory British Standards to provide control of quality. The role of standards will shortly be enhanced, as will be seen below. Nevertheless certain legal limitations on the use of products already exist by virtue of statutory requirements, in particular those relating to occupational health and exposure to hazardous substances. The Control of Substances Hazardous to Health Regulations 1988 (COSHH)[33] require employers to assess and control the risks posed by substances in the workplace. In practice this may involve a builder who is responsible for selection of materials abandoning the use of certain products altogether and substituting something less hazardous, or at least changing the way in which the material is prepared, applied or used. In other cases the necessary provision of personal protective equipment and other control measures may make the use of particular product too inconvenient or prohibitively expensive. Where design and specification is in the hands of consultants and other professional advisers the builder is still obliged to carry out the assessment and to take the appropriate steps; the risks posed by materials therefore have to be considered at design stage so that contractors can be informed of any special hazards.

Designers already have general obligations under the Health and Safety at Work etc Act (HSWA) with regard to the employees of contractors. However, proposals for new legislation by the Health and Safety Commission concerning the management of construction safety contained in a 1989 Consultative Document[34] include more specific obligations which would be imposed on all designers, firstly to design with a view to the health and safety of construction workers, and secondly to ensure that adequate information is provided at the tender stage about aspects of materials or design which might pose risks. Additional information on potential hazards in the course of subsequent work on the building, including its eventual demolition, would also have to be given to the building owner to pass on to contractors for the purposes of any future work.

Manufacturers' Warnings and Labelling

These specific responsibilities for designers would be new, although there are existing obligations to design safely articles for use at work[35] and suppliers of most types of consumer products (including DIY products) are required to supply goods which meet a statutory 'safety requirement' – the legal test for which takes account of any instructions or warnings which are given with the goods[36]. Considerable emphasis has been placed in current legislation on requiring manufacturers to supply safety information with products; the main provision is Section 6 of HSWA under which anyone who manufacturers, supplies or imports substances or articles into the United Kingdom for use at work must ensure that they are safe and without risks to health when being used, handled, processed or stored. The section also requires there to be adequate testing and examination of products so that the information obligations can be met. Until recently it had been the case that manufacturers and suppliers simply had to have available safety information for when it was requested but the wording of the Act was strengthened in 1988[37] to include a positive obligation to provide hazard data to customers. There is also now a continuing obligation to provide revised hazard data to customers who have already been supplied with a product if additional risks to health and safety become known. Failure to provide information of this nature can also lead to civil liability to injured persons under the European Product Liability Directive[38] because inadequate instructions and warnings can cause a product to be regarded as 'defective' for these purposes.

A number of other European countries have requirements similar to Section 6 but which go further and specify the provision of a written Material Safety Data Sheet. A European Directive on 'preparations' adopted in 1988[39] will in due course require there to be a system of specific information in data sheet form relating to dangerous preparations (mixtures or solutions for more than one substance) but at present EEC law focuses on classifying, labelling and adequately packaging harmful materials, with support from a notification procedure for manufacturers and importers of new chemical substances[40]. A further proposed Product Safety Directive[41] for consumer products which is under development would impose additional general obligations on manufacturers and other suppliers to ensure that products do not present unacceptable risks to safety or health 'either directly or indirectly' and this would also include obligations with regard to instructions for use and safety information.

In the UK the Notification of New Substances Regulations 1982 were enacted to implement the relevant EEC law on developing new products; their effect is to prohibit the supply of any 'new substance' which is subject to the Regulations which has not first been duly notified to the Health and Safety Executive or to an equivalent body in another Member State. (Broadly speaking a new substance under the Directive is any substance which is not contained in the list which has been compiled in the form of the European Inventory of Existing Commercial Chemical Standards −'EINICS'). Where these substances are supplied above certain threshold quantities, manufacturers and importers have to send a detailed technical dossier to the HSE or the equivalent body in other Member States containing an evaluation of the effect a new substance might have on man and the environment. There are less rigorous notification procedures where smaller amounts are being supplied.

There is at present no legal obligation to evaluate the effects of existing chemicals on man and the environment, but the Department of the Environment has published a Consultation Paper[42] on possible new statutory powers which would enable the Government to designate a substance as being subject to review and to require information on its properties and use from the manufacturer. Similar EEC legislation is under consideration.

Information about hazards from materials is also required by the UK's

Classification, Packaging and Labelling of Dangerous Substances Regulations 1984[45]. These have general application to any substance or preparation which is supplied or conveyed by road and packages. In order to come within the scope of the Regulations the substance or preparation in question has to be contained in an Approved List[44] which has been designated for these purposes, or alternatively has to have certain characteristic properties which create a risk to health and safety when it is supplied. Under these Regulations manufacturers and suppliers are subject to requirements that packaging a substance should be secure and compatible with the substance in question. The packaging also has to show particulars of the classification of the substance according to the Approved List criteria together with indications of the 'general nature of the risk' (eg 'irritant') and the corresponding risks symbol and phrase. These details therefore provide the user with a minimum level of safety data and details of basic precautions against mis-use. It is however, sometimes wrongly assumed by manufacturers and suppliers that compliance with these Regulations means that safety data is being effectively provided for the purposes of the more general provisions of the Health and Safety at Work Act described earlier but this is not the case; very often more extensive data will be needed in order for the user to assess risk and to ensure that the material in question is used safely.

These requirements tend to concentrate, albeit not exclusively, on human health rather than on more general risks to the environment and it is not surprising therefore that attention has begun to focus on the issue of 'Green Labelling'. The marketing potential of such labelling has been recognised and exploited, but unregulated labelling and questionable claims that products are 'environmentally friendly' have been a cause for concern. Legislation in the UK has been considered specifically in relation to consumer products which will be developed in conjunction with the other European Community Member States. This may entail introducing codes of practice for environmental claims and possibly strengthening the Trades Descriptions Act. The overall objective will be that manufacturers would assess the impact of a product on the environment 'from cradle to grave', i.e. the stage of its manufacture (including the use of raw materials) through to its use and ultimate disposal as waste. In order to be entitled to apply the official label, manufacturers would have to be operating to the highest technical standards.

European proposals will be put forward in due course but numerous practical difficulties will have to be overcome for the official European labelling scheme to function: keeping up to date with developments in scientific knowledge, verifying self-certification of compliance by manufacturers, standardising test methods, and above all determining the criteria for 'environmentally friendly' products will need to be worked out before the European system can be properly implemented.

The fact that regulation of 'Green Labelling' will probably be restricted to consumer products may lessen the impact in the building industry, although DIY products would probably be covered and the manufacturers of industrial materials may be able to participate in voluntary self-regulatory schemes and codes of practice.

Construction Products Directive

In the immediate future, the construction industry will feel the impact of another European development which is aimed at encouraging safer building materials. In December 1988 the European Community adopted its Construction Products Directive[45] which has two main objectives:

- first, the removal of technical and regulatory restrictions on trade in construction products between Member States;
- second, the introduction of certain uniform standards relating to health and safety.

The Directive itself does not attempt to specify technical standards for construction products; instead, it establishes a framework of technical criteria to be developed in the future and provides for a Standing Committee on Construction (made up of representatives of the Member States) with decision making powers in relation to specifications and procedures for obtaining the appropriate certifications or technical approvals for products. It is thought that the Construction Products Directive is likely to encompass a larger number of products than are presently subject to British Standards and Agrément Certificates.

The Directive introduces a requirement that construction products may only be placed on the market if they are fit for their intended use which is to say, in terms of the Directive, that they enable the construction work in question to meet the relevant 'essential requirements'. As the Department of Trade and Industry booklet on the Directive explains, 'the essential requirements apply to construction works, not to construction products as such, but they will influence the technical characteristics of those products'[46].

The essential requirements are not described in detail in the Directive, but an Annex sets out in broad terms objectives relating to various aspects of building works, namely mechanical resistance and stability, safety in case of fire, hygiene, health and the environment, safety in use, protection against noise, energy economy and heat insulation. The Standing Committee will elaborate on these broad objectives and produce 'interpretative documents' expanding the essential requirements into substantive criteria of product quality. The interpretative documents will then be used as the basis for the formulation of European standards for individual products by the European Standards Bodies CEN and CENELEC. Compliance with the essential requirements may be shown by manufacturers fixing the characteristic EC mark on the product or accompanying commercial documents. Products which satisfy the Directive and carry the EC Mark will be presumed to be fit for their intended use. The most straightforward route for manufacturers to use the EC Mark will be compliance with a specific harmonised European standard produced by CEN or CENELEC (published in the UK in the form of a British Standard in precisely the same terms). Where there is neither a harmonised European Standard for a product nor a recognised national standard then it may be possible to obtain a European technical approval which is a formal assessment of fitness for use, based on the essential requirements, granted by a recognised standard body in one of the Member States. In the UK the recognised body will be the British Board of Agrément. This route will be used chiefly by the manufacturers of innovative products and the technical approval will normally be granted for a limited period only. Manufacturers of products which have only minor relevance to safety (which will be contained in a specific list being drawn up for the purposes of the Directive) will not have to conform to European standards or technical approvals and will not bear the EC mark.

The Member States are required to enact legislation implementing the Directive no later than June 1991, and the Building Regulations will have to be reviewed in the implementation process. In practice national standards and technical specifications will be relevant for some time to come because the European standards will take time to produce. The impact of the Directive remains to be seen and depends very much on the interpretation of the essential requirements and the formulation of harmonised product standards and testing requirements. Nevertheless, the Directive is bound to have a significant effect on the way in which building materials are chosen and specified.

HAZARDS IN THE CONSTRUCTION PHASE

Health and Safety at Work etc Act 1974 (HSWA)

This Act contains the principal legislation governing site safety during construction, although earlier legislation contained in the Factories Act 1961 remains of considerable importance because of the number of wide-ranging Construction Regulations made under that Act.

Sections 2 to 4 and 7 of the HSWA impose 'general duties' on employers to ensure – as far as is reasonably practicable – that the health and safety and welfare of employees is safeguarded, and likewise in relation to other persons who 'may be affected' by the employer's conduct. This would include visitors to buildings and the public generally. Section 4 of the Act goes further in requiring anyone who has 'control', to any extent, of premises to take reasonable measures to protect the health and safety of persons using the premises. There is also a duty imposed on employees by Section 7 to take reasonable care for their own safety and that of their colleagues, and to cooperate with their employers. The duties imposed on the employer are not absolute and the qualification of the duty in terms of reasonable practicability means that this is not a strict liability statute. In practice however the onus is on employers to prove that they discharge the duty and Courts have expected very high standards of care before exonerating defendants. As well as the ultimate sanction of prosecution, enforcement of the duties is carried out by inspectors with extensive powers to issue statutory notices suspending or prohibiting unsafe systems of working.

The HSWA does not contain detailed guidance on how these general obligations should be complied with in specific cases. Instead, the legislation is designed to provide a framework for introducing regulatory controls over specific activities which are established through powers conferred upon the Secretary of State to make health and safety regulations, and upon the Health and Safety Commission to issue Approved Codes of Practice which the Courts can take into account in determining whether the duties under the Act have been complied with. An important example of this framework in this context is the Control of Substances Hazardous to Health Regulations 1988 and the associated codes of practice which are discussed below.

Important new European legislation is now being developed for occupational health and safety, and a Directive on 'Temporary and Mobile Worksites' (ie construction sites) is being prepared. This will deal with the overall management of health and safety on sites, and more specifically is expected to include requirements to appoint competent persons who would have statutory duties to plan and implement safety measures from the design stage through to completion. This draft Directive is one of a number of 'daughter' Directives to be adopted pursuant to the main 'framework' Directive on health and safety at work[47] which was adopted in 1989. The general requirements for this framework directive resemble the requirements of the Health and Safety at Work Act but the Health and Safety Commission will in due course be publishing proposals for amendments to the UK Act to implement changes required by the Directive. Other 'daughter' Directives which touch upon health issues and which will lead to UK legislation in due course include those on Personal Protective Equipment[48] and the use of Work Equipment at Work[49].

At present in the UK the general duties under the HSWA in relation to management of health and safety issues on construction sites is not put in force by any specific health and safety regulation framework, although the separate regulations made under the Factories Act 1961 cover a wide range of mandatory safety precautions, most of which are concerned more with avoiding physical risks, for example collapsing structures or inadequate scaffolding. Detailed guidance (albeit advisory rather than mandatory) has also been published by the Construction Industry Advisory Committee of the Health and Safety Commission (CONIAC) setting out procedures for the management and co-ordination between designers, building owners, main contractors or management contractors, and sub-contractors[50]. A recent Consultative Document on possible new Construction (Management and Miscellaneous Duties) Regulations has been issued by the Health and Safety Commission[51] which would, if adopted, introduce various new legal duties under the HSWA regime which would include:

- specific requirements for anyone in control of the sites to ens⸱⸱ that adequate safety arrangements are in place;
- appointment of competent health and safety advisors;
- information being provided by any person who enters into a contract with the contractor about the state or conditions of the land which might affect health and safety;
- a positive obligation to check the competence of contractors before their appointment;
- duties on designers to provide information about safety (see above).

In practice UK legislation is not likely to be enacted in isolation from the European proposals, and these proposals will probably be largely assimilated in due course into the draft Temporary and Mobile Worksites Directive.

The Control of Substances Hazardous to Health Regulations 1988 (COSHH)

These European proposals deal with safety generally but the UK has already introduced its own important legislation dealing specifically with health risks from materials in the form of the COSHH Regulations. Although these are not entirely comprehensive (in that they do not extend to risks arising from 'articles' as opposed to 'substances') they affect virtually all businesses and work situations. Even apparently innocuous substances can be hazardous in certain circumstances, and the Regulations relate not only to risks arising from actual use of substances but to other potential risks to ancillary workers, for example maintenance staff and inspectors.

The COSHH Regulations imposes a series of duties on employers to protect their employees and others who may be exposed to substances hazardous to health. Consequently main contractors and management contractors owe duties to their own employees and others working on sites under their control; they should also check the adequacy of the safety arrangements of their sub-contractors. Sub-contractors themselves owe a duty to their employees, and to others working on site. The self-employed also have duties to protect their own health.

'Substances hazardous to health' may be substances already classified as toxic, harmful, corrosive or irritant under existing dangerous substances legislation, or substances for which 'maximum exposure limits' are specified in the COSHH Regulations. The Regulations also apply for micro organisms and dust of any kind in substantial concentrations. These designations of hazardous substances under the COSHH Regulations do not however constitute an exhaustive definition — the duties will arise in connection with any substance which creates comparable hazards to health. Certain substances are exempt from the rules, in particular those which are hazardous only by virtue of their radioactive, explosive or flammable properties, or solely because they are at high or low temperatures or high pressure. The implications for those carrying out construction works are enormous, given the range of potentially harmful materials used, and the Health and Safety Commission has therefore published guidance material ('The Control of Substances Hazardous to Health in the Construction Industry') for developers and contractors.

Central to the COSHH Regulations is the duty placed upon employers to carry out assessments of the risk to health created by work that is liable to expose their employees (or others) to substances hazardous to health, and to consider the steps that need to be taken by them to meet the other requirements of the Regulations. The main Approved Code of Practice explains how to carry out assessments for the purposes of the legislation; more specific Codes of Practice deal with risks from carcinogens, pesticides and fumigation. Other requirements of the COSHH Regulations include duties to provide protective equipment if risks to health cannot be guarded against by other measures; to give safety information and training to staff; to monitor exposure levels and keep health records of employees in certain cases; and to restrict exposure to certain designated substances within specified limits.

The importance of the COSHH Regulations lies not just in the extensiveness of the obligations created but the sheer range of its application; virtually all the materials and products mentioned later in this book are subject to these rules when used in the work-place. In only a few cases work with certain substances is not covered by the COSHH Regulations; asbestos and lead are excluded because they are subject to their own separate regulatory codes under the Control of Asbestos at

Work Regulations 1987[52] and the Asbestos (Licensing) Regulations 1983[53] (which require in most instances the use of licensed contractors to work with asbestos), and the Control of Lead at Work Regulations 1980[54]. The common theme of these regulations, as with the COSHH Regulations, is assessment of risk from exposure by employers backed up by detailed Approved Codes of Practice explaining how to achieve compliance.

Other legislation will also come into play in circumstances where building operations give rise to health hazards not only to workmen on site but also to others in the neighbourhood. In particular, the Public Health Act 1936 may be used by local authorities to deal with what are known as 'statutory nuisances' which can include air pollution of various kinds as specified in the statute. These include dust and effluvia, accumulations and deposits of materials, or any premises in a condition prejudicial to health or a nuisance. Local authorities are empowered to issue abatement notices against such nuisances which have to be subsequently enforced by an order of the Court if disregarded. The Environmental Protection Bill proposes that local authorities in future will be given more effective powers to issue notices which would take immediate effect and would give rise to a criminal offence if ignored.

DEMOLITION AND DISPOSAL OF MATERIALS

Demolition of buildings gives rise to many of the same problems which arise during the construction phase, and the health and safety legislation described above will apply equally in these circumstances. There is no specific obligation to carry out surveys of buildings for hazardous materials before demolition but this would normally be one aspect of the general duties under the HSWA, and failure to do so, or at least to protect employees against foreseeable risks from exposure if work is commenced, could therefore breach the statutory duties. As with all construction works, notice must be given to the HSE of demolition of a building which could lead to an inspection and service of improvement or prohibition notices if the demolition works are not being carried out satisfactorily.

Disposal of Waste

As well as potential health hazards, demolition inevitably creates the need for disposal of waste materials. The Control of Pollution Act (COPA) makes it an offence to deposit any household, commercial or industrial waste on land, unless the disposal site is duly licensed by the local waste disposal authority. COPA also makes it an offence to knowingly permit or cause such deposits to take place.

The provisions of the Environmental Protection Bill will extend the scope of liability in connection with waste, but these basic offences will continue to exist under the new legislation. The definition of waste is wide, and the fact that the material may be of use to someone other than the waste producer, for example for re-cycling or for some other practical purpose, does not prevent the application of the legislation[55]. This would pose considerable problems in relation to construction works where waste of various sorts is typically re-used as a construction material. Exemptions have therefore been made in the Collection and Disposal of Waste Regulations 1988[56] which permit waste arising from construction or demolition work, tunnelling or other excavation, to be deposited on land where there is going to be future construction. This is not however an unqualified exemption and hazardous wastes cannot be used in this way[57].

Hazardous wastes are treated differently to ordinary wastes by virtue of the Control of Pollution (Special Waste) Regulations 1980[58], the principal effect of which is to impose notification procedures and requirements for consignment notes where substances meeting the criteria of the Regulations are being disposed of. Amendments to the existing Regulations will in due course extend these criteria to cover more materials[59]. The Regulations can apply to a number of persons who at different times may be dealing with special waste: in particular the controls apply to any person who produces special waste, or who transports it, or who actually disposes of the waste. In principle every consignment of waste has to be accompanied by a number of copies of the consignment note when it leaves the place of its production. In addition a copy consignment notice must be sent to the local authority responsible for supervision of the disposal of waste in the area in which the disposal takes place.

The obligations imposed by COPA, although not insubstantial, have become widely regarded as inadequate to deal with current problems of waste disposal and contaminated land. The Environmental Protection Bill contains proposals for the re-organisation of the waste disposal functions of local authorities with the creation of new Waste Regulation Authorities which will exercise an independent regulatory function, and moreover the introduction of a new 'duty of care' to take a reasonable measure in connection with waste applying to producers, importers, holders, carriers and persons who treat or dispose of waste. Such persons would have to take all reasonable measures to prevent any unlawful keeping, treating or disposal of waste by others and to prevent its escape either from their control or that of anyone else. When the waste is transferred this will have to be to an authorised person, with a sufficient written description of the waste accompanying it. The Department of the Environment is developing a Code of Practice with statutory force to give practical guidance on how to discharge the duty. In addition to the usual criminal liabilities in this area of the law it is proposed that there will be civil liability for any damage caused by unlawful deposits of waste.

There are also proposals for a European directive on waste which go further than the provisions of the Environmental Protection Bill, although the Community proposal is confined to the imposition of civil liability to pay compensation for damage caused[60]. This would create a significantly greater potential liability for clean-up costs for contaminated sites than is currently proposed in the UK. Even under the proposed Directive, however, liability would not be retrospective and would only arise out of 'incidents' occurring after the Directive comes into force. Nor would liability under the Directive be indefinite; claims would have to be brought within three years beginning with the day on which the claimant became aware, or should have become aware, of the damage or injury to the environment and the identity of the waste producer, and in any event no claim could be brought thirty years after the event which caused the damage. The only limits to liability for claims arising within the thirty year period would be *force majeure* or contributory negligence on the part of the claimant. No financial ceiling on liability would be provided for in the Directive under the current terms of the draft. The proposed Directive is intended to further the realisation of the 'polluter pays' principle, and the producer would retain liability until proper disposal is ensured under the conditions laid down by the Directive. In practice this would mean that handing waste to a carrier to take it to a disposal site would not of itself mean the waste producer would relinquish responsibility for any damage; in order to be relieved of these responsibilities, the producer would first have to comply strictly with the conditions contained in the Directive. The European Community is also likely to develop directives on disposal of specific wastes and one will in due course take effect governing the licensing of installations for collection and storage of PCBs and PCTs[61].

Recycling

For various reasons but in particular the economic cost of disposing of waste, recycling has now become the focus for future legislation in this area. It remains to be seen whether legislation is a desirable approach given that plant and facilities are not yet readily available for a comprehensive system of recycling, and attempts to encourage the use of existing processes, such as recycling waste paper, have overwhelmed the market's capacity to absorb the waste materials. The Environmental Protection Bill would impose a new duty on waste collection authorities to draw up plans for the recycling of waste. In particular, authorities would have to prepare statements of the arrangements made or proposed to be made for dealing with collected waste. Authorities would be empowered to make arrangements with the waste disposal contractors for them to use waste for the purposes of producing heat or electricity, and they could buy or otherwise acquire waste with a view to having it recycled. But there are no positive obligations proposed in the bill to require producers of waste to engage in recycling.

The European Community, which has since 1975 had a Directive in place encouraging the recycling of waste[62], is presently looking at the terms of a possible directive on recycling waste plastics and other containers. A number of European countries already have legally enforced measures setting recycling targets[63].

BUILDINGS IN OCCUPATION

Once a building is built and occupied numerous other statutes and regulations will affect the occupier in relation to the health and safety of the occupants and visitors, and protection of the environment. In the main this legislation is directed at business rather than domestic premises.

The principal relevant statutes are the Health and Safety at Work Act etc 1974 (HSWA), which is a general application to all employers, the Factories Act 1961 and the Offices Shops and Railway Premises Act 1963. These lay down general requirements in relation to the 'indoor environment' in relation to such things as lighting, temperature, ventilation and hygiene. In each case reference needs to be made to the individual statutes and related guidance materials in order to understand whether premises fully comply with the legislation. In addition, consideration has to be given to health issues as required by the general duties of the HSWA and, specifically in relation to substances, assessments need to be carried out pursuant to the COSHH Regulations, even in apparently low risk situations such as offices. The European Communities framework Directive on safety and health of workers at work referred to earlier and another of its 'daughter' Directives on the minimum safety and health requirements for the workplace[64] are likely to result in further UK legislation supplementing the Health and Safety at Work Act; the extent of the changes required in English law to comply with the Directives are not yet clear but it is probable that more general obligations will be introduced to assess formally risks in the work place and positively to provide instruction or training to staff, together with designation of individuals responsible for protecting against occupational hazards.

Fire precautions

There are other statutes relevant specifically in relation to fire risks, and in particular the Fire Precautions Act 1971 which is now varied by

the amending provisions contained in the more recent Fire Safety and
Safety at Places of Sport Act 1987. These requirements apply in
addition to the provisions on fire safety contained in the Building
Regulations 1985 which concern means of escape in the case of fire
and the control of fire spread. Fire certification provisions under the
1971 Act apply to certain factories, offices and other premises as set
out in regulations designating premises for these purposes. Under the
new certification arrangements, exemptions can be granted by fire
authorities for designated premises where certain conditions are met,
whereupon the occupier becomes subject to a regime of self-regulation,
for which the guidance contained in a Home Office Code of Practice is
particularly relevant[65].

Indoor Environment

Problems with conditions inside buildings which have been traditionally
considered in the light of this legislation have recently begun to be
regarded by some people as part of a generalised problem described as
Sick Building Syndrome, (or similar phrases) – see Chapter C5. Although
the 'daughter' Directive on workplaces deals generally with issues relating
to the indoor environment, no legislation has yet been directed towards
sick building syndrome, and this is unlikely to happen given the lack of
any clear definition of the condition and the large number of possible
causes which research has indicated may be responsible for the health
effects attributed to the syndrome. In the event of these problems
becoming a legal issue for building occupants and their employers, it will
be necessary to have regard to the existing legislation on indoor
environment outlined above in addition to the common law duties and
general occupier's duties to maintain safe premises contained in the
Occupiers Liability Act 1957. Breach of any of the duties laid down in
these statutes might lead to enforcement notices or even prosecutions by
inspectors and could additionally support claims for damages in
compensation. If the source of the 'sickness' problem were traced to plant
installed in the building, for instance air-conditioning equipment, then the
employer may have no defence to a claim because of the strict liability
imposed on him under the Employers' Liability (Defective Equipment)
Act 1969 which makes an employer directly responsible to employees for
any injuries or health problems caused by equipment used at work[66].

Emissions from buildings

Emissions into the atmosphere and to water sources are also covered by a
number of statutes, some of which have already been considered, such as
the Public Health Act 1936 which is to be amended by the

Environmental Protection Bill. The Clean Air Acts 1956 and 1968 deal with the emission of smoke from trade premises and various other regulations deal with industrial emissions. Under the terms of the Environmental Protection Bill, industrial emissions will be subject to a new regime of 'Integrated Pollution Control' administered by Her Majesty's Inspectorate of Pollution, which will regulate emissions from certain industrial processes. Discharges of effluent direct to water courses are subject to the Water Act 1989 but these affect mainly premises used for industrial operations. In most cases, discharges of liquid effluents will be made to sewers; for domestic waste this discharge is allowed by right under the Public Health Act 1936 but premises used for business are subject to provisions that the discharges are notified to the local sewerage undertaker as required by the Public Health (Drainage of Trade Premises) Act 1937. Discharges of this nature have to accord with the terms of the relevant consent granted to the occupier which may restrict the types or amount of effluent discharged.

Legionnaires' Disease

Attention has turned in recent years to the particular problems attached to the emission of possible bacterial contamination from buildings leading to outbreaks of diseases classed broadly as 'Legionellosis'. It has not been part of the general policy of legislation since the introduction of the HSWA to 'over-regulate' businesses with legislation of a very specific nature such as would be required to legislate on Legionnaires' Disease and, where cases have arisen in the past, building owners have been convicted under the HSWA itself for failing in their general duty to ensure the safety of their employees or others who could be affected. The new COSHH Regulations would also now apply given that micro-organisms are specifically included among substances to which exposure must be prevented or controlled. In the absence of a specific regulatory regime, civil claims have also been brought relying on the general common law and the duties imposed on all occupiers under the Occupiers Liability Act 1957.

A number of enquiries have followed recent outbreaks of the Disease and it has been widely felt that these obligations, expressed in general terms in the legislation, have not always been fully appreciated by those charged with responsibility for building management. Accordingly, the Health and Safety Commission has published a Consultation Document[67] on possible future action which could involve new regulations, possibly imposing duties to register the existence of wet cooling towers or to obtain a licence to operate them, together with strict requirements for periodic examinations and certification by qualified personnel. Another possibility to be mooted is a total prohibition on new wet cooling towers although this seems unlikely. For the time being it appears that legislation would be confined largely to wet cooling towers which are regarded as being the chief cause of outbreaks of the disease, although the terms of the Approved Code of Practice set out in draft in the Consultative Document contemplate guidelines which would apply to all work activities and business premises where water is used or stored and there is a means of creating water droplets which may be inhaled. This would extend the scope of the controls to a broader range of plumbing, heating and ventilation equipment, and make it easier for enforcing authorities to point to evidence of specific failures to comply with the general duties of HSWA through non-compliance with the Code.

Legionnaires' disease is covered in detail in Chapter C3.

CONCLUSIONS

* Traditionally there has been little legislation, apart from basic sanitation and hygiene requirements, aimed directly at improving problems of health and the environment associated with buildings, although developments at the European level, in particular with Environmental Assessments and the Construction Products Directive, have begun to alter the position.

* Bans on individual products such as asbestos and CFCs also play their part in this process but, to be effective, regulation has to extend from the initial conception and construction of a building, throughout its occupation, and until the demolition and disposal of its components; hence the importance of legal obligations being imposed on manufacturers of materials and on designers and managers of building projects, and on those who dispose of waste.

* While the present regulatory system has many imperfections, the pace of legal developments in all these areas is quickening; the principle that 'ignorance of the law is no excuse' makes it essential for all concerned with building and development to monitor and respond to these changes.

REFERENCES

Reference is not made here to Acts of Parliament whose full title and date is given in the text. The aim is to give specific reference to Statutory Instruments, European Directives, Section of Acts etc., which bear on the specific point made in the text.

(SI refers to UK Statutory Instrument; OJ refers to Official Journal of the European Community)

1 The author has endeavoured to present the law as at June 1990.

2 *Council Directive 85/337/EEC on the Assessment of the Effects of Certain Public and Private Projects on the Environment*, OJ No. L 175, 5 July 1985, page 40

3 *The Town and Country Planning (Assessment of Environmental Effects) Regulations 1988*, SI 1988 No. 1199, as amended by the Town and Country Planning (Assessment of Environmental Effects (Amendment)) Regulations 1990, SI 1990 No. 367

4 *Environmental Assessment (Salmon Farming in Marine Waters) Regulations 1988*, SI 1988 No. 1218

5 *Environmental Assessment (Afforestation) Regulations 1988*, SI 1988 No. 1207

6 *Land Drainage Improvement Works (Assessment of Environmental Effects) Regulations 1988*, SI 1988 No. 1217

7 *Highways (Assessment of Environmental Effects) Regulations 1988*, SI 1988 No. 1241

8 *Harbour Works (Assessment of Environmental Effects) Regulations 1988*, SI 1988 No. 1336

9 *Harbour Works (Assessment of Environmental Effects) (No. 2) Regulations 1989*, SI 1989 No. 424

10 *Electricity and Pipe-line Works (Assessment of Environmental Effects) Regulations 1990*, SI 1990 No. 442

11 Department of the Environment, Circular No. 15/88, 12 July 1988

12 See the case of R-v-Swale Borough Council and Medway Ports Authority, ex parte the Royal Society for the Protection of Birds (The Times, 11 April 1990) for judicial comment on the interpretation of the Town and Country Planning (Assessment of Environmental Effects) Regulations 1988

13 *Building Regulations 1985*, SI 1985 No. 1065

14 House of Commons Environment Committee, *Contaminated Land, Volume 1*, First Report on Session 1989/90

15 Law Commission Report, *Let the Buyer be Well Informed*, December 1989

16 *Reporting of Injuries, Diseases and Dangerous Occurrences Regulations 1985*, SI 1985 No. 2023

17 Department of the Environment, Circular No. 17/89, 26 July 1989

18 Series of Waste Management Papers published by DoE and Her Majesty's Inspectorate of Pollution

19 *The Comprehensive Environmental Response, Compensation and Liability Act* ('CERCLA' or 'Superfund'), 42 U.S.C. S.9603

20 *Title III of the Superfund Amendments and Reauthorisation Act, the Emergency Right to Know Act of 1986,* ('SARA Title III' or 'Community Right to Know') 33 U.S.C. S.11004

21 *The Clean Water Act,* ('CWA') 33 U.S.C. S.1321

22 *The Resource Conservation and Recovery Act,* ('RCRA'), 42 U.S.C. S.6922, 6923, 6924

23 *The Hazardous Materials Transportation Act,* ('HMTA'), 49 U.S.C. S.1803–1805

24 *Toxic Substances Control Act,* ('TSCA'), 15 U.S.C. S.2607(e)

25 *Section 92, Public Health Act 1936* (which is being superseded by the provisions of the Environmental Protection Bill)

26 *The Asbestos (Prohibitions) Regulations 1985,* SI 1985 No. 910 as amended by *The Asbestos (Prohibitions) (Amendment) Regulations 1988,* SI 1988 No. 711

27 *The Asbestos Products (Safety) Regulations 1985* SI 1985 No. 2042 as amended by *The Asbestos Products (Safety) (Amendment) Regulations 1987,* SI 1987 No. 1979

28 *The Control of Asbestos at Work Regulations 1987,* SI 1987 No. 2115

29 *The Control of Pollution (Supply and Use of Injurious Substances) Regulations 1986,* SI 1989 No. 902

30 *Proposed Council Directive to amend Directive 76/769/EEC on the Marketing and Use of Certain Dangerous Substances in Preparations,* OJ C 24, 1 February 1990, page 15

31 Regulation 3322/88, OJ L 297, 31 October 1988

32 *The Control of Pesticides Regulations 1986,* SI 1986 No. 1510

33 *The Control of Substances Hazardous to Health Regulations 1988,* SI 1988 No. 1657

34 *Construction Management: Proposals for Regulations and Approved Code of Practice,* Health and Safety Commission Consultative Document CD12(F)

35 *Section 6(1) and (2), Health and Safety at Work etc., Act 1974*

36 *Section 10, Consumer Protection Act 1987*

37 *Section 36 and Schedule 3, Consumer Protection Act 1987*

38 *Council Directive 85/374/EEC on the Approximation of the Laws Regulations and Administrative Provisions of Member States Concerning Liability for Defective Products,* OJ L 210/29 1985

39 *Council Directive 88/379/EEC on the Approximation of the Laws Regulations and Administrative Provisions of Member States Relating to the Classification, Packaging and Labelling of Dangerous Preparations,* OJ L 187, 6 July 1988

40 *Council Directive 79/831/EEC amending for the sixth time Council Directive 67/548/EEC, OJ L 196/1 1967 on the Classification, Packaging and Labelling of Dangerous Substances,* OJ L 259/10 1979

41 *Amended Proposal for a Council Directive concerning general product safety,* OJ C 156/8 27 June 1990

42 *Statutory Powers to Evaluate and Control the Environmental Hazards of Existing Chemicals*, Department of the Environment, April 1988

43 *The Classification, Packaging and Labelling of Dangerous Substances Regulations 1984*, SI 1984 No. 1244 (as amended by SI 1986 No. 1922, SI 1986 No. 1951, SI 1988 No. 766, SI 1989 No. 2208 and SI 1990 No. 1255)

44 *Information approved for the Classification Packaging and Labelling of Dangerous Substances for Supply and Conveyance by Road*, Health and Safety Commission Authorised and Approved List, Third Edition

45 *Council Directive 89/106/EEC on the Approximation of the Laws Regulations and Administrative Provisions of Member States relating to Construction Products*, OJ L 40/12, 11 February 1989

46 *The Single Market, Standards: Construction Products*, Department of Trade and Industry, London

47 *Council Directive 89/391/EEC on the Introduction of Measures to Encourage Improvements in the Safety and Health of Workers at Work*, OJ L 183/1, 29 June 1989

48 *Council Directive 89/656/EEC Concerning the Minimum Safety and Health Requirements for the Use of Personal Protective Equipment by Workers at Work, (Third Individual Directive Within the Meaning of the Framework Directive of 12 June 1989 (89/391/EEC))*. OJ L 393/18, 30 December 1989

49 *Council Directive 89/655/EEC Concerning the Minimum Safety and Health Requirements for the Use of Work Equipment by Workers at Work, (Second Individual Directive Within the Meaning of the Framework Directive of 12 June 1989 (89/391/EEC))*, OJ L 393/13, 30 December 1989

50 *Managing Health and Safety in Construction: Part I, Principles and Application to Main Contractors/Sub-Contractor Projects (1987) and Part II: Management Contracting (1988)*, Health and Safety Commission, London

51 Health and Safety Commission, Consultation Document CD12(F)

52 *The Control of Asbestos at Work Regulations 1987*, SI 1987 No. 2115

53 *The Asbestos (Licensing) Regulations 1983*, SI 1983 No. 1649

54 *The Control of Lead at Work Regulations 1980*, SI 1980 No. 1248

55 See Long-v-Brooke (1980), Criminal Law Review 109

56 *Collection and Disposal of Waste Regulations 1988*, SI 1988 No. 819

57 Department of the Environment, Circular 13/88, 31 May 1988

58 *Control of Pollution (Special Waste) Regulations 1980*, SI 1980 No. 1709

59 See DoE Consultation Paper, *Special Waste and the Control of its Disposal*, January 1990

60 *Proposal for a Council Directive on Civil Liability for Damage Caused by Waste*, OJ C 251/3, 4 October, 1989

61 *Proposal for a Council Directive on the Disposal of Polychlorinated Biphenyls and Polychlorinated Terphenyls*, OJ C 319/57, 12 December 1988

62 *Council Directive 75/442/EEC Waste*, OJ L 194/39 1975

63 See European Parliament Written Question No. 2218/88, OJ C 305/30, 4 December 1989

64 *Council Directive 89/654/EEC Concerning the Minimum Safety and Health Requirements for the Workplace, (First Individual Directive within the Meaning of the Framework Directive of 12 June 1989 (1989/391/EEC)*, OJ L 393/1 1989, 30 December 1989

65 *Code of Practice for Fire Precautions in Factories, Offices, Shops and Railway Premises not Required to have a Fire Certificate*, Home Office, 1989

66 See Article by Holloway, Property Journal, June 1990, page 18

67 *The Control of Legionellosis: Proposals for Statutory Action*, Health and Safety Commission Consultative Document, CD18(F)

Section B

Materials and the Building Structure

DUSTS AND FUMES

Alan Bradley

Institute of Occupational Medicine Ltd

INTRODUCTION

Dusts and fumes occur naturally in the environment, and the human body has evidently developed an ability to survive a certain amount of exposure to them. Of concern are the health hazards arising from exposure either to 'excessive' quantities of dusts or fumes and/or to those harmful to human health in even modest concentrations.

Other chapters dealing with specific materials and/or environments cover aspects of the dust and/or fume hazard produced. Dusts and fumes are produced in the construction and use of buildings in many ways, e.g. dust is produced from the use of impact machines to break down buildings during demolition and fumes are formed during welding or arc-cutting operations. In this chapter an attempt is made to define what is meant by the terms dust and fume, to describe their harmful effects on the body in general terms, and then to guide the reader through the various phases of the construction process discussing some of the more common dusts and fumes produced in each phase.

DEFINITIONS

Airborne dust consists of solid particles rendered airborne by some physical action such as the crushing or grinding of solid substances. It can also be produced by dispersion into the air of fine powder from a bulk source or from previously settled airborne dust. Fume is formed from a material which is solid at ambient temperature. Usually it is the airborne solid particle formed by vaporization of the parent material, oxidation of the vapour and condensation of the oxide. One of the most common fumes found in construction is welding fume.

THE EFFECTS OF DUSTS AND FUMES ON THE BODY

Demolition, construction, maintenance and DIY operations can produce dust and fumes which may be harmful if they are inhaled, ingested or come into contact with the skin. Inhalation is the most common mode of entry for dusts and fumes. The criteria when assessing the potential risk from dust or fume exposure is the amount of the hazardous material likely to be inhaled and the ability of the material to reach a target area in the body and to cause harm in that area. The potential risk therefore depends on:

- the exposure level;
- the site of deposition in the respiratory tract;
- the rate of clearance from the lung;
- the toxicity and solubility of the dust;
- the rate of absorption into the body.

Exposure Level

The exposure level of a substance is equal to the concentration of the substance in the air multiplied by the time which a person spends in the dust or fume. Concentrations of dusts and fumes are usually expressed as milligrams of substance per cubic metre of air (mg m^{-3}) or, in the case of fibrous dusts, as the number of fibres per millilitre of air.

Site of Deposition

Inhaled particles may be deposited in the nasopharyngeal (nose and throat), tracheobronchial (upper lung) or alveolated (lower lung) regions of the respiratory tract. The site of deposition is determined by the falling speed of the particles. The large particles settle in the nasopharyngeal region, particles up to about 15 microns (μm) in aerodynamic (ie effective) diameter may deposit in the tracheobronchial region and only particles with aerodynamic diameter up to 7μm can be deposited in the alveolated region.

Clearance

Some of the very fine dusts reaching the lower lung are not deposited and are exhaled. The remainder which deposit are affected by a defence system which clears the deposited dust to the upper lung; from there an escalator system of small hairs and mucous fluids permits clearance by spitting or swallowing. This system removes about 95% of inhaled particles.

Toxic Effects

Depending on the physical and chemical properties of the uncleared dusts, short- or long-term health effects may be caused at the site of deposition.

Soluble dusts may be absorbed and cause systemic effects, such as:

- wood dusts: nasal cancers;
- lead: absorbed at site of deposition or ingestion after
              ciliary clearance, systemic effect;
- quartz: silicosis;
- asbestos: asbestosis, mesothelioma, lung cancer;
- chromium   contact dermatitis, perforated or ulcerated septa,
  compounds: lung cancer.

DUST OR FUMES AND CONSTRUCTION PHASES OF A PROJECT

Planning and design

Planners and designers of a construction project can take some steps to
reduce hazards from dust and fumes at all phases of a construction
programme, although the extent of control they have on actual
operations may be limited. Firstly the potential hazards of the materials
being specified must be assessed. Wherever practical, the materials with
the lowest potential risks should be selected at each phase, but risk
reduction can rarely be the sole or prime criteria for material selection.
Secondly, clients and their professional advisors or agents should ensure
that contractors and subcontractors are contractually required to meet
appropriate standards laid down by legislation. Of major importance are:

- The Health and Safety at Work etc. Act 1974
- The Control of Asbestos at Work Regulations 1987
- The Control of Lead at Work Regulations 1980
- The Control of Substances Hazardous to Health Regulations 1988.

The Health and Safety Commission produce Approved Codes of Practice
which explain the Regulations in detail and describe how operations to
meet the Regulations should be carried out in a practical manner.
Typical of these Codes of Practice are two which apply to asbestos:

- Approved Code of Practice (The Control of Asbestos at Work), 1988
- Approved Code of Practice, Work with Asbestos Insulation,
  Asbestos Coating and Asbestos Insulating Board, 1988.

Also available from the Health and Safety Executive (HSE) are several
series of Guidance Notes. These deal with specialist subjects in great
detail and, whilst they do not carry the full force of the law, they do
represent what the HSE consider to be good safe practice. Typical

titles in the environmental hygiene (EH) series include:

- EH2   Chromium – Health and Safety Precautions
- EH7   Petroleum-based Adhesives in Building Operations
- EH16 Isocyanates – Toxic Hazards and Precautions
- EH35 Probable Asbestos Dust Concentrations at Construction Processes
- EH44 Dust in the Workplace – General Principles of Protection
- EH54 Assessment of exposure to fume from welding and allied processes
- EH55 Control of Exposure to Fume from Welding, Brazing and Similar Processes

There is much more relevant legislation and associated information available, and clients and their professional advisors and agents should research the relevant legislation prior to contract writing and ensure that only legislation current at that time is included.

Under the new Control of Substances Hazardous to Health Regulations, all employers are required to protect the health of their employees and other people likely to be affected by exposure to substances at work. This protection is carried out by assessing the potential risk associated with substances potentially hazardous to health. The assessment involves looking at the way hazardous substances are used and then making a judgement about the possible risks to health. Reference should be made to the appropriate HSE Guidance Note giving advice on the application of the Regulations to the construction industry.

When some controlled materials, such as asbestos, are involved a statement of the method of working is often required by the HSE, and the client and his professional advisors or agents can request copies of this.

Demolition

During demolition, which nowadays so often precedes new construction, dust from two major sources may be encountered: that left by previous users of the building, or that produced by demolition activities.

When buildings are demolished, the vibrations caused by the use of impact machines can re-entrain deposited dusts from ledges. Some of these dusts, e.g. grain dust, vegetable dusts and wood dusts, in high airborne concentrations, can be extremely explosive if they come into contact with a naked flame. Others such as lead dust and its compounds can be hazardous after only a relatively short exposure by either inhalation or ingestion. Other dusts such as chromium compounds can cause contact dermatitis.

Prior to any demolition of industrial premises which are heavily contaminated with dust, an investigation to assess the potential risk is recommended. This may take the form of a historical data search to find out what processes were carried out in the building and what materials were involved; sampling and analysis may be required. Care should be also taken, prior to demolition, to study the structure of the building for the possible presence of hazardous materials such as asbestos and lead that are covered by specific regulations which require that special removal practices are used. Other potentially hazardous materials which are not covered by specific regulations are covered by the Control of Substances Hazardous to Health Regulations; it is therefore the employer's duty to control the exposure of his employees and others to these substances. Usually special work practices will have to be devised for working with them.

The process of demolishing a building is a violent operation and highly concentrated dust clouds are often raised from the structural material being broken. Much of this dust such as cement, brick etc. is coarse and not very toxic. There is little evidence that lifetime exposures of lower than the occupational exposure limit of the so-called nuisance dusts cause permanent damage to health. However, quartz (which can cause silicosis) is found in sand, granite and to a lesser extent other building materials, and so care must be taken to protect the work-force by control measures such as regularly damping down rubble.

Gas-cutting operations melt the metal being cut and during these operations fume is produced from the parent metal. Typically the fumes are the oxides of the various major and trace metals in the structure being cut. These can include, among others:

- iron, which causes siderosis;
- zinc, which causes metal fume fever;
- lead, which causes lead poisoning.

Particulate matter can also be produced by burning-off paints and other treatments on the metal. It is often impractical to fit local exhaust ventilation at the source of the fume in operations such as demolition; nevertheless this should be done wherever practical. Cutting should only be carried out where there is an ample supply of fresh air and the operator should wear, as an added precaution, an approved respirator. Cutting should not be carried out in confined spaces unless mechanical ventilation is applied continuously into the space.

Development on Previously Used Land

An increasing amount of development is occurring on land previously used for industrial purposes. In these cases the project manager should ensure that a site survey is carried out to identify any contaminants in the land to be worked. Contaminated land is dealt with in detail elsewhere (Chapter C9) and so it is only necessary here to consider the dust that may be raised in construction operations and contaminants that may be left on site and later raised as dust to which the user of the development may be exposed.

Construction Phase

There are many potential sources of dust and fume in the construction phase, the most common being dust raised in building operations, fumes from welding and burning, and fumes from brazing and jointing cables.

During the construction phase, dust is raised by digging and loading operations and from vehicle movement. The dust can contain some of the soil contaminants and therefore must be controlled during these operations by use of water and protective clothing. Wheel washing facilities should be provided so that contaminated soil is not transported from the site on vehicle wheels. This material can easily be deposited on public roads, later becoming airborne into the atmosphere by other vehicles. Often, dust raised on site passes over the site boundary. Normally this causes a nuisance problem rather than a health problem to the public. On these occasions environmental health officers have enforcement powers to stop the dust release.

Dusts are raised during building by the handling and mixing of dry powders such as cement, plaster, lime etc. and by similar operations involving bulk materials such as sand and gravel. Usually the dusts from these operations are of relatively low toxicity except possibly for those such as sand which may contain quartz. Control of exposure in these circumstances is usually by careful handling, good housekeeping and the use of disposable respirators.

Problems of more concern in building operations are associated with high dust concentrations from the cutting and trimming of stone, slate or marble and to a lesser extent of blocks, bricks and concrete. With stone, slate or marble, these operations should be carried out using water as a dust suppressant at the contractor's workshops where local exhaust ventilation can be applied. Where it is necessary to carry out operations on these materials on site, portable local exhaust ventilators fitted with suitable filters must be used and HSE-approved respirators are also recommended as an additional precaution.

Isocyanate paint spraying can raise both airborne vapours and particulates. Most modern isocyanate paints contain either methylene bisphenylisocyanate (MDI) or hexamethylene diisocyanate (HDI), which are safer than toluene-2,4-diisocyanate (TDI) which is vaporous (the other two are particulate). Isocyanates are sensitizing agents and should be used with extreme care. Operators should use an approved respirator giving adequate protection during spray operations. Positive pressure respirators fitted with a particulate/organic vapour cartridge may be used during brush applications. In both types of application an exclusion zone should be set up around the work area to avoid exposure of other persons to the isocyanates.

The installation of fibrous materials such as man-made mineral fibre is dealt with elsewhere (Chapter B4).

During construction, welding operations are quite common, with cutting operations being less frequent. During welding, fumes are produced from the welding rod, from pre-applied coatings and from the parent metal itself. The fumes consist mainly of metal oxides. Typically present may be iron, manganese, copper, tin, nickel and zinc, plus many other trace metals. Welding fume can be adequately controlled by the use of local exhaust ventilation to collect the fumes at source. Unfortunately, because local exhaust ventilation equipment can be fairly bulky and requires time to be spent on positioning the equipment, it is rarely used in the construction industry. With the implementation of the Control of Substances Hazardous to Health Regulations, a welder's employer is required to assess the hazard and to control it to acceptable standards. The site management team should make sure this is done.

Maintenance and the Building User

Maintenance operations produce dust and fumes in many ways. Some of these operations can also be encountered in partial demolition and/or refurbishing programmes. Operations which may affect the building occupants include:

* entry panels or ceiling tiles that are removed in order to expose services may contain fibrous materials, including asbestos. Their origin should be identified and a check made with the manufacturer. If that proves impossible, and the panels are suspected of containing asbestos, an analysis before disturbance might be prudent. If asbestos is found the panels should be removed only under strictly controlled conditions laid down by the HSE;
* stripping of paint by sanding can produce dust containing lead whilst stripping by hot guns can produce lead fume. Paints can contain harmful metals other than lead, e.g. cadmium. The sanding down of hard woods can produce dust which may cause nasal cancer. As with most carcinogens, the lower levels of exposure have not been fully investigated but there is no known safe level for carcinogens;
* texture paints applied many years ago may contain asbestos as the

texturing agent. Rubbing down of these surfaces can be extremely hazardous;

- even the simple common operation of breaking down structural walls may produce dust containing quartz which causes silicosis. Exposure is unlikely to be high enough to cause ill health to the building user but persons working regularly on maintenance may be subject to risk.

It is obvious from the above list that maintenance contractors need to plan operations carefully in order not to affect the building occupants or the contractor's own employees. The maintenance contractor should therefore consider the following actions:

- ensure that building ventilation systems are either blanked off or totally switched off to avoid the transportation of dust or fumes from the immediate area of work;
- screen off the work area using wooden frames covered in double plastic sheets;
- use a temporary ventilation unit to apply negative pressure to the screened area and fit it with a filtration unit to collect the dust or fumes;
- create exclusion zones where only workmen are allowed to enter. Move occupiers from areas immediately adjacent to the area being worked. For major hazardous materials such as asbestos consider fully evacuating whole floors or the whole building;
- ensure that the work-force are protected by approved protective clothing which they have been trained to wear and which has been properly maintained.

The Building in Normal Use

During normal everyday use there is little significant hazard to the occupant from dust and fumes originating from the materials in the building. The proven exception is from gradual deterioration of sprayed asbestos or asbestos insulation which can produce low concentrations of fibres to which the occupier may be exposed. However, in the case of asbestos insulation, there may be less risk to health in leaving it in place if it is well sealed than would be the case if it were removed.

Research also suggests that some ill health may be caused by other dusts such as household dust including house mites; this is at the level of allergic reaction and is described elsewhere (Chapter C6).

CONCLUSIONS

* Airborne dust and fumes can be raised at almost any phase of a construction programme, and all of them are, to some degree, harmful.

* Of the dusts raised during building and demolition operations, those originating from common building materials such as cement, lime and plaster are not particularly dangerous in normal concentrations.

* Fumes from gas cutting of metals and paint burning, and dusts from wood, lead and chromium compounds, asbestos and quartz have well defined toxic effects. Many dusts form explosive mixtures with air. Dusts raised during the redevelopment of land previously used for industrial purposes may contain other toxic materials.

* Planners and designers should take steps to reduce the risks by using the information and guidance provided by the Health and Safety Commission, the Health and Safety Executive and others to specify materials and methods of use.

* Contractors should be required to follow current legislation and guidance to control dusts and fumes at source whenever possible, or to use efficient approved personal protective clothing. Good control can only be achieved by ensuring that equipment is well maintained and that all the workforce know of the risks and are efficiently trained to use the controls provided.

* If these steps are taken, risks to the health of the workforce and community will be contained to currently acceptable levels.

* As with other hazardous activity, it is possible that currently acceptable risks will need to be reduced and construction professionals will need to keep up to date with developing guidance and legislation.

BIBLIOGRAPHY

Harvey B. (Editor in Chief), *Handbook of Occupational Hygiene*, Croner
   Publications, London, 1990
Clayton, G.D. & F.E. (Editors), *Patty's Industrial Hygiene and Toxicology*, John
   Wiley & Sons, New York, 1978

Acts and Regulations from Her Majesty's Stationery Office:

   The Health & Safety at Work etc Act, 1974
   The Control of Asbestos at Work Regulations, 1987
   The Control of Lead at Work Regulations, 1980
   The Control of Substances Hazardous to Health Regulations, 1989
   Asbestos Licensing Regulations, 1983

Approved Codes of Practice from the Health and Safety Commission:

> *Work with Asbestos Insulation, Asbestos Coating and Asbestos Insulating Board, 1988*
> *The Control of Asbestos at Work, 1988*
> *Control of Substances Hazardous to Health*
> *Control of Carcinogenic Substances, 1988*

Guidance Notes from the Health and Safety Executive:

> *EH 2 Chromium – Health and Safety Precautions*
> *EH 7 Petroleum – based Adhesives in Building Operations*
> *EH10 Asbestos – Control limits and measurement of airborne dust concentrations (revised), 1988*
> *EH16 Isocyanates – Toxic Hazards and Precautions*
> *EH18 Toxic substances – a precautionary policy*
> *EH35 Probable asbestos dust concentrations at construction processes*
> *EH40/90 Occupational exposure limits, 1990*
> *EH44 Dust in the Workplace – General Principles of Protection.*
> *COSHH Assessments – A step-by-step guide to assessment and the skills needed*
> *EH54 Assessment of Exposure to Fume from Welding and Allied Processes*
> *EH55 Control of Exposure to Fume from Welding, Brazing and Similar Processes*

GASES, VAPOURS AND MISTS

Alastair Robertson

Institute of Occupational Medicine Ltd

INTRODUCTION

Many potentially hazardous gases, vapours and mists can be encountered during demolition, land decontamination, construction and building occupancy. The risks from exposure depend on the chemical involved and the extent of exposure. It is the aim of this chapter to outline some of the more common problems and provide some suggestions for their control, rather than define and detail the hazards associated with each gas, vapour and mist which could be encountered during all phases of construction and occupancy.

The chapter has been divided into four sections. The first deals with general aspects, including health effects, legislation and broad principles of control. The remaining three sections cover, in turn, site preparation, construction, and occupancy, outlining hazards, sources and control measures. Chlorofluorocarbons (CFCs) and pesticides other than wood preservatives are not covered in this chapter, as each is the subject of a separate chapter. As these two classes of chemicals are by far the major environmental problems associated with gases, vapours and mists in the construction industry, environmental aspects are not considered further here.

BACKGROUND

Gases and Vapours : Definitions and Properties

There is a clear distinction between the terms gas and vapour, despite confusion about them in some quarters. Gases or, more correctly, permanent gases cannot be compressed into liquids or solids at normal ambient temperatures, whereas vapours *can* be compressed into liquids or solids. The differences are made more obvious by considering some simple examples. Oxygen, methane and carbon monoxide are all permanent gases, whereas gaseous phases of solvents, such as benzene, trichloroethane and hexane, would be classified as vapours.

Although hazards associated with gases and vapours are primarily a function of their chemical structure and reactivity, the risks are often influenced by the physical properties of the material, particularly where hazards are associated with vapours. It is therefore important to begin by describing some of these basic properties.

The concept of vapour pressure is very important. Any solid or liquid has a vapour pressure at ambient temperatures; in other words, there will be molecules or atoms of the material in the gas phase above it. For many materials, such as wood, iron and glass, the vapour pressure is so infinitesimally small that it is totally irrelevant. The higher the vapour pressure of a material, the more likely it is that the material will exist in the gas phase in significant concentrations, and, even though their vapour pressures are low, the vapours of certain materials (e.g. mercury) can be hazardous to health. Many organic solvents which are commonly used in the construction industry have vapour pressures sufficiently high for vapour concentrations of 30% or more to exist in the air, and occupational exposure limits are invariably only a very small fraction of such concentrations. While these very high levels would normally only occur in enclosed spaces, the consequences can be tragic when they are encountered; many deaths by poisoning, asphyxiation and explosions have occurred.

The vapour pressure is also an indicator of the volatility of a material or, in other words, how quickly it will evaporate. This can be very important in assessing and controlling risks to health associated with vapour exposure. There is little doubt that, the higher the volatility of a solvent, the higher the likely exposure of an individual using the material concerned. One of the principles of occupational hygiene control is the substitution of a hazardous material by a less hazardous material. If the less hazardous material is much more volatile, this approach could actually increase risks to health as vapour concentrations of the substitute could be much higher. This effect has been observed in reverse with mastics. The risks were reduced by going from a xylene-based mastic to one based on mesitylene (which is less volatile but nominally more harmful) as the airborne vapour levels were much lower with the substitute material.

With evaporation, the major point to note is that a small volume of liquid will produce a large volume of gas, with clear consequences. If 1 litre of, say, xylene from paint is evaporated and dispersed in a room of dimensions 10 m x 5 m x 2 m (100 m³) and there is no ventilation, the resulting concentration will be around 2,000 parts per million (ppm). The occupational exposure standard is 100 ppm.

Evaporation is not the only means by which gas and vapour concentrations can build up to hazardous levels. Leaking high pressure gas lines are an obvious source of rapid increases in concentrations. Similarly, combustion can cause acute problems, with carbon monoxide being an all too common cause of fatalities.

The final physical property of gases and vapours of interest is diffusion. Gases and vapours do not need air movement to move across workplace areas. Even in calm air they diffuse from areas of high concentration to areas of low concentration. Toxic gases can therefore be found in unexpected areas and more people may be exposed in a process or operation than would otherwise be predicted. Diffusion is being increasingly utilized in gas sampling instrumentation (see Appendix 1).

Mists – Definition and Properties

A mist is a suspension of liquid droplets in air. In the context of construction and building, mists are most likely to occur as part of a spraying process (painting, pesticide treatment etc.), in contrast with gases and vapours which are more commonly unwanted by-products of the operation.

Mists behave similarly to dusts. Their hazards are functions of their chemical structure and reactivity, and of their aerodynamic size distribution which determines where the droplet would be deposited in the respiratory tract. (The relationship between particle size and deposition in the respiratory tract is discussed in Chapter B1.)

Health Effects, Legislation and Control

The numbers of health effects from exposure to gases, vapours and mists in the construction industry are almost as numerous as the chemicals used. There are sensitizers, irritants and carcinogens. Many organic solvents are central nervous system depressants while some gases and vapours cause liver, kidney or lung damage.

Because of their physical properties, gases and vapours are much more likely to present an acute hazard in the industrial environment than dusts, fumes or mists. Indeed, most gases and vapours may, if concentrations are allowed to rise out of control, cause serious and immediate risks to health. However, their health hazards are not restricted to acute effects. Many of the hazards listed above can arise from prolonged or chronic exposure at relatively low concentrations.

The law requires that the health of employees is protected and in the field of gases, vapours and mists the Health and Safety at Work etc Act 1974 and the Control of Substances Hazardous to Health (COSHH) Regulations 1988 are the prime items of legislation to be followed. The Health and Safety Executive have produced much useful guidance for employers seeking to comply with these regulations, the COSHH Regulations Approved Codes of Practice, and the HSE Guide to the COSHH Regulations being particularly helpful. In certain instances the risks of fires and explosions are also great where gases and vapours are involved, and the Highly Flammable Liquids and Liquified Petroleum

Gases Regulations 1972, as amended by the Classification, Packaging and Labelling Regulations 1984, apply. (Fire and explosion hazards are considered in detail in Chapter B8.)

The indoor environment is another area of growing concern. The COSHH Regulations and the Health and Safety at Work Act both apply, but problems seem to occur in the office environment which are difficult to relate to normal occupational practice and exposure limits. These difficulties are often associated with recirculation of building air and a lack of ventilation, thus allowing gas and vapour concentrations to build up to noticeable levels. The Factories Act 1961 and the Offices, Shops and Railway Premises Act 1963 require that there is an adequate supply of fresh air, and the Health and Safety Executive gives guidance on the definition of adequate in Guidance Note EH22 Ventilation of the Workplace. This was revised in 1988 and covers a wide range of buildings, including offices, shops, factories, laboratories, residences, conference rooms and board rooms. In almost all instances, allowance is made for smoking. Minimum outdoor air supply figures per person and by floor area are given. Slightly higher fresh air values per person are recommended however, and these range from 8 to 25 litres per second per person according to the location and floor area.

Good control of the risks from exposure to gases and vapours starts at the planning stage. Any new building must have adequate ventilation and supplies of fresh air and, where possible, the use of materials which will emit gases and vapours after installation should be avoided. During site preparation, construction and maintenance, contractors and subcontractors should comply with the appropriate health and safety legislation, a duty which can usefully be reinforced by making compliance a condition of contract. Lastly, and perhaps most importantly, the work-force should be encouraged to respect the materials they work with and to be aware of the potential hazards.

DEMOLITION AND SITE PREPARATION

The obvious sources of gases and vapours in demolition are cutting and burning. When clean or rusty metal is being dealt with, the major gas problems are carbon monoxide and oxides of nitrogen. It is difficult to avoid producing these, and ventilation control is clearly impracticable in many circumstances. If possible, workers should avoid standing and working directly in the plume, and in open spaces this will frequently give sufficient protection. However, respiratory protection is often necessary and, if so, the appropriate respirators should be selected. The HSE has produced, over the years, lists of approved respirators with information on their performance and where they should be used. The problems are substantially increased, however, if metal coated with paint, plastic or similar material is being cut. Most organic polymers give off toxic gases and smoke when burnt, and it is good practice to remove these coatings before flame cutting. When this is not practicable, suitable respirators must be worn by the workers involved. It should also be remembered that, if these control measures are to be effective, the workforce must be made aware of hazards and be appropriately trained.

Demolition of industrial premises can lead to other problems. Various unwanted chemicals are often left when the building becomes unoccupied. CFCs and volatile flammable solvents are particularly common, and contractors should be aware of the possibilities of finding PCBs (polychlorinated biphenyls) in old transformers. Clearly, any such material should be removed and properly disposed of before the main structural demolition starts. It is a relatively simple job if the materials are stored in sound drums or similar containers, but problems arise if the containers are immovable or rusting or if the liquids are left in pipework or similar transport systems. The best way of avoiding these hazards is sound, careful planning. The previous use(s) of the building should be ascertained, any information on stored chemicals should be collected and, if any drawings of the building remain, these should be inspected to identify the probable locations of any special hazards. Any pipework should be carefully drained and, if there are any doubts about the contents, these should be analysed before any work is started.

Many areas of land have been contaminated by previous industrial activities and in some cases gases and vapours are still emitted when the land is disturbed. There are two types of problem. The simpler is where there are underground tanks of chemicals on sites. It is better if these can be identified in advance of reclamation, but this is not always possible and developers should be aware that in certain industrial locations unpleasant surprises may be lurking six feet below the surface. In either case, once discovered, the tank can be drained and the material removed safely. Personal protection may be necessary, but only for relatively short periods and for clearly defined tasks. The more complex problems arise when the ground itself is impregnated with volatile materials, either from leaking storage tanks or from years of illicit dumping. Serious health hazards may arise and, in certain circumstances, special working practices may need to be developed to prevent explosions. Long-term usage of respirators may be required to reduce health risks, but vehicle drivers can often be adequately protected in air-conditioned cabs. The problems of working on contaminated land are discussed in detail in Chapter C9.

CONSTRUCTION

A large number of chemical products which can emit hazardous gases and vapours are used in the construction industry. These products are often used for fitting out once the building shell is complete and natural ventilation is relatively poor. In consequence the associated risks generally occur during construction and even immediately after occupation. These hazards have tended to multiply with changing construction methods, and the ever-increasing numbers of adhesives, solvent cleaners, flooring, paints, insulation materials and mastics, which can all emit gases and vapours.

Hazards

It is only possible here to present some general principles relating to hazards and their control, and to identify some of the more common problems.

The most ubiquitous vapours found during construction are organic solvents. White spirit, toluene, xylene and trichloroethane are among the most commonly used, and are found in adhesives, paints, flooring materials, mastics and cleansing-degreasing fluids. There is surprisingly little published information on the exposures of workers using these materials, but the literature, together with the experience of the staff of the Institute of Occupational Medicine Ltd, Edinburgh, suggests that, unless some care is taken, high airborne concentrations can occur when any of these materials is used. In addition, inhalation is not the only route of exposure when solvents are used. Absorption through the skin can be a major route and, of course, continuing contact with the skin can cause dermatitis. It should be remembered that gloves are often permeable to organic solvents and use of the wrong type of glove may therefore be worse than using no gloves at all.

A number of other vapours are associated with certain types of adhesives. Some of these contain quite hazardous materials (e.g. isocyanates, epichlorohydrin, styrene and formaldehyde) and care should be taken to prevent overexposure. Paints can also pose specific problems. During normal application vapour concentrations can be high and care should be taken to ensure that ventilation is adequate and to use paints with solvents of relatively low toxicity. Paints with extremely hazardous solvent bases such as carbon tetrachloride are still available and should be avoided. Spray painting is clearly more hazardous with vapour concentrations being higher and mists and even biocides posing problems. Paints containing lead should not be sprayed. Roofing and flooring often involve heating of pitch or bitumen and both give off fumes. Pitch fumes are much more hazardous than those from bitumen as they contain much higher levels of known carcinogens, and bitumen should be used in preference wherever possible. However, in neither case should tar or bitumen boilers be allowed in unventilated areas and, when out of doors, the workers must be instructed against working directly in the plumes of fumes being emitted.

Sprayed insulation can cause considerable risks during application. Polyurethane insulation is now the most commonly used. The unpolymerized sprays contain isocyanates which are known sensitizers and may cause asthma, and strict precautions must be taken to control exposure. The use of prepolymers can greatly assist in this although, in any case, proper ventilation is required and respirators are often necessary. Similarly, care is also necessary if urea-formaldehyde, or related sprayed insulation, is used. The British Standards Institution have published standard specifications for cavity wall insulation of this type and a code of practice for its installation. The problems with these formaldehyde-based resins do not disappear once application is completed since formaldehyde can be emitted at quite high rates for considerable periods, even years, after application.

The hazards outlined above are all associated directly with the materials being used. Other problems are associated with the work carried out, in particular welding, cutting and burning. When clean metal is involved, the probable gaseous emissions are carbon monoxide and oxides of nitrogen in addition to metal fume (covered in Chapter B1). If painted or coated surfaces are involved, a vast range of gaseous materials can be given off depending on the coating. Wherever possible, coatings should be removed before any welding or flame cutting is carried out. Soldering is another source of particulate fume and hazardous vapours. The problems are exacerbated if coatings, usually polyvinyl chloride (PVC) insulation, are heated with the wire to be soldered. Such practices should be avoided.

Control

It is necessary under the Health and Safety at Work Act and the COSHH Regulations to prevent or control adequately exposures to hazardous substances. An important first step is to inform the workforce of the potential hazards associated with the work and the need for and means of controlling exposure. Proper education in occupational health matters does more to reduce exposure than expensive engineering controls which are often ineffectual if the work-force does not believe they are necessary.

Next, there is a hierarchy of control measures which can be applied: elimination of the substance; substitution by a less hazardous material; segregation of the source from the workforce; local exhaust and general ventilation; and, as a last resort, respiratory protective equipment. A working method is required with a health and safety standard at least equal to that required in the safety data sheets provided with each material. These sheets may be difficult to interpret from time to time (e.g. the phrase 'well ventilated area' may mean on top of the British

Telecom Tower in a gale) but, with a little care and good common sense, practicable and effective control measures can be achieved.

OCCUPANCY

The occupier of a building can be exposed to mists, gases and vapours in several ways. The general indoor environment may be polluted from outdoor sources, building materials, or indoor activities. Maintenance can produce these materials and there may be specific industrial processes which cause occupational hygiene problems.

The Indoor Environment

One consequence of the energy crises of the 1970s was the search for increased energy efficiency in building design. As a result, there is less fresh air being drawn into buildings and ventilation often includes the recirculation of air. Despite advances in air-conditioning systems, an unwanted and unforeseen consequence has been an increase in indoor air pollution.

Gases and vapours are important components of indoor air pollution. With the exception of formaldehyde from particle board, gas and vapour concentrations in the indoor environment are generally well below occupational exposure limits or, indeed, levels which would be expected to cause health effects or irritation amongst those exposed. However, recent work has shown that very low levels of organic vapours in the office environment can cause eye, nose and throat irritation. In addition, while certainly not the sole cause, low levels of organic vapours have been implicated as contributing to sick building syndrome (see Chapter C5). There is therefore a burgeoning literature characterizing gases and vapours in indoor air, identifying sources, controlling exposure and quantifying risks.

Sources can be conveniently classed in four categories:

- *combustion*:   smoking, unventilated heaters etc
- *activities:*   painting, cleaning, cooking, photocopying, solvent use
- *outside*:   outdoor air, soil contamination, water supplies
- *construction materials*:   insulation, mastic, furnishings

Many gases and vapours have been detected indoors at measurable concentrations, and the species found clearly depend on the source. Some examples are given in Table B2.1. The range of pollutants and their airborne concentrations are normally greater indoors than outside.

Concentrations depend primarily on the rates of emission and the size and ventilation of the building or room concerned. In many ways indoor pollution from combustion and outdoor sources is beyond the scope of this book but, as both can be substantial contributors to indoor gas and vapour levels, they deserve a brief mention.

Cigarette smoking is a major source of combustion gases and smoke. It has been recognized as a nuisance for many years by non-smokers, but risks to health from passive smoking have only recently been quantified, and many organizations are either banning smoking or restricting it to designated areas. Other combustion sources such as gas cookers, paraffin heaters and gas and solid fuel fires all produce a wide range of gaseous pollutants. There has been some controversy surrounding the effects of gas cookers on the respiratory health of children but, generally, these contribute little to indoor pollution unless they are not properly vented.

Air pollution is generally greater indoors than outside. Consequently, pollution entering from outside is not normally a problem but, where it is, it is difficult to control. It can arise from contaminated land under or around the building, adjacent industrial or municipal operations, and even through the water supply. The problem is perhaps best addressed at the planning stage by proper land decontamination or careful site selection. However, if these are not practicable or conditions change, odours can only be removed by ensuring that air entering the building passes through air filtration units.

Vapour- and gas-generating activities are common in all buildings. During office activities such as gluing, the use of felt tip pens and correction fluids, photocopying and a wide range of printing, including some laser printers, concentrations are generally low, but they produce odours, and even irritation in some individuals. People also produce odours. Everyone has encountered unpleasant body odours, but cosmetics also emit a range of vapours in addition to perfumes and these too can cause workers to complain. As an antidote to these difficulties, it is best to ensure that there is an adequate supply of fresh air to the building. If felt to be appropriate, charcoal or similar filters can be used to reduce odours and solvents from recirculating air, though their effectiveness is variable and temperature dependent.

Building materials and furnishings such as adhesives, mastics, paints, carpets, insulating materials, pesticides, plastics and particle board, are the fourth major source of gases and vapours in the indoor environment. Examples of the vapours emitted are given in Table B2.1.

In general, emissions from building materials are worst in newly occupied buildings, and concentrations decline quite rapidly thereafter. Nevertheless, care should be taken to avoid or minimize the use of such materials wherever possible. This can be done at the initial design stage but changes can still be made during construction. However, it may still

Table B2.1 Some example of gases and vapours commonly found in the indoor environment

	Combustion	Plywood, particle board etc.	MMMF board
Inorganic			
Carbon monoxide	√		
Nitrogen dioxide	√		
Sulphur dioxide	√		
Carbon monoxide	√		
Nitric oxide	√		
Organic			
Alkanes			
n-Hexane			
n-Heptane			
n-Octane			
n-Nonane			
n-Decane			
Terpenes			
α-Pinene		√	
Limonene		√	
Aromatic hydrocarbons			
Benzene	√	√	
Toluene	√	√	
Xylene			
Ethylbenzene			
Trimethylbenzene			
Styrene		√	
Naphthalene	√		
Chlorinated bydrocarbons			
Methylene chloride			
1,1,1-Trichloroethane			
Trichloroethylene			
Chloroform			
Tetrachloroethylene			
Chlorobenzene			
Dichlorobenzene		√	
Oxygenated species			
Formaldehyde	√	√	√
Acrolein	√	√	
Acetone			
Methyl ethyl ketone		√	
Pentanal			√
Hexanal		√	√
Benzaldehyde		√	√
Methanol			
Ethanol			
Butanol		√	
Ethyl acetate			
Ethoxyethanol			
Phthalic acid anhydride			

PAINTS AND VARNISH	ADHESIVES AND MASTIC	CLEANING MATERIALS: POLISH, CLEANING LIQUIDS	COSMETICS AND DEODORIZERS	FLOORING: CARPETING, LINOLEUM, PVC
√ √ √ √ √	√ √ √ √	√ √ √ √ √	√	√ √ √ √ √
		√ √	√ √	
√ √ √ √ √	√ √ √ √	√ √ √	√ √ √	√ √ √ √
√ √ √	√ √ √ √	√ √ √	√	√ √
√ √ √	√ √ √ √ √	√ √ √ √ √		√

be necessary to use many materials which slowly emit gases and vapours. Good ventilation is usually the key to avoiding odour and irritation problems in these circumstances, although recently, in an attempt to reduce emissions in the first few weeks of occupancy, some new buildings have been 'baked out' prior to occupancy.

There are a number of emitters which persist for months and even years. The most important are pesticides (see Chapter C8) and materials bonded with urea-formaldehyde, including particle board, blockboard and plywood. Of these, particle board is recognized as the greatest problem. Its urea-formaldehyde resins can slowly emit formaldehyde for considerable periods. Formaldehyde is an irritant, an allergen and a suspect carcinogen, and it is often found in elevated concentrations in buildings where particle board is used. Very high levels have been observed, but in recent years emissions have been reduced by using improved resins, and purchasers should now ensure that they only buy these low emission boards. Further reductions in emissions can be made by sealing all boards. Unfinished undersides of desks and even small drilled holes for optional fittings have been shown to increase emissions significantly. Urea-formaldehyde insulating foams may produce similar problems, but the use of these materials is now uncommon in construction.

Maintenance

The hazards from gases and vapours during building maintenance are similar to those encountered during construction (see above). Paints, adhesives, bituminous materials, pesticides and cleansing solvents are all used, and even welding and cutting may be necessary. The major additional consideration is that occupants as well as operatives may be exposed to some risk.

Buildings should, whenever practicable, be constructed so that emissions of gases and vapours are minimized during maintenance and, when materials which emit gases and vapours must be used, care should be taken to select those where risks will be least. However, there are difficulties. In almost all buildings, large areas require painting, carpets need to be replaced and stuck down from time to time, roofing and floors wear out, and solvent-based cleaners and polishes are very widely used. As a result, as far as protecting the operatives is concerned, the same guiding principles outlined for construction should be followed: the Health and Safety at Work Act and the COSHH Regulations and good occupational hygiene practices should be adopted.

Maintenance work may be carried out in-house or by contractors. It is often easier to control contractors (through their contract) than unsupervised in-house maintenance which is frequently carried out by a handyman, who may use some unnecessarily toxic material which happens to be cheap. The in-house work must be carried out to meet the same health and safety standards as any other maintenance. During maintenance, unwanted odours may pervade the building. These may cause complaints and even some irritation and should be minimised. A knowledge of ventilation flows around the building is essential, and a building maintenance manual could be a useful source of this information.

Wood Preservatives

Wood preservatives are pesticides used to protect wood from biological attack such as wet rot, dry rot, wood-boring insects etc. Each contains at least one active ingredient and some of the most common are listed in Table B2.2. Many, particularly those developed some time ago, are highly hazardous to health and must be handled and used with the utmost care.

Table B2.2 Some common active ingredients in wood preservatives

	Fungicide	Insecticide	IARC(1) carcinogen classification	Measurable(2) vapour pressure
Arsenic pentoxide	√		1	
Copper naphthenate				
Copper sulphate	√			
Creosote	√		2A(3)	√
Cypermethrin		√		√
Dichlofluanid	√			
Disodium octaborate	√			
Dodecylbenzyltrimethylammoniumchloride	√			
Lindane		√	2B	√
Pentachlorophenol		√	2B	√
Pentachlorophenyllaurate		√		
Permethrin		√		
Sodium dichromate	√	√	1	
Tributyltinoxide		√		√
Zinc naphthenate				

(1) International Agency for Research on Cancer
Category   1   Carcinogenic to humans
            2A   Probably carcinogenic to humans
            2B   Possibly carcinogenic to humans
(2) $>10^{-6}$ mm mercury at room temperature
(3) Coal tar creosote

In the construction industry, there is potential exposure to wood preservatives at all stages from site preparation through to occupancy, but it is likely that, during site preparation and building, exposures will be limited to handling pre-treated wood and risks will be relatively slight. (There is always a possibility that containers of pesticides could be encountered during demolition. These should be dealt with in the same manner as any other toxic chemical.) Greatest risks are likely to occur during maintenance when wood preservatives are being applied and immediately thereafter.

The use of wood preservatives is subject to both the Health and Safety at Work Act 1974 and the COSHH Regulations 1988. However, there are additional restrictions imposed by the Food and Environment Protection Act 1985 and the Control of Pesticides Regulations 1986. These regulations require that industrial and professional applications of pesticides, including wood preservatives, are carried out by suitably trained staff who are aware of the potential hazards to themselves and others. Approval schemes are also required by the regulations and these are run by the Ministry of Agriculture, Fisheries and Food and the Health & Safety Executive (HSE). The HSE scheme is obviously more relevant to construction, and lists of approved wood preservatives are regularly produced. This list gives the marketing company, the product name, the active ingredient, the approved use and the approval number. The approval also includes instructions for use.

The regulations go a long way towards ensuring that pesticides are used safely, but other precautions will minimize any risks to users and occupants.

- Careful selection of the preservative is important. In principle the least toxic material which can do the job should be used, but the most efficient preservative is often selected regardless of its toxicity. Slightly volatile chemicals should also be avoided. For example, elevated airborne lindane concentrations have been reported in buildings 10 years after application, and the safety of lindane and other chlorinated pesticides has been questioned in recent years. The procedures used for application are also important. Ideally wood preservatives should only be applied when buildings are unoccupied; areas for treatment should be emptied and then sealed off to avoid or at least minimize unwanted contamination. Where appropriate, carpets, curtains and soft furnishings should be removed prior to application. The preservative must not be allowed to contaminate the water supply or any food in the building.

- The application should be selected on the basis of minimizing risks to the health of operators and occupants. The best method of application is to paint on the preservatives as a water-based paste or solution. Organic solvents are also used as carriers, but these often have the disadvantage of being potential hazards themselves. Nevertheless painting organic solvent solutions of wood preservatives can be a safe and specific means of application. Where neither is feasible, spraying is probably the next best alternative, but only if it is carried out carefully and with due regard to the potential hazards. Smoke bomb applications are best avoided because they are indiscriminate and uncontrolled, and their efficacy has been questioned.

• Finally, after application has been completed, care should be taken to ensure that the treated area is fit for habitation. It should be inspected to ensure that there is no exposed area with unwanted contamination. The area should be left ventilated but unoccupied for at least 24 hours to allow airborne pesticide levels to drop. Note that the carriers used in wood preservatives often have odours and they may be irritants in themselves. They are, therefore, often mistakenly identified by occupants as the pesticides, giving rise to undue concern and loss of confidence in the contractor. It may be best in these circumstances to delay re-occupation until the area is odour-free.

Wood preservation treatment is usually carried out by specialist contractors who should be obliged by the terms of their contract to adhere to the relevant legislation. The contractor selected should be willing to use the modern less toxic pesticides and have a good reputation for responding to complaints in a satisfactory way.

Finally, the active ingredients of many wood preservatives can significantly damage the environment. Pesticides are commonly found in water and food at levels which could have a damaging effect on health. Bird and insect populations have been unwittingly reduced and pesticides, particularly tributyltin oxide, have had very serious effects on the fauna of rivers and waterways. Most incidents of this nature have been caused by the agricultural industry or users of antifouling paints on boats. Nevertheless those involved in construction should recognise that they too have a part to play. Wood preservatives should be used carefully, and any excess or waste preservatives should be disposed of through reputable licensed waste disposal contractors.

CONCLUSIONS

* There are hundreds of gases and vapours to which construction workers and occupants may be exposed, and there is a likelihood of the numbers of such gases and vapours increasing as new products are introduced.

* Depending on the concentration, any of these gases and vapours can present hazards to health or cause irritation during demolition, site preparation, construction, and occupancy of buildings.

* Gases, vapours and mists may present dangers of explosion and/or toxicity, and may arise from cutting and burning, adhesives, paints, organic solvents, sprayed materials, preservatives and resins.

* Careful planning at all stages can minimise any health problems – particular attention should be paid to the selection of building and other construction materials and both the hazards to the construction worker and those to any future occupant should be considered.

* During any work, safe work practices which meet current Health & Safety Regulations should be documented and followed.

* Workers should be instructed on the hazards of the gases and vapours to which their work exposes them and on the importance of taking appropriate control measures.

* Low levels of gases and vapours may cause considerable irritation to office workers and have been implicated as contributing to Sick Building Syndrome. Careful selection of construction materials and furnishings, ample and controllable fresh air and good work practices minimise these problems.

* All maintenance work liable to produce any hazardous substances must be carefully managed and controlled.

* The first considerations in the selection and use of wood preservatives should be the health and safety of the operator applying the material and the health and safety of future occupants of the building.

BIBLIOGRAPHICAL REFERENCES

UK Acts of Parliament and Regulations

The Health and Safety at Work etc Act 1974.

The Factories Act 1961.

The Offices, Shops and Railway Premises Act 1963.

The Highly Flammable Liquids and Liquified Petroleum Gases Regulations 1972.

The Control of Substances Hazardous to Health Regulations 1988.

Food and Environment Protection Act 1985.

Control of Pesticides Regulations 1986.

Health and Safety Commission (1988), *Control of Substances Hazardous to Health (General ADP) and Control of Carcinogenic Substances (Carcinogens ACOP). Control of Substances Hazardous to Health Regulations 1988 Approved Codes of Practice*, HM Stationery Office, London.

Health and Safety Commission (1988), *Control of Substances Hazardous to Health in Fumigations, Control of Substances Hazardous to Health Regulations 1988 Approved Code of Practice*, HM Stationery Office, London.

Health and Safety Executive (1988), *Control of Substances Hazardous to Health Regulations 1988, COSHH Assessments A step-by-step guide to assessment and the skills needed for it*, HM Stationery Office, London.

Health and Safety Executive (1977), *Petroleum-based Adhesives in Building Operations.* Environmental Hygiene 7.

Health and Safety Executive (1977), *Spraying of Highly Flammable Liquids.* Environmental Hygiene 9.

Health and Safety Executive (1977), *Ventilation in the Workplace.* Environmental Hygiene 22.

Health and Safety Executive (1989), *Occupational Exposure Limits 1989.* Environmental Hygiene 40/89.

Health and Safety Executive (1988), *Certificate of Approval (Respiratory Protective Equipment) 1988. F2486 (1988).*

Pesticides 1990 Reference Book 500. Pesticides Approved under the Control of Pesticides Regulations 1986, HM Stationery Office, London.

Health and Safety Commission (1990), *Information approved for the Classification, Packaging and Labelling of Dangerous Substances for Supply and Conveyance by Road* (3rd Edn), Authorised and Approved List, HM Stationery Office, London.

Other Publications

ASHRAE (1981), *Ventilation for Acceptable Indoor Air Quality*, American Society of Heating, Refrigeration and Air-Conditioning Engineers, Atlanta, GA.

Black, M.S., Bayer, C.W. and Brackett, H.L. (1987), *An office building IAQ problem involving volatile organic compounds* in *Practical Control of Indoor Air Problems*, Proceedings of the ASHRAE Conference IAQ 87, Arlington, VA, pp. 72-87.

British Standards Institution (1985), *Code of Practice for thermal insulation of cavity walls (with masonry or concrete inner and outer leaves) by filling with urea formaldehyde (UF) foam systems*, BS 5618: 1985 BSI, London

British Standards Institution (1985), *Specification for urea formaldehyde (UF) foam systems suitable for thermal insulation of cavity walls with masonry or concrete outer leaves.* BSI London BS 5617 : 1985

Daugbjerg, P. (1989), *Is particle board in the home detrimental to health?* Environ. Res., 48, 154-63.

Girman, J., Alevantis, L., Kullasingham, G., Petreas, M. and Webber, L. (1987), *Bake-out of an office building* in *Indoor Air '87, Proceedings of the 4th International Conference on Indoor Air Quality and Climate* (eds B. Siefert, H. Edson, M. Fisher, H. Ruden and J. Wegner), Berlin, Vol 1, pp. 22-6.

Grandjean, P. (1986), *Occupational health aspects of construction work*, Euro Reports and Studies 86, World Health Organization, Copenhagen.

International Agency for Research on Cancer (1987) IARC, *Monographs on the evaluation of carcinogenic risks to humans – overall evaluations of carcinogenicity : an updating of IARC monographs – Volumes 1 to 42 – IARC, Lyon, France*

Krause, C., Mailahn, W., Nagel, R., Schulz, C., Seifert, B. and Ullrich, D. (1987), *Occurrence of volatile organic compounds in the air of 500 homes in the Federal Republic of Germany* in *Indoor Air '87, Proceedings of the 4th International Conference on Indoor Air Quality and Climate* (eds B. Siefert, H. Edson, M. Fisher, H. Ruden and J. Wegner), Berlin, Vol. 1, pp. 102-6.

Levin, H. (1987), *Protocols to improve indoor environmental quality in new construction* in *Practical Control of Indoor Air Problems*, Proceedings of the ASHRAE Conference IAQ 87, Arlington, VA, pp. 157-70.

Meyer, B., Andrews, B.A.K. and Reinhardt, R.M. (1986) *Formaldehyde Release from Wood Products*, American Chemical Society, Washington, DC.

Miksch, R.R., Hollowell, C.D. and Schmidt, H.E. (1982), *Trace organic chemical contaminants in office spaces*, Environ. Int., 8, 129-37.

Molhave, L. (1982), *Indoor air pollution due to organic gases and vapours of solvents in building materials*, Environ. Int., 8, 117-27.

Molhave, L., Bach, B. and Pederson, O.G. (1986), *Human reactions to low concentrations of volatile organic compounds*, Environ. Int., 12, 167-75.

Tichener, B.A. and Mason, M.A. (1988), *Organic emissions from consumer products and building materials to the indoor environment*, J. Air Pollut. Control Assoc., 38, 264-8.

Vince, I. (1987), *Sick Building Syndrome*, IBC Technical Services, Devon.

Wallace, L. and Clayton, C.A. (1987) *Volatile organic compounds in 600 US homes; major sources of personal exposure* in *Indoor Air '87, Proceedings of the 4th International Conference on Indoor Air Quality and Climate*, (eds B. Siefert, H. Edson, M. Fisher, H. Ruden and J. Wegner), Berlin, Vol. 1, pp. 183-92.

Wallace, L.A., Pellizari, E., Leaderer, B.,Zelon, H. and Sheldow, L. (1987), *Emission of volatile organic compounds from building materials and consumer products*, Atmos. Environ., 21, 385-93.

ASBESTOS

John Addison

Institute of Occupational Medicine Ltd

INTRODUCTION

Natural fibrous silicate minerals known as asbestos are common throughout the rocks of the world. As a result, the useful properties of asbestos were recognized and exploited even as early as prehistoric times. It was used in various minor ways for thousands of years until, with the rapid industrial expansion of the last century, the asbestos industries were started. Only after new industries had become major employers of national importance did it gradually become evident that working in environments dusty with asbestos carried severe risks to health. Asbestos was recognized as a hazardous material and the study of patterns of disease in exposed populations (epidemiology), toxicology, occupational hygiene, mineralogy and many other sciences have subsequently enhanced our understanding of the complex relationships between asbestos and disease.

DEFINITION OF ASBESTOS

There is no entirely satisfactory definition of asbestos at the present time. There are two main types – chrysotile, and the amphibole minerals. Conventionally the term 'asbestos' has been applied to those naturally occurring fibrous silicate minerals which have been exploited commercially for their useful properties of incombustibility, resistance to chemical attack, low thermal conductivity etc. When such a definition is used in legislation it is usually followed by a list of the asbestos minerals such as chrysotile (white asbestos), amosite (brown asbestos), crocidolite (blue asbestos), anthophyllite, fibrous tremolite and fibrous actinolite.

The main weakness of this definition lies in the fact that, apart from chrysotile, all these minerals are much more common in forms which are not asbestos but are mineralogically almost indistinguishable from genuine asbestos. While the definition attempts to avoid this weakness by using the term 'fibrous' in the description of the materials, this term itself is not defined. This lack of precision leads to problems which will be considered later. However, despite these disadvantages, the working definitions given above, based upon the normal concept of the form of asbestos fibres, have been adequate for most situations.

THE MINERALS

Chrysotile

Chrysotile, also known as white asbestos, is mineralogically quite distinct from the other forms of asbestos in being a member of the serpentine mineral group. Chrysotile production has been very widespread, major deposits having been worked in British Columbia and Quebec in Canada, in the Ural mountains of Russia, in Zimbabwe, South Africa, India and China among many others. Chrysotile is the only asbestos mineral produced in Europe in comparatively small mines at Balangero in North Italy and in Cyprus and Northern Greece.

It is normally white or very pale coloured with a soft curly texture and silky appearance; it is flexible and inelastic and very easily splits longitudinally down to extremely fine fibres (fibrils). The surface of chrysotile fibres is chemically reactive which makes it useful in the manufacture of asbestos cements but does make it more prone to chemical degradation. Its flexibility and low elasticity make it easy to spin and weave into ropes and textiles. Chrysotile has also been used in lightweight insulations, laggings and friction products, as a filler in plastics, roofing felts and gaskets, and in filters in the drinks industries.

The Amphibole Minerals

The amphiboles are a group of some 50 very varied and widely occurring minerals related by a common crystal structure. The most usual forms for any of the amphiboles are coarse prismatic or rod-shaped crystals, although some may also be found in the finely fibrous forms typical of asbestos. The five main types of amphibole asbestos listed earlier are those which have at some time been used commercially, although other types, which are more mineralogical curiosities, have also been found. The main characteristics of the five key minerals are given below.

Amosite or brown asbestos, more properly called fibrous grunerite, was named after its first and only producer AMOSA (Asbestos Mines of South Africa). It is a grey or white needle-like fibre with a vitreous lustre (glassy); it is relatively flexible and elastic and was used mainly in insulation board, ceiling tiles, some asbestos cements and laggings, but rarely in textiles or ropes.

Crocidolite, or blue asbestos, is a fine soft blue-grey fibre with very good tensile strength, thermal resistance and chemical resistance, and was produced in South Africa and Western Australia. It was probably the highest quality fibre of the commonly available types but was more expensive so that its use was more specialized. However, in sensitive or high risk situations, such as in warships, in railway rolling stock and as spray on steel frame buildings, the use of crocidolite was thought to be justified. In addition it was in very widespread use as an additive to chrysotile in cements, boards, ropes etc., and in gaskets, pipe seals and battery cases where its acid and chemical resistance was useful.

Anthophyllite, a grey needle-like fibre similar to amosite, is a much less common asbestos mineral which was produced in Finland for some years. Its occurrence in lagging samples is rare and it was not used to any great extent in commercial products in the United Kingdom. The presence of anthophyllite as a contaminant in other natural raw materials such as talc may be of more concern than its use as asbestos.

Tremolite is a fine white asbestos which was used for high temperature applications. It is extremely resistant to chemical attack and has excellent tensile strength. It is produced in Korea, Pakistan and India, but also occurs in some chrysotiles as a contaminant and in other materials such as some talcs, vermiculites and other minerals.

Actinolite was considered to be a very rare asbestos mineral occurring only as a contaminant in amosite from the Prieska area of South Africa (hence the name prieskaite which is sometimes used). It is a green asbestos variety and has a fairly wide occurrence although not in any commercial quantities. It is only likely to be encountered as a contaminant of other minerals.

Asbestiform and Non-asbestiform Minerals

There are no straightforward rules for deciding the extent of the hazard from exposure to a mineral such as an amphibole. The asbestos varieties of amphibole are undoubtedly very harmful materials indeed; but there is increasing evidence that, whatever the chemical composition or crystal structure of the fibre, it will be equally harmful if the shape and durability are the same as the amphibole asbestos minerals. For example, erionite, the zeolite mineral, is very harmful to health in its fine fibrous forms even though it is not an asbestos mineral. However, not all amphibole minerals can achieve the fine fibrous form even though all their other chemical and physical properties appear to be the same. As a result it is becoming apparent that the non-asbestiform amphibole minerals are no more harmful than other low toxicity dusts such as kaolinite. The problem for the scientist in evaluating materials, particularly as trace contaminants in other minerals, is in deciding whether, for example, the tremolite found in a vermiculite sample is of the asbestos type or the non-asbestos type. This judgement may still be subjective even though it may be based upon the most detailed examination of the mineralogical evidence. A more adequate definition of asbestos is necessary, which depends upon identifying either a fundamental property of asbestos or a fundamental predictor of harmfulness, before a purely objective judgement can be made. In the meantime a certain amount of amphibole or even asbestiform amphibole must be acceptable in raw materials for otherwise, because of the ambiguous nature of amphiboles, there may be no acceptable mineral raw materials at all.

ASBESTOS-RELATED DISEASES

There are a number of diseases which have proved to be related to asbestos exposure, the three main examples being (a) asbestosis, (b) bronchial carcinoma and (c) mesothelioma. There are other diseases for which the association with asbestos exposure is less clear. There are also less serious medical conditions which are clearly related to asbestos exposure.

Asbestosis is fibrosis of the lung parenchyma, i.e. the development of fibrous scar tissue in the areas of the lung where the oxygen exchange takes place. It results in inadequate oxygenation of the blood, restricted breathing and increased resistance to breathing in the small airways. The earliest complaint is usually coughing followed by breathlessness. As the disease progresses the symptoms become more distinctive: X-ray shadows become more obvious; crackling of the lung can be heard on examination and the breathlessness increases. With advanced asbestosis the patient dies of cardio-respiratory failure. The severity of the disease is considered to be related to the amount of exposure experienced by the patient. The disease is also progressive in that, even when removed from exposure, the condition may continue to worsen. However, if it is recognized in its early stages and the patient is removed from exposure, the progression may be very slow or even arrested.

There is good evidence to suggest that the risks of disease for crocidolite asbestos are greater than for amosite, and are greater for amosite than for chrysotile. Current levels of exposure to chrysotile in factories in the United Kingdom, if kept at less than 0.5 fibres per millilitre of air, are effectively controlling the disease to very low levels.

Increased risk of **bronchial carcinoma** or lung cancer, a tumour on the epithelial cover of the lung airways, is associated with exposure to asbestos. There is a general relationship between the amount of exposure and the degree of risk, but no threshold level has been established below which there is no risk. As with asbestosis, the risks appear to be greatest with exposure to crocidolite and least with chrysotile.

The risks of lung cancer are very much higher if the exposed person is a cigarette smoker, since there is an apparent multiplicative effect between the two separate risks. The risk of lung cancer is ten or more times higher for a smoker exposed to asbestos than for a non-smoker. Unfortunately the strong relationship between smoking and lung cancer makes attribution of the cause of lung cancer very difficult in a smoker with casual or very low asbestos exposure. In the past, compensation for lung cancer has not been awarded on the basis of asbestos exposure unless the cancer has been accompanied by asbestosis.

Mesothelioma is a tumour which develops in the membranes which line the inside of the chest cavity and cover the lungs (pleural) or the intestines (peritoneal). In its early stages of growth it causes few symptoms, but once at the stage that it can be diagnosed it is rapidly fatal, causing death within about 2 years. There is no known treatment although various therapies may delay death for a few months. The association of the disease with exposure to asbestos is very strong indeed, and it may arise after only a short exposure. The tumour is usually diagnosed 20–50 years after first exposure to asbestos. A proportion of the 500 or so cases each year in the United Kingdom have no identified asbestos exposure and a few of these cases must be accepted as spontaneous.

There is no known level of exposure to asbestos without risk of mesothelioma, and because of its rarity as a disease and its unique association with fibrous silicate minerals it is one of the few cancers with a demonstrated environmental cause. For example, the fibrous zeolite mineral erionite in Turkey and the tremolite asbestos in the rocks and soils of certain areas of Turkey, Cyprus and Greece have been shown to cause mesothelioma in the local rural populations. Crocidolite and other amphibole asbestos such as very fine fibre tremolite are generally considered to be more carcinogenic than coarser fibre amphiboles or chrysotile. Indeed chrysotile is not now thought to present any real risk of mesothelioma at all.

Other Diseases/Conditions

At various times increased risks of developing a number of other tumours have been attributed to asbestos exposure. These include gastro-intestinal, laryngeal and ovarian cancers. However, the evidence for any of these is not strong and the risks which might be attributed to casual or low level exposure will be extremely low.

There are a number of other pleural conditions, that are not life-threatening, which are associated with exposure to asbestos but are also caused by other factors. Pleural plaques are benign broadening and thickening of the chest lining producing shiny smooth yellow elevations on the surface. Pleural effusion is the production of fluid in the pleura which is sometimes found in asbestos workers; it may develop into pleural fibrosis. These conditions may also calcify and in the case of fibrosis may impair breathing.

ASBESTOS PRODUCTION AND USE

In 1985 and for some years before this, annual world production of asbestos was about 4 million tons of which over 90% was chrysotile. In the United Kingdom, the use of chrysotile, actinolite, tremolite and anthophyllite is permitted, but only chrysotile is now in common use in new products. In 1986 only 40,000 tons of chrysotile were imported in comparison with the maximum in 1973 of 195,000 tons. Nevertheless a total of about 6 million tons has been imported to the United Kingdom, used and distributed since the beginning of the century, and although the majority (more than 95%) of this was chrysotile, significant amounts of crocidolite and amosite were imported prior to the introductions of voluntary bans and prohibitions in 1970 and 1985.

The variety of products containing asbestos and used in the past is enormous, although the gradually increasing restrictions on use have reduced this so that today only asbestos cements and friction materials constitute major uses of chrysotile asbestos. Nevertheless existing buildings may contain any of the materials described below in broad categories.

Low density materials (<500 kg m^{-3}), such as sprayed asbestos coatings, laggings, quilts, blankets, ropes, yarns, cloths and lightweight preformed sectional insulation made from calcium silicates or magnesia, all contain loosely bonded asbestos and are easily damaged to release fibres. The use of asbestos in sprays and thermal insulations has now been prohibited, and large-scale use of loose products is not advisable. While the new use of asbestos spray and lagging is now prohibited, these materials are unfortunately still commonly found in older buildings and can only be dealt with by strict adherence to the relevant regulations. Disturbance of such low density materials can lead to very high airborne fibre concentrations.

Medium density insulating boards in the 500-700 kg m^{-3} range were in very widespread use between the 1950s and mid-1970s under a variety of trade names. They contain mostly amosite, sometimes with chrysotile, in a matrix of Portland cement or hydrated lime and silica. They are found in all types of industrial, commercial, public and private buildings as wall panels, ceiling tiles, acoustic panels and many other situations. Their use declined as substitutes became available and none have been manufactured in the United Kingdom since 1980. Even careful handling of these products can produce fairly high airborne fibre concentrations, and any mechanical working (e.g. power drills or saws) will produce very high concentrations.

Asbestos cement products are high density materials in the range 1200-1500 kg m^{-3}. All three main asbestos varieties have been used mixed with Portland cement or autoclaved calcium silicate, although all asbestos cement now manufactured in the United Kingdom contains only chrysotile asbestos. Asbestos cement is found in sheet form, pressed and semi-pressed, corrugated sheets, tiles and slates, flues, pipes, drains, water tanks, cores of steel sheets etc. In general the asbestos fibres are very firmly bound in the cement matrix so that only if the material is mechanically damaged or worked or if it has deteriorated with age will fibres be released. Release of fibres from corroded or weathered asbestos cement does occur, but the rate of release is very low and would not present a major airborne dust hazard unless the fibres accumulated after release, e.g. in drains or gutters. The possibility that release of fibres into potable water supplies might constitute a risk of cancer has been examined in great detail but so far the evidence has been negative.

Other assorted materials such as bitumen, plastics, mastics, sealants, paints and putties have all been used with asbestos fillers in the past and some are still used. As with asbestos cement, the rate of release of fibre from such materials in normal use is very low and the associated risks are therefore correspondingly small. However, if they are mechanically worked or abraded or become seriously corroded, then fibres may be released more easily.

In general, as the knowledge of the relative harmfulness of the asbestos minerals and of the fibre concentrations involved in materials handling has developed, so there has been a move away from the use of friable materials with easily released fibres, and from materials made of or with amphibole asbestos types. With the use of chrysotile asbestos cement as the major single product involving asbestos, the risks to the building industry end user – the occupant – or to the environment are now comparatively small.

However, work with new asbestos materials currently constitutes only a tiny proportion of all asbestos work; large numbers of companies are now involved in asbestos removal and abatement, and in particular with the more hazardous materials. It is within this relatively new industry that the exercise of caution and the imposition of regulations is most necessary. The work-force in the removal industries is at special risk, and decisions about the removal of existing asbestos installations from buildings should also take this into consideration.

MEASURING THE RISKS FROM ASBESTOS

Asbestos is potentially very hazardous to health, but only when it is in the form of airborne respirable dust is it generally thought to pose a risk of disease to exposed persons. The degree of risk is difficult to measure accurately, especially with the very low asbestos fibre concentrations experienced by the general public. Even in buildings with damaged sprayed amphibole asbestos the airborne regulated asbestos fibre concentrations rarely exceed 0.0005 fibres per millilitre of air (20 times lower than the clearance limit concentration for re-occupation of premises after asbestos removal). Doll and Peto (1985) assessed the risk as follows: 'Exposure to this level for a working week in an office for 20 years in adult life or for 10 years or so at school, or to lower average levels for more prolonged times at home is calculated to produce a lifetime risk of death of 1 in 100,000. If 20% of the population experience such exposure, this would imply that one death in a year was caused in the whole country.' While this statement applies strictly to chrysotile asbestos, nevertheless the risks from amosite or crocidolite are unlikely to be more than two or three times greater.

Clearly these risks from the exposures experienced by the general public are very small compared with risks of road traffic accidents or domestic accidents. Despite this it is emphasized that reduction of exposure will reduce the risks further, however small they were in the first place, since no known level of exposure below which there is no risk has been established.

Maintaining as low a level of exposure as possible to airborne asbestos fibres does not necessarily mean removing asbestos materials from every installation. Indeed, the opposite may be preferable, since high level exposures of asbestos removal contractors are probably inevitable, as are the elevated exposures (up to 0.01 fibres per millilitre of air) experienced over a long period by the normal inhabitants upon re-occupation. In such a situation the risk to school children during the six months following asbestos removal might be greater than that during the whole of their school life had the material not been removed at all. Very careful assessment of the situation is necessary before a course of action involving possible risks to the health of the population is embarked upon.

ASBESTOS SURVEY, ABATEMENT, DEMOLITION, WASTE DISPOSAL

Survey

The assessment of a building for the extent and state of any asbestos involves careful searching and sampling of materials by competent qualified people. Like all work with asbestos, these operations must be carried out in accordance with the relevant regulations. The procedure may involve damage to the fabric of the building and release of asbestos fibres, and so appropriate precautions must be taken to protect the health of occupants and to avoid contaminating the building with loose fibres. Once the location of all asbestos has been established, then a judgement can be made about actions to be taken.

There are no strict rules about the judgements which have to be made in this assessment. A number of 'point-scoring' systems have been devised but they are not always applicable and ultimately the decision will be subjective. Sampling of the air in a building and counting of fibres can give a more objective guide as to the need for remedial action, but care must be taken that airborne fibres are identified properly and that external environmental concentrations are also assessed. It may be necessary to undertake some form of electron microscope analysis in such situations.

The type and amount of asbestos should be considered since not only do the different asbestos types involve different degrees of hazard but they also affect the physical behaviour of the material. For example, cement products made with amosite or crocidolite tend to be more friable and less resistant to abrasion than chrysotile products.

The type of material containing the asbestos is obviously very important: asbestos cement materials containing chrysotile might not be considered to be a serious hazard, while a soft chrysotile lagging or spray in the same situation would not be acceptable and its removal would be recommended. Generally the hazard is related to the resilience of the material and the ease with which fibres may be released into the air. The state of repair of the material must also be considered, and any damage such as abrasions and scratches on the surface, detachment of spray coatings from surfaces or of paints and sealants from asbestos surfaces must be noted. Any fraying of edges, cracking or minor breakages are just as important to the survey as major damage, although the decisions about resulting actions may differ. Generally minor damage can be repaired with little risk although compliance with the relevant regulations is still essential.

The position of the asbestos material is extremely important. Asbestos materials can be found in almost any area of a domestic or public building and, depending on the site, the resulting actions may be very different. For example, asbestos cement soffits which are unlikely to be disturbed for maintenance would not constitute a serious hazard and would not require action other than management and recording. However, asbestos cement wall panels at low levels in a high activity area where the possibility of damage was high would almost certainly justify removal.

Evaluation of the circumstances and decisions about actions are not always so obvious. For example, a high ceiling lined with asbestos insulation board may release large amounts of fibre if there is violent activity in the room above the ceiling. Inaccessible asbestos cement panels or sprayed asbestos coatings may in fact be a source of contamination for an air-conditioning system or may be frequently disturbed inadvertently by people involved in unrelated maintenance work.

The nature of any activity in the vicinity of asbestos materials in a building requires further consideration. High levels of violent activity are more likely to disturb materials or loose fibres, producing greater hazards. Asbestos panels on or near vibrating machinery will release asbestos fibres unless they are totally sealed. Similarly, any materials near scaffolding or heavy equipment which is frequently moved will have a high risk of damage and will require strong physical protection or removal.

The level of detail to which a survey might extend depends on the future use or activities. For example, in-depth investigation of fully enclosed areas, wall cavities, underfloor areas or similarly inaccessible places would be recommended prior to demolition of a building, but might not be necessary for normal occupation of a building in good condition.

Finally, the practical considerations of ease and effectiveness of any remedial actions as well as financial costs must be taken into account. Obviously, the easily undertaken low cost actions can be done immediately − the old ironing board will be disposed of by the local authority services. Higher cost complex actions involving risks to occupants of buildings and many others require careful planning.

Removal from Occupied Buildings

Only after all the relevant factors have been considered can a decision be made to undertake measures such as:

- leaving the material in place but instituting a management system;
- leaving it in place but sealing or enclosing and introducing a management system; or
- removing or disposing of the material.

The first two might involve minor repairs and maintenance work, some of which may require licences, but should also involve careful recording of sites, labelling of materials, dissemination of information concerning the materials to all interested parties, including later contractors for other works etc., and the provision of regular and frequent re-inspection. Any asbestos removal should be carried out in accordance with the Control of Asbestos at Work Regulations, assisted by the Guidance Notes provided by the Health and Safety Executive (HSE). In particular, if work is carried out involving the removal, repair or disturbance of asbestos insulation or asbestos coating, then it must be done by a contractor licensed by the HSE. It is a condition of most licences that notification is made to the enforcing authority before work begins.

Any work involving asbestos should be carried out by suitably qualified and experienced persons. Lists of licensed contractors are held by the HSE, and the Asbestos Removal Contractors Association (ARCA) offer advice. The past performance of any contractor should be examined carefully, and the contractor should provide a full method statement and demonstrate that he is complying with all the appropriate legislation. It is often useful on large contracts to have an experienced and competent independent body monitoring the work of the removal contractor, advising the owner-occupier of any deficiencies, evaluating the job upon completion and undertaking airborne asbestos clearance monitoring. HSE Guidance Note EH51 requires that the site be thoroughly examined and the air tested and found clear of asbestos before any enclosures around the work are removed and the area or building is re-occupied.

If the original purpose of the asbestos was for fire protection then it may have to be replaced by other suitable material so that the relevant fire regulations are met and insurance policy conditions are not broken. This may best be done in consultation with the local fire authorities.

Demolition

Demolition of buildings can create very large amounts of dust and it is important that any asbestos present is removed in a controlled way in order to minimize the risk to the health of the public and the work-force. Sprayed asbestos and asbestos insulation should be removed by a licensed contractor before demolition begins. Asbestos cement components should be dismantled and lowered to the ground, i.e. treated according to the appropriate Approved Codes of Practice and Guidance Notes in order to reduce asbestos exposure to a minimum. The enforcing authorities must be notified of demolition work, as must local authorities who may impose their own conditions on the demolition.

Waste Disposal

All raw asbestos or asbestos waste must be kept or transported only in suitable sealed containers and these containers must be appropriately labelled in accordance with (a) the Control of Asbestos at Work

Regulations 1987, (b) the Classification, Packaging and Labelling of Dangerous Substances Regulations 1984 as amended, (c) the Dangerous Substances (Conveyance by Road in Road Tankers and Tank Containers) Regulations 1981, and (d) the Road Traffic (Carriage of Dangerous Substances in Packages etc) Regulations 1986. Wastes should be double sealed in large appropriately labelled plastic bags, decontaminated before removal from any enclosure and then stored in a sealed skip before transport to the disposal point.

All asbestos wastes are classed as controlled wastes under the Control of Pollution Act 1974 and must be disposed of only at a licensed site. On the grounds of a greater hazard of human carcinogenicity, certain asbestos wastes are classed as 'special wastes' if 'dangerous to life'. DoE Waste Management Paper 23 (1981) indicates that this applies to any measurable quantity of crocidolite and any other form of asbestos material containing at least 1% of free asbestos fibres. Thus sprayed coatings and laggings as well as broken or damaged insulation boards or even severely broken or pulverized asbestos cement are classified as special wastes. Other materials such as sound asbestos cement bitumen felt, reinforced plastics etc would generally be controlled wastes unless they contained crocidolite.

Further information about control and waste management and a code of practice are contained in the DoE Waste Management Paper 18 'Asbestos Wastes' 1979, under revision. The control of Pollution (Special Waste) Regulations 1980 are in addition to the legislation covering controlled waste and carry implications for transport, disposal sites, documentation labelling of waste and containers and many other factors.

BULK ASBESTOS SAMPLING AND ANALYSIS

Any sampling of bulk materials suspected of containing asbestos should be carried out by suitably qualified persons, and strict care and attention should be given to the relevant regulations to ensure that no hazards are generated by the collection of samples. No formal guidance on sampling and identification of asbestos in bulk materials has been issued by the HSE although there are useful suggestions in documents such as Asbestos Materials in Buildings (Department of the Environment, 1986). Asbestosis Research Council (ARC) Technical Note 3 contains more detailed information about procedures and sampling strategies. Any damage caused by the sampling must be made good at that time and the person should be properly equipped with protective clothing.

The sampling scheme should be such that any variations in the nature of suspected asbestos-containing materials can be identified, with particular attention being paid to patched and repaired areas in pipe and boiler laggings and to ensuring that the full depth of laggings is sampled.

Obviously it is not acceptable to the owners or occupants of premises that perfectly sound well-decorated walls or ceilings should be damaged to provide samples, and a degree of ingenuity or agility may be required to obtain suitable samples from unobtrusive areas. Also, in such situations the size and number of samples may have to be minimized as far as possible while still consistent with the aims of the sampling exercise. All samples must be sealed individually in containers, fully labelled and documented, and the sampling site must be recorded at the time of sampling. Great care must be taken to ensure that no cross-contamination can occur and all implements used should be scrupulously clean to avoid this.

There is no formally recommended method for identification of asbestos in bulk samples, although the HSE and the National Testing Laboratory Accreditation Scheme (NATLAS) recognize methods based upon polarized light microscopy and dispersion staining microscopy as being the most suitable for the purpose. Identification should only be carried out by fully trained personnel in recognized analytical laboratories and preferably by laboratories registered in the NATLAS scheme.

Identification of the asbestos types by analysis is required by regulations before work starts which may expose, or may be liable to expose, workers to asbestos unless the material is assumed to contain crocidolite or amosite and is treated as such in any subsequent work.

AIRBORNE FIBRE SAMPLING AND ANALYSIS

Wherever work is carried out with asbestos materials, or when asbestos materials have been removed, there will be a requirement to carry out air sampling and evaluation of airborne fibre concentrations. Sampling may be required for purposes of monitoring under the Control of Asbestos at Work Regulations, for assessment of air quality outside an enclosure where asbestos work is going on, for final clearance of an area where asbestos work has been completed or to investigate whether asbestos materials are releasing fibres into the air. The method of sampling consists of drawing air through a thin membrane filter at a known flow rate for a given period of time. Depending on the purpose of the sampling, the flow rate, sampling time and sampling strategies may be different, but at all times they should comply with HSE Guidance Notes EH10 and EH42.

For final clearance monitoring according to the Guidance Note, at least two air samples should be collected for each area up to 25 square metres and more as appropriate for larger areas. The minimum total volume of the two air samples should be 480 litres but higher volumes of up to 2000 litres may be preferred. Air sampling rates up to 8 litres per minute may be used, and so a survey of airborne dust should take at least half an hour and would preferably be longer.

The membrane filter used to collect the dust is of a type that, when placed on a glass microscope slide and exposed to acetone vapour (or other solvents), becomes optically transparent so that the dust particles can be examined and the fibres counted at high magnification using a phase contrast optical microscope. The main advantages of the phase contrast microscopy method are that it is quick, practical and can be carried out on or near the site of the asbestos work to give an immediate response in clearance monitoring. The exact details of the procedures are given in the HSE document MDHS 39/3 (1990). All sampling and fibre counting should only be carried out by fully qualified persons. In particular the laboratory undertaking the fibre counting should be NATLAS accredited, one condition of which is that the laboratory participates successfully in the RICE (Regular Interlaboratory Counting Exchanges) fibre counting scheme operated by HSE.

No structure erected to enclose asbestos work may be removed until the area has been carefully inspected and seen to be free of visible dust or debris, the air inside the enclosure has been tested and has been shown to contain less than 0.01 fibres per millilitre of air (Guidance Note EH10, Rev 1900). Air testing for obtaining a Clearance Certificate should not be carried out by the company involved in the actual asbestos removal operation or by any related company.

One disadvantage of the fibre-counting method (MDHS 39/3) is that any fibre meeting the size criteria set out in the regulations (length greater than 5.0 microns, diameter less than 3.0 microns and aspect ratio greater than 3:1) must be counted when it is found during a systematic search of the membrane filter sample, irrespective of its nature or identity. In other words, fibres such as cotton, wood, paper or glass fibre must all be counted as if they were asbestos. This causes no major problems with clearance monitoring where the inside of the enclosure should be scrupulously clean of all dust or debris in any case, but in other situations there may be many sources of non-asbestos fibre dust which could give comparatively high fibre counts. Phase contrast microscopy cannot differentiate consistently between asbestos and other fibres, and so it may be necessary in such situations to use more sophisticated analytical methods in order to allay the anxieties of the occupants of buildings.

Scanning electron microscopy (SEM) with chemical analysis of individual particles using energy dispersive X-ray spectrometry (EDXS) can discriminate satisfactorily against non-asbestos fibres, excluding organic, metal or glass fibres from the fibre count. The degree of confidence in asbestos fibre identification is very high indeed, but since no information about crystal structure of the fibres can be obtained using SEM, it is impossible to make a completely unambiguous identification. Transmission electron microscopy (TEM) with EDXS may also provide crystal structure data in the form of electron diffraction patterns which, together with the morphological and chemical information, can therefore give a full identification of the fibres.

However, these electron microscopy methods are progressively more expensive to use and time-consuming, and so the justification for their use must be carefully examined beforehand.

ASBESTOS IN FIRES

It has recently become evident that in very severe fires asbestos cement may explode and be spread over a wide area. While the heating process itself may change much of the asbestos into other non-fibrous minerals, the debris in such a case will almost always contain some unchanged asbestos and will require careful collection and disposal. Any asbestos material still in position after a fire may be more hazardous if the fire has made it more friable and likely to release fibres.

ASBESTOS AS A CONTAMINANT

Chrysotile and the amphibole minerals are both very widespread in their natural occurrence, so it is not unusual to find that other mineral or rock raw materials may contain either or both. For example, the chemical and physical conditions which promote the formation of vermiculite in commercial deposits are similar to those in which tremolite or actinolite may form. In some cases these accessory minerals (accessory to the commercially exploited mineral) have been identified as asbestos minerals and have been shown to be a serious health hazard (McDonald et al 1986). This does not mean that all vermiculite deposits contain or are likely to contain tremolite or actinolite asbestos, and in fact many deposits are free of asbestos. It does mean however that the sources of raw materials such as vermiculite should be checked before use and, in the case of uncertainty, the materials themselves should be tested. In this context, it is important to note that even very small proportions of asbestos fibre in a dry loose aggregate could generate hazardous airborne fibre concentrations if the material is handled carelessly (Addison et al, 1988).

Despite this, in principle it must be accepted that a raw material can be used safely even when it contains identifiable asbestos, i.e. that the proportion of asbestos is so low that it constitutes no measurable additional increased risk to the health of persons exposed, that release of asbestos from the installed material would present no measurable increased risk to third parties and that disposal of the materials after use would produce no measurable increase in environmental contamination.

An unwillingness to accept such a principle could lead directly to serious difficulties with all types of mineral raw materials since all might be suspected of containing minute trace amounts of asbestos or other fibrous minerals. The consequence is that all materials would have to be tested to progressively lower limits, shown to be free of asbestos or any other fibrous minerals, and shown to constitute no foreseeable hazard to health before they could be used anywhere.

REGULATIONS ASSOCIATED WITH ASBESTOS

A large number of UK regulations have been effected over recent years concerning asbestos. All work comes under the Health and Safety at Work etc. Act 1974, and the following Statutory Instruments implement recommendations of the Advisory Committee on Asbestos or comply with requirements of European Communities Directives on asbestos.

- The Asbestos (Licensing) Regulations 1983 require work on asbestos insulations or coating to be carried out only by persons licensed by HSE.
- The Asbestos (Prohibition) Regulations 1985 (and as amended, 1988) prohibit the import, use in manufacture and sale of crocidolite and amosite, and asbestos spraying and asbestos insulation.
- The Asbestos Products (Safety) Regulations 1985 (and as amended, 1988) prohibit the supply of crocidolite and amosite, and of products containing them and require labelling of products containing asbestos.
- The Control of Asbestos at Work Regulations 1987 are intended to protect the health of persons at work and other persons who may be affected from risks to their health associated with exposure to asbestos arising from work activities. They set out comprehensive regulations supported by a very detailed Approved Code of Practice.

The legislation supports the HSE Guidance Note EH10: Asbestos Exposure Limits and Measurement of Airborne Dust Concentrations (revised February 1988), which establishes workplace limits, how they can be achieved and how they can be measured, the last with reference to MDHS 39/3: Asbestos Fibres in Air, Optical Microscopy and the Membrane Filter Method, 1990. In addition, various Guidance Notes and approved Codes of Practice (e.g. HSE: Work with Asbestos Insulation and Asbestos Coating, 1984; HSE Guidance Note EH37: Work with Asbestos Insulating Board, 1984; HSE Guidance Note EH36: Work with Asbestos Cement, 1984) give detailed information on how materials should be handled and what levels of exposure to airborne asbestos fibres can be expected. Finally, publications such as Asbestos Materials in Buildings (Department of the Environment, 1986) give good detailed advice on a very wide range of aspects of asbestos.

In addition to these regulations associated with asbestos at work, there is a large body of legislation associated with public health which places various duties upon owners, landlords, and people working upon premises with respect to notifications of demolition, emissions of dust, disposal of rubbish, provision of a safe dwelling fit for habitation, maintenance and repairs, and the requirement to take reasonable care to ensure that tenants and other people are safe from personal injury or disease caused by a defect in the state of the premises. A list of the major items of legislation, codes of practice and other useful and relevant publications is given below.

CONCLUSIONS

* Asbestos is very harmful to health but only poses a risk to exposed persons when it is in the form of airborne respirable dust. The degree of risk is very difficult to assess, especially at low airborne concentrations and although the risk may be very small indeed there is no known level of asbestos exposure at which there is no risk.

* Asbestos removal contractors will inevitably be exposed to high airborne asbestos fibre concentrations. Also, exposure and therefore the risks experienced by the normal occupants of a building will also be higher as a direct result of the asbestos disturbance than it would have been had the asbestos been left in place.

* Surveying and evaluation of asbestos in buildings must be done very carefully by qualified experienced persons and take into account a wide range of factors before a decision is made about asbestos removal or maintenance.

* Expensive complex asbestos removal programs involving risks to occupants of buildings and to many other people must not be considered without very careful planning.

* Sampling and analysis of bulk materials or for airborne dusts should always be done by suitably qualified and equipped persons and laboratories, and always in accordance with the appropriate HSE guidance. Such laboratories should be accredited under the NATLAS Scheme.

* It must be accepted that raw materials or products can be used safely even when they contain identifiable asbestos. Asbestos can be detected in such small amounts that any increased risk from human exposure to it or to the environment would be undetectably small.

GUIDANCE LITERATURE

Health and Safety Executive publications available from HM Stationery Office, London:

A Guide to the HSW Act, 2nd edn (1983), HSE Health and Safety Series Booklet HS(R)6.

A Guide to the Asbestos (Licensing) Regulations 1983, (1983), HSE Health and Safety Series Booklet HS(R)19.

Asbestos: Exposure Limits and Measurement of Airborne Dust Concentrations, (1988), HSE Guidance Note EH10.

Probable Asbestos Dust Concentrations at Construction Processes, (1984) HSE Guidance Note EH35.

Work with Asbestos Cement, (1984), HSE Guidance Note EH36.

Work with Asbestos Insulating Board, (1984) HSE Guidance Note EH37.

Occupational Exposure Limits 1990, (1990), HSE Guidance Note EH40/89.

Respiratory Protective Equipment for Use Against Asbestos, (1985) HSE Guidance Note EH41.

Monitoring Strategies for Toxic Substances, (1984), HSE Guidance Note EH42.

The Provision, Use and Maintenance of Hygiene Facilities for Work with Asbestos Insulation and Coatings, (1986), HSE Guidance Note EH47.

Training Operatives and Supervisors for Work with Asbestos Insulation and Coatings, (1988), HSE Guidance Note EH50.

Enclosures Provided for Work with Asbestos Insulation, Coatings and Insulation Board, (1989), HSE Guidance Note EH51.

Asbestos: Health Precautions in Industry, 2nd edn (1975), Health and Safety at Work No. 44.

Health and Safety in Demolition Work, Part 1: Preparation and Planning, (1984), HSE Guidance Note GS29/1.

Health and Safety in Demolition Work, Part 2: Legislation, (1984), HSE Guidance Note GS29/2.

Health and Safety in Demolition Work, Part 4: Health Hazards, (1985), HSE Guidance Note GS29/4.

Asbestos, (1980), HSE Guidance Note MS13.

Welding, (1978), HSE Guidance Note MS15.

Working with Asbestos. A guide for Supervisors and Safety Representatives, (1985),
   HSE Asbestos Manufacturing Guidance Booklet 1.

Good housekeeping when working with asbestos, (1985), HSE Asbestos Manufacturing
   Guidance Booklet 2.

**Health and Safety Executive publications available from HSE Publications Sales
Points:**

*Asbestos Fibres in Air, Light Microscope Methods for Use with the Control of Asbestos
   at Work Regulations (1988)*, HSE Methods for the Determination of Hazardous
   Substances MDHS39/3.

*Man-made Mineral Fibre. Airborne Number Concentration by Phase-contrast Light
   Microscopy (1988)*, HSE Methods for the Determination of Hazardous Substances
   MDHS 59.

Other Publishers

Asbestos Cement Manufacturers' Association (1983), *Q & A: Living and Working
   with Asbestos-Cement Products*, Asbestos Institute Publication No. 1487, Asbestos
   Cement Manufacturers' Association, Montreal.

Asbestos Information Centre (1983), *Asbestos in Building*, Asbestos Information
   Centre Publication No. 1492, AIC, London.

Asbestos Information Centre (1983), *Asbestos in the Home*, Asbestos Institute
   Publication No. 1494, Asbestos Information Centre, Montreal.

Asbestosis Research Council (1978), *Recommendations for the Sampling and
   Identification of Asbestos in Asbestos Products*, Technical Note 3.

Institute of Waste Management (1988), *Code of Practice for the disposal of Asbestos
   Waste.*

Reports

Health and Safety Commission: Advisory Committee on Asbestos (1979), *Asbestos,
   Vol. 1: Final Report of the Advisory Committee*, HM Stationery Office, London.

Health and Safety Commission: Advisory Committee on Asbestos (1979) , *Asbestos,
   Vol. 2, Final Report of the Advisory Committee*, Papers commissioned by the
   committee, HM Stationery Office, London.

Acheson and Gardner, M.J. (1983), *Asbestos. The control limit for asbestos. An update of the relevant sections of 'The ill-effects of asbestos on health'*, prepared by
   the authors for the Advisory Committee on Asbestos and published in Health and
   Safety Commission (1979) *Asbestos, Vol. 2: Final Report of the Advisory
   Committee*, HM Stationery Office, London.

Addison, J., Davis, L.S.T., Robertson, A. and Willey, R.J. (1988), *The release of
   dispersed asbestos from soils*, IOM Report TM/88/15, Institute of Occupational
   Medicine, Edinburgh.

Doll, R. and Peto, J. (1988), *Effects on Health of Exposure to Asbestos*, HM Stationery Office, London.

Health and Safety Executive (1986) , *Alternatives to Asbestos: a Review*, HM Stationery Office, London.

McDonald, J.C., McDonald, A.D., Armstrong, B. and Sebastion, P. (1986), *Cohort Study of mortality of vermiculite workers exposed to tremolite*, Br. J. Ind. Med.pp 436-444.

OTHER SELECTED PUBLICATIONS ON ASBESTOS

Legislation

Factories Act 1961, HM Stationery Office, London (9 & 10 Eliz. II Ch. 34).

Control of Pollution Act 1974, HM Stationery Office, London (Eliz. II Ch. 40).

Health and Safety at Work etc. Act 1974, HM Stationery Office, London (Eliz. II, Ch. 37).

Social Security Act 1975. Asbestos-related diseases without asbestosis. Supplement to the report (Cmnd 8750) by the Industrial Injuries Advisory Council in accordance with Section 141 of the ... Act on the question whether asbestos-related diseases without asbestosis should be prescribed under the Act (Cmnd 9104), HM Stationery Office, London.

Council of the European Communities Directive of 19 September 1983 on the protection of workers from the risks related to exposure to asbestos at work (second individual Directive within the meaning of Article 8 of Directive 80/1107/EEC). Official Journal of the European Communities, L263, 25-36; Corrigendum L327, 40, 1983.

Asbestos Products (Safety) Regulations 1985, Health and Safety Executive, London (SI 1985 No. 2042).

The Asbestos (Prohibitions) Regulations 1985, HM Stationery Office, London (SI 1985 No. 910).

The Control of Asbestos at Work Regulations 1987, HM Stationery Office, London (SI 1987 No. 2115).

Codes of Practice

Department of the Environment (1979), *Asbestos Wastes.* A Technical Memorandum on Arisings and Disposal including a Code of Practice, DoE Waste Management Paper No. 18, HM Stationery Office, London.

Department of the Environment (1981), *Special Wastes: A Technical Memorandum Providing Guidance on their Definition*, DoE Waste Management Paper No. 23, HM Stationery Office, London.

Department of the Environment (1986), *Asbestos Materials in Buildings, 2nd edn*, HM Stationery Office, London.

Health and Safety Commission (1987), *The Control of Asbestos at Work Regulations 1987: The Control of Asbestos at Work*, Approved Code of Practice COP 21 (with addendum, March 1988), HM Stationery Office, London.

Health and Safety Commission (1988), *Work with Asbestos Insulation, Asbestos Coating and Asbestos Insulation Board*, Approved Code of Practice COP 3, HM Stationery Office, London.

Health and Safety Executive (1981), *Construction: Health and Safety 1979-80*, HM Stationery Office, London (NIG 9).

Health and Safety Executive (1983), *Construction: Health and Safety 1981–82*, HM Stationery Office, London.

Health and Safety Executive (S. Grant, Chairman) (1983), *Report of the Asbestos Working Group 1982/3*, HSE, Bootle.

Ogden, T.L. (1982), *The Reproducibility of Asbestos Counts*, HSE Research Paper RP18, Health and Safety Executive, London.

Walton, W.H. (1982), *The nature, hazards and assessment of occupational exposure to airborne asbestos dust: a review*, Ann. Occup. Hyg., 25, 117-247; Corrigenda, 28, 466, 1984.

World Health Organization (1981), *Methods of Monitoring and Evaluating Airborne Man-made Mineral Fibres*. Report on a WHO Consultation (J. Dodgson, Rapporteur), WHO Euro Reports and Studies 48, WHO Copenhagen.

Books

Bogovski, P., Gilson, J.C., Timbrell, V. and Wagner, J.C. (eds) (1973), *Biological effects of asbestos*. In Proc. Working Conf., International Agency for Research on Cancer, Lyon, 2-6 October 1972, IARC Scientific Publications No. 8, IARC, Lyon.

Craighead, J.E. (Chairman) (1982), *Asbestos-associated diseases.The Pathology of asbestos-associated diseases of the lungs and pleural cavities: diagnostic criteria and proposed grading scheme*. Report of the Pneumoconiosis Committee of the College of American Pathologists and the National Institute for Occupational Safety and Health, American Medical Association, Chicago, IL (Arch. Path. Lab. Med., 106 (11), 541-99).

Dewees, D.N. (1986) , *Controlling Asbestos in Buildings. An Economic Investigation*, Resources for the Future, Washington, DC.

Hodgson, A.A. (1987), *Alternatives to Asbestos and Asbestos Products, 2nd edn*, Anjalena Publications, Crowthorne.

Michaels, L. and Chissick, S.S. (eds) (1979), *Asbestos, Vol. 1: Properties, Applications and Hazards*, Wiley, Chichester.

Morgan, W.K.C. and Seaton, A. (1984), *Occupational Lung Diseases, 2nd edn*, W.B. Saunders, Philadelphia, PA.

Parkes, W.R. (1982), *Occupational Lung Disorders, 2nd edn*, Butterworths, London.

MAN-MADE MINERAL FIBRES

Jim Dodgson

Consultant in Occupational Hygiene

INTRODUCTION

Production of man-made mineral fibres (MMMF) has increased considerably over the last 30 years to meet the needs of energy conservation, better insulation and structural reinforcement. Part of the growth in production is due to the wide use of MMMF as a potentially safe product compared to asbestos. However, concern with the health hazards associated with asbestos fibres has led to extensive investigations of the possible hazards associated with other fibrous materials. In this chapter, the types of MMMF currently being produced are described, their main properties are summarized and the present evidence on potential health risks in relation to the use of MMMF in buildings is reviewed.

MAN-MADE MINERAL FIBRE MATERIALS

Definitions

A wide range of synthetic mineral fibres is now available for use in the building and construction industries. There are three main types of MMMF:

- *'Vitreous' fibres,* which are amorphous and glassy, made from molten blast furnace slag or other readily fusible slags, natural rocks and minerals such as basalt, diabase or olivine, and borosilicate or calcium aluminium silicate glass. In this category, there are also three main types:

  - continuous-filament glass fibres
  - mineral wools
  - special purpose glass fibres

- *Ceramic fibres,* produced from high temperature fusion of aluminosilicate minerals such as kaolin or mixtures of alumina and silica or zirconia. These are generally amorphous but some conversion to the crystalline form (ie mullite, chrystabolite) can occur during use at high temperatures;

• **Refractory fibres,** usually crystalline, of alumina, silica, zirconia, graphite, silicon carbide, potassium titanate etc. which are obtained by high temperature fusion or chemical methods.

The physical and chemical properties of these fibres differ considerably in terms of their physical strength, temperature resistance, insulation properties, physical size and solubility in acid or alkali media. These differences largely decide their industrial uses, together with considerations of manufacturing costs and availability. The chemical composition of the various MMMF largely determines their acid resistance and solubility in various solutions; this is relevant, for example, in considering factors which affect clearance of fibres from the lungs. Thermal conductivity, however, is mainly a function of fibre diameter; the finer diameters are less thermally conductive.

The melting points of ceramic and refractory fibres are substantially higher than those of mineral wools and are mainly used for high temperature insulation or jointing in and around industrial furnaces or other specialized industrial situations. Unlike asbestos, MMMF fibres do not split longitudinally into finer fibres or fibrils but may break transversely into shorter fibres of the same diameter.

Manufacturers characterize their MMMF products by their 'nominal diameter', which is a length-weighted measure of mean fibre diameter, and this nominal diameter is the measure used in this chapter.

Each type of MMMF is briefly reviewed below.

Vitreous fibres

Continuous-filament glass fibres are produced to a predetermined diameter by mechanically drawing extruded threads of molten glass through a small orifice of defined size. These long filaments are usually made in relatively large diameters ranging from about 6 to 25 μm but with a very narrow size distribution about the selected diameter. For this reason few respirable fibres (i.e. those of less than 3 μm diameter which can penetrate to the lungs) are obtained.

Mineral wools (also referred to as insulation wools) are made from slag, rock or glass by a combination of blowing and spinning processes to obtain fibres from the melt. A small quantity of mineral oil and resin binder (about 0.5%) is normally added during fibre formation to assist dust suppression and adhesion. In the USA the term mineral wool is often used to describe mixtures of slag and rock wool only. The processes used for manufacturing mineral wools produce a range of fibres of different lengths and diameters together with non-fibrous particles of similar mineral composition formed from solidified droplets.

The nominal diameter of mineral wools now being manufactured is about 2–6 μm. However, the fibre diameter distribution in these materials is rather broad, and some of the fibres present have diameters less than 3 μm. Earlier manufacturing processes for slag and rock wool gave nominal diameters similar to present-day values. Prior to about 1960 the earlier glass wool processes generally produced materials of larger nominal diameter (10–25 μm), although some finer products were made (Cherrie et al., 1986).

Recent research (Dodgson et al., 1987a) has shown that fine fibres (less than 3 μm in diameter) were still present in the older products of relatively small nominal diameter. Technical developments in production to improve insulation properties of the mineral wools reduced the proportion of coarse fibres. Present production material is close to the optimum size for insulation purposes taking into account the cost and effectiveness of manufacturing and transporting bulkier products; further major changes in fibre size are unlikely.

Mineral wool is supplied in a variety of forms for acoustic and thermal insulation or fire protection. These products include loose fibre, flexible lightweight rolls or quilts, and flexible, semi-rigid and rigid bats, slabs and boards of varying densities. They can be supplied with or without facing materials, including laminates on boards. While most products contain mineral oil and resin binder, increased binder is usually added during manufacture when compressing mineral wool for rigid or semi-rigid products.

Special purpose glass fibres are made by further heat attenuation of glass fibres, usually without added oil or binder. None is currently known to be manufactured in the United Kingdom but they are imported for use (e.g. in filter manufacturing). These fine glass fibres have much smaller diameters than the mineral wools, being in the range 1–3 μm. Some superfine glass fibres (less than 1 μm in diameter) are also manufactured.

Ceramic and refractory fibres

Ceramic fibres are usually produced from the molten aluminosilicates by means of similar methods to those used for mineral wool. Nominal fibre sizes generally range from about 1 to 3 μm, although coarser grades are manufactured (WHO, 1988, Cherrie et al, 1989). Unlike mineral wools, the mineral oil added during fibre formation is subsequently removed and is absent from the final products.

HEALTH EFFECTS

Areas of Concern and Exposure Limits

Man-made fibres have been produced for more than 40 years and their effects on workers' health have been examined intensively. Complaints of skin and eye irritations arising from close contact with MMMF materials are well known, particularly from workers handling MMMF for the first time or after a period of absence from contact. These complaints do not usually persist with continued exposure (Hill, 1976; Health and Safety Commission, 1979) except in a minority of cases. Good personal hygiene and good housekeeping lessen irritation (Konzen, 1987). This includes occasional washing of exposed surfaces during the working day, showering, and separate washing of work clothes. The acute effects of MMMF on eyes have recently been attributed to the degree of exposure to MMMF dust and the use of protective goggles has been recommended (Stockholm et al., 1982). The evidence of such effects was reviewed by the World Health Organization (WHO) in 1988. The data available were considered insufficient to derive exposure response relationships for either dermatitis or eye irritation in workers exposed to MMMF.

Substantial exposure to MMMF can result in irritation of the upper respiratory tract although the effects are usually transitory and have not been considered to be a long-term health risk at current levels of exposure in the manufacturing industry (Hill, 1976; Health and Safety Commission, 1979). The occurrence of respiratory symptoms might be expected to be related to dust exposure but early studies of this relationship were inconclusive. Nevertheless, after reviewing the evidence then available, the Health and Safety Commission (1979) proposed and subsequently introduced a UK control limit, now a 'maximum exposure limit', of 5 mg m^{-3} of fibre in air (COSHH Regulations 1988) for exposure to MMMF in recognition of the fact that these respiratory effects implied that MMMF could not simply be treated as a biologically inert dust. In addition, a control limit of 5 fibres per millilitre for respirable fibres was proposed for MMMF workers to minimize the potential carcinogenic risks suggested in the earlier experimental studies with animals (see Appendix), but it was never implemented. The Commission recognized the tentative and subjective nature of these proposals and considered it important to check them against research results as they became available. More recently, the Health and Safety Executive (1984) introduced a recommended limit of 1 fibre per millilitre for superfine MMMF (i.e. fibres with a nominal diameter of less than 1 μm) but this limit is no longer in force. Having reviewed recent research on the carcinogenicity of MMMF, the Health and Safety Commission (1989) now propose to introduce a 2 fibre per millilitre maximum exposure limit for MMMF in addition to the 5 mg m^{-3} maximum exposure limit.

Conclusions from Recent Research

An account of extensive investigations of health effects and results from recent research is given in the Appendix to this chapter. Although conclusions concerning the potential carcinogenicity of MMMF are not clear, authoritative reviewers have summarised the main findings as follows.

Doll (1987) has concluded (tentatively) from the results of the epidemiological studies, taking into account the animal experimental results and the experience of the asbestos industry and the continuous-glass-filament sector of the MMMF industry, that 'MMMF are not more carcinogenic than asbestos fibres and exposure to current mean levels of respirable fibres in the manufacturing industry of 0.2 fibres per millilitre or less is unlikely to produce a measurable risk after another 20 years have passed'. This statement is consistent with the review by the WHO Task Group (WHO, 1988). The latter draws attention to the higher potential risks of lung cancer where substantially higher dust concentrations occur – in ceramic fibre production, in the manufacture of small-diameter ($<$ 1 μm) glass wool and in the user industry, particularly during spraying or blowing operations in confined spaces if protective equipment is not used. Similarly, the International Labour Organisation (ILO, 1989) concluded that, 'With the adoption of appropriate control and preventative measures ... any risks associated with the production and use of the insulation wools should be minimal.'

BUILDING APPLICATIONS

MMMF products are widely used in the building and construction industry. The main applications are summarized in Table B4.1. There are potential risks of exposure to fibres during installation of MMMF products, during maintenance operations and subsequently during normal occupation of the buildings. These potential risks are considered below.

Housing

Mineral wools are commonly used in roll form for thermal insulation of roofs, lofts and attics or as lightweight cladding of walls, and in a shredded or loose form for infilling wall cavities or lofts. Compressed mineral wools in the form of flexible semi-rigid or rigid bats and slabs of varying densities are also used for filling wall cavities or partitions for

Table B4.1 Uses of man-made mineral fibres			
CONTINUOUS FILAMENT	GLASS, ROCK AND SLAG-WOOL	SPECIAL PURPOSE GLASS FIBRE	CERAMIC AND REFRACTORY FIBRES
Reinforcement of cement, plastics paper and rubber products; textiles and electrical insulation	Thermal and acoustic insulation, tiles, pipes; ventilation and air-conditioning ducts.	High performance thermal and acoustic insulation (e.g. aircraft); high efficiency air filters: ear plugs	High temperature (> 1000°C) thermal insulation in furnaces; joints, gaskets

both thermal and acoustic insulation, particularly in timber-frame buildings. Boards and slabs with or without laminated or other surface finishes are used for cladding inner or outer walls, as partitions or as roof linings. Mineral wool ceiling and wall tiles are also made by compression for cladding purposes. Ceramic and refractory fibres are only used to a minor extent domestically in some heating equipment, ceramic hobs and hand-held paint strippers.

Industrial and Other Large Buildings

In addition to the above uses, mineral wool rolls are used for lightweight cladding of plant, pipes etc. Bats, slabs and boards also have further applications in industrial buildings or large apartment blocks, including use as acoustic ceiling panels and fire protection of structural steel. Rigid slabs are used for thermal, acoustic and fire insulation in boiler and ventilation rooms in the form of wall cladding or floor insulation and can be load bearing. Mineral wool pipe sections produced by compression are used for insulating heating or other pipe runs in buildings and associated plant. Loose-fibre spray is also used for insulation or fire protection purposes on structural steel and basement or car park roofs.

Mineral wools are used as baffles in ventilation or air-conditioning ducts, and high efficiency filter systems frequently include special purpose or superfine glass fibres in the matrix. Use of ceramic and refractory fibres is largely confined to high temperature applications in excess of 1,000°C, e.g. in furnace linings and associated pipework.

Exposure to Man-made Mineral Fibres during Installation

Attention has been drawn (see Appendix to this chapter) to fibre emission levels when using and installing mineral wools, and it has been pointed out that products containing mineral oil produce markedly lower emissions. The highest respirable fibre concentrations (1 fibre per millilitre or more) occur when spraying or blowing loose material in confined spaces or laying mineral wool roll blanket in lofts. Actual exposure levels will often be less than these values since workers are usually not continuously employed on such operations. Nevertheless, the use of respiratory protection should be actively encouraged and practised during spraying or blowing; containment and exhaust ventilation should also be used to minimize fibre emissions. In most cases lightweight filtering facepiece respirators should provide sufficient respiratory protection (British Standard 6016, 1980) but more efficient devices may be required if control of fibre emissions is inadequate.

Installation work in more open areas with better natural ventilation and involving less disturbance of the mineral wool product has been associated with substantially lower fibre emission levels (WHO, 1988). These are generally comparable with or lower than those currently experienced in the manufacturing industry. Work on compressed materials (bats, slabs, boards and pipes), particularly pre-formed, encased or faced products, would be expected to produce low emission levels. Cutting or drilling of these materials will increase emissions, but fibre concentrations will be minimized if this work is carried out in the open or using extract ventilation.

The release of respirable fibres within domestic houses during installation of mineral wool loft insulation or disturbance of existing insulation has been measured (Dodgson et al., 1987). Fibre levels were generally less than 0.01 fibres per millilitre. Within 24 hours of disturbance or installation, fibre levels inside the houses were below the detection limit (0.005 fibres per millilitre). Actual levels measured by high volume samples or pooled samples were about 0.0002 fibres per millilitre or less. Similar studies in other types of buildings have not been reported, but similar results might be anticipated.

Use of ceramic and refractory fibres which do not contain mineral oil is largely confined to furnace linings and associated pipework. Although not strictly part of the building operation, installation work on furnaces with these materials may be expected to release respirable fibre concentrations in excess of 1 fibre per millilitre into the building unless the work is properly contained by sealing off the work area and using extract ventilation.

The effects of ageing on the emission of fibres may be important during removal, maintenance or demolition work. The oil content of mineral wools and the effectiveness of binders may be expected to diminish during prolonged exposure to high temperatures. This could increase fibre emission during the above operations. The effects of heat on ceramic fibres, particularly the formation of chrystabolite, should also be taken into account. In both cases, exposures should be minimised by effective containment, ventilation and respiratory protection procedures.

Exposure to Indoor Air

Measurements of respirable fibre concentrations in the home, school or work environment following installation of mineral wool are extremely low (see above). Some release of fibre will occur if the materials are disturbed during maintenance or disposal or are installed in places where damage can easily occur. For example, pipework insulated with roll, blanket or pipe sections of mineral wool in transit areas of schools, factories etc. should be protected with a tough metal scrim to avoid scuffing. Mineral wool products containing mineral oil and binder should be employed wherever practicable to minimize fibre emission.

The release of fibre from loft insulations in houses can occur when entering or working in the loft, and fibres could enter the water system if water tanks in the roof space are not properly covered with a well-fitted lid. Contamination of other rooms could occur from fibres released through structural gaps, e.g. at the inner leaf of the external wall or through down-lighters and around pipes from the loft to lower rooms. The above measurements (Dodgson et al., 1987) indicate that long-term exposure levels arising from disturbance of loft insulation should be extremely low.

Similarly neither cavity-wall timber-frame insulation nor compressed and pre-formed sections (bats, slabs, boards and pipes) should release significant amounts of fibre in normal use, particularly if they are combined with facing materials, although care will be needed to minimize exposure during maintenance work. Whenever possible, compressed sections should be used in preference to loose fibre or roll blankets to minimize fibre emission.

Loose mineral wool insulation around hot- and cold-water tanks is usually encased in polyethylene. Alternatively, rigid compressed boards may be employed. Such tanks are often accessible in airing cupboards and there is a small risk of contaminating clothes if the insulation is not properly encased. The use of casings to cover and protect the insulation around boiler and ventilation plant in large buildings should avoid these problems. Some release of fibres might be expected during maintenance when the casing is removed but not otherwise.

The respirable fibre levels of MMMF in indoor air measured to date are generally very low compared with present levels in most sectors of the production and user industry and extremely low – by several orders of magnitude – compared with some past occupational levels associated with lung cancer risks. The WHO drew attention (1988) to the absence of increased lung cancer risk among workers employed under the improved conditions in the MMMF industry and followed up for a sufficient length of time. Nevertheless, there is insufficient data from occupationally exposed populations to permit quantitative extrapolation to the low exposure levels of indoor air or the general environment. The WHO conclude: 'The overall picture indicates that the possible risk of lung cancer among the general public is very low, if there is any at all, and should not be a cause for concern if the current levels of exposure continue'.

CONCLUSIONS

* When using MMMF, good personal hygiene and good housekeeping practices should be adopted to minimise any possible skin or eye irritations, and protective goggles should be supplied for operatives and used by them.

* Compliance with current statutory requirements for control of exposure to less than five milligrams per cubic metre should avoid any long-term upper respiratory health affects from MMMF.

* The evidence of carcinogenity from exposure to MMMF is less clear, but the need to minimise any potential risks by limiting exposures to respirable fibres has been recognised.

* Elevated concentrations of respirable fibres have been associated with the blowing or spraying of mineral wool and during the laying of roll blankets in confined spaces. Similar levels may be prevalent during the installation of similar ceramic or refractory fibre insulation which contains no mineral oil or oil-free mineral wool. Even though time-weighted average exposures may not be high, fibre emissions should be minimised by using containment and exhaust ventilation procedures; protective equipment should also be used in these situations, as advised by the WHO, to minimise any potential risks of lung cancer.

* Fibre emissions during the handling and installation of compressed and pre-formed mineral wool products (bats, slabs, boards and pipes) are generally comparable with the current lower levels in the manufacturing industry which have not been associated with increased lung cancer. It would be prudent to use these materials where possible, taking care to minimise fibre emissions during cutting or drilling.

* Fibre concentrations in indoor air diminish rapidly to very low levels following installation or maintenance work. Emissions can be further reduced by careful building design to minimize the ingress of fibres to the interior of buildings or by using faced products or encapsulation. Occupiers of buildings containing MMMF are exposed to extremely low fibre concentrations which should not cause concern.

* Simple protective measures using suitable clothing, gloves, goggles or filtering facepiece respirators can be utilized during building maintenance or DIY work, should skin, eye or respiratory tract irritations occur.

APPENDIX

PREVIOUS INVESTIGATIONS OF HEALTH EFFECTS, AND RESULTS OF RECENT RESEARCH.

Experimental Investigations of Fibre Carcinogenicity

The implantation of glass and other natural and synthetic fibres in the pleural or peritoneal cavities of animals has led to the development of tumours similar to mesothelioma caused in man by asbestos (Stanton and Wrench, 1972; Pott et al. 1974; Stanton et al. 1977). This work was originally designed to show how asbestos fibres might produce their carcinogenic effect. The conclusion was that carcinogenicity was more closely related to the physical size and shape (length and diameter) of the fibres than to differences in mineralogical composition. Fibres of length greater than 8 μm and diameter less than 0.25 μm were the most carcinogenic. These studies attracted interest in the possible health hazards of inhaling respirable fibres from MMMF materials (i.e. the fine fibres that can penetrate to and deposit in the lungs) and stimulated extensive research on the long-term risks to health in the manufacture and use of MMMF products.

Results of Recent Research

Large-scale epidemiological, environmental and animal studies into the possible health hazards of MMMF have been funded by the European and US manufacturing industries for more than 10 years. The research has been carried out by independent institutes in Europe and the United States, and the results were first reported in 1982 at a meeting organized by the WHO in Copenhagen. These investigations were continued and the results of the extended research were reported at a similar meeting at the same venue in 1986. Research conducted by other groups not involved in the industrially sponsored work was also presented at these meetings. The published proceedings (WHO, 1983, 1987) include peer reviews (Doll, 1987). The results were further assessed by a WHO Task Group (WHO, 1988) concerned with estimating the risks associated with exposure to MMMF. These conclusions have been given in the main text.

Environmental exposure to man-made mineral fibres

Environmental surveys of respirable fibre concentrations in mineral wool manufacturing plants show that current exposure levels are generally low. Mean concentrations of respirable fibres were mainly less than 0.1 fibres per millilitre in both the American and European studies, although levels exceeding 1 fibre per millilitre occurred occasionally. Mean respirable fibre concentrations at continuous-fibre plants were less than 0.02 fibres per millilitre. All of these fibre levels are considerably lower than those previously experienced in the asbestos industry. The airborne MMMF fibres were also substantially thicker and longer than asbestos, and the proportion of very fine potentially carcinogenic fibres, was very much lower. Mean concentrations of total dust at the MMMF plants were usually around 5 mg m⁻³ or less, although some higher mean values occurred. Much of the airborne dust was not fibrous. These environmental data were used in the epidemiological studies.

Evidence was presented at the 1986 WHO Meeting which indicated that the emission of respirable fibres from MMMF was strongly dependent on the nominal diameter of the material (the finer the nominal diameter the greater the fibre emission), the opposing effect of added mineral oil and resin binder which acts as a dust suppressant, and the degree of manual handling. The addition of 0.5%–1% of mineral oil to mineral wool was shown to reduce emission of respirable fibres by a factor of 5–10.

Estimates of past exposure levels (Dodgson et al., 1987a) and simulation studies (Cherrie et al., 1987) in the rock and slag wool industry, which took account of changes in the product, manufacturing methods, production rates and improvements in ventilation, suggested that mean respirable fibre concentrations in the early period of the rock and slag wool industry might have been 1–2 fibres per millilitre, or even more, during the dustiest work. Levels in the glass wool industry were probably similar to current levels.

Airborne levels of respirable fibres measured in the ceramic fibre industry were substantially higher than for mineral wool manufacture, being as high as 2 fibres per millilitre for production and secondary production work but generally less than 0.5 fibres per millilitre for other work (Esmen and Hammad, 1985; Cherrie et al., 1989). Such values are consistent with the nominal size of the product and the absence of mineral oil.

Substantial fibre concentration data are available for the application of mineral wools in the user industry (WHO, 1988). Respirable fibre concentrations vary markedly depending on the degree of disturbance and confinement. Spraying or blowing operations with loose-fill mineral wool in domestic lofts have produced short term mean concentrations of 8.2 fibres per millilitre (maximum 21 fibres per millilitre) (Head and Wagg, 1980). Corresponding values for laying mineral wool blanket in lofts seldom exceed 1–2 fibres per millilitre. Other installation work is associated with concentrations of less than 1 fibre per millilitre. Similar data for the use of ceramic or refractory fibres are not available.

Respirable MMMF concentrations have also been monitored indoors in offices, schools and domestic buildings containing mineral wool insulation at varying periods after completion of building or installation work (Dodgson et al., 1987b; WHO, 1988). The level of fibres encountered was generally less than 0.001 fibres per millilitre when measured by electron microscopy methods. When phase contrast optical methods were used (the routine method for industrial monitoring) higher values were obtained since this technique cannot distinguish organic or other mineral fibres from MMMF.

Epidemiological studies

Reports on the progress of epidemiological studies in Europe (Simonato et al., 1987) and the United States (Enterline et al., 1987), together with that of a smaller study in a Canadian glass wool plant (Shannon et al., 1987), included observations on 41,185 workers and provided information on 7,862 deaths. Taken together (Doll, 1987) the data show no excess mortality when compared with national death rates for any cause of death other than lung cancer. Nor was there any evidence of any risk of mesothelioma (the tumour in the lining of the lung which can be caused by amphibole asbestos fibres). The extra deaths from lung cancer were found to increase with time since first exposure, being greatest for workers who had been followed up for 20 years or more after first being exposed. The excess was highest for the rock and slag wool workers and not statistically significant for glass wool workers when their death rates from lung cancer were compared with those for people in the localities near the plants. In the US study there was evidence that the risks of dying from lung cancer were greater for those employed in the manufacture of small-diameter glass fibres. No excess lung cancer mortality was found for those employed in the manufacture of continuous glass filaments. The excess of lung cancer deaths associated with rock and slag wool may possibly be attributed to work in the early periods of the industry during which the respirable fibre levels were estimated to have been at least 10 times higher than current levels. No excess of lung cancer deaths has been observed among European rock and slag wool workers during the period of lower fibre exposures associated with current methods of production. In the US study, there was no association of the increased death rates with either the intensity or the duration of the fibre exposure, as would be expected if exposure to fibres was the cause of the increase. It is possible that this increase in mortality may be related to other occupational factors (e.g. use of asbestos, arsenic, or polyaromatic hydrocarbons) or non-occupational factors (e.g. smoking). Nevertheless it was concluded that, on balance, the weight of the evidence pointed to the fibres themselves being at least partly responsible for the observed risk (Doll, 1987; WHO, 1988).

Epidemiological studies of respiratory illness among workers in the manufacturing industry were also reported at the 1982 WHO Conference. Respiratory symptoms and impairment of lung function were not related to past exposure to MMMF, although some small radiographic opacities in the lungs of a limited number of exposed men were reported. There was an absence of corresponding data for the user industry. Further epidemiological investigations are needed to clarify the findings. These have been started but no results are yet available. There has been no evidence of excess mortality from non-malignant respiratory disease in the above large-scale investigations in Europe and the United States.

Animal inhalation studies

Several groups have reported animal research studies designed to test the carcinogenic and fibrogenic potential of MMMF when animals are allowed to inhale the fibres. This type of exposure mirrors that experienced by man more closely than that induced by implantation. The results were compared with those from unexposed animals and animals exposed to asbestos and the findings have been reviewed (Davis, 1986; Kuschner, 1987; WHO, 1988). These investigations supported the hypothesis that MMMF in general production are not likely to cause lung cancer, pulmonary fibrosis or mesothelioma. The absence of carcinogenic effects was considered consistent with the physical and chemical properties of MMMF: these fibres have larger diameters than airborne asbestos and would be expected to be less carcinogenic; MMMF can only split transversely, thus producing shorter fibres of the same diameter, whereas asbestos splits longitudinally to form finer fibres; MMMF are also more soluble than asbestos. These factors would be expected to assist natural clearance from the lungs.

Conclusions

Doll (1987) has concluded (tentatively) from the results of the epidemiological studies, taking into account the animal experimental results and the experience of the asbestos industry and the continuous-glass-filament sector of the MMMF industry, that 'MMMF are not more carcinogenic than asbestos fibres and exposure to current mean levels of respirable fibres in the manufacturing industry of 0.2 fibres per millilitre or less is unlikely to produce a measurable risk after another 20 years have passed'. This statement is consistent with the review by the WHO Task Group (WHO, 1988). The latter draws attention to the higher potential risks of lung cancer where substantially higher dust concentrations occur — in ceramic fibre production, in the manufacture of small-diameter (< 1 µm) glass wool and in the user industry, particularly during spraying or blowing operations in confined spaces if protective equipment is not used. Similarly, the International Labour Organisation (ILO, 1989) concluded that, 'With the adoption of appropriate control and preventative measures ... any risks associated with the production and use of the insulation wools should be minimal.'

REFERENCES

British Standard 6016: *Filtering Facepiece Respirator* (1980).

Cherrie, J., et al. (1986), *Past exposure to airborne fibres and other potential risk factors in the European man-made mineral fibre production industry*, Scand. J. Work Environ. Health, 12 (Suppl. 1), 26-33.

Cherrie, J. et al. (1987), *An experimental simulation of an early rockwool/slagwool production process*, Ann. Occup. Hyg., 31 (4B), 583-93.

Cherrie, J.W. et al. (1989), *A Report on the Environmental Conditions at Seven European Ceramic Fibre Plants*, IOM Report TM/89/07, Institute of Occupational Medicine, Edinburgh.

Davis, J.M.G, *A review of experimental evidence for the carcinogenicity of man-made vitreous fibres*, Scand. J. Work Environ. Health, 12 (suppl. 1) 12-17.

Dodgson, J., Cherrie, J. and Groat, S. (1987a), *Estimates of past exposure to respirable man-made mineral fibres in the European insulation wool industry*, Ann. Occup. Hyg., 31 (4B), 567-82.

Dodgson, J. et al. (1987b) , *Assessment of Airborne Mineral Wool Fibres in Domestic Houses*, IOM Report TM/87/18, Institute of Occupational Medicine, Edinburgh.

Doll, R. (1987), *Symposium on MMMF, Copenhagen, October 1986: overview and conclusions*, Ann. Occup. Hyg., 31 (4B), 805-19.

Enterline, P.E. et al. (1987), *Mortality update of a cohort of U.S. man-made mineral fibre workers*, Ann. Occup. Hyg., 31 (4B), 625-56.

Esmen, N.A. and Hammad, Y.Y. (1983) , *Recent studies of the environment in ceramic fibre production (1983)*. In Euro Reports and Studies 81, WHO, Copenhagen, pp. 222-31.

Head, I.W.H. and Wagg, R.M. (1980), *A survey of occupational exposure to man-made mineral fibre dust*, Ann. Occup. Hyg., 23, 235-58.

Health and Safety Commission (1979), *Discussion Document: Man-made Mineral Fibres*. Report of a Working Party to the Advisory Committee on Toxic Substances, HM Stationery Office, London.

Health and Safety Commission (1988), *Control of Substances Hazardous to Health Regulations, 1988, Schedule 1*, HM Stationery Office, London.

Health and Safety Executive (1984), *Toxic Substances Bulletin, December 1984*, HM Stationery Office, London.

Health and Safety Commission (1989), Consultative Document : *Draft Control of Substances Hazardous to Health* (Amendment) *Regulations 1990 and Draft amendments to the Control of Carcinogenic Substances Approved Code of Practice and the Control of Substances Hazardous to Health* Approved Code of Practice, HSE, London.

Hill, J.W. (1976), *Health aspects of man-made fibres. A review*, Ann. Occup. Hyg., 20, 161-73.

ILO (1989), *Draft Working Document on Safety in the use of Mineral Wool and Synthetic fibres of a meeting of experts Geneva 17-25 April 1989*, International Labour Organisation, Geneva.

Konzen, J.L (1987), *Fibreglass and the skin*, in *Occupational and Industrial Dermatology*, Ed Howard I Maibach, Year Book Medical Publishers Inc.

Kuschner, M (1987), *The effects of MMMF on animal systems: some reflections on their pathogenesis*, Ann. Occup. Hyg. 31 (4B), 791-797.

Pott, F., Huth, F. and Friedrichs, K.H. (1974), *Tumorigenic effect of fibrous dusts in experimental animals*, Environ. Health Perspect., 9, 313-15.

Shannon, H.S. et al. (1987), *Mortality experience of Ontario glass fibre workers – extended follow-up*, Ann. Occup. Hyg., 31 (4B), 657-62.

Simonato et al. (1987), *The International Agency for Research on Cancer historical cohort study of MMMF production workers in seven European countries: extension of follow-up*, Ann. Occup. Hyg., 31 (4B), 603-23.

Stanton, M.F. and Wrench, C. (1972), *Mechanism of mesothelioma induction with asbestos and fibrous glass*, J. Natl. Cancer Inst., 48, 797-821.

Stanton, M.F. et al. (1977), *Carcinogenicity of fibrous glass: pleural response in the rat in relation to fibre dimension*, J. Natl. Cancer Inst., 58, 587-603.

Stockholm, J. et al. (1982), *Ophthalmologic effects of man-made mineral fibres*, Scand. J. Work Environ. Health, 8, 185-90.

WHO (World Health Organization) (1983), *Biological effects of man-made mineral fibres*. Report on a WHO/IARC meeting in Copenhagen 20-22 April, 1982. In Euro. Reports and Studies 81, WHO, Copenhagen.

WHO (World Health Organization) (1987), *Man-made mineral fibres in the working environment*. In Proc. Int. Symp. Copenhagen, 28-29 October 1986, Ann. Occup. Hyg., 31 (4B).

WHO (World Health Organization) (1988), *Environmental Health Criteria 77: Man-made Mineral Fibres*, WHO, Geneva.

METALS

Roy M. Harrison

University of Essex

INTRODUCTION

Metal toxicity has caused problems for mankind for many centuries. Lead was much used in Roman times and its toxic effects have been well recognized for over two centuries. The effects of mercury on the brain gave rise to mental illness in hat-makers – 'mad-hatters' – for many years. In general, metal toxicity has been observed initially through its adverse effects on occupationally exposed workers. It is only more recently that concern has arisen over possible ill effects caused by low level exposure of the general population to toxic metals from the environment in which they live.

Metals have many applications in building. In most instances they are quite innocuous, although in some cases they do give cause for concern. The metals most widely used in building are aluminium, plain and galvanized (i.e. zinc-coated) iron and steel, stainless steel, copper and lead. Other metals (e.g. chromium) are components of paints and also require consideration, and both chromium and cadmium may be used in bright finishes on metalwork. This chapter reviews the metals used and found in buildings and the potential hazards to construction workers and occupants.

TOXICOLOGY

Aluminium

Aluminium is an abundant element in the natural environment. Normal adult daily intake is within the range 10–100 mg and is without known adverse effects.

The main route of intake is dietary, but absorption via the gastrointestinal tract (stomach and gut) is very inefficient. Bypass of this barrier, either by industrial exposure to bauxite fumes (small airborne particles of aluminium oxide) or through kidney dialysis with non-deionized aluminium-coagulated tapwater, can lead to serious toxic effects.

Concern has arisen recently over possible associations between aluminium and Alzheimer's disease, a degenerative brain disorder comprising one category of pre-senile and senile dementia. Some studies have shown an increased aluminium content in the brains of patients with Alzheimer's disease, although this could be the result of the disease process rather than the cause of it (Lee, 1989). One recent epidemiological study has shown a slight increase in the incidence of Alzheimer's disease in areas with higher levels of aluminium in tapwater (Martyn et al., 1989). At the time of writing, the subject is highly controversial with other non-aluminium-related causes of the disease also postulated; no firm opinion can be given on the risks, if any, associated with environmental exposure to aluminium.

Cadmium

Cadmium is an element of high toxicity, with well-recognized adverse effects upon the kidney and the ability to damage bones in long-term exposure. The main source of human intake of cadmium is the diet, although drinking water and air also contribute to exposure. Contaminated beverages from dispensers containing cadmium-plated fittings have caused acute effects in children.

Chromium

Chromium can exist in several chemical oxidation states known as valence states. Biologically, chromium(III) and chromium(VI) are the most important and these are chemically and toxicologically distinct. Chromium(VI), also known as chromate, is considerably more toxic. Most of the evidence about chromium(VI) is from industries where the metal is used. The effects include the following.

- *Dermatitis*: chromium(VI) can act as an allergen causing contact dermatitis on exposed skin. When inhaled, chromium(VI) can cause perforation of the nasal septum and inflammation of the larynx and liver.

- *Ulceration:* penetration of the skin through cuts and abrasions can lead to serious ulceration.

- *Carcinogenesis*: epidemiological (statistical) studies suggest that inhalation of chromium(VI) can be a cause of lung cancer (bronchial carcinoma). There is also slight evidence from animal studies that ingested chromium(VI) may be associated with a higher incidence of malignant tumours. There are clear indications that some chromium(VI) compounds are more potent carcinogens than others. 'Evident carcinogens' include calcium chromate, zinc potassium chromate and lead chromate.

The greatest potential exposure to chromium(VI) in the home is through old chromium-based paints. The organic matrix of the paint may to some extent limit the availability of the chromium for absorption if ingested, but it will not eliminate it entirely. It is reported (Browning, 1969) that an infant who had eaten paint containing a relatively insoluble chromium compound showed symptoms suggestive of encephalitis (a serious condition involving inflammation of the brain). Unfortunately, however, this aspect of chromium(VI) toxicity has been little investigated and it is difficult to draw firm conclusions as to the degree of risk.

The recommendation by the World Health Organization (1984) of an upper limit of 0.05 parts per million on levels of chromium in drinking water is a recognition of the considerable toxicity of chromium(VI).

Copper

Copper is an essential trace element and the human body regulates its level of copper by means of a homeostatic (i.e. self-regulating) mechanism. Acute exposure to large doses of copper has known adverse health effects, but chronic (long-term) low level exposure to the metal is not believed to be associated with any ill effects.

Lead

Human exposure to lead arises from a number of sources, the most important being diet – drinking water and beverages – inhaled particles and, for children, ingested dust. The relative contribution of each source is very variable depending upon the dietary habits of the individuals, the nature of the plumbing system and tapwater that they use and the lead content of the air and dusts to which they are exposed (Harrison and Laxen, 1977; Royal Commission on Environmental Pollution, 1983).

Acute exposure to high doses of lead causes clear symptoms of poisoning. These are rarely observed nowadays in the United Kingdom but a few cases arise annually, almost invariably in children who consume old lead-rich paint. Small children may develop the habit known as 'pica' of ingesting materials not normally regarded as foodstuffs, and so they may chew or ingest flakes of paint (Bicknell, 1975). Children also inadvertently consume surface dust as a result of hand-to-mouth activity, and if such dusts are enriched with paint flakes or with debris arising from the abrasion of old paintwork, appreciably elevated exposures can occur.

The topic of subclinical effects of lead exposure is far less clear-cut.

Many independent studies have been carried out to determine whether levels of lead exposure insufficient to cause clinically-recognizable poisoning give rise to impaired intellectual development and behavioural problems in children. Such studies have normally taken blood lead or tooth dentine lead as an indicator of exposure and have sought correlations with performance in intelligence tests and behavioural evaluations. It is generally found that children with higher lead exposure perform less well in the tests, but when allowance is made statistically for parental and socio-environmental factors (i.e. that children from lower socio-economic groups tend both to live in high lead content inner city environments and to show poorer test performances), most studies have revealed a connection between intellectual deficit and lead exposure that is only small and not statistically significant (Urbanowicz et al., 1987). However, some of the most recent studies, including the lead study by Edinburgh of over 500 children (Fulton, 1987), have shown small statistically significant adverse effects of lead on various measures of ability, educational attainment and behaviour.

There is no widely accepted no-effect threshold for adverse effects of lead exposure and indeed many researchers argue that there is a continuum of effects, very slight at low levels of lead exposure and increasing as lead exposure increases. As a result of this concern, government policy has been progressively to reduce population exposure to environmental lead, and whilst the European Economic Community Directive 77/312/EEC defines a blood level concentration of 35 µg dl[1] (micrograms per 100 millilitres) as an upper limit (Official Journal of the European Communities, 1975), UK government advice (Department of the Environment and the Welsh Office, 1982) recommends that action should be taken to reduce environmental exposure when an individual, particularly a child, has a blood concentration in excess of 25 µg dl[1]. Concentrations of lead in the blood of the UK population are currently declining. As a general policy, where viable alternatives exist, lead is being replaced in environmentally sensitive applications.

Most modern building materials are low in lead, and the exposure risks arise in the main from older materials, particularly leaded water pipes, and solders (even in copper pipes), gunmetal tap fittings and old lead-rich paintwork. However, the most serious risk is in soft water areas, where lead pipes have not generally been installed for years. Lead-free solder for copper pipes is now often specified and this practice is to be encouraged.

Use of lead in the workplace is subject to the Control of Lead at Work Regulations 1980 which should be consulted if any work with lead is undertaken.

Iron, Steel and Stainless Steel

Iron is abundant in the natural environment and is an essential trace element for humans. Thus there are well-defined problems associated with iron deficiency, whereas poisoning is possible but only by very large doses. Accidental ingestion of ferrous sulphate tablets is a well-recognized cause of iron poisoning, especially in children. Occupational exposure to high concentrations of iron oxides in air is associated with a benign (harmless) accumulation of dust in the lung known as siderosis.

The average adult daily intake of iron is about 20 mg, and exposure through use of iron in building materials is likely to add only a very small amount to this. The World Health Organization recommends upper limits for iron in drinking water, but because of taste and discoloration effects rather than toxicity (World Health Organization, 1984).

Steel is made by alloying iron with carbon. Other elements (e.g. manganese, silicon, chromium, vanadium, tungsten, molybdenum, titanium, phosphorus, zirconium, aluminium, copper, cobalt and nickel) may be added to impart special properties to the steel, but are normally present in concentrations of a few per cent at most. Stainless steels are so called because of their corrosion resistance, are subject to only very slow rates of degradation due to weathering, and hence release their chemical constituents at an insignificant rate. Adverse health effects due to the release of minor components of steels are therefore most unlikely.

Zinc

Zinc is an essential trace element, and the human body has a homeostatic (i.e. self-regulating) mechanism by which levels of zinc are regulated. Excessive intake is eliminated by enhanced excretion; consequently cases of zinc deficiency are probably more common than cases of zinc poisoning (Nriagu, 1980). Zinc intake can be important in limiting the toxic effects of cadmium. Zinc poisoning can occur as a result of very large doses of zinc, either inhaled as fine particles (causing zinc fume fever) or from consumption of acid foods prepared in galvanized iron containers (this effect has also been ascribed to the cadmium impurity commonly present in zinc). Chronic effects from lower doses are probably of little practical relevance, and copper in the diet would be expected to exert an ameliorating effect. The limits for zinc in drinking water recommended by the World Health Organization (1984) relate to aesthetic and nuisance considerations rather than toxic effects. Overall, therefore, modest exposure to zinc is more likely to be beneficial than deleterious to health.

USES OF METALS IN BUILDINGS

Some uses of metals in buildings may lead to the dispersal of metal particles within and outside the building while others do not. Specific uses are reviewed below.

Pipework, Boilers and Tanks

Pipes used for hot and cold water supply present a possible hazard as a result of leaching or abrasion of both external and internal surfaces. In particular, cold-water pipes and storage tanks are a known source of metals in drinking water, which arise from simple dissolution of the material of the pipe into the water. Of special note in this regard are lead and copper pipes, but the materials of solders and joints must also be considered. Occasionally water drawn from the hot tap is used for cooking or drinking and in this case contact with storage tanks as well as boiler surfaces or immersion heater elements is also inevitable. The higher temperature will often lead to enhanced metal concentrations relative to cold water. This topic is considered in more detail in Chapter 9.

Pipes used in hot-water central heating systems and for transmission of gas, as well as water supply pipes, may represent a source of metals in the home due to abrasion of outer surfaces. Such abrasion processes generally proceed at only a very modest rate and appreciable metal dispersal from this source is unlikely.

Cast iron is used in rainwater pipes and fittings, drainage pipes and fittings and manhole covers. Iron is an abundant element in the environment (especially in soils) and no problems due to iron release are envisaged.

Ducting and Flues

Ducting for hot-air central heating and flue pipes are frequently of metallic construction, generally galvanized steel. Metal ducting is usually concealed within walls or beneath floors and is not subject to substantial abrasion. It should not therefore be an appreciable source of release of metals into the building. Double-walled stainless steel is used in flue pipes. Provided that it can meet the technical criteria of lack of corrosion and leakage and adequate internal insulation to prevent risk of burning of skin or of combustible materials coming into contact with it (stainless steel is a good conductor of heat), it provides a safe material for flue pipe construction.

Railings and Ironmongery

Many items are used in construction which come under the heading of railings and ironmongery. In general, they are made of iron or steel and are subject to mild abrasion. As such they are likely to be harmless. Use of other metals, or platings, might give cause for concern. Bronze (an alloy of copper and tin) and brass (an alloy of copper and zinc) are also used in cladding, fittings, railings and ironmongery. The combination of little dispersal into the environment and low toxicity means that they are relatively safe.

Windows and Leaded Lights

The traditional leaded light offers some possibility, however slight, of abrasion and the consequent release of lead, and the opportunity for sucking or chewing by a child. Although the risk of release of appreciable quantities of lead is very small, the recommendation must be against the use of the traditional leaded lights. Copper, however, offers a far smaller toxic hazard and is to be preferred on health grounds.

Rationalized design (i.e. bonding the strip of metal on to the glass) restricts the lead to the outer surface of the glass, but the lead is nonetheless accessible and might even part from the glass if the adhesive is inadequate. For this reason this design cannot be endorsed on health grounds. The alternative in which lead is sealed within a double glazing unit, however, offers no hazard unless the window is broken, and then there is only a slight opportunity for exposure if replacement of the window is promptly carried out.

Modern linseed oil putties do not contain lead. However, older putty is likely to do so and due care should be taken in maintenance work. In particular, dry sanding should be avoided as this will disperse leaded dusts.

Modern Roofing Materials

Plastic-coated galvanized steel and plastic-coated aluminium are extensively used for roofing, particularly in industrial and warehouse applications. Clearly, if the plastic coating remains intact, there is no metal-associated hazard. If the plastic coating is breached, however, some weathering of zinc (from the galvanization) and aluminium is certain. These materials are unlikely to become airborne to any significant degree; the only likely route of any importance is leaching by rainwater. Since both the zinc and the aluminium form sparingly water-soluble oxidized coatings, it is fairly certain that the concentration of dissolved metals would be modest and would represent no hazard to health even if the drainage water were collected for drinking (indeed galvanized iron water pipes and aluminium cooking utensils are used with no known ill effects), unless the rainwater was highly acidic.

Coatings on Iron to Prevent Corrosion

Zinc, as a coating (galvanization) on iron to prevent corrosion, should not present a hazard as neither the zinc nor the iron is appreciably toxic unless ingested in considerable quantities.

Components of Paints

Historically a number of metals have been used in paints. One, lead, has been a well-recognized source of problems. Another, chromium, in its chromium(VI) form is potentially toxic, although firm evidence linking chromium(VI) in paints to adverse human health effects is lacking. Chromium(VI) in the form of zinc chromate and zinc tetroxychromate is used in some metal primers, but not normally in decorative paints. Thus it is not usual to find chromium(VI) in recent indoor paint-work. Currently manufactured metal primers containing more than 1% chromium(VI) pigment carry a warning on the can.

Cadmium Pigments and Lead in New Paints

Cadmium pigments have been used in the past but are not now in common use in paints used in buildings. The pigments are generally of low availability to humans and toxic hazards are believed to be low. Following recent voluntary agreements between the government and the UK paint industry (Paintmakers' Association of Great Britain, personal communication), lead compounds are no longer used in the production of retail decorative paints. There may be lead impurities in some of the materials used, but levels of lead in such paints are normally very low (< 25 ppm). Lead-containing paints in the form of white lead and calcium plumbate primers are available to the trade. The former are normally used only in specialized exterior applications and the latter as metal primers. The European Commission is proposing to ban the use of white lead pigment in paints in the near future. Paints containing more than 1% soluble lead pigment, or decorative paints containing more than 0.25% (2500 ppm) total lead in whole paint, are labelled with warnings.

Lead in Old Paints

Old paintwork can contain high levels of lead. Chemical analysis is required before it can be stated with any certainty whether or not a particular piece of paintwork has a significant lead content, but history gives a useful general guide. Before the First World War, lead-based paint was used very extensively on walls, wood and metal, both indoors and outdoors. All paintwork and priming dating from before the First

World War is likely to contain significant amounts of lead. Technical changes after about 1920 caused steady reductions in both the average lead content of leaded paints and their use, first for indoor work and later even for outdoor priming.

The overall reduction in lead content has continued to the very low levels in domestic decorative paints used today. So leaded paintwork is very likely to be found on the exteriors of inter-war buildings and is not uncommon on interior surfaces, especially in the priming coats, and there is the likelihood that unsuitable leaded paint or primer has been used since the war. It must also be borne in mind that (a) recent unleaded paint-work may conceal older lead-based paint or primer and (b) older woodwork may have some leaded primer left on it after it has been stripped. Exterior metal work of whatever age is very likely to have at least a lead-based primer on it unless it has been stripped recently and deliberately repainted with low-lead paint and primer. A small flake of paint is all that is needed for an inexpensive test to establish the lead content.

Leaded paintwork only becomes a serious hazard when it is disturbed, and then only if the disturbance is such that people breathe or eat dust or debris. Sound leaded paintwork, free from peeling, cracking, chipping or other deterioration, poses no problem except in the case of children suffering from 'pica' (see above).

Although children with pica do not always chew paint or painted surfaces, where a child has this condition the only completely reliable safety measure is to remove the child to a place which is known to be free from leaded paint, especially on accessible surfaces. Failing that, the child should be closely supervised and all accessible surfaces in the home should be stripped and repainted with low-lead paint, taking care to follow the precautions set out below.

Removal of Leaded Paint

Once lead paint is detected it does not necessarily follow that it needs to be removed. Wholesale removal is generally neither feasible nor cost-effective and, if not done with scrupulous care, will probably make matters worse by releasing lead dust and particles around the home to be inhaled and ingested. When paintwork is sound and children are not exposed to it, it is unlikely to present any serious hazard, whatever its lead content, if it is left alone or simply covered with modern paint in the course of normal redecoration. Preparation of sound paintwork should be restricted to cleaning using ordinary domestic cleaning solutions and very light surface abrasion with 'wet and dry' paper in order to scratch the surface and give a key for the following coats. However, there may eventually come a time when the paint will of necessity need to be stripped off because of decay or a major refurbishment.

Where leaded paint is flaking or crumbling, or needs to be removed for some other reason, there are a number of precautions which should be taken by both professional and amateur decorators. Dry sanding, whether for surface preparation or complete removal of the paint, is hazardous, particularly when power tools are used. The large quantities of dust released may be directly breathed in and also contribute to high indoor lead concentrations for extended periods. The hazards fully justify the advice that dry sanding should never be performed indoors for the removal of leaded paint. Burning or other stripping methods using heat can generate lead-rich fumes which may be dangerous to the decorator and occupant if they are exposed for long periods. Hot-air tools are now widely available which soften the paint without generating fumes, provided that the temperature is below 500°C, and allow it to be scraped off. However, it is quite easy to overheat the paint with these hot-air machines set at the lowest level and so they must be used with care; there is also the danger of generating lead-rich dust as the machine will blow particles or flakes of paint about as the paint is being scraped off, causing widespread dust contamination.

Wet sanding avoids the hazards of both dry sanding and burning but is slow for large areas and messy for domestic purposes. Chemical paint strippers will give satisfactory results, but they are expensive, caustic to the skin and give off fumes which are hazardous if breathed to excess.

It must be concluded that there is no completely 'safe' method of removing lead-based paints, but in overall terms chemical strippers appear to pose the least hazard, provided that adequate ventilation can be assured. It is essential that DIY decorators provide adequate through ventilation, for which it is usually necessary to open sufficient windows and doors so that air moves through the whole house while stripping is in progress. (In addition, such ventilation is also advisable when painting and also until the paint has dried since the solvents used in some paints are hazardous if breathed to excess.) Professional decorators should take adequate precautions to protect themselves from dust and fumes using appropriate breathing apparatus.

Paint Dust Removal

Dust is released by alterations and refurbishment of older property and by paint stripping. It is possible that the dust in floor and roof voids together with service ducts may contain raised levels of lead dust due to previous redecoration of high lead content paints and general environmental levels. Care should therefore be exercised, particularly with refurbishment, so that all dust is collected by vacuum equipment of proven efficiency at each stage of the work and properly disposed of as below.

Paint flakes and scrapings, together with dust from refurbishment and alterations, should be collected in stout sealed plastic bags and may be disposed of, in small quantities, through the normal local authority waste collection arrangements. Large quantities may require special arrangements with the local authority.

Roof Flashings and Coverings

Lead is the traditional material for roof flashings and coverings and its low weathering rate is evidenced by the existence of intact lead sheeting on buildings of considerable age. The natural weathering processes of the atmosphere are very unlikely to generate aerosols of lead, and the hazards which exist are associated with rainwater leaching. If there is any possibility that roof drainage water is used for cooking or drinking, alternative materials should be used (although the author could find no indication in the literature of lead levels in roof drainage water due to the use of lead flashings). In most instances, however, roof drainage water is discharged directly to a sewer or soak-away and no direct human exposure is likely. In circumstances where gutterings leak or where for some other reason lead-contaminated waters fall upon the ground around the house, some enrichment of lead in the soil is likely. On the assumption that lead weathering rates are low, however, such enrichments are likely to be small and no appreciable risks are anticipated.

The alternative materials for flashings and coverings are copper, zinc, aluminium and stainless steel. These again are unlikely to cause any air contamination but may cause some pollution of drainage waters. Their generally low toxicities, however, give no cause for concern, but as a general rule water drained from roofs should never be used for drinking.

Structural Frames, Roof Trusses etc.

Steel, galvanized steel and aluminium may be used for structural frames, roof trusses etc. Their low accessibility, low weathering rates and modest toxicity give reassurance that no problems should arise.

Metals in Interior Dusts

Dusts may be either airborne or deposited. The former present a source of human exposure by inhalation, the latter by hand-to-mouth activity, especially by children, and by inhalation of deposited dusts which have been made airborne again by activities in the building.

Metal concentrations measured in suspended dusts indoors are normally lower than out of doors and should not present a health risk.

There are circumstances, however, in which the generation of dust within the house (e.g. by dry sanding leaded paintwork, see above) causes elevated concentrations of inhalable dusts. Such circumstances should be avoided.

Deposited dusts collect on surfaces and their total abundance is critically dependent on the frequency with which the house is cleaned. These dusts come from many sources, the most abundant often being small particles of soil brought in from outdoors on footwear or by the wind. Other contributors are food fragments, animal-derived dusts and abrasion products from household materials such as paint and plaster. The importance of soils is often reflected in a correlation of household indoor dust metal levels with those in the garden soil.

The metals which have been regarded as especially important in indoor deposited dusts are lead and cadmium. The Royal Commission on Environmental Pollution (1983) regarded dusts as a major source of lead exposure for children. In the case of cadmium, soil levels are generally rather low and impurities in rubber carpet-backing materials are often the main source of cadmium contamination. The existence of lead or cadmium-containing artefacts within the building will contribute to metals in dusts, but is not likely to be a major factor unless the artefacts are both extensive and subject to abrasion or another cause of deterioration. Vigorous activity in the house (e.g. running, sweeping) may make deposited dusts and lead available again to exposure by inhalation. In this context, cleanliness, especially during maintenance work, is the best policy.

METALS IN RECLAIMED LAND

Land previously used by metallurgical or engineering industries or for the storage and breaking of scrap may be contaminated with metals. Threshold trigger concentrations exist for arsenic, cadmium, chromium (total and hexavalent), lead, mercury, selenium, copper, nickel and zinc. This topic is covered in more detail in Chapter C9.

CONCLUSIONS

* Environmental exposure to metals has long been known to be associated with possible adverse consequences for health. Of the metals used in buildings, those currently giving cause for concern are lead, cadmium and aluminium.

* The health risks of high lead exposure are well documented, but so-called sub-clinical effects on children's intellectual development and behaviour are not clearly established and remain controversial. The

main possibilities for lead exposure arise in older housing and are associated primarily with water pipes and lead-rich paint. Whilst the former may be replaced without adverse consequence, disturbance of old paint, especially by sanding, can lead to appreciable dispersal of lead and subsequent exposure of both the operative and the occupants of the house. If old paint is to be removed, stripping is desirable, but requires good ventilation.

✻ Postulated causal links between aluminium exposure and Alzheimer's disease are not proven and it is currently unclear whether environmental exposure to aluminium carries a risk to health. Nonetheless, exposure through diet is likely to prove far more significant than any exposure arising from building materials.

✻ Whilst both cadmium and chromium in the (VI) valence state are appreciably toxic and may be used in some applications in building, the likelihood of appreciable exposure is very small.

REFERENCES

Bicknell, A.O.J. (1975), *Pica, a Childhood Symptom*, Butterworths, London.

Browning, E. (1969), *Toxicity of Industrial Metals*, 2nd edn, Butterworths, London.

Control of Lead at Work Regulations 1980, HM Stationery Office, London

Department of the Environment and the Welsh Office (1982), *Lead in the Environment*, DoE Circular 22/82 and WO Circular 31/82, HM Stationery Office, London.

Fulton, M., Raab, G.M., Thomson, G.O.B., Laxen, D.P.H., Hunter, R. and Hepburn, W. (1987), *Lancet*, 1221–6.

Harrison, R.M. and Laxen, D.P.H. (1981), *Lead Pollution: Causes and Control*, Chapman and Hall, London.

Lee, P.N. (1989), *Epidemiological research on Alzheimer's disease: past, present and future*, Environ. Technol. Lett., 10, 427–34.

Martyn, C.N., Osmond, G. and Edwardson, J.A. (1989), *Lancet*, 59–62.

Nriagu, J.O. (1980), *Zinc in the Environment, Part II, Health Effects*, Wiley, New York.

Official Journal of the European Communities, L105, 10–12, 25 July 1975.

Royal Commission on Environmental Pollution (1983), *Lead in the Environment, Ninth Report*, Cmnd 8852, HM Stationery Office, London.

Urbanowicz, M.A., Hunter, J., Yule, W. and Lansdown, R. (1987), *Social factors in relation to lead in the home environment*, in *Lead in the Home Environment* (Eds I. Thornton and E. Culbard), Science Reviews, London.

World Health Organization (1984), *Guidelines for Drinking Water Quality*, WHO, Geneva.

PLASTICS, RESINS AND RUBBERS

Morris Greenberg

Mount Sinai Medical Center, New York

INTRODUCTION TO PLASTICS AND RESINS

Plastics are complex, man-made organic chemicals of high molecular weight which find many uses in construction either as substitutes for traditional materials or for their special properties. Those special properties derive from their molecular structure of long chains of atoms in which the patterns of atoms usually form repeating units, which are in turn derived from the smaller molecules of the chemicals used to form them. The small molecules are often called monomers, and the long chains resulting from combining them are usually referred to as polymers. Most polymers are the result of carefully engineered chemical synthesis, but natural polymers, such as rubber, pitch, bitumen and cellulose, have been used for thousands of years in construction and other activities.

The terms polymer and resin are commonly used as synonyms. In addition, in recent years, the term 'resin' has often been used as a synonym for 'plastic', although most people refer to a product as 'plastic' when it is solid − a plastic gutter or downpipe, for example − and use 'resin' for the usually very viscous liquids which are converted to solid form by the addition of other reagents or exposure to the atmosphere, eg epoxy resins.

Plastics can arrive on site in the form of fully fabricated components such as pipes, tanks, gutters, baths and board, or in the form of polymer reagents and additives that are reacted on site. Table B6.1 lists most of the applications of polymers in construction. In a number of them workers can be exposed, to varying degrees, to the reactive chemicals involved in the polymerization process and to the solvents and additives.

This chapter provides guidance on the general principles of the potential health hazards of plastics used in construction, together with examples of the more notorious problem areas in on-site use of plastics. It would require a book in its own right to describe in detail the potential health hazards of plastics used in construction, so wide are their applications and so complex and variable are the formulations and additives associated with them (Malten and Zeilhuis, 1964).

In general, finished products as delivered to construction sites present no appreciable toxic hazard to workers. The monomers, catalysts, copolymers,

Table B6.1 Typical uses of formed plastics in construction

	LDPE	PVC	EPS	PE	PP	UPVC	PU	UF	GRP
Substructure									
Damp-proof course	√								
Damp-proof membrane	√	√	√						
Thermal insulation			√				√	√	
Superstructure									
Gaskets and water stops		√				√	√		
Infill panels						√	√		√
Copings						√			√
Interior panels			√			√	√		√
Partitions						√			√
Formwork			√		√				√
Roofing		√		√	√	√			√
Dome lights		√				√			√
Thermal insulation			√				√	√	
Roofing systems		√					√		√
Architectural cladding panels						√	√		√
Finishings									
Draught excluders		√			√	√			
Window frames		√				√			
Sills						√			√
Doors						√			
Architraves						√			√
Skirtings						√			√
Handrails						√			√
Bannisters		√							√
Floor tiles		√		√	√		√		
Ceiling tiles		√	√						
Services									
Prefabricated plumbing		√		√	√	√			
Ducts and chutes						√			√
Tanks		√		√	√	√			√
Soil systems		√		√	√	√			
Pipes and fittings		√		√	√	√			
Drainage		√		√	√				
Manholes		√				√			√
Conduit systems and covers						√			
Cable trays						√			√
Light fittings					√				√
Baths									√
Basins									√
Sealing tapes									
Siteworks									
Fences and posts						√			√
Fencing		√				√			
Lamp posts									√
Septic tanks				√					√

This is by no means a complete applications list. A very comprehensive analysis of plastics use in construction can be found in *Plastics in Building*. **LDPE**, low density polyethylene; **PVC**, poly(vinyl chloride); **EPS**, expanded polystyrene; **PE**, polyethylene; **PP**, polypropylene; **UVPC**, unplasticized PVC; **PU**, polyurethane; **UF**, urea-formaldehyde; **GRP**, glass-reinforced plastic;

HPDL	PF	CPE	ABS	CPVC	MDPE	HDPE	PS	HIPS	PTFE
√									
	√								
		√							
√									
√									
			√	√	√				
						√			√
			√						√
√							√	√	
√								√	
									√

HPDL, high pressure decorative laminate; **PF**, phenol-formaldehyde; **CPE**, chlorinated polyethylene: **ABS**, acrylonitrile butadiene styrene; **CPVC**, chlorinated PVC; **MDPE**, medium density polyethylene; **HDPE**, high density polyethylene; **PS**, polystyrene; **HIPS**, high impact polystyrene; **PTFE**, polytetrafluoroethylene.

plasticizers, stabilizers, fillers, antioxidants, colours and flame retardants have largely been reacted or bound at the factory. In practice chemical reactions rarely involve irreversible equimolecular combinations: in the case of polymerization, some residual unreacted monomer may be found which slowly escapes into the atmosphere, the rate being dependent upon the plastic and temperature. The rate of release is high immediately after the reaction and then falls rapidly, except for certain materials, to insignificant levels.

There are certain common areas for concern related to the use of plastics, together with some individual, product-specific problems. These may occur when the plastics are handled as fully formed plastic products, when they are manipulated on site, when they are polymerized on site, when they are involved in fires or when they are ultimately scrapped. For certain plastics in certain applications there may be a potential hazard from components of the plastic that are released at various stages of its lifetime where formulation or application has not conformed to proper standards.

The monomers and reactants used in the polymerization processes may be toxic and carcinogenic, and the degree of toxicity or carcinogenicity may not be known. In addition to volatilization there may be loss of compounds that are to some degree soluble in water: this can be important where plastic is used for pipes and tanks containing water. Before they may be used to contain drinking water, their formulation and performance need to be approved.

They may also have an environmental impact, but here again data may be lacking. When hazards to health are reviewed, it is not uncommon to find, even for materials produced for 40 or more years, that full animal, human and ecological studies are sparse and of little use for resolving human and environmental health impacts.

Many of the reagents will not present a problem for the resident or subsequently for the environment. However, their very reactivity will present potential problems if they are to be mixed on site by the construction worker. Subsequent environmental impacts of 'dumped' materials have not been fully explored. Biodegradability, which is usually considered to be a 'good thing', implies a rapid release of compounds present in the mixture; where these are heavy metals or mineral fibres they contribute to the health hazard of land that is to be reclaimed. Incineration is not necessarily an advantageous alternative since the residual ash may be toxic and present problems of disposal, and the gaseous effluent may be corrosive unless treated. Components in the plastic may interact with those present in other refuse to increase the yield of undesirable compounds available for release into the general environment, unless state-of-the-art incineration of the standard required for toxic wastes is employed.

Because of the large number of chemical compounds that can be used in a particular plastic and the variety of plastics, it is inappropriate to deal with the whole field in detail here. The above general observations and the examples given below should give the reader sufficient idea of the complexity of the situation and the points to consider for determining the potential hazard of a material at the various stages of its life cycle to worker, resident and the environment. As previously warned, there are often insufficient data on various aspects of the problem, even for old familiar plastics.

EXAMPLES OF PLASTICS USED IN CONSTRUCTION

Polyvinyl chloride (PVC)

This polymer is widely used in construction. It is formed from the monomer vinyl chloride which is an animal and human carcinogen at the parts per million level. In its early manufacture and use, relatively substantial levels of monomer were measured in air from materials in store after polymerization, and lower levels have been measured subsequently after installation in a building. Subsequent technological developments have reduced residual monomer emission substantially. As a carcinogen for which a threshold (i.e. a level below which it has been demonstrated that no tumours will occur) has not been determined, it must be considered to present a cancer risk at these low levels. However, it has been considered that even under worst-case conditions this risk is currently minimal and by inference acceptable. Any concern in this context would have been less for the worker than for the householder exposed to substantial quantities of newly installed PVC material in a draught-proofed house for a greater period of time.

Various products made primarily of PVC can incorporate plasticizers (for example, phthalate esters), stabilizers (lead stearate, organo-tin, barium, cadmium and zinc salts), reinforcers and fillers (celluloses, asbestos fibre, silicates), antioxidants (phenolics, amines, sulphur-containing esters), ultraviolet radiation blockers (carbon black, organo-nickel, benzophenones), colours (inorganic minerals, organic soluble or insoluble salts or metal complexes, colours deposited on aluminium) and flame retardants (antimony, bromine, chloride-containing compounds). According to the special technical properties required, other plastic products may include all or some of the components listed above together with mixed polymers. While a number of the component materials are substantially locked in, gaseous monomer is released, as noted earlier, and so are less volatile agents. For example, phthalate plasticizer for a flooring product, which may constitute up to 10% of the mixture, has been calculated under worst conditions to give rise to concentrations in air that reach occupational exposure limits (Curwell et al, 1986). It has further been calculated that this could be reduced to a tenth by moderate ventilation; it is unlikely that even a reduction of this magnitude would be acceptable for domestic exposure. However, further significant reduction can be achieved by treating the surface of the flooring with sealant.

Urea-formaldehyde

The installation of urea-formaldehyde foam in wall cavities requires controlled mixing and application, and that the inner wall surface should be impermeable, these conditions being laid down in BS 5618:1985. This places a premium on the expertise of the specialist installer and the knowledge of the specifier of construction materials, and for the person overseeing the operation to be knowledgable and vigilant. The financial consequences of a botched job and complaints of loss of amenity can be considerable. Operatives require respiratory protection against the undoubted irritant and possibly allergenic effects of formaldehyde, which can be classified as an animal carcinogen and a probable human carcinogen.

In so far as respiratory protection against the other effects will cover the carcinogenic properties, the hazard is potentially one for the resident who is unprotected and spends some 90% of time indoors (150 hours a week, compared with the 40 hour working week). If, contrary to specification, urea-formaldehyde foam is installed in a wall cavity and the wall to the room is permeable to gas, or is penetrated by services around which there are spaces connecting the wall cavity with the room, levels of formaldehyde within the room may rise. Perception of the aroma of formaldehyde may lead to complaints of irritation of the eyes, nose, throat and chest, and may be followed by recurrent cough, wheeze and breathlessness.

Other complaints of a more general nature may be made and attributed to formaldehyde. On occasion it may be possible to confirm a causal association between formaldehyde exposure and signs and symptoms of disease in individual cases. Sometimes in an 'epidemic', usually in an institution, it may be difficult to establish this causal association confidently.

Skin contact with phenol-formaldehyde wood adhesive is associated with various forms of rash as well as the respiratory complaints associated with exposure to the component vapours.

Polyurethane Resin and Foam

Among the applications of polyurethane are protective and decorative finishes (paints and varnishes), damp proofing (combined with pitch), grouting, formwork, and foamed insulant. These products consist of polyisocyanate and polyol or some other reagent as separate components which are reacted *in situ*, as in the case of foam insulant, or partially prereacted in prepolymer form as in paints and varnishes. Although some polyisocyanates cause irritation on skin contact, their major skin hazard relates to their high chemical reactivity which can lead to sensitization. Volatile polyisocyanates when inhaled lead to respiratory symptoms (discomfort, cough, wheeze, breathlessness). A fuller discussion of the signs and symptoms and course of the condition is given elsewhere (Chapter C6). The polyisocyanates vary in their volatility, with the less volatile being claimed to be safer. However, they are highly reactive and on warming reach concentrations in air capable of initiating 'allergy'. Once a person is sensitised, extremely low concentrations of polyisocyanate can initiate a severe disabling reaction. The inhalation of particulate from paint spray is an effective way of producing respiratory sensitization to polyisocyanates. Deaths have been reported in association with polyisocyanate exposure.

When polyurethane is to be sprayed or during *in situ* foam insulation, the operative requires high-efficiency personal respiratory protection, not the derisory cotton muslin pad. This restricts safe use, and problems with polyurethanes are for the construction worker and the casual do-it-yourself (DIY) enthusiast rather than for the resident, if they fail to follow the manufacturer's instructions.

Epoxy Resins and Glues

Not surprisingly, the highly reactive components of epoxy resins and glues react vigorously with skin chemicals and lead to various forms of dermatitis after repeated skin contact. Subsequently there may be a brisk response to low concentrations and small exposures. The problems are largely for construction workers and DIY enthusiasts. Safe 'no touch' techniques appropriate to these products have operated in factories and, with similar training and supervision, could protect construction workers.

Polytetrafluoroethylene (PTFE)

PTFE is used as sealing tape, as jointing tape in screwed pipework (and therefore including drinking water systems), and for its non-stick properties. In fine powder form it is used as a dry lubricant in aerosol dispersants. When heated in flame it breaks down in a complex manner. Inhalation of the fumes gives rise to local irritation and a general influenza-like effect of fever and muscle and bone pain. This has been called polymer fume fever because of its similarity to metal fume fever. It is suspected that, on site, minute fragments of PTFE swarf have mixed with tobacco and on smoking have given rise to fume fever. This could take place when operatives are shaping pads on site. The irritant effect of substantial breakdown is shared with PVC (see above), but the fever effect with minute quantities is a curiosity. Although a transient phenomenon over in a day or so, it is so dramatic that cautions are routinely provided with non-stick kitchen utensils and should be found with bulk material and cans of dry lubricant.

THE CONTROL OF HEALTH AND ENVIRONMENTAL HAZARDS FROM PLASTICS

As previously mentioned, the chemical compounds involved are too numerous to be itemized and evaluated as toxic hazards in the context of this publication. As a general principle the essential components of plastics and resins must be considered according to the evidence for their toxic irritant, sensitizing and on occasion carcinogenic properties.

On occasion, as in the case of polyurethanes, the role of such potential contaminants as toluenediamine may also need to be considered. Most of the chemicals employed in formulations have been formally evaluated by national and international agencies for their human health hazards and for their environmental health impacts. The International Programme on Chemical Safety (IPCS) publishes a series of environmental health criteria documents in parallel with the International Agency for Research on Cancer (IARC) publications. In the United Kingdom, the Health and Safety Executive reviews some chemical agents and evaluates their health hazards and sets standards for their control. It is the responsibility of the manufacturer, importer or supplier of substances to provide, to each person they supply, adequate safety information to ensure that the substances will be safe when used, stored or transported. These legal obligations are in practice normally discharged by providing a comprehensive safety data sheet of potential hazards and safety precautions. The Health and Safety Executive, the Department of Trade and Industry and the Department of the Environment are responsible in collaboration with other ministries for protection of worker, consumer and general public, and general and special facets of the environment. There is a considerable body of legislation and governmental guidance in this area. In the case of construction materials, some progress has been made by standards bodies to consider health impacts of products. Legislative and advisory initiatives notwithstanding, there is still an opportunity for those specifying products and processes in construction to make a positive contribution to human and environmental health.

Fire Hazards

The common polymers break down readily when heated. According to the type of plastic the products of pyrolysis will vary in irritancy and toxicity (some contribute to the hazard by producing thick black smoke and others drip fiery droplets to produce secondary fires). When pyrolysis products are tested on laboratory animals under controlled conditions it is possible to rank them for their toxic and irritant properties. Cyanide generation from polyurethane and hydrogen chloride from PVC might seem to lead to significant additional danger. However, when one considers the atmosphere in a fire involving wood, with oxygen depletion, carbon monoxide and a range of irritant and toxic gases and fumes, which together make life unsustainable anyway, the effect of the addition of cyanide and hydrogen chloride is probably marginal.

INTRODUCTION TO NATURAL AND SYNTHETIC RUBBERS

Natural rubber has a useful but limited range of properties and is not available in sufficiently large quantities to provide for total modern demand for rubber. Synthetic rubbers were therefore originally produced as substitutes, but have been developed for their special properties and for applications for which natural rubber is unsuitable or unavailable.

In the formulation of rubber products, synthetic polymers are used singly or mixed with other synthetic polymers or with natural rubber. Compounded rubbers contain a wide range of organic and inorganic compounds of varying degrees of toxicity, but in general the hazard is for the factory worker and there is reason to believe that this has reduced over the years.

Natural Rubber in Construction

Historically, natural rubber was used extensively in roofing sheets, flooring materials and underlay, so refurbishing and demolition will involve their disposal. While in position, it is not anticipated that their presence will pose a significant toxic hazard to residents. In the event of a fire, in an enclosed space, the toxicity of the smoke can be expected to be as lethal as that from other polymers such as wood.

The process of stripping these materials is harmless to construction workers except where they incorporate mineral fibres that are released from the aged matrix. The environmental impacts of rubber and its numerous additives when disposal is by incineration or dumping have not been evaluated.

The use of *Latex Based Adhesives* requires considerable care. Repeated skin contact may lead to dermatitis as a result of defatting of the epidermis by the solvent or by over-vigorous cleaning of the skin by solvent or by abrasive means. Petroleum solvents are flammable but their non-flammable substitutes share their narcotic properties and may have specific organ toxicity. When large areas of adhesive are employed in poorly ventilated places, inhalation of particular solvents will lead progressively to loss of vigilance, loss of balance and co-ordination and impaired consciousness. Repeated excessive exposure will produce mood changes and lead to liver or kidney disease. Chlorinated hydrocarbons are associated with the development of threatening or fatal irregularity of the heartbeat. Some are suspect carcinogens but there are inadequate data for evaluation of their carcinogenicity or to monitor their environmental impact.

Synthetic Rubbers in Construction

The following are the more common synthetic rubbers used in construction. Their potential health effects and hazards are dealt with in the next section.

Polyisoprene This polymer resembles natural rubber in structure and function and is found in construction for such purposes as vibration dampening in the form of blocks under bridge beams on motorways. (Plastic/rubber composites are also used for resilient load bearing seating).

Styrene-butadiene This mixed polymer is the most widely used general purpose rubber.

Poly-butadiene This polymer may be used on its own or mixed with other rubbers to give them such properties as low temperature flexibility, crack resistance on flexing, and resistance to abrasion. It is used for example in sheeting to form a membrane on flat roofs.

Neoprene (Polychloroprene) This material is resistant to ozone attack and to fire and finds application in external gaskets for windows and doors.

Butyl Rubber Formed by polymerizing isobutylene with a small percentage of isoprene, this rubber has low gas permeability, ozone resistance and weather resistance. It has good chemical and thermal resistance and is used as sheeting for flat roofs, in cable insulation and in adhesives.

Ethylene Propylene Terpolymer (EDPM) This has replaced ethylene polypropylene as an ozone and water resistant material in window gaskets.

Nitrile Rubbers These rubbers are copolymers of acrylonitrile (18–50%) with butadiene. Their premium properties include oil and solvent resistance. This has no general application in construction but will be of use in specialist structures.

Polysulphide Rubbers These specialist rubbers have low gas and vapour permeability and are used variously in jointing interior wall panels, and in petrol, diesel and fuel oil hoses and in tank linings.

Silicone Rubbers These siloxane elastomers are stable over the temperature range +250°C to −75°C, are chemically inert, resistant to many solvents and gas permeable. They are used as sealants between structural panels (internal and external), around external door and window frames, and around bathroom, kitchen and sanitary fittings.

Polyurethanes Commonly used in construction as wood sealants and as a paint component, they are soft and hard elastomer products with resistance to oil, solvents and abrasion, with application in special situations.

POTENTIAL HEALTH EFFECTS OF SYNTHETIC RUBBERS USED IN CONSTRUCTION

Various of the monomers have been suspected by the International Agency for Research on Cancer, as being human carcinogens. On review (IARC 1987) their overall classification has varied from 'Probable Carcinogen' (Acrylonitrile), 'Possible Carcinogen' (Butadiene, styrene), and 'Insufficient data for evaluation' (Chloroprene, Propylene and Polychloroprene). Following polymerization and formulation, residual monomer should be at such a low concentration as to present the construction worker and resident with a hypothetical cancer hazard of a very low order. For the construction worker, solid rubber components should present no problem. There will be skin contact problems and inhalation hazards of liquid and semi-solid preparations from the solvents and from other chemical components modifying the properties of the polymer, as in adhesives and sealants. No direct hazard is foreseeable to residents from the presence of synthetic rubbers in construction. In the event of fire, those rubbers containing chlorine in the molecule, or certain additives will be more irritant, though as with natural rubber the overall toxicity of the smoke and the resulting atmosphere will be lethal.

The environmental impact of these polymers, their solvents and additives has not been evaluated during installation, incineration or landfill.

THE USE OF NATURAL AND SYNTHETIC RUBBERS IN CONSTRUCTION WORKER PROTECTION

Historically, natural rubber formed the basis of outer wear, gloves and boots to protect against the effects of abrasion, corrosion and chemically active materials like cement, and to protect against water and to enhance grip. Apart from the sogginess of the skin of hands and feet resulting from constant wear (with consequent fungal infection), dermatitis and depigmentation of the skin has resulted from chemicals in the mixture that leached out in sweat. Further, the inappropriate use of rubber as protection against oils and solvents soluble in rubber aggravated the hazard. The selection of protective clothing against skin hazard must take account of the microclimatic conditions produced and their effects on the skin, and the necessity for choosing the special type of material resistant to the oil, solvent or other chemical to be protected against.

CONCLUSIONS

No data are available from which actual hazard to workers or residents can be derived. Predicted quantitative cancer risk is based on experimental studies of the toxic hazards of component chemicals. The results are then extrapolated to man with substantial caveats as to the degree of confidence in the predictions. There are individual reports of individuals or small groups of workers or residents contracting skin and respiratory disease as a result of exposures to such materials as epoxy resins, polyurethane components and urea-formaldehyde. The complaints correspond to those experienced by factory workers.

* In general, construction workers face minimal carcinogenic and toxic hazard from handling formed materials, and they may be formulated to present little more hazard to residents. If standards for installation and usage are observed, residents face minimal risk.

* The greatest potential for skin and respiratory problems is for construction workers, if they are inadequately trained, equipped or supervised, when they are using polymer-based mixtures as adhesives, as surface treatments, as additives to other materials such as concrete, and/or during in situ wall cavity or roof space plastic foam applications (polyurethane, urea-formaldehyde).

* Residents have been reported to be affected by formaldehyde released from urea-formaldehyde cavity foam when standard procedures have not been followed.

* By appropriate selection of applications and the control of installation processes, the technical and economic advantages of plastics can be exploited while minimizing human health hazards.

* The environmental impact of disposal of plastics during renovation and following demolition remains to be determined and requires to be considered on a case by case basis. When plastics are dumped in land fill, there will be leaching of metals and poorly biodegradable organic compounds. On incineration, according to the formulation, a range of toxic and irritant gases will be emitted, presumably safely, to the atmosphere. However, the halogen-containing plastics are believed to contribute to dioxin synthesis when burnt in other than state-of-the-art incinerators.

REFERENCES/BIBLIOGRAPHY

Environmental Health Criteria Documents: available from World Health Organization, Geneva

No 15 Tin and Organo-tin compounds.
No 26 Styrene.
No 28 Acrylonitrile.
No 49 Acrylamide.
No 74 Diamine Toluenes.

Plastics in Building (1987/8 edn), British Plastics Federation, London.

Malten, K. E., & Zielhuis, R. L., *Industrial toxicology and dermatology in the production & processing of plastics*, Elsevier Publishing Co, Amsterdam, 1964.

Control of Substances Hazardous to Health Regulations (1988), SI 1988 No. 1657, HM Stationery Office, London.

International Agency for Research on Cancer, *Supplement 7 in the Series: Monographs on the evaluation of the carcinogenic risk of chemicals to humans*, IARC, Lyon, 1987.

British Standards Institution, *Thermal insulation of cavity walls (with masonry or concrete inner and outer leaves) by filling with urea-formaldehyde foam systems*, BS5618, 1985.

IARC, *Monographs on the evaluation of carcinogenic risks to humans, overall evaluations of carcinogenicity: an update of IARC monographs vols 1 – 42 Supplement 7* IARC Lyon 1987 (Deals with carcinogenicity of certain monomers and rubber solvents).

OTHER NATURAL MATERIALS

Morris Greenberg

Mount Sinai Medical Center, New York

INTRODUCTION

Earlier chapters have dealt with potential significant health risks from a number of individual natural and man-made materials used in construction. This chapter reviews the health hazards of a number of other natural materials.

Materials used in construction include a range of massive and coarse and fine particulate minerals, timber and wood derivatives and bitumen and asphalt products. Such materials are used singly or are found as mixtures of natural materials or combined with man-made materials. Trade terminology can be misleading and can present a barrier to the evaluation of the nature and extent of hazard in a product. Thus the term 'granite' has been applied to masonry material whose crystalline silica content, in which the health hazard principally lies, varies between 40% and zero. The description of decorative woods can be profoundly misleading in terms of identifying timber species and therefore the likely hazard.

NATURAL MINERAL FIBRES OTHER THAN ASBESTOS

The mineralogist defines a fibrous mineral as one that crystallizes in habits resembling organic fibre. The hygienist uses the convention of a fibre being a particle whose aspect ratio (maximum dimension to minimum dimension) is equal to or greater than 3 : 1. (Some have argued over the years for a greater aspect ratio but the greater biological basis has yet to be finally determined.) When counting fibres by optical microscopy it is not possible to detect fibres with diameters of 0.2 μm or less. Optical microscopy is the method specified for regulatory purposes. When electron microscopy is employed on the same specimens the fibres counted will be greater. When comparing environmental hygiene measurements, therefore, the microscopy technique employed must be taken into account.

Around 1970, experimental studies showed that a number of long fine mineral fibres could produce tumours similar to those produced by asbestos. The unnatural conditions of the experiment led to reservations in extrapolating the results to human health potential and the human health hazard was held to apply exclusively to asbestos.

A few years later a phenomenal number of malignant mesothelial tumours diagnosed in a small Turkish village were found to be associated not with asbestos exposure but with a fibrous mineral of the zeolite group (Baris et al., 1978). This gave an added impetus to studying fibre forms of other common minerals, it being realized that this was a common mineralogical phenomenon. A limited number of human but extensive animal and cell studies have been carried out from which the message is that it would be prudent to minimize exposure to fibrous dusts. The probability of causing tumours experimentally is in part chemical in relationship and part dimensional: particles of length greater than 7 μm and with diameters variously stated as less than 1.5 or 0.5 μm are considered as most hazardous (Stanton, 1974). In the present state of knowledge, it is not possible to discount shorter fibres as free of hazard. The commonly held opinion that fibres of low durability are of no account lacks adequate scientific supportive data.

A comprehensive list of mineral fibres has not been attempted here. A number of clays and various calcium silicates have been studied in the laboratory with interesting results, and a few occupational population studies that require confirmation have been reported. They add force to the recommendation for prudence in handling dusty minerals about whose physical nature one is ignorant. On the other hand, a number of products are routinely analysed and declared to be free from fibre inclusions (e.g. vermiculite, various calcium silicates).

STONE

Masonry, whether it is high silica granite or sandstone, that is worked off site and thus does not require to be worked on site presents no health problems either to construction workers or residents of the building. The health of the workforce who prepare the masonry is of course at risk and suitable preventative and protective measures need to be taken. (The use in the past of certain granites has led to raised domestic levels of ionizing radiation in buildings with substantial stonework in construction (see Chapter C4).) A crystalline silica hazard will be generated if dry abrasive techniques are used subsequently for cleaning. Sand blasting has long been abandoned in the United Kingdom on health grounds. Substitute blasting materials, although relatively innocuous, if effective may generate siliceous dust from the masonry being cleaned. Operatives may have personal protection but there may be general environmental contamination. Wet methods are intrinsically less dusty in execution but spread dust on drying out. The use of hydrofluoric acid for stone cleaning requires careful training and supervision of dilution and handling techniques and efficient personal protection if severe chemical burns are to be avoided.

Crushed stone used for construction purposes in general presents no significant health effect even when rich in silica (except for an unprotected crusher operator and handlers). The presence of mineral fibre has been observed in the USA in material used for loose surfacing of roads and car parks.

Health Hazards of Crystalline Silica

The very heavy exposures to which sand blasters were exposed over 30 years ago in the United Kingdom and more recently in North America led to a rapidly progressive lung disease terminating with death within 2 years. Similar deaths were common amongst rock drillers in civil engineering work. Less heavy exposure experienced by masons and crusher operators leads to a form of scarring of the lungs called silicosis, although, commonly, mixed dusts are involved. This interferes with oxygen and carbon dioxide exchange, makes the lungs less elastic, interferes with breathing and obstructs the circulation through the lungs. Tuberculosis was once a serious complication of silicosis. Currently there is concern that silica may play a role in the development of lung cancer (Goldsmith, 1987). Experimental studies and some human population studies are causing sufficient concern that the current exposure standards of 0.1 mg m^{-3} for silica, based on the criterion of silicosis, are being questioned. The uneasiness about carcinogenicity suggests the desirability for reducing exposure to siliceous dust to as low as is reasonably practicable (see Chapter B1). The current practice of cutting grooves and chases in concrete, masonry and siliceous bricks and blocks is an example of where care should be taken.

Fire and Silica

Siliceous materials are non-combustible. Their metamorphosis at temperatures of 1,000–1,200°C to more toxic forms would be of little significance as an added health hazard in the event of fire.

SLATE

Slate is a highly siliceous material but as long as it is not ground further on site it presents no hazards.

CLAY

The term clay covers a number of products with varying amounts of crystalline silica and fibrous mineral inclusions. Converted to ceramics and not subsequently machined on site, they present no further hazard. There are special purpose clay products that are used in certain drilling operations whose composition may indicate the need for care where there may be exposure to dust.

VERMICULITE

Vermiculite has been used as a loose-fill or block-form thermal insulation material, and as aggregate for lightweight plaster. As a dusty, largely non-siliceous material with the propensity for infiltrating the upper storey through gaps left by services it has been considered as merely a nuisance dust. However, studies of miners exposed to vermiculite and a review of certain batches of material has given cause for concern. All vermiculite except that mined in South Africa contains asbestos. As a consequence, since origin is often difficult to establish, it is considered prudent to request that the material be provided fibre-free. This is obviously desirable for loose-fill use but in block form the friability of the product and the likelihood that the binder will unlock the mineral over time dictate a fibre-free specification. It is not combustible, and while mineral transmutation will occur at high temperature to more toxic minerals, it is unlikely in practice to add significantly to the hazard of fire.

ASPHALT AND BITUMEN

Asphalt and bitumen are derived from natural deposits or are products of petroleum distillation and are widely used as roofing materials. They have often replaced coal and wood-derived material with similar physical properties of adhesion and waterproofing. They have the merit of having a considerably smaller burden of carcinogenic compounds in their composition. Nevertheless prudence dictates limited contact with skin and by inhalation. The main concern is for the construction worker in regular contact, which is a situation that is complicated by other additives (see Chapter B6).

There is an optimum temperature for these materials in use. A sufficient flow quality can be achieved at a temperature that limits the evolution of fumes. Apparatus of the correct design, adequate operator training and supervision are required to achieve these technical and hygiene aims.

A number of skin disorders has been reported from regular contamination including the development of sensitivity to sunlight. Decontamination of soiled skin by vigorous means can lead to dermatitis. For the resident, the hazard, if any, is of an extremely low order; however, if after installation of waterproofing the subsequent treatment fails to seal the layer, volatile constituents may be sensed for a long period and give cause for concern. Concern by specifiers for the aroma of materials and for correct methods of installation should obviate complaints by householders.

TIMBER

In bulk, timber in general presents no health hazard in itself. Wood dusts of inhalable particulate size, on the other hand, may possess toxic, immunological and carcinogenic properties. The strength of evidence for carcinogenicity is not definitive but the suspicions are sufficient to prompt greater care than hitherto.

These properties are specific to particular species of plant. Unfortunately one cannot rely on the trade name for identification of species or potential hazard. These names are largely descriptive of the appearance of the wood. The hazard is less for the construction worker than for the carpenter, joiner and factory worker who are exposed to high levels of dust during the sanding and machining processes during production. On site fitting with equipment that lacks the dust retention features available in factories may present a hazard. One on site process that offers opportunities for heavy dust exposure is sanding during floor resurfacing.

Health Effects of Wood Dust Exposure

Complaints of irritation of the eyes, nose, throat and chest with cough, wheeze and breathlessness may follow exposure to many wood dusts, with exposure histories much as described in the section dealing with allergies (Chapter C6). These complaints may be short lived, ceasing with cessation of exposure, or may persist long after cessation of exposure, deteriorating to become a severe disability. Canadian Red Cedar (Thuja plicata) which is not a true cedar, is notorious. It produces an 'allergic' syndrome and many publications in the literature give virtually identical accounts of its respiratory effects. The major differences between publications relate to the elucidation of the underlying mechanisms of action. There are certain chemical substances found widely in the vegetable kingdom that possess powerful pharmacological actions that set in train clinical effects that resemble the effects produced by plant materials with genuine allergic effects. The handling of certain woods is also recognized as giving rise to irritant or allergic rashes.

The original report on furniture workers exposed to native hardwoods indicated that they were subject to an excess of nasal cancer (Acheson et al., 1972). Follow-up analyses seemed to suggest that this only related to furniture workers employed during a particular period, which cast some doubt on wood dust as the active agent. However, as a result of the original report, a number of surveys of furniture workers and others exposed to other woods, both soft and hard, indicated that other cancers were possibly associated with exposure to various wood dusts. The position is unclear. The apparent cessation of the 'epidemic' in the original study remains to be confirmed, as do the findings in the other groups of workers.

In all these studies, the authors discuss the role of the wood dusts *per se*. Certainly, a study of wood chemicals would give plausibility for wood dust as the responsible agent. In addition they discuss the roles played by the agrochemicals used to protect trees and subsequently timber from spoiling, citing studies of groups of workers in other industries exposed to certain herbicides and fungicides in whom health effects were observed. Untreated woods can act as a good substrate for a variety of organisms that can lead to human allergic disease, so that on human health grounds safe chemical or environmental controls are required for structural wood.

Preservatives

Currently, all wood preservatives used in the United Kingdom need to be approved; this controls the formulation, protection of the operative and conditions of use. There are numerous chemicals in use. Organotins, pentachlorophenol and c-benzene hexachloride are chemicals that have given rise to much controversy as to suitability. They can be acutely toxic to workers handling them with inadequate protection, but the controversy relates to whether there is a potential hazard to the household. In the interim many of the complaints levelled against them (sore eyes, headaches, chest symptoms) are attributed to the pungent solvents with which they are formulated. The matter is not resolved for all persons who have reviewed this area. In the interim it would seem desirable, if they are to be used, to constrain these preservatives to the underfloor space and not to allow volatiles to enter the living space. Fungal control by means of damp-proofing techniques and underfloor ventilation seems less controversial and will not lead to hazard for the worker, resident or environment, unlike the three agents referred to.

Burning Wood

Burning wood generates a range of toxic and irritant gases and fumes, the proportions varying with the ventilation. Experimental studies show exposure to be extremely hazardous, in practice not significantly less than for man-made polymers.

PLY, BLOCK AND COMPOUND BOARD

The resin binder in ply, block and compound board presents the main cause for concern currently. On breakdown it has been found in a number of cases to yield measurable amounts of formaldehyde, particularly when the board has not been treated with an impermeable surface. Levels of 0.060–0.94 mg m^{-3} (mean 0.39 mg m^{-3}) were measured at one site where untreated particle board had been used for floors, ceilings and walls. Yields of formaldehyde would be expected to vary with the resin mix, conditions of curing, age of product and temperature and ventilation conditions in the building. These concentrations are far lower than those found in industry, but concern has been expressed about the lower domestic exposures because of the long hours of exposure involved. At high levels of formaldehyde exposure there are no doubts as to its irritant properties and there is reason to believe that true allergy may develop in certain individuals. Animal experimentation has produced tumours in certain species at high concentration. At present it is still being debated whether exposure to low concentrations constitutes a health risk. As it is possible by product design and building design to minimize exposure to formaldehyde, it seems prudent to do so (See Chapter B6).

In the event of fire, it is not anticipated that the pyrolytic products of the binder resin would add significantly to the substantial toxic effects of the burning wood material.

CELLULOSE FIBRE

There is no published experimental toxicological evidence for this material. Studies in related fields suggest that such an investigation would be reassuring. Studies of workers in industries where related materials are manufactured (wood, paper pulp) suggest a possible cancer hazard. An evaluation of the suitability for loose lay in the loft would require information about the dustiness of the material over time and the nature of such fire retardants, fungicides, pesticides and preservatives as have been added.

CONCLUSIONS

Stone

* Early concern about silica dust was due to exposure to substantial quantities leading to silicosis, a scarring of the lung with loss of function and ultimately to death. More recently, suggestions that this

dust might be associated with lung cancer have been an incentive to minimize exposure.

* In civil engineering, where hard rock drilling and excavation have been carried out in the past, numerous deaths from lung disease have resulted unnecessarily. More recently it has been possible to carry out a massive hydroelectric tunnelling operation on time through high silica content rock with good environmental control at acceptable cost.

* Unsuspected lung changes attributed to siliceous aggregate have been found in unprotected workers specializing in cutting grooves in concrete. Vigilance is merited even for familiar hazards.

* Indications of a possible lung cancer hazard in workers heavily exposed to environments rich in crystalline silica support the policy that it is prudent to reduce exposure to mineral dust to as low as is reasonably practicable. This applies to construction workers and residents.

* Stone rich in crystalline silica need not present a health hazard to construction workers or residents if it does not require to be worked on site and if satisfactory techniques are employed subsequently for cleaning.

Wood

* Wood and wood products and their treatments are too familiar to have been considered hazards until relatively recently. Exposure to wood dust and timber treatments should be minimized to protect construction workers from possible ill effects.

* Regulatory and standard-setting bodies approve wood treatment products and manufacturers describe how they may be safely used. As long as materials that are acceptable for use only by trained, supervised and adequately equipped specialist operatives in specific circumstances are not made available to non-specialists, this may be satisfactory. The standards set have addressed protection of residents in treated buildings.

* Surface treatments (paints, varnishes, stains) need to be considered similarly for their suitability for safe use to be determined.

* The fire hazards of the natural polymer cellulose are not markedly less than those of plastics in terms of toxicity.

* Wood itself would have no adverse environmental impact when disposed of in landfill. Current thinking requires timber and wood

treatments to have no adverse environmental impacts at any stage of the product life cycle.

Asphalt and Bitumen

* Asphalt and bitumen have the merit of having a much smaller burden of carcinogenic compounds than earlier coal and wood-derived material. However, prudence dictates limited contact with skin and inhalation. Operator training, correct design, and supervision should ensure that the materials are used at their correct temperature and that hygiene risks are kept to a minimum.

Other Issues

* The recognition of the potential for certain mineral fibres other than asbestos to cause cancers in man and in laboratory animals has altered public policy on mineral fibre use. Review of the mineralogical literature has shown how common fibrous inclusions can occur in mixed minerals and how 'massive' minerals may also coexist in fibrous forms. This has led to attention being drawn to special purpose clays, certain calcium silicates and vermiculite as potential health hazards under certain conditions of use. Concern is primarily for the construction worker although in certain applications there is a potential impact on residents.

REFERENCES

Acheson, E.D., Cowdell, R.H. and Rang, E.H. (1972), Br. J. Ind. Med., 29, 21–30.

Baris, Y.I., Sahin, A.A., Ozesmi, M. et al. (1978), Thorax, 33, 181–92.

Control of Substances Hazardous to Health Regulations (1988), SI 1988 No. 1657, HM Stationery Office, London.

Goldsmith, D.F. (Ed.) (1987), *Silica, Silicosis and Cancer. An International Symposium*, Praeger Publishers, New York.

Health and Safety Executive (1990), *Occupational Exposure Limits, Guidance Note EH 40/90*, HM Stationery Office, London.

Stanton, M. (1974), J. Natl Cancer Inst., 52, 633–4.

FIRE

Frank Smith and John Hume

Warrington Fire Research Consultants and Warrington Fire and Materials Centre

INTRODUCTION

In the United Kingdom approximately 900–1,000 people die and 11,000 –12,000 are injured each year as a result of fires in buildings. It is reasonable to ask whether it is possible to reduce these numbers by careful selection of building materials.

An uncontrolled fire in a building will generally undergo four relatively distinct phases: ignition, growth, full development and decay. If fire fighting does not interrupt this process, the fire may take several hours to pass through all these stages. However, the period of about three minutes in the growth stage of the fire between ignition and full development is of particular importance to life safety. During this period heat builds up within the room on fire until temperatures at the ceiling reach around 600°C, at which stage (provided that there is sufficient oxygen) all combustibles in the room simultaneously ignite under the influence of the heat radiating down on them. This phenomenon is known as flashover and marks the transition from a growing to a fully developed fire. After flashover, temperatures in the room on fire rise rapidly, typically to more than 1,000°C.

Life is not sustainable within a fully developed fire, and so escape from the room on fire must be made before this occurs. As far as occupants of the room of origin of a fire are concerned, the important question is whether escape is impaired or enhanced by the materials used in the building construction. This is largely related to the ease of ignition, the rate of burning and the rate of heat release of the materials. The toxicity of the smoke and gases produced will be a secondary factor.

However, the smoke and gases will be important to occupants of other rooms in the building, who will generally need to escape before the fire can spread from the room of origin. Also important to this group will be the ability of the structure to withstand the fire and prevent its spread, i.e. the fire resistance and fire compartmentation of the structure. More important still will be the suitability of routes allowing escape from the fire.

EFFECT OF FIRE ON MATERIALS

Some materials are basically inert to high temperature and fire, undergoing little or no chemical or physical change. Many of the most common building materials are in this category, including brick, concrete, cement mortar, and clay tiles. Such materials – all essentially chemically inorganic – present minimal hazard in a fire. Other building materials undergo physical changes at high temperatures but are non-combustible or of limited combustibility. ('Limited combustibility' is a term applied in building regulations for materials which reach a set (low) level of performance under BS 476: Part 11.) Common examples are glass, steel and plasterboard. Again, the health hazards associated with the involvement of such materials in fire are negligible. Glass will shatter and steel will buckle in a fully developed fire, but this will not occur at an early stage when occupants are present. Non-combustible materials cannot contribute to the severity of a fire either by burning or by producing heat. In theory some can undergo non-oxidative thermal degradation (pyrolysis) evolving toxic smoke and fumes, but in practice this is not a problem.

The hazards of a fire result from the burning of combustible material – principally or entirely chemically organic material – with the evolution of heat, and from toxic smoke and gases. As pointed out earlier, by far the most important factor affecting the contribution that any individual material will make to this hazard will be its ease of ignition, burning rate and heat release rate, particularly in the early stages of a fire. Experience shows that the first parts of a building structure to be affected by fire are wall and ceiling linings, and so these should be chosen with particular care. One hundred and forty-six people died in a club at St Laurent du Pont in France in 1970 when very rapid fire spread occurred across polyurethane foam used as a wall and ceiling lining to create a grotto effect; 48 died at the Stardust Club in Dublin partly, as was reported to the official tribunal, because carpet had been used as a wall lining. Easily combustible wall and ceiling linings lead to very rapid fire spread which can entrap people before they have a chance to escape.

Approved Document B of the Building Regulations (1985) recognizes this fact and stipulates acceptable linings by reference to BS 476: Part 7 and, as far as the highest category of linings (Class 0) is concerned, also to BS 476: Part 6. It should be remembered, however, that the Building Regulations represent a minimum standard, and if the intended use of a building suggests that escape may be difficult for some occupants, i.e. they are likely to be old, infirm, disabled, intoxicated or under the influence of drugs, then consideration should be given to providing surfaces that have a better spread-of-flame rating than that legally required.

The use of combustible materials in parts of the building structure other than wall and ceiling linings does, of course, have an effect on the total severity of a fire and the ability of a building to survive fire. However, it cannot be said that the use of a combustible cavity wall insulation material, for example, significantly affects the fire hazard experienced by occupants, as they are unlikely to be in the vicinity of the fire when such originally-unexposed materials become involved.

SMOKE AND TOXIC FUMES

The majority of fire deaths (about 60%) are attributable to smoke and toxic fumes rather than burning. This percentage increased rapidly during the 1960s (from 5% in 1955 to 52% in 1970) and is on a slower but nevertheless upward trend still. The increase is partly due to more accurate reporting by better-informed police surgeons and coroners, but largely it is because of the growing use of synthetic polymers within buildings. Most of these are in furnishings and furniture (foam-filled furniture) but some are part of the building fabric, e.g. UPVC window frames and rainware. This has led to a widespread perception that the smoke produced by burning plastics in a fire is different in kind (and more noxious) than that produced by traditional materials such as wood.

Much research has been directed to this question and to attempts to develop a standard test for 'smoke production potential'. Yet the complexity of the mechanisms of smoke production in a fire have so far defeated all attempts to devise a test for smoke production potential which is either reproducible or representative of what could happen in real fires. (What ventilation conditions should be used, for example? Cellulosics, such as wood, tend to produce more smoke when oxygen is limited. Some synthetics, however, tend to produce most smoke when free burning.) It has not even been possible to rank materials in order of their potential to produce harmful or toxic smoke in fires. It is therefore not possible at the present time to select building materials on the basis of their reduced potential to produce smoke and toxic fumes, even if it should be decided to do so. A notable exception to this is the selection of low smoke and fume (LSF) cabling instead of PVC cabling, which should be considered whenever cabling constitutes a major part of the fire load of a building.

More encouraging research has been undertaken into the more general area of smoke and toxic fumes and their effects on people. This has shown that, despite the fact that smoke may contain well over a hundred different chemical constituents, all smoke, whether produced from burning cellulosics or synthetics, tends to have similar physical, physiological and psychological effects which together can affect the ability of people to escape from fire and hence the hazard of fire.

There is a strong body of opinion that the only important factor is the optical density of smoke, i.e. whether people are able to see through it. If people cannot see their way to escape, death often results as they become trapped by the fire. Research has shown that 10% of people will turn back rather than travel through smoke with an optical density of 0.1 bels/m, i.e. a visibility of 10 m.

Considering optical density alone, however, may be an oversimplified approach. Although it must be a major factor – probably the major factor – and is particularly important where occupants are unfamiliar with their surroundings (i.e. public buildings), the subtle incapacitating effects of the major smoke toxicants are also relevant. It is now apparent that such effects can drastically impair a person's ability to escape, even though escape may still be technically feasible. That being the case, it is then immaterial whether death is clinically due to carbon monoxide poisoning or hydrogen cyanide poisoning. (These are the two most important smoke toxicants, and the majority of fire deaths are in fact attributable to the former.)

Compounding the narcotic (sleep-inducing) and incapacitating effects of major smoke toxicants are the additional factors of reduced oxygen availability and high carbon dioxide concentration. Reduced oxygen (below about 14%) produces lethargy (and sometimes euphoria). Carbon dioxide is itself narcotic above a 5% concentration, but at lower concentrations it has the effect of inducing hyperventilation which can increase the rate of toxicant absorption by the body. Also important is the heat content of smoke itself, which can cause heat exhaustion and scorching of the respiratory tract.

There is some debate about the relative importance of the irritants present in smoke. It has been stated that they encourage escape by producing in sufferers an overwhelming desire to flee from them. However, they are just as likely to produce panic and disorientation. They are also responsible for long-term effects (see below).

Table B8.1 lists the main characteristics and constituents of smoke and their effects. Carbon monoxide, hydrogen cyanide and irritants such as acrolein, nitrogen oxides and formaldehyde are produced in virtually all fires, although the proportion of each varies widely with the conditions of burning such as temperature and oxygen content. Irritants such as hydrogen chloride and sulphur dioxide will only be present if chlorine– or sulphur-containing chemicals are involved in a fire; but their additional presence should not be taken to suggest, for example, that in all cases smoke from burning PVC is worse than that from burning wood. What is important is not what is in the smoke but whether occupants have time to escape before serious smoke conditions occur. It was thought that the total effect of exposure to several fire toxicants might be worse than the sum of their individual effects, but, at the time of writing, there is no evidence that such synergistic effects occur.

Table B8.1 Common fire toxicants			
CHEMICAL	POSSIBLE SOURCES	EFFECT	TENTATIVE ESTIMATE OF SHORT-TERM (10 MIN) LETHAL CONCENTRATION IN SOME HUMANS (PPM)
Carbon dioxide	All combustible materials containing carbon	Hyperventilation followed by difficulty in breathing. Asphyxiant	100,000
Carbon monoxide	All combustible materials containing carbon	Lethargy, disorientation	8,000
Hydrogen cyanide	Materials containing nitrogen, e.g. nylon, polyurethane, polyacrylonitrile	Asphyxiant	350
Nitrogen oxides	Polyurethanes, celluloid	Pulmonary irritant	250
Ammonia	Wool, melamine, nylon	Pungent unbearable odour Eye and nose irritant	1,000
Hydrogen chloride and other halogen acids (HBr and HF)	PVC, fire retardants, fluorinated plastics	Respiratory irritants	HC 1,500 HBr 500 HF 400
Acrolein	Polyolefins and cellulosics	Respiratory irritant	30
Isocyanates	Polyurethanes	Respiratory irritant	100
Sulphur dioxide	Rubber, other sulphur-containing materials	Respiratory irritant	500

Compiled from various sources. Death from irritants at these concentrations need not be immediate.

SUPERTOXICANTS

It has been suggested that some materials can burn to produce substances which are so toxic that even if present in very small quantities they can be lethal. Such supertoxicants are rare, but test evidence with rats suggests that a supertoxicant can be produced if polytetrafluoroethylene

(PTFE) (which can be used as a cable and terminal insulant and as part of roofing membranes) is subjected to certain heating conditions associated with a standard test procedure. The exact nature of this supertoxicant has never been identified, although it is known that heated PTFE can release fluorine-containing compounds such as perfluoroiso-butylene (PFIB) and carbonyl fluoride. However, toxicity from PTFE in a fire has not been known to be a problem, particularly as PTFE is difficult to ignite and does not support combustion, although it will burn under extreme fire conditions.

LONG-TERM HEALTH EFFECTS

There is insufficient evidence to gauge accurately the long-term health effects of a relatively brief exposure to non-lethal fire atmospheres. Neither carbon monoxide nor hydrogen cyanide have long-term effects, and complete recovery from exposure to them can be obtained within a few hours of removal from exposure. Irritant gases, however, can cause inflammation of the air passages leading to the lung and of the lung itself. Resulting pulmonary oedema (accumulation of fluid in the lungs) can be fatal 24 hours or so after exposure to fire atmospheres.

There is no doubt that known human carcinogens, such as benzopyrene, can be present in smoke, but it has not been possible to show whether cancers have resulted because of this.

ASBESTOS

Fire can have the effect of dispersing hazardous materials which would otherwise remain concealed or protected in some way. The most obvious of these is asbestos, which has been known to be dispersed over large areas during and immediately following a fire. This risk, however slight, is therefore an additional reason for not incorporating this material into buildings, and for removing it when it is already present after taking advice of specialist consultants.

THE PROBLEM IN PERSPECTIVE

Finally, two additional factors must be borne in mind if fire hazard is a consideration when selecting building materials. The first is that the building structure is usually by far the smaller part of the total fire load (i.e. total combustibles) of a building, and contents are more important. Moreover, contents are usually the item first ignited in a fire – only about 8% start in a building's structure. Thus the nature of the contents of the room of fire origin has more effect on fire growth during the critical first few minutes than the structure of that room, or for that matter the contents of other rooms or the structure of the building as a whole. There is thus more scope for reducing fire hazard by controlling contents than by controlling building materials.

The second factor is that fire hazard can also be mitigated by fire protection measures other than control of materials. The science of fire engineering is concerned with designing buildings (and of course other structures and plant) in such a way that they cost-effectively resist the effects of fire and present an acceptable risk to occupants should a fire occur. 'Acceptable' and 'cost-effective' are important here – it is not possible to design absolute safety against fire.

In the United Kingdom it has been standard practice not to tackle the question of fire and buildings head on, but instead to assume that the Building Regulations (and more recently Approved Document B/2/3/4 of the English and Welsh Building Regulations) set out an acceptable level. Then it is just a case of 'following the rules'. Occasionally, where circumstances make the following of the rules prohibitive, design alternatives are justified by comparing the safety they offer with the level implicit in the Approved Document.

There are several faults with such an approach, not least that, despite the fact that the Building Regulations are ostensibly only concerned with the safety of life, the recommendations in Approved Document B, developed pragmatically over the years, have as much to do with protecting property from fire as protecting people. Moreover, the Approved Document sets out a minimum standard; it does not make it clear how a concerned designer can provide an increased level of fire safety.

The Approved Document B approach to fire safety is largely 'passive', i.e. it relies on the inherent performance of a building's structure. The Approved Document limits the potential spread of fire by dividing large buildings into small fire-resisting compartments, and then ensures that the building will survive most fires without structural collapse by specifying a set degree of fire resistance depending on the building's use (occupancy). In addition, the risk that a rapidly growing fire could entrap people before they escape is regulated by control over the flame-spread characteristics of linings. On top of these controls is added a requirement to provide adequate escape routes for people in the event of fire. The rules governing this are outlined in Approved Document B1 – Mandatory Rules for Means of Escape in Case of Fire.

What the Approved Documents do not consider to any extent is the provision of fire safety by means other than passive protection, particularly 'active' means such as water sprinklers and fire alarm and fire detection systems. It is possible, however, to incorporate such features into the fire safety design of a building, possibly as part of a case for reducing passive fire protection measures such as compartmentation. (NB:

Approved Document B is currently (1990) under revision by the Department of the Environment. Possible changes include provisions to allow 'trade-offs' between passive protection and sprinklers.)

Therefore an adequately 'fire-safe' building is not just a collection of adequate materials. Fire is a phenomenon that involves a complete building, including its occupants, and a well-designed fire safety strategy recognizes this fact. In terms of life safety alone the most important features of such a strategy are to stop fires starting by good housekeeping and fire safety management and, failing this, to ensure that people are not overcome by fire or smoke at an early stage and can then escape safely. In some buildings – large and/or tall buildings, buildings with especially flammable contents, and buildings such as hospitals where the occupants are handicapped in some way – increased fire safety requires a detailed strategy which will include some or all of the fire protection techniques described above. Elsewhere, however, it is possible to suggest simpler remedies.

In simple terms, the most cost-effective way of reducing fire deaths and injuries is:

- good management;
- to control linings; and
- to fit smoke detectors in buildings where people sleep, particularly domestic houses.

CONCLUSIONS

* The answer to the question whether building materials can be chosen to increase the period that occupants have in which to escape a fire is 'yes', but this must be a modified 'yes'.

* Reduced fire hazard is best achieved by selecting materials that are non-combustible or of limited combustibility, or, failing that, which are difficult to ignite and do not rapidly spread fire or generate large amounts of heat. These factors are particularly important when selecting lining materials which are generally the first part of a building structure to be involved in fire. They are less important as regards other building components which are unlikely to be involved until after the occupants have escaped.

* Although smoke and toxic gases are the main killer in fires, lack of suitable tests means that it is usually not possible to select materials on the basis of their reduced potential to produce smoke and fumes. A notable exception here is the use of LSF cable instead of PVC cable.

BIBLIOGRAPHICAL REFERENCES

British Standard 476:
Part 6: Fire Propagation Test: 1981
Part 7: Surface Spread of Flame Test: 1987
Part 11: Method for Assessing the Heat Emission from Building Materials: 1982
British Standards Institution, London.

The Building Regulations (1985), Approved Document B1, Mandatory Rules for Means of Escape in Case of Fire, Department of the Environment and The Welsh Office, HM Stationery Office, London.

The Building Regulations (1985), Approved Document B 2/3/4, Fire Spread, Department of the Environment and The Welsh Office, HM Stationery Office, London.

Kaplam, H.L., Grand, A.F. and Hartzell, G.E. (1983), *Combustion Toxicity,* Technomic, Lancaster, PA.

Proc. Conf. on Smoke and Toxic Gases from Burning Plastics, QMC Industrial Research Ltd and the Fire Research Station, January 1982.

Report of the tribunal of enquiry on the fire at the Stardust, Arlane, Dublin, Eire, Government Publications Office, Dublin.

Smith, D.A. (1985), *Smoke and Toxicity,* presented at Interflam '85, University of Surrey, Guildford.

UK Fire and Loss Statistics, Home Office, HM Stationery Office, Annually.

Section C

The Internal and External Environments

INDOOR AIR QUALITY AND VENTILATION REQUIREMENTS

Paul Appleby

Building Health Consultants Ltd

INTRODUCTION

The average person will spend more than 90% of their time in an artificial environment of one sort or another. Much of this time is spent working in an office or a factory. In many countries expanding economies and centralisation of services have led to a concentration of office space in the cities. The cost of land has shaped buildings into deep-plan high-rise structures. The cost of materials and the popularity of mirror glass has led to the sprouting of hundreds of 'glass boxes' in the world's cityscapes.

These boxes are sealed to keep out noise and pollution – mainly from traffic – and access to a window has become associated with status. Hence clerical staff, VDU operators and other junior personnel are relegated to the internal reaches of the building, whilst senior staff occupy individual offices at the perimeter. Occupants of areas remote from windows commonly experience problems relating to continuous exposure to artificial illumination, lack of a link with the outside world and lack of control over ventilation and heat. On the other hand, the perimeter offices may suffer from environmental problems associated with solar gain or draught whilst densely-light-absorbing mirror glass can give the impression of winter in summer and dusk during day.

Regardless of whether buildings are sealed or not, a strategy is required to ensure that (a) inhaled air does not reach an unacceptably high odour level, and (b) undetected contaminants do not pose a hazard to occupants' health. The following strategy, expressed in a preferential sequence, should be adopted to eliminate or reduce occupational exposure to airborne contaminants:

- elimination of contaminant;
- substitution with a less toxic or less malodorous contaminant, as appropriate;
- reduction of contaminant emission rate;

- segregation of occupants from potential sources of toxic or malodorous contaminants;
- provide ventilation, at source or dilute to acceptable concentration;
- personal protection: e.g. workers wear air-fed respirators.

This last control measure is only appropriate for high emission/high toxicity industrial exposure, and should only be adopted if other measures are not feasible technically or economically.

The above measures are not mutually exclusive, and some combination will usually be necessary, with some form of ventilation always required. The quantity and quality of outdoor air introduced to the space must be compatible with these aims. It is the quality of the air in the breathing zone of the occupants which is important, hence it must be introduced in such a manner that each occupant receives maximum benefit from the outdoor air which enters the buildings via windows or the external louvres of a ventilation plant.

This chapter begins by defining comfort and health, and the distinction between them, in the context of indoor air quality. It then examines potential sources of indoor contaminants, how they can be sensed by humans as odours or irritants, and introduces the concept of odour intensity and total odour loads. The next sections deal with control of exposure to indoor contaminants, outlining the different methods of ventilation, the methods by which ventilation rates can be established accounting for all sources of odour and contaminants, the influence of room air movement on the effectiveness of ventilation, and the overall economic implications of ventilation rate. In this context, the feasibility of using filtration to reduce ventilation rates is also discussed. Finally, the role of maintenance in ensuring good indoor air quality is examined.

Poor air quality and lack of ventilation are two contributory factors to the collection of conditions and symptoms called 'sick building syndrome' which is dealt with in Chapter C5.

COMFORT AND HEALTH

Ventilation requirements and design must be based on some combination of parameters which keeps odours below acceptable limits for 80% of the occupants and ensures minimum deleterious health effects. Standards are either comfort-based (e.g. the provision of adequate outdoor air, reducing concentrations of specific contaminants below their detection threshold or reducing total odour loads) or health-based (e.g. reducing concentrations below specific occupational exposure limits).

Comfort has been defined[1] as 'that condition of mind which expresses satisfaction with the ... environment', whereas the World Health Organisation have defined health as '... a state of complete physical, mental and social well-being, not merely the absence of disease and infirmity.' It could be argued that any occupant who expresses dissatisfaction with their environment is not healthy by this latter definition. It is clear that this state of complete well-being represents the ideal. However if a pragmatic concept of an 'acceptable' indoor air quality is adopted, this ideal may not be met for a certain proportion of building occupants.

Most comfort standards are based on the concept of an acceptable level of dissatisfaction, normally taken as 20%. The North American standard 'Ventilation for Acceptable Indoor Air Quality'[2,3] uses this level of dissatisfaction in its definition of acceptable indoor air quality. A more elaborate model for acceptable indoor air quality may be evolved by combining this concept with the World Health Organisation's basis for establishing comfort guideline values for individual chemicals[4]. Thus, indoor air quality may be said to be 'acceptable' if less than 50% of the occupants can detect any odour, less than 20% experience discomfort, less than 10% suffer from mucosal irritation and less than 5% experience annoyance for less than 2% of the time. Although not defined by WHO, in this context annoyance probably refers to the case during which odour and irritant effects are sufficiently prominent to be distracting.

A comfortable indoor air quality is therefore taken primarily to be one which is not unacceptably malodorous. However some contaminants which cannot be detected by the olfactory sense may produce mucosal irritation or long term health effects, some of which might be irreversible or life-threatening. In this context, Occupational Exposure Limits[5] provide limits on occupational exposure to airborne substances hazardous to health, and are primarily used for assessing compliance with the UK Health & Safety at Work etc Act 1974. In theory, they apply equally to the non-industrial and the industrial workplace. Where a single substance dominates (high 'signal to noise' ratio) these may be used to determine dilution ventilation rates or as an indicator of the toxicity of the substances and hence aid the evolution of a strategy for the control of exposure of the form outlined earlier. In most non-industrial environments the signal to noise ratio is low and ventilation strategy must be based on empirical data and past experience.

Occupational Exposure Limits are designed for healthy people working a normal working week, with no allowance for other stresses. Some individuals may suffer health effects due to exposure to some contaminants at concentrations below the Occupational Exposure Limit. For example, some sensitised individuals may experience allergic reactions.

Extreme discomfort associated with inadequate ventilation has produced symptoms similar to those associated with sick building syndrome (see Chapter C5), and resulted in lost productivity and absenteeism.

SOURCES OF INDOOR CONTAMINANTS

Exposure to non-industrial atmospheres usually involves exposure to a cocktail of thousands of substances all having relatively low concentrations compared to their occupational exposure limits. Typical individual concentrations are frequently in the order of one thousandth of the occupational exposure limit, or less[6]. Substances found range from the relatively harmless products of metabolic processes to low concentrations of highly toxic and, in some cases, carcinogenic substances.

Appendix 1 provides an account of the main airborne contaminants which have been found in non-industrial buildings. Table C1.1 gives a list of some common organic compounds found in past surveys of office atmospheres and sources which have been identified for them.

In general terms, potential sources of contaminants include:

- the ground: natural source of gases such as radon and methane;
- the ground: gases emanating from earlier dumping of waste;
- outdoor air: industrial pollutants, vehicle exhaust, dust etc.;
- building materials: organic compounds, radon gas;
- building furnishings and materials: mainly organic compounds;
- cleaning, photocopying and other processes: organic compounds, particulates, ozone;
- products of complete and incomplete combustion: heaters without flues, cooking, tobacco smoking: thousands of chemicals, including respirable suspended particulates (RSP);
- mouldy surfaces;
- poorly maintained water spray equipment, such as spray humidifiers: bacteria, amoebae, spores;
- internals of ventilation and air-conditioning systems: particulates, micro-organisms, organic compounds;
- human and animal occupants: mainly water vapour, CO_2 and particulates, plus low emissions of thousands of organic compounds.

Any one contaminant may emanate from a number of sources.

ODOUR AND IRRITATION

The sensations of odour and irritation are used by the individual as a means of assessing indoor air quality. Perception of an odour is a comfort effect, whereas irritation is usually defined as an acute health effect.

Table C1.1 Sources of some common organic compounds found in office atmospheres

CHEMICAL	POTENTIAL SOURCE
Acetone	Lacquer solvent, tobacco smoke
Benzene	Tobacco smoke, adhesives, spot cleaners, paint remover, particle board
2–Butanone (MEK)	Caulking, particle board, floor & wall coverings, fibre board, tobacco smoke
Carbon tetrachloride	Grease cleaners
Chlorobenzene	Paint solvent, DDT, phenol
Chloroform	Clothes washing
Ethylbenzene	Floor/wall coverings, insulation foam, chipboard, caulking, jointing, fibreboard, calcium silicate sheet, adhesives, lacquer, grease cleaners
Methylene chloride	Paint removers, aerosol finishers
Styrene	Insulation foam, jointing, fibreboard, tobacco smoke
Perchloroethylene	dry cleaning
Toluene	Adhesives, sealing tape, wall paper, jointing compound, calcium silicate sheet, floor covering, vinyl, caulking, paint, paraffin stoves, tobacco smoke, grease cleaners
1,1,1 Trichloroethane	Cleaning fluid, dry cleaning, correction fluids
Trichloroethylene	Paint solvents, grease cleaners
Xylene	Adhesives, jointing, wall paper, caulking, floor coverings, lacquers, grease cleaners, shoe dye, tobacco smoke
Hexane	Floor covering, wall paper, chipboard, gypsum board, insulation foam, tobacco smoke
Heptane	Floor covering, varnish, kerosene stoves
Ethanol	Fibreboard, solvents, tobacco smoke
Ethyl acetate	Linoleum, varnishes, perfumes, artificial leather
Cyclohexane	Tobacco smoke, lacquers, resins, paint removers
n-Nonane	Wall paper, caulking, floor covering, chipboard, adhesives, cement, jointing, floor varnish, kerosene stoves, floor wax
n-Decane	Floor adhesive, floor wax, wood stain, polyurethane, room freshener
n-Undecane	Wall paper, gypsum board, floor/wall coverings, jointing compounds, chipboard, floor varnish, paint, paint removers
n/i-Butanone	Edge sealing tape, jointing compound, linoleum, floor lacquer, cleaners, paint removers, tobacco smoke

The human nose is extremely sensitive to low concentrations of some chemical substances. For example it can detect 1 mg m[-3] of toluene[4], one of the most common volatile organic compounds to be found in the non-industrial atmosphere, whereas the UK Occupational Exposure Limit, time weighted for a 40 hour working week (OEL TWA) is 375 mg m[-3].

A substance which enters the nasal cavity may be sensed by two separate detection systems. The olfactory sense, which is responsible for odour detection, and the common chemical sense, which is sensitive to irritants. These two senses interact – for example, it is possible for an odour to be disguised by irritation and *vice versa*[7]. A single substance may evoke sensations of both odour and irritation. Humans are known to adapt to odours with time, whereas irritation may be compounded with time[8, 9]. In the specific case of exposure to environmental tobacco smoke, a recent study[10] has found that irritation intensity increases by a factor of 2 during the first hour of exposure, after which steady state occurs. The same study found that perceived odour intensity fell off by a factor of 50% and levelled out after only a few minutes.

Many of the sources mentioned above produce odours, some of which may be perceived as pleasant, some unpleasant. Some evolve from the release of potentially harmful substances, although it is not usual for exposure to airborne contaminants in non-industrial buildings to be associated with irreversible health effects. Exceptions have been thought to include exposure to radon gas (mainly in homes) and lead from emissions in vehicle exhaust – see Chapters C4 and B5. Because odour perception is highly subjective, it is extremely difficult to measure. Olfactometers have been developed for use by trained panellists[11, 12] but no automatic sensor has yet been developed which accurately simulates the response of the nose. Sensors are available which give an approximate indication of air quality. For example CO_2 sensors provide a signal which is indicative of the contribution of body odour to the overall odour levels. Unfortunately odours are also emitted by processes and materials which do not emit CO_2.

An 'air quality' sensor adsorbs gases onto the porous surface of a semiconductor, the conductivity of which changes with the amount of gas adsorbed. Gases are alternately adsorbed and desorbed. Unlike the nose, it cannot distinguish between different potencies of odour; an air quality sensor calibrated to respond to body odour would not give a good indication of the odour associated with tobacco smoke, and vice versa.

Studies have indicated[13] that general perceptions of odour are at their lowest at humidities in the range of 45 to 65% sat (rh) at normal comfort temperatures, although this varies with the nature of the contaminant. However the odour emission rate from many materials, such as paint, rubber, upholstery, floor coverings, etc., tends to reduce with falling humidity. The adsorption of odours onto internal surfaces, and their subsequent desorption as temperature, air velocity and vapour pressures change, can lead to a considerable increase in odour levels as conditions become favourable for desorption. During one recent study[14] a panel of non-adapted people were asked to compare the odour intensity in bars after all occupants had left with that generated by the equivalent smoking level in a non-adsorptive chamber. On average, odour intensities were judged to be higher in the unoccupied bars. This was thought to be primarily due to the desorption of gaseous components of tobacco smoke, which had been adsorbed onto internal surfaces, along with the particulate matter, during occupancy.

It has been suggested[15] that for every occupant and associated odours in an air conditioned building, there could be up to 6 or 7 odour equivalents (clfs) associated with environmental tobacco smoke, building materials, furniture, mould spores and the internal components of the air handling system.

One study of eight air handling units[16] found that perceived odour intensity increased by an average of 0.81 decipol through an air handling unit (range 0.19 to 1.67), where 1 decipol is the odour intensity perceived by a trained panellist of the odours emitted by a standard person (1 olf) ventilated by 10 litres per second of odourless air.

Odours are released from the fungicides used to treat filter material and thermal wheels, as well as the lubricants and fan belts associated with motors and fans. Poorly maintained air handling systems release odours from accumulated dirt in filters and other internal surfaces. Bio-fouling of cooling coils, moisture eliminators and spray ponds is a particular problem. This study[16] found that the filters were major polluters in nearly all of the ventilation systems examined. Spray humidifiers and rotary heat exchangers (used for transferring heat from air flowing in one duct to another) were major polluters in the units in which they were found.

VENTILATION

Ventilation can be defined as the movement of air through a space whereby used air is continually replaced with air from outside that space. This air may all originate from an external source, i.e. 'fresh' air, or some proportion of the air leaving the space may be recirculated.

The forces that set up this throughput of air may be natural, mechanical, or some combination of the two. Naturally induced forces are generated from wind pressure, internal convection currents or the two forces working together, via cracks or openings in the fabric of the building. The resultant air movement may be adventitious, in which case it is called infiltration, or deliberate and controllable, in which case it is known as natural ventilation. Mechanical, or forced, ventilation is generally employed when natural forces cannot be relied upon to satisfy building or user requirements. The normal prime mover used is a fan, comprising of a bladed impeller rotated by the action of an electric motor and thus creating additional capital and running cost when compared with a naturally driven system. There are many different types of forced ventilation, depending on the sophistication of control required. They range from a simple propeller fan mounted in a window through to full air-conditioning, with separate supply and extract air distribution systems and facility to recirculate room air, filter, cool, heat, control humidity and even cater for different load patterns in different zones of a large building.

Regardless of the level of sophistication every space has certain basic ventilation needs, dictated by the nature of the contaminant-producing processes which occur within the space. Contaminants evolve continuously, even in empty buildings where fabric and furnishings may emit a cocktail of constituent substances, such as formaldehyde, VOCs and temporary lodgers which have been adsorbed onto surfaces during occupancy, such as odours. When the space is occupied, additional 'fresh' air is required to dilute body odours and tobacco smoke as appropriate (see below). In addition there may be other processes requiring either dilution of low levels of contaminant emission or make-up air to replace that removed by a local exhaust system or combustion process.

Heat can be looked upon as another form of contamination. Temperature rise in a space can be limited by the movement of outside air through that space. Depending on the dynamics of heat flow at the internal surfaces and cyclic variations in outdoor temperature, it is usual for peak internal space temperature to decrease with an increase in throughput of outdoor air. Furthermore, ventilation can generate air movement which can create a beneficial cooling effect at the surface of the body. Another potential source of contamination is water vapour and in some applications, particularly domestic, ventilation may be used to limit condensation. Ventilation may also have an important part to play in the control of smoke and protection of escape routes during a fire.

Since outdoor air may require treatment for much of the year and fan energy is related to the total volume flow, ventilation strategy is very closely tied to the economic strategy for a particular project. Over-ventilation wastes energy, may result in over-sized hardware and can lead to draught or process problems. Under-ventilation may lead to some combination of odour, contamination, heat or moisture problems, and has been a major contributing factor in some cases of sick building syndrome (SBS) (see Chapter C5), and chronic or acute illness and even death in some industrial applications.

The ventilation options available are characterised by the degree of control they offer over air movement and indoor air quality (airborne contaminants). For example, natural ventilation provides limited control over air movement, dependent on careful positioning of openings in the fabric to make use of wind or convection forces as available. These forces have been observed to cause the ventilation rate to vary by a factor of 5 with changing weather conditions[17]. Control over indoor air quality will fluctuate with natural forces, although the purity of the incoming air cannot be controlled at all. The ventilation efficiency, or index (see below) will depend on the position of openings and the prevailing forces. Internal buoyant forces can produce a 'stack' effect which induces low level input and moves contaminants upwards. If there is enough incoming air then the contaminants will stratify above the occupied zone. This is displacement or buoyancy-assisted ventilation, where make-up and exhaust can either occur by natural or mechanical means. Mechanical ventilation provides the designer with far more choices, although at greater cost. High-emission and toxic contaminants (including heat) can be controlled at source. General contamination and heat gain can be either diluted or displaced, and air can be distributed to wherever it is most needed. Contaminants can be removed from outdoor air and extract air, as appropriate, and the building can be sealed to reduce infiltration of air and noise from outside. Supply air condition can be automatically controlled to provide constant internal conditions if desired.

VENTILATION RATES

In recent years there has been a tendency to blame many of the complaints from people working in air-conditioned office buildings on a lack of 'fresh' air. Investigations[18,19] have shown that a perception of inadequate fresh air is frequently associated with lack of air movement, stuffiness, or the inability to open windows. There is usually very little correlation between the incidence of this complaint and the ventilation rate provided.

Infiltration of outdoor air into naturally ventilated buildings in winter is frequently below recommended quantities, particularly for occupants working 5 or 6 metres from a window, yet SBS-related symptoms associated with these free-running buildings would appear to be less common than in the sealed air-conditioned buildings. So just how important is 'fresh' air? Should more attention be focused on other aspects of air-conditioned buildings, such as remoteness of some workers from a view or daylight, lack of personal control and prolonged VDU operation?

Outside air must reach certain minimum standards to be considered suitable for supply to occupants within a confined space. The new ASHRAE Standard[1] uses ambient air quality standards produced by the US Environmental Protection Agency as a basis for their definition of 'fresh air'. This specifies long-and short-term limits for common pollutants only. If examination of records shows that these are exceeded then it is recommended that suitable air cleaning apparatus be installed.

Non-smoking environments

Exposure to CO_2 at low concentrations is not harmful to human health. An acceptable concentration is considered to be 2,500 ppm, which may be achieved, in theory, by supplying 2.5 litres per second of outdoor air for each sedentary occupant. Accordingly, after the oil crisis of the 1970s, a ventilation rate of 2.5 litres per second per person was adopted in North America as a minimum for sedentary activity with no smoking. At about the same time in the UK, CIBSE were recommending a minimum of 5 litres per second per person.

However, chamber studies carried out in North America[20] and Denmark[21] have shown that these rates were inadequate when considering odour levels perceived by non-adapted people, and that the density of occupants has no bearing on fresh air requirements. These studies showed that there is a difference in perception between people entering a space and those who are acclimatised. Even with no smokers present, up to 40% of people entering a room supplied with 2.5 litres per second of air per person will be dissatisfied, whereas if 8 litres per second is available dissatisfaction was found to reduce to the acceptable level of 20%. Minimum fresh air requirements have been increased accordingly, both in the USA and in the UK[22], to 8 litres per second per person (see Table C1.2). This corresponds to a maximum CO_2 concentration of 1,000 ppm.

Environmental Tobacco Smoke

Leaderer[20] has shown that allowances for environmental tobacco smoke (ETS) have also been inadequate in the past, particularly when catering for non-smokers entering the space. The issue is complicated by the fact that smoke evolves at a rapid rate and there may be high local concentrations, the decay of which depend on room air movement. The plume is very sensitive to cross draughts from supply air jets, opening doors and wakes generated by passers by.

CIBSE recommendations[22] are based on attaining 80% satisfaction among non-adapted occupants. They refer to rooms in which there is 'some', 'heavy' and 'very heavy' smoking, corresponding with ventilation rates of 16, 24 and 32 litres per second per person respectively.

The new ASHRAE Standard is based on chamber studies which indicated that, for typical smoking levels in US offices, 80% of adapted occupants could be satisfied if provided with 8 litres per second per person. However the fresh air rate proposed for 'office space', having a

Table C1.2 Fresh air requirements of a number of countries

COUNTRY	APPLICATION	FRESH AIR RATE	SOURCE
UK	odour control light smoking heavy smoking v heavy smoking	8l/s/pers 16l/s/pers 24l/s/pers 32l/s/pers	CIBSE Guide (1986) Section B2: Ventilation & Air-conditioning Requirements
USA	offices (some smoking) auditoria conference rms smoking lounges	10l/s/pers 8l/s/pers 10l/s/pers 40l/s/pers	ASHRAE Standard 62-1989
Finland	office room open office smoking room	10l/s/pers 1l/s/m^2 10l/s/pers 1.5l/s/m^2 10l/s/pers	National Building Code of Finland: Indoor Climate and Ventilation in Buildings (1987)
Sweden	non-smoking areas smoking areas	5l/s/pers 10l/s/pers	Swedish Building Code SBN 1988: Air Quality
Nordic countries	non-smoking areas smoking areas	10l/s/pers 20l/s/pers	Nordic Building Regs 1989 (Prelim.)
FRG	non-smoking areas with some smoking	5.6l/s /m^2 14–19.4l/s/m^2	DIN 1946 Part 2 (DE6)
Italy	offices, conference rooms, theatres, restaurants	8.3-19.4 7-8.3 11-13.9 (l/s/pers)	Standard UNI–CTI
Japan	general spaces	CO<10 ppm CO_2<1000 ppm RSP<0.15mg/m^3	Building Sanitation Management Standards Law

l/s/pers = litres per second per person

maximum occupancy density of 1 person per 14 square metres, is 10 litres per second per person. The areas listed as requiring the minimum rate, such as auditoria, reception areas and classrooms, are either of a transitory nature or less likely to contain smokers. Table C1.3 gives selected recommendations extracted from the proposed ASHRAE 'Outdoor requirements for ventilation' compared with recommendations from other countries.

Fanger et al[15] found that a further 2 olfs were contributed to the emission of odours by cigarette smoking: this is with 30% of their panel being smokers, although they provide no information on smoking rates.

Table C1.3 Comparison of UK Occupational Exposure Limits (OELs), WHO guidelines and ASHRAE standards

SUBSTANCE	OEL (g/m^3)	WHO GUIDELINE (g/m^3)	ASHRAE STANDARD 62-1989 Outdoor air (g/m^3)	Indoor air (g/m^3)
Carbon monoxide	55×10^3	10×10^3	$10 \times 10^3 (8h)$	
Carbon dioxide	9×10^6			1.8×10^6 (continuous)
Formaldehyde	1.5×10^3	100 (30min.)		
Particulates	10×10^3	70 (thoracic particles)		
Nitric oxide	30×10^3			
Nitrogen dioxide	6×10^3	210 (1 hour) 80 (24 hour)	100 (1 year)	
Ammonia	18×10^3			
Acrolein	250			
Ozone	200	150-200 (1h) 100-120 (8h)	235 (1h)	100 (continuous)
Sulphur dioxide	5×10^3	500 (10min)	365 (24h)	
Toluene	375×10^3	7.5 x 10³ (24 hour) 1.0 x 10³ (30 min.)		
Styrene	215×10^3	800 (24h) 70 (30 min.)		

Intermittent and Transitory Occupancy

For applications in which odours are likely to accumulate, on fleecy surfaces, cluttered shelving etc., it is useful to provide pre-dilution by bringing in the ventilation plant some time before the occupants arrive. For rooms with smooth surfaces it may be possible to hold back fresh air provision until the odour levels are approaching unacceptable levels.

The new ASHRAE Standard[2] provides a technique for determining the lead and lag times depending on the room volume per person and their fresh air allowance. Nomograms are provided which can be used to determine how long before occupants enter a space (lead time) a particular ventilation rate should be provided in order to deal with overnight desorption of contaminants adsorbed during the previous day, along with overnight outgassing from non-human sources. The nomogram is based on typical adsorption/desorption rates for spaces with carpets, soft furnishings, and textured walls and ceilings. For example, for an office density of 30 m³ per person and a fresh air rate of 16 litres per second per person a lead time of 2 hours would be required.

Similarly, for low emission spaces, containing minimal fleecy surfaces or shelving, it can be determined that the fresh air damper could be kept closed for 30 minutes (lag time) after occupants first enter, assuming the same density and fresh air allowance as above.

Control methods are available which can be used to adjust fresh air rate according to the prevailing contamination levels. CO_2 or air quality sensors, mentioned earlier, can be installed in the space or in extract ductwork and arranged to adjust the mixing dampers or switch fans accordingly. These methods can be used to provide automatic control over lag and lead operation and adjust fresh air volumes for transient and intermittent occupancy. However Fanger[15] found no correlation between CO_2 concentrations and odour perception, a finding which may throw some doubt on the validity of using CO_2 sensors for control of ventilation systems.

Control of Specific Contaminants and Total Odour

In the past, ventilation rate recommendations have not taken account of ventilation efficiency or odours released by the building and services. The new ASHRAE Standard[2] allows for the designer to calculate an appropriate ventilation rate from first principles. This 'Indoor Air Quality Procedure' involves the calculation of a dilution or displacement ventilation rate, based on limiting concentrations for non-industrial exposure to contaminants and a prediction of the ventilation efficiency or index. There are very few published limits for non-industrial exposure to contaminants. Table C1.3 gives a comparison between comfort, environmental protection and occupational exposure limits for some airborne contaminants found in buildings.

Fanger[23] provides a method by which a ventilation rate can be calculated using a form of dilution equation based on diluting the total malodorous contaminant load, the 'olf load', to an acceptable perceived air quality level in decipol, assuming a perceived outdoor air quality level in decipol.

Since little data is yet available on odour emissions from specific sources, Fanger provides typical 'olf loads' for different types of building, based on field studies using panels of 'sniffers'. For a typical office he suggests an olf load of 0.4 olf per square metre, whilst for a 'low-olf' building an olf load of 0.1 is suggested. This implies that if a building is designed with low emission materials, smooth cleanable internal surfaces, minimal shelving, and smoking is prohibited, ventilation rates can be reduced to a quarter of that required for a typical office building. For example, for acceptable indoor air quality, with 20% dissatisfaction, he suggests a perceived air quality of 1.4 decipol, whereas a typical outdoor vote in a (Danish) town gives 0.2 decipol. A typical office would need around 32 litres per second per person to achieve acceptable indoor air quality, whereas a 'low-olf' building would need 8 litres per second per person.

The ventilation rate can be further reduced if a ventilation index greater than 1.0 is predicted (see below).

The Economics of Outdoor Air Provision

Air entering a building from outside, through openings in the fabric or via central air handling plant, may require heating when it is at a temperature below room air, unless it can be used for 'free' cooling. Air-conditioned buildings require the provision of outdoor air which is cooled and dehumidified in the summer and, where necessary, humidified in the winter.

Eto and Mayer[29] have used computer modelling to predict the increase in energy consumption and overall costs which are likely with the adoption of the new ASHRAE ventilation standard[2]. They predicted that with an increase in ventilation rate from 2.5 to 10 litres per second per person, the annual energy operating costs would rise by 5% on average, whilst total building construction costs would rise by 0.5%. These are averages for 13 buildings spread across all the main climatic zones of the United States and Canada, built to modern standards of construction and insulation, and using local energy tariffs.

At 1990 prices, a typical office building built to current UK Building Regulations might cost about £1,000 per square metre, including building services and internal finishes. Air-conditioning might cost from £100 to £300 per square metre, depending on type and module size. Applying Eto and Mayer's computer predictions suggests that increasing fresh air provision by 7.5 litres per second would cost approximately £5 per square metre.

Leary[30] gives estimated energy costs for air-conditioning at £7.75 per square metre per annum (at 1986 prices) for a basic building with no energy conservation features. Annual recurring maintenance and replacement costs are given as £5.6 to £16.6 per square metre for air-conditioning, over a 20-year period. If again we apply Eto and Mayer's predictions[29] to Leary's, an increase in fresh air rate by 7.5 litres per second per person would cost around £0.40 per square metre.

Gillingham[31], using 1985 figures for the UK, has suggested that the overall cost of owning and operating an air-conditioning system may be about £13 per square metre per annum more than a non-air-conditioned property. This he compared with an annual bill for rents and rates of about £550 per square metre for the City of London, or £130 to £190 per square metre for Greater London, down to a minimum of £50 per square metre in the provinces. On the other hand, annual salaries and other associated overheads could amount to £5,000 per square metre.

Although this is a fairly crude analysis, based, in part, on extrapolating USA computer predictions onto UK computer predictions, it gives an idea of the economic impact of ventilation in the context of indoor air quality and the design of air-conditioning systems. For example, it could be estimated that for a 10,000 square metre office building costing £10m, an extra £50,000 in first costs would be required to increase outdoor air provision per person from 8 litres per second to 16 litres per second, and hence comply with CIBSE's latest recommendations for rooms in which there is some smoking. Running costs may increase by £6,000 per annum compared to other running costs, including salaries etc which might add up (for the example 10,000 square metre building) to £10m per annum (allowing for inflation from 1986 to 1990).

ROOM AIR MOVEMENT AND VENTILATION EFFECTIVENESS

Although the provision of an appropriate quantity of outdoor air is the ammunition in the battle to provide acceptable indoor air quality, the accuracy of the aim has to be ensured by a correctly designed system for creating room air movement. Sufficient uncontaminated outdoor air must be available to dilute locally produced contamination throughout the occupied zone of a building. This air must be provided in such a way as to ensure an acceptable quality of inhaled air for each occupant.

The precise contaminant distribution within a room depends on the room air movement and may be quantified in terms of the ventilation effectiveness, which is determined as:

$$\text{Ventilation effectiveness} = \frac{\text{contaminant concentration in extract air}}{\text{contaminant concentration in inhaled air}}$$

This is sometimes known as the ventilation index. In theory, values for ventilation effectiveness could lie between zero and infinity. For example, if all the air supplied to a room were extracted before it diluted any of the contaminants in the occupied zone, then the ventilation effectiveness would be zero. At the other extreme, if all the contaminants released were carried away in the extract system, resulting in no measurable concentration in the inhaled air, then the ventilation effectiveness would be infinity.

Little is known about the ventilation effectiveness resulting from natural ventilation. Clearly it will vary with window operation, wind direction and heat sources. Best results are likely to occur in tall rooms and if openings are provided close to the floor and ceiling and when the convection currents are the main driving force.

Most air-conditioning and ventilation systems rely on grilles and diffusers to discharge supply air across a ceiling, which may also contain extract openings. Heat transfer and contaminant dilution rely on the mixing of supply and room air, most of which occurs above the heads of the occupants. The usual aim is to create uniform temperature and air purity throughout the occupied zone, with a ventilation effectiveness of unity. Usually some short-circuiting occurs, resulting in values less than unity. The momentum from supply jets can generate draughts and transfer contaminants, such as tobacco smoke, from source to recipient.

Systems which discharge air into the lower part of the room[24] are not usually designed to mix the supply and room air. Room air movement is primarily due to upward room convection currents, displacing room-generated contaminants which stratify above head level. Hence values for ventilation effectiveness are usually much higher. Unfortunately contaminants which are generated below head level, such as smoke evolving from a cigarette lying in an ashtray, may find their way into the breathing zone of nearby occupants.

FILTRATION

It may be possible to reduce the quantity of outdoor air drawn into the building via a central air handling plant by providing a filtration system which is capable of reducing the concentration of entering contaminants to a level which is acceptable to the occupants. In sealed buildings occupied by non-smoking people this will entail removing bioeffluents and CO_2 expired by the occupants and the normally low concentrations of other contaminants released by the fabric, furnishings and cleaning operations.

Filtration of environmental tobacco smoke presents a particular problem, because not only does it contain particles ranging in size from 0.1 to 0.7 microns, all of which are respirable, it contains a number of gases and vapours, some of which are irritants.

Filtration load can be reduced by locating the fresh air inlet as far as possible from sources of contamination, such as local traffic. A properly installed fine matrix fibreglass bag filter might remove 100% of entering particulates larger than 6 microns, particles of 1 to 6 microns at 98–99% efficiency, whilst efficiencies fall off rapidly down to around 0.1 microns, below which virtually all particles get through. It can be estimated therefore that efficiencies for removing the particulates found in environmental tobacco smoke may be between 20 and 40% for this kind of filter.

A matrix of fibreglass will not remove gases or vapours from the air. Some gases and vapours can be removed by scrubbing, i.e. absorption into a liquid, normally water. This requires water to be agitated so that a large surface area is presented to the entering air stream. Dust is also scrubbed from the air, and provision must be made for removal of the resultant sludge, otherwise micro-organisms may proliferate. Spray humidifiers are low efficiency scrubbers, indeed historically they have been known as 'air washers'. High efficiency tower, orifice and venturi scrubbers are used for cleaning industrial exhausts, but are not suitable for commercial air-conditioning. An activated carbon filter adsorbs certain airborne gases and vapours onto its surface by a physical process of surface adhesion. A typical activated carbon filter may be prepared from coconut shells exposed to very high temperatures, a process which purges all fluids and impurities and creates an enormous area for adsorption. Adsorption efficiencies vary considerably for different substances. Many low volatility substances, such as CO_2 and CO, are not removed at all, whilst for others, such as SO_2 and NO_2 and formaldehyde, the mass adsorbed onto the carbon is very low.

The more stages of filtration are incorporated into the air handling system the cleaner the supply air will be, although it must be remembered that particles will be released from the inside surfaces of equipment and ductwork, particularly if it is allowed to become soiled through prolonged maintenance intervals or poorly fitted filters. However clean air is not cheap, and penalties will be paid in terms of filter replacement costs, maintenance labour time and fan running costs. The latter increase in proportion to the pressure drop across the filters.

Activated carbon filters are particularly costly to run because the cells typically need replacing every 6 to 12 months at 1989 costs of around £500 per cubic metre per second. If the carbon cells are not replaced when saturated, they will eventually break up and coat all downstream surfaces with a fine layer of carbon and contaminants, which is very difficult to remove.

MAINTENANCE

In general, inadequate maintenance leads, amongst other things, to poor indoor air quality. Ventilation systems and buildings should be designed to be easily cleaned and, if possible, to contain no inaccessible surfaces and have the minimum of surface areas on which chemicals can be adsorbed or trapped. In the UK, attention has focused on maintenance after investigations into a number of serious outbreaks of Legionnaires' Disease have laid a significant proportion of the blame at the door of the maintenance personnel. This has already led to building owners being prosecuted under the UK Health and Safety at Work Act for failure to provide and maintain 'plant and systems ... that are safe and without risk to health'. As a result, the building services industry's professional body, the Chartered Institution of Building Services Engineers, and the contractors' association, the Heating and Ventilating Contractors' Association, are working together to improve maintenance standards by improving the professional standing of maintenance personnel and publishing standard maintenance specifications. The pressure on consultants and contractors to become quality assured should also improve the communications and documentation procedures at handover of the building and its services to the client and operating and maintenance personnel.

The National Institute for Occupational Safety & Health[25] found poor maintenance to be the root cause of many of the environmental problems in the buildings they have investigated in North America. This was also one of the conclusions of the Building Use Studies survey of 47 buildings in the UK[19]. Dust and micro-organisms can accumulate inside air handling systems. If dust penetrates the filters then it will settle out on all available surfaces, such as heating and cooling coils, sound attenuators, spray ponds and the internal walls of ductwork. In areas where moisture can collect, such as fresh air inlets subject to rain penetration, spray humidifier ponds, drip trays beneath cooling coils and moisture eliminators, micro-organisms can thrive on a mixture of iron oxides and sludge. This contamination can result in strong odours being emitted into the supply air and, in severe cases, large concentrations of micro-organisms have been carried in the supply air into the workplace producing allergic responses including, rarely, humidifier fever. For this reason spray humidifiers should be avoided and cooling coil drain trays well drained, and coils, moisture eliminators and drain rays regularly cleaned and disinfected.

It is vital that appropriate filters be installed, that they are accessible and equipped with a 'change filter' indicator. Ideally all air handling equipment and ductwork should be provided with access doors to facilitate regular internal cleaning. The Heating and Ventilating Contractors Association[26] suggest cleaning intervals of 3 to 6 months for air handling unit internals including all coils, 6 to 24 months for supply ductwork and 12 to 24 months for extract systems, depending on the condition of incoming air and the use of the system. 'Deep' cleaning of ductwork which has not been provided with suitable access panels may be time consuming, disruptive and expensive, and building owners are well advised to invest in adding airtight access panels at appropriate positions. Turning vanes, sound attenuators and ductwork lined with sound absorbent material present particular cleaning problems. All this has considerable economic implications which will inevitably weigh heavily against the use of air-conditioning and mechanical ventilation systems in providing environmental control of buildings.

A room with soft furnishings, textured wall coverings, carpets etc. may have thousands of square metres of surface on which airborne chemicals can be adsorbed or dust particles trapped, and the trapped dust actually increases the area available for adsorption. As temperatures and vapour pressures change, some of the adsorbed chemicals may be emitted from certain surfaces, thus adding to the odour burden in the room. In some cases this emission occurs when the room is not occupied and contaminants can be purged by introducing fresh air some hours before occupants arrive.

Abildgaard[27], whilst showing a good correlation between concentrations of airborne dust and bacteria in room air, measured the highest concentrations of both in carpeted buildings, the oldest carpets being associated with the highest readings. It is clear that smooth, easily cleanable surfaces pose far fewer maintenance and air quality problems. Furthermore, soiling from environmental tobacco smoke leads to increased cleaning times and shorter intervals between cleans, resulting in an increase in cleaning costs.

CONCLUSIONS

* The health of building occupants may be compromised by exposure to a wide range of airborne contaminants, both in the home and at work. More commonly, occupants experience unacceptable discomfort, which may be unpleasant and distracting. In either case productivity may suffer and absenteeism increase.

* There is a need to distinguish between comfort and health in the context of indoor air quality and ventilation requirements. Ventilation requirements and design must be based on some combination of parameters which keeps odours at an acceptable level for at least 80% of the occupants and ensures minimum deleterious health effects. Standards are either *comfort-based* (e.g. the provision of adequate outdoor air, reducing concentrations of specific contaminants below their detection threshold or reducing total odour loads) or *health-based* (e.g. reducing concentrations below specific occupational exposure limits).

* Poor maintenance has been identified as the root cause of many of the environmental problems in the buildings in North America. This was also one of the conclusions of the Building Use Studies survey of 47 buildings in the UK. Prompt and conscientious maintenance is crucial to avoidance of health problems in all buildings, and particularly those with air-conditioning.

* Any preventive strategy should focus firstly on the source and then on ventilation. In the future, specifiers must take steps to reduce emissions by selecting low emission and low absorption building products. Building interiors and equipment must be easy to maintain, and preventive maintenance regimes must be evolved by the designers and communicated to the users.

* All buildings require some form of ventilation, whether generated by natural forces or mechanical. Well constructed naturally ventilated buildings may not provide adequate ventilation during the winter months if the windows remain closed, whereas opening windows in winter may lead to draught and complaint. Trickle ventilators incorporated into window frames may overcome this problem.

* Investigations have found that naturally ventilated buildings in general have worse indoor air quality than air-conditioned ones, but the incidence of sick building syndrome is lower. This seems to point to other causes for sick building syndrome (see Chapter C5), although SBS is known to be triggered by a combination of factors.

* In non-industrial buildings environmental tobacco smoke is usually one of the most obvious indoor air contaminants. In many working environments exposure can be limited by providing separate amenity for smokers and banning smoking from the workplace. Exposure in the home is virtually impossible to control, other than by health promotion propaganda via the media.

* Much guidance on indoor air quality and ventilation is available to the designer, but there is no consistency in the advice and there are new developments under way. For example, Swedish codes may soon reflect the trend, which is already prevalent in some Scandinavian countries, for full fresh air ventilation plant, with no recirculation but heat transfer by air-to-air heat exchanger. This follows the widespread adoption of displacement ventilation in those countries, which requires 100% outdoor air to maintain stratification of contaminated air above head level[24]. By contrast the new ASHRAE Standard[2] allows for a reduction in outdoor air rate, provided particulate and gaseous contaminants are removed from the air by filtration, so that the level in the space is equivalent to that which would be obtained if the recommended fresh air rates were employed. It also allows provision for a reduction in outdoor air rate to account for uneven contaminant emissions in multiple-room buildings, allowing for the air returning from low contamination zones to help with dilution in contaminated regions. The American approach to ventilation, which allows the designer to minimise outdoor air supply, is no doubt born from concern about the massive amounts of energy required to ventilate their buildings, with floor areas commonly in the tens of thousands of square metres, which are very difficult to ventilate efficiently, particularly with the widespread use of variable air volume air-conditioning and supply and extract air terminals in close proximity.

* In this rapidly developing field, designers and specifiers must keep abreast of new developments, and seek out the latest available guidance applicable to their project.

REFERENCES

1. ISO 7730: *Moderate thermal environments – Determination of the PMV and PPD indices and specification of the conditions for thermal comfort.* International Standards Organisation (1984)

2. ASHRAE Standard 62-1989 – *Ventilation for Acceptable Indoor Air Quality*, American Society of Heating Refrigerating and Air–conditioning Engineers, Atlanta, USA, (1989)

3. J.E. Janssen, *Ventilation for acceptable indoor air quality.* In CIBSE/ASHRAE Conference, Dublin, S. Ireland, September 15-17, 1986. Chartered Institution of Building Services Engineers, Balham, UK, 40-49, (1986)

4. *Air Quality Guidelines for Europe*, World Health Organisation, Geneva, (1987)

5. *Occupational Exposure Limits.* Guidance Note EH4. Health and Safety Executive, Bootle (revised annually)

6. Berglund, B., *The role of sensory reactions as guides for nonindustrial indoor air quality.* Preprint for American Industrial Hygiene Conference, St Louis, USA, May 21-26 (1989)

7. Cain, W.S., *Perceptual Characteristics of Nasal Irritation.* John B. Pierce Foundation Laboratory, New Haven, USA, (1989)

8. Cain, W.S., See, L.C., and Tosun, T., *Irritation and odour from formaldehyde: chamber studies.* In IAQ '86: *Managing the Indoor Air for Health and Energy Conservation*, American Society of Heating Refrigerating and Air-conditioning Engineers, Atlanta, USA, 126-137, (1986)

9. Gunnarsen, L., Fanger, P.O., *Adaptation to indoor air pollution*, in *Healthy Buildings '88*, eds B. Berglund and T. Lindvall, Swedish Council for Building Research, Stockholm, 3, 157-167, (1988)

10. Clausen, G.H., Nielsen, K.S., Sahin, F., and Fanger, P.O., *Sensory irritation from exposure to environmental tobacco smoke*, in *Indoor Air '87, Berlin*, eds B. Seifert et al, 2, 52-56, (1987)

11. ASHRAE Handbook: *Fundamentals*, Chapter 12: *Odors*. American Society of Heating, Refrigerating & Air-conditioning Engineers, (1989)

12. Bluyssen, P., *Olfbar*, Laboratory for Heating and air-conditioning, Technical University of Denmark (1989)

13. McIntyre, D.A., *Indoor Climate*, Applied Science, London, (1980)

14. Pejtersen, J., Clausen, G.H., and Fanger, P.O., *Olf-values of spaces previously exposed to tobacco smoking*, in *Healthy Buildings '88*, eds B. Berglund and T. Lindvall, Swedish Council for Building Research, Stockholm, 3, 197-205, (1988)

15. Fanger, P.O., Lauridsen J., and Clausen, G., *Air pollution sources in offices and assembly halls, quantified by the olf unit*, Energy & Buildings, 12, 7-19, (1988)

16. Pejtersen, J., Bluyssen, P., Kondo, H., Clausen, G., and Fanger, P.O., *Air pollution sources in ventilation systems*, Laboratory of Heating and Air-conditioning, Technical University of Denmark, (1989)

17. Jones, W.R., and Stricker, S., *Ventilation requirements and natural air leakage in residences*, in *Ontario Hydro Research Review No.4*, Ontario, Canada (1981)

18. Griffiths, I.D., Huber, J.W., and Baillie, A.P., *Effective ventilation in offices: The occupants' perspective*, in *Effective Ventilation – the 9th AIVC Conference*, Air Infiltration and Ventilation Centre, Coventry, UK, 1, 311-328, (1989)

19. Wilson, S., and Hedge, A., *The Office Environment Survey: A Study of Building Sickness*, Building Use Studies, London, (1987)

20. Leaderer, B.P., and Cain, W.S., *Air quality in buildings during smoking and non-smoking occupancy*, ASHRAE Trans, American Society of Heating, Refrigerating & Air-conditioning Engineers, Atlanta, USA, 89, 2A & 2B, 601-623, (1983)

21. Fanger, P.O., *Body odour and carbon dioxide, minimum ventilation rates*, IEA energy conservation in buildings and community systems programme, Annex IX final report, (1986)

22. *CIBSE Guide, Section B2*, Chartered Institution of Building Services Engineers, London, (1987)

23. Fanger, P.O., *The new comfort equation for indoor air quality*, in *IAQ 89: Human Equation – Health and Comfort*, April 17-20, 1989, San Diego. ASHRAE, Atlanta, USA (1989).

24. Appleby, P.H., *Displacement ventilation, a design guide*, Building Services J, 11(4), 53-56, (1989)

25. Wood, J., Morey, P., and Stolwijk, J., *Indoor air quality and the sick building syndrome: A view from the United States*, in CIBSE International Symposium Advances in air-conditioning. CIBSE, London, (1987)

26. HVCA, *How to Avoid Sick Building Syndrome*, Heating & Ventilating Contractors Association, London (1990)

27. Abildgaard, A., *The interaction between dust, micro-organisms and the quality of cleaning*, in *Healthy Buildings '88*, eds B. Berglund and T. Lindvall, Swedish Council for Building Research, Stockholm, 3, 197-205, (1988)

28. Mant, D.C., and Muir-Gray J.A., *Building Regulation and Health*, Building Research Establishment, Watford (1986).

29. Eto, J.H., and Mayer, C., *The HVAC cost of increased fresh air rates in office buildings*, ASHRAE Trans 94(2), 1988

30. Leary, J., *The case for decentralised building services*, Electricity Council Internal Paper V1201PDS1,1 London, 1987

31. Gillingham, D.S., *Air-conditioning – an ever expanding market*, in *Air-conditioning impact on the built environment*, ed A Sherratt, CICC, Nottingham, 1986

APPENDIX

CONTAMINANTS OF INDOOR AIR AND THEIR SOURCES

This appendix is largely based on a study carried out by Mant and Muir-Gray (28) at the Building Research Establishment (BRE), as part of a review of building regulations and health. It is incorporated here with some amendments and with the permission of the authors and BRE. Many of the contaminants are dealt with in more detail in other chapters.

Water Vapour

The moisture content of indoor air is generally about that of outdoor air, particularly in dwellings. At the temperature and humidity found in most UK buildings, there are no direct health effects associated with exposure to water vapour. Low humidities may, however, be associated with discomfort from dryness and mucosal irritation. This is because irritants such as dust and formaldehyde are not irrigated away so efficiently. There is also some evidence of an increased risk of respirable infection. High humidities in association with cold surfaces result in condensation which can damage building fabric and stimulate colonisation by moulds and other micro-organisms (see below).

Carbon Dioxide

Carbon dioxide (CO_2) is a constituent of outdoor air, being the product of many natural and man-made processes. Typically concentrations outdoors fall between 350 and 400 ppm. It is usually higher than this indoors, resulting from metabolic production by occupants and the flueless operation of combustion equipment. Concentrations which result from occupants alone will depend upon the dilution available from outdoor air per person and the activities and hence metabolic rates of the occupants. There are no known health effects associated with exposure to CO_2 at the concentrations reported in non-industrial buildings. However, metabolic carbon dioxide can be used as an indicator of ventilation rate and hence problems arising due to exposure to other less detectable contaminants.

Carbon Monoxide

Carbon monoxide (CO) is produced by incomplete combustion. Within buildings it may result from tobacco smoking, cooking and heating appliances without flues. Outdoors it emanates from vehicle exhausts and chimneys. Outdoor concentrations usually fall between 3 and 17 ppm, averaged over an 8 hour period.

The primary toxic action resulting from exposure to CO is hypoxia. This results from CO combining with haemoglobin in the blood, hence supplanting the oxygen, and resulting in tissue injury.

Indoor concentrations rarely reach a level which could cause concern. However death or injury has resulted from backflow of combustion products from incorrectly installed water heaters. High concentrations can occur in tunnels and multi-storey car parks during rush hour periods.

Oxides of Nitrogen

Oxides of nitrogen are a minor product of combustion of common fuels. Within buildings they may be produced by gas cookers, heating appliances without flues and tobacco smoking. There is evidence from animal studies that exposure to nitrogen dioxide can reduce the lung's defence against bacterial infection. A number of epidemiological studies have indicated increased incidence of respiratory infection in children living in homes using gas rather than electric cooking. It is thought that the causative agent might be nitrogen dioxide, although the evidence is not conclusive. At this level of exposure the health effects are probably small.

Environmental Tobacco Smoke

Environmental tobacco smoke (ETS) is a mixture of exhaled mainstream smoke (MS) and the sidestream smoke (SS) which evolves between puffs. ETS comprises a mixture of several thousand constituents, some of the more commonly measured of which are: particulates, nicotine, carbon monoxide, benzene, nitrogen dioxide, acrolein and formaldehyde.

It has been suggested that ETS is one of the most important sources of indoor air contamination and, since exposure is not always voluntary, one of the more controversial. It is a difficult contaminant to deal with, being generated from a randomly located point source with locally high concentrations.

Acute effects include objectionable smell and irritation of the eyes, nose and throat, as well as a reduction in visibility. Irritation can be further exacerbated by low humidities as mentioned above. Long term effects are less well established. A number of epidemiological studies have shown increased respiratory disease amongst children of smoking parents and a positive association between exposure to ETS and an increased relative risk of lung cancer. Based upon the best available evidence, the annual risk of mortality due to average exposure to ETS is estimated to be 1 in 15,000, or midway between an acceptable risk[28] and a risk considered to be unacceptable in any circumstances.

Organic Compounds

Organic compounds arise from many sources within buildings, including the building materials, preservatives, sealants and finishing products, furnishings, combustion, tobacco smoking, occupants, personal care products, cleaners, correcting fluids, and reprographic facilities (see Table C1.1).

Thousands of chemicals have been identified in the atmosphere of non-industrial buildings, but there is as yet little known about emission characteristics of known or suspected sources. Similarly, knowledge of health effects resulting from exposure is limited, and usually restricted to industrial workplace exposure, where the concentrations found are generally several orders of magnitude higher than those found in non-industrial buildings. Little is known about the effects of exposure to low concentrations of these substances, particularly the effects of exposure to mixtures.

Organic compounds can be categorised by their boiling point, which dictates their rate of emission into the surrounding atmosphere as follows:

- VVOC – very volatile, boiling point range : <0°C to 50–100°C
- VOC – volatile, boiling point range: 50–100°C to 240–260°C
- SVOC – semi-volatile, boiling point range : 240–260°C to 380–400°C
- POC – particle-bound, boiling point: >380°C.

At the normal temperatures found in buildings VVOCs may evaporate fairly rapidly, unless they are locked in by an impermeable layer. VOCs may take 6 months to several years to be fully liberated, whereas SVOCs may take 15 to 30 years to disappear from the source. POCs are generally only liberated by combustion.

Formaldehyde is a VOC which has been of particular concern due to its presence in urea-formaldehyde foam insulation (UFFI), chipboard and some textiles. In the UK, emission rates are restricted by codes of practice covering the manufacture of particle board and the composition and installation of UFFI. Because it is soluble in water it has a particularly strong irritant effect on the eyes, mucous membranes and the respiratory tract, and easily enters the bloodstream. It has a pungent odour which can be detected at concentrations as low as 0.1 ppm, which is below most countries' occupational exposure limits. The chronic effects have not been established for humans, although nasal cancer has been induced in laboratory animals, whilst sensitised individuals have developed asthma and dermatitis. Based on animal studies, the annual risk of mortality from cancer, due to exposure in buildings insulated with UFFI, has been estimated to be in the range of 1 in 250,000 to 1 in 150 million.

Wood preservatives comprise a mixture of solvent (VOC) and active ingredients (SVOCs) such as pentachlorophenol (PCP), gamma-hexachlorocyclohexane (gamma-HCH or lindane), dieldrin and tributyl tin oxide (TBTO). They have been cited as possible sources of ill health. This has been based on well-documented toxicological effects due to occupational exposure of wood treatment operatives. Exposure to the active ingredients in treated buildings is usually through the inhalation of dust particles which have the compound attached to them. As well as being irritants and nerve poisons, some of these compounds target organs, such as the liver, and can accumulate there from a number of sources, since they are commonly used in agriculture and find their way through the food chain. Estimated health risks based upon expected exposure in treated buildings against an acceptable daily intake indicate a negligible risk from exposure to PCP and gamma-HCH, but a possible risk from exposure to dieldrin, the use of which is now being voluntarily controlled.

Non-viable Respirable Suspended Particulates (RSP)

Respirable particulates are those non-viable dust particles which penetrate the defences of the respiratory system and penetrate deep into the alveoli. This includes most of the particles smaller than 4 microns in diameter, whilst a significant proportion of those smaller than 7 microns will penetrate into the upper respiratory tract.

A significant proportion of indoor airborne particulates are external in origin, especially in naturally ventilated buildings, but may be generated indoors from a number of sources. Occupants generate dust from their clothing, whilst movement of people, machinery and air continually redistributes dust between the internal surfaces of rooms. Tobacco smoking is an important source of RSP. In poorly ventilated heavy smoking areas visibility can be reduced and concentrations may well exceed standards.

Fibres

The fibrous material of most concern is asbestos, which is known, from studies in the occupational field, to be carcinogenic and to cause chronic, disabling lung disease (see Chapter B3). Asbestos has in the past been used for a number of purposes, most particularly as sprayed insulation. Recent analysis of epidemiological studies of occupational exposure has yielded an annual risk estimate of death from cancer, due to exposure to all types of asbestos, of approximately 1 in 700,000. This is close to the defined acceptable risk. With the widespread withdrawal of asbestos-bearing building products exposure in new buildings should be negligible.

Man-made mineral fibre (MMMF) products (see Chapter B4) are still widely used, particularly within air handling systems in the form of filters, sound attenuators and internal insulation. MMMFs are known to irritate the skin, eyes and upper respiratory tract, although so far there is no firm evidence that they can produce lung disease.

Viable Particulates (airborne micro-organisms)

Biogenic aerosols formed from bacteria, mould spores and amoebae are commonly found in indoor air, from which they may settle on a suitable substrate and, if temperature and humidity are favourable and a suitable nutrient available, they may form colonies, multiply, become airborne and enter the respiratory system of occupants. Viruses, on the other hand, may simply be transmitted from person to person by an airborne route; they do not survive for long outside the host body.

Health effects are of two broad types:

(a) *allergies*, ranging from allergic rhinitis (inflammation of the nasal mucous membrane) to extrinsic allergic alveolitis (irritation of the lungs), which is potentially extremely debilitating, and occupational asthma, and

(b) *infections*, which can be viral, as with the common cold, or bacterial, as with Legionnaires' Disease, a sometimes fatal form of pneumonia.

Airborne concentrations of micro-organisms vary considerably depending on whether conditions for growth exists. Control can only be by eliminating the conditions for growth.

Radon (see Chapter C4)

Radon-222 is a chemically inert radioactive gas which is one of the series of isotopes which starts life as uranium and decays through numerous steps until it eventually becomes completely stable as lead. Radon is a gas with a relatively short half life of 3.8 days which is present in the earth's crust globally and can be absorbed into water and natural gas supplies, as well as particular types of building material manufactured from radon-bearing minerals.

Radon can outgas into the atmosphere from these various sources and either enter the lungs directly or after decay into radon-daughters, which are chemically active electrically charged ions which become attached to any convenient particulate matter. There are four radon-daughters all of which have half lives of less than 30 minutes, two of which are alpha-emitting helium nuclei (polonium). Because radon is a gas, it is normally inhaled and exhaled again before the emission of alpha particles can do much damage, but because the radon-daughters are attached to dust particles which can become lodged in the lung further decay can produce irreversible damage to lung tissue and perhaps lung cancer. It is thought that a significant proportion of the lung cancers are caused by radon exposure, the WHO having estimated that about 10% of these cancers could be attributed to radon.

The concentration of radon (expressed in Becquerels per cubic metre) varies with geographical location. Greatest exposures occur in basements and ground floors. Exposure can be reduced by careful selection of building materials, effective sealing of basement floors and walls, pressurisation of basements, and provision of adequate dilution or displacement ventilation.

WATER QUALITY

Christopher Forster

University of Birmingham

INTRODUCTION

Until recently, the prime requirement for public supply of drinking water in the United Kingdom was that it should be 'wholesome'. This meant that the organizations supplying the water had three main responsibilities:

- to ensure that the water was fit for human consumption, i.e. that it was free from pathogenic organisms and from harmful dissolved or suspended matter;
- to ensure that the water was aesthetically attractive, i.e. free from taste, colour and odour;
- to ensure that the water was chemically suitable for household purposes, e.g. that it was sufficiently soft for washing purposes.

This requirement for quality was not clearly defined in terms of chemical composition. There were recommended limits, however, for bacterial concentrations. These existed to ensure that drinking water was not a vector for the transmission of diseases originating from sewage. The European Community (EC) has now issued a series of Directives which define the quality of many types of water, including drinking water, quite precisely. Similar definitions are provided for England and Wales by the Water Supply (Water Quality) Regulations 1989 (see Table C2.1). The standards for drinking water place restrictions not only on the numbers of bacteria that are indicative of pollution by sewage but also on a range of chemicals that have the potential, in some way, for being hazardous to human health. These hazards range from the initiation of cancer to direct or cumulative poisoning. Restrictions are also placed on other chemical species which could have an effect on the more general characteristics of the water (e.g. taste, hardness). Two levels of restriction are defined in the EC Directive on Drinking Water: the imperative, or mandatory, concentration and the guide value. For drinking water, the former is the maximum admissible concentration (MAC) (Table C2.2) whilst the latter is the target that would ultimately be achieved in an ideal situation. In the United Kingdom, drinking water is produced from a variety of sources:

Table C2.1: Maximum Admissible Concentrations for Contaminants in Drinking Water in the Water Supply (Water Quality) Regulations 1989

CONTAMINANT	MAXIMUM ADMISSIBLE CONCENTRATION
Aluminium	200 micrograms per litre
Coliforms	
• faecal	Nil per 100 millilitres
• total	Nil per 100 millilitres
Copper	3000 micrograms per litre
Faecal streptococci	Nil per 100 millilitres
Lead	50 micrograms per litre
Manganese	50 micrograms per litre
Nitrates	
• as N	11.3 milligrams per litre
• as NO_3	50 milligrams per litre
Organo–chlorine compounds:	
• Tetrachloromethane	3 micrograms per litre
• Trichloroethane	30 micrograms per litre
• Tetrachloroethane	10 micrograms per litre
Poly–aromatic Hydrocarbons	0.2 micrograms per litre
Pesticides	
• individual	0.1 micrograms per litre
• total	0.5 micrograms per litre
Sodium	150 micrograms per litre (80 percentile over 36 months)

groundwater which collects in underground aquifers and which is obtained by pumping from boreholes; upland catchment reservoirs which collect rainfall and snow run-off; and lowland rivers. The degree of treatment that any water receives before it is passed into the distribution system varies with its quality. For example, some borehole waters may need little more than disinfection whilst lowland river waters may need extensive treatment to remove suspended solid material, colloidal matter and dissolved compounds as well as disinfection. An EC Directive specifies the quality of the raw water in relation to the treatment processes that are used.

In considering the effect that the quality of water can have on the built environment, two categories of human being need to be defined. The first includes the builders, the destroyers (i.e. demolition workers) and the modifiers (i.e. do-it-yourself enthusiasts); the second includes maintenance workers and the occupiers of the buildings.

Table C2.2: Maximum admissible concentrations for contaminants in drinking water in the EC Drinking Water Directive

CONTAMINANT	MAXIMUM ADMISSIBLE CONCENTRATION
Aluminium	200 micrograms per litre
Coliforms	
• faecal	Less than 1 per 100 millilitres
• total	Less than 1 per 100 millilitres
Copper	3000 micrograms per litre
Faecal streptococci	Less than 1 per 100 millilitres
Lead	50 micrograms per litre
Manganese	50 micrograms per litre
Nitrates	
• (as N)	11.3 milligrams per litre
• (as NO_3)	50 milligrams per litre
Organochlorine compounds	1 microgram per litre[a]
Polycyclic aromatic hydrocarbons	200 micrograms per litre
Pesticides	
• individual	0.1 micrograms per litre
• total	0.5 micrograms per litre
Sodium	150 micrograms per litre (80 percentile over 36 months)

[a] Guide value, excluding pesticides.

WATER OTHER THAN POTABLE WATER

Although the bulk of this chapter describes the potential risks associated with the various constituents of drinking water that are proscribed by the EC Directive on Drinking Water, it is pertinent to examine the hazards in the other types of water likely to be encountered by building or demolition workers: groundwater and sewage. Groundwater ought not to present a risk unless it has been seriously contaminated by:

- sewage leaking from a cracked sewer;
- the infiltration of surface water from an industrial site where toxic or hazardous chemicals were used, either historically or currently;
- leachate from a waste disposal site.

In the case of leachate from a waste disposal site, the major problem is likely to occur when the site has been closed and landscaped so that its existence may pass unnoticed.

If it can be assumed that contaminated groundwater will not be ingested, the only significant threat will be from contaminants that can be absorbed into the body either through the skin or through abrasions. The range of toxic chemicals that could act in this way is far too great for any discussion of them to be attempted here. However, chemicals of this type are unlikely to be encountered unexpectedly since their existence, at the point of origin, ought to be recorded because of their toxicity. The exception is when their origin is a tip or industrial site whose records either have been obscured by time or originally were inadequate. For further details of chemical hazards from contaminated land see Chapter C9.

If the groundwater has been contaminated with foul sewage, any problem will be biological rather than chemical. In general, provided that sensible rules of hygiene prevail, this should not be serious even if pathogenic bacteria and viruses are present. There are two situations, however, when care needs to be exercised. Soil or groundwater that has been contaminated with sewage may contain the spores of the bacteria that cause tetanus (*Clostridium tetani*) or gas-gangrene (*Clostridium welchii*) and, if wounds or abrasions became infected with these spores, the corresponding disease could develop. The solution to this problem is to provide good washing and first aid facilities and to consider whether the work-force should be offered immunization against tetanus. Sewage may also contain the organisms, spirochaetes, that cause Weils disease (Leptospirosis). These microbes are excreted in the urine of infected rats and can penetrate the skin even through small skin cracks so that contact with water contaminated with them can spread the disease.

ALUMINIUM

Although aluminium does not occur naturally as the free metal, it is the most common metal in the earth's crust, being present in most forms of rock. Some soluble forms of aluminium (silts, complexes) will therefore be present in the natural waters that are the starting point for the production of drinking water. Usually the concentrations of these compounds will be low (around 0.05 milligrams per litre (mg l^{-1})) unless the pH value of the water has been reduced by inputs of acidic water (produced either naturally or by man-made pollution). A recent survey of European waters by Sollars et al. (1989) found that the aluminium concentration in raw waters typically ranged from 0.002 to 0.844 mg l^{-1}, although two higher values, 2.38 and 3.09, were reported from Italy. Aluminium is also used in the treatment processes that are used to produce drinking water, the most usual form used for this purpose being aluminium sulphate. The presence of aluminium in public supply water is therefore to be expected.

Increasing concern has recently been expressed about the possible link between Alzheimer's disease and the exposure to aluminium, in particular in drinking water. Alzheimer's disease is a form of dementia, and patients suffer losses of memory, of emotional stability and of the control of bodily functions. The full course of the disease may be as little as 2 years or as long as 20. However, the prevalence of the disease is not known with any great precision. Indeed, it has been suggested that many sufferers may die with the disease undiagnosed. A recent review of the epidemiology of this disease stated that there are clear *a priori* grounds for suspecting that this link with aluminium does exist (Lee, 1989). However, it emphasizes that none of the findings proves a causal relationship.

In the Drinking Water Directive, the MAC value for aluminium is 0.2 mg l^{-1}, a value which is not dissimilar to that required by other, non-EC, countries. The survey by Sollars et al. (1989) showed that, of the 85 works or regions in the United Kingdom and mainland Europe for which data were available, 17 reported annual maximum concentrations of aluminium in excess of the MAC value whilst only five had annual mean concentrations which exceeded the MAC. In other words, the aluminium problem was, in general, under control. Certainly, in the United Kingdom the water supply companies are achieving steady improvements. For example, the commissioning of new treatment works by one UK Water Authority has resulted in the mean aluminium concentration in the final water being reduced from 0.53 to 0.05 mg l^{-1} at one works (Briens et al., 1989) and from 0.59 to 0.07 mg l^{-1} at another (Hudson et al., 1988). Even so, these figures need to be placed in an overall context if the water-associated risk is to be assessed. In the built environment the people at risk, if indeed there is a risk, come from both the categories defined previously. These people will also ingest aluminium from sources other than water. A study made in 1985 by the Ministry of Agriculture, Fisheries and Food estimated that the daily intake of aluminium was between 6 and 7 mg per person with the contribution from water being between 0.5% and 11%. This value was based on a water concentration appreciably higher than that found in the European survey. This means that the actual maximum water contribution will probably be around 5%. The major contribution comes from food, some 6 mg per day. In addition, certain drugs (antacids, buffered aspirin) contain aluminium and these can contribute significantly to the daily input. One American survey (Epstein, 1984) indicates that the intake from antacids could be as high as 1,000 mg per day. However, although these facts seem to suggest that aluminium in drinking water, at the present level of performance of the treatment plants, is not a significant risk, it must be recognized that the precise nature of the aluminium species either in potable water or in many foods is unclear. Also, it is not known whether the different species have different roles, if indeed they have any at all, in the initiation of Alzheimer's disease. The overall risk significance is therefore not known.

TRIHALOMETHANES

In the United Kingdom, chlorine is the main disinfecting agent used in the production of drinking water. However, as well as killing bacteria, chlorine can react with organic compounds in the water to form chloroform-related compounds, the trihalomethanes (THMs). This group of chemicals, the most common of which is chloroform, has been found to cause cancer in test animals. For this reason restrictions are placed on the concentrations of THMs in drinking water. The World Health Organization (WHO) suggests a guide concentration of 30 micrograms per litre (μg l^{-1}) and the EC Drinking Water Directive specifies a guide value for the organochlorine concentration (excluding pesticides) of 1 μg l^{-1}, with a supplementary note that THM concentrations should be as low as possible. Approximately 80% of the drinking water sources in England and Wales are surface waters, which may contain dissolved organic material (either naturally occurring or from pollution) and which therefore have the potential for THM formation during treatment. The water companies are fully aware of this problem (Edge and Finch, 1987; Greene and Fadzean, 1988) and many of them are examining how their chlorination procedures can be modified to minimize the production of THMs. A problem can arise with upland sources where natural colour in the raw waters peaks at a similar time to the microbial contamination. The high levels of chlorination needed to cope with the latter problem produce high THM concentrations (up to 440 μg l^{-1}) in the final water (Greene and Fadzean, 1988). In these cases, colour removal prior to chlorination is being proposed. In other cases, with lowland sources, the simple expedient of moving the point of the pre-chlorination stage can reduce the THM concentration significantly (by about 60%), resulting in concentrations well below the MAC value (Timmins, 1985). No matter how effective the control at the treatment works, there is the possibility that THM production will continue in the distribution system, particularly if free chlorine is present (Edge and Finch, 1987). However, it is unlikely that this will result in appreciable concentrations of THMs.

The values for THM concentrations that have been reported in drinking water range from less than 5 μg l^{-1} in a French study to 10 μg l^{-1} (Italy) and 21 μg l^{-1} (USA) (Aggazzotti and Predieri, 1986).

Chlorinated organics can also be formed within buildings when chlorine is added to water. Thus, if chlorine is used to disinfect swimming pools or whirlpool spas, haloforms will be produced from the organic matter excreted by the human users of these facilities. An Italian study (Aggazzotti and Predieri, 1986) has reported maximum chloroform concentrations of 179 μg l⁻¹ in swimming pools, whilst Canadian workers (Benoit and Jackson, 1987) have found values of up to 674 μg l⁻¹ in spas. It is therefore important to exercise a rigorous control over the length of time that water is kept in these systems. Alternative types of disinfectant (e.g. ozone) could also be considered. In attempting to assess the risk from THMs (or other chlorinated organics), the question of what concentration of a carcinogen will initiate cancer must be asked. Whilst this question will not be answered with any precision at present, the size of the risk from a lifetime's exposure to known compounds in drinking water has been estimated at less than 1 in 10^5 when their concentrations are in the microgram per litre range (Fawell et al., 1987). This suggestion is borne out by the results of two American studies (Cech et al., 1987; Young et al., 1987). If a degree of protection additional to that afforded by the EC Drinking Water Directive is required, then additional private in-house treatment could be considered. The most effective would be to use adsorbers packed with granular activated carbon (in much the same type of unit as is used for in-house water softening). A number of such units are available commercially.

POLYCYCLIC AROMATIC HYDROCARBONS

The group of compounds known as polycyclic aromatic hydrocarbons (PAHs) is ubiquitous in nature. Many of the compounds are carcinogenic and both the UK Regulations and the EC Directive restrict their presence in drinking water by requiring that the sum of the concentrations of specified PAHs should not exceed 0.2 μg l⁻¹. The EC Directive specifies five reference substances (of which one is given twice); the UK Regulations specify six. Three, possibly four, of these six are carcinogens although it is far from certain whether this is of significance when the compounds are present in the trace quantities normally found in drinking water. However, it must also be recognized that other PAHs may be present and that the relationship between the concentrations of measured total PAH and actual total PAH is vague and difficult to measure (Crane et al., 1981). Crane found that river waters which were used as drinking water sources contained PAH concentrations that ranged up to about 0.2 μg l⁻¹ and that, under high flow conditions, some rivers contained PAH concentrations of over 1,000 μg l⁻¹. Despite this, all the treatment plants examined in the survey achieved a high removal of PAHs. This is because, in water, PAHs are adsorbed to particulate matter which is readily removed by the standard treatment processes of coagulation, settlement and filtration. Some water at the point of consumption did contain levels that were comparable with the MAC value. However, these high concentrations were made up almost entirely of a single member of the PAH group, fluoranthrene, which is not considered to be carcinogenic. The most likely source of this compound was thought to be the coal tar lining of the distribution mains. This type of pipe is clearly unsuitable for use in the distribution of drinking water and no new mains of this type have been produced in the United Kingdom since 1977. However, it is not known how much still remains in service. Nevertheless, the risk to water users is not likely to be significant as long as there is compliance with the EC Directive at the point where the water leaves the treatment works. If additional in-house protection were required, adsorbers similar to those described in the previous section could be used.

OTHER ORGANIC POLLUTANTS

A large number (>600) and a wide variety of organic compounds have been detected in drinking water (Fielding et al., 1981). Most of them are the result of human activity that causes pollution of groundwater or surface water sources. However, a recent survey in Holland has shown that, when polyethylene piping was used for water supply, some organic compounds in contaminated soil could permeate through the pipe and adversely affect the treated water quality (Vonk, 1985). The permeation through concrete or asbestos cement pipes (see Chapter B3) was negligible.

Despite the wide variety of types of compound that have been found, in this chapter attention will be focused on two classes (other than the THMs and PAHs): pesticides, and solvents. The solvents which are found most commonly in groundwater studies (both in America and the UK) are chlorinated solvents such as trichloroethene. The EC Directive places no restriction on this type of solvent as such, relying on a 'blanket' limit for organochlorine compounds of 1 µg l⁻¹. The WHO specifies guideline values for some of the chlorinated solvents; the UK Regulations specify maximum concentrations. For trichloroethene, the limit is 30 µg l⁻¹. The Directive is therefore more stringent. However, a survey published in 1985 (see Lewis et al., 1987) showed that some 35% of the groundwater sources examined contained trichloroethene concentrations which exceeded this value. Moreover, only a small proportion of the UK water companies were monitoring groundwater supplies for these solvents. This, therefore, seems to be an area for possible concern since it is not known how effectively the various treatment processes will remove these compounds (certainly they have been detected in treated water (Fielding et al., 1981)) or what the long-term effects of their ingestion will be.

The EC Drinking Water Directive defines pesticides as persistent organochlorine compounds, organophosphorus compounds and carbamates, but its restrictions also apply to herbicides, fungicides and polychlorinated biphenyls and triphenyls. The restriction is an MAC value of 0.1 µg l⁻¹ for individual compounds and of 0.5 µg l⁻¹ in total. These various types of biocidal compound, because of the way in which they are used, can and do contaminate water sources very readily. For example, during the period 1984–6, a survey of surface water and groundwater sources showed that there was significant contamination (0.1–1.0 µg l⁻¹) with the herbicide triazine. The survey also showed that there were seasonal variations, the minima occurring during the winter months. Therefore, in this particular case, the water companies are faced not only with the problem of monitoring and removing this type of compound but also of doing this with a seasonally variable pollutant. It is not known whether or how other members of this proscribed group will vary. Pesticides are therefore another area where concern might be expressed. (The risks from pesticides in amenity areas are covered in Chapter C8.) In both cases (solvents and pesticides), if in-house protection were to be required, adsorption filters could be used (see earlier).

RADIOACTIVE MATERIAL

Radioactive material can enter the water cycle, and therefore treated water, either as a result of an accident (e.g. Windscale, 1957; Three-mile Island, 1979; Chernobyl, 1986) or from natural sources. In the latter case, the radioactivity is most likely to arise from radon gas (Castle, 1988). The EC Drinking Water Directive provides no specific guidance about the acceptable levels of radioactivity in drinking water and in two recent examinations of the problem (Jones and Castle, 1987; Castle, 1988) the WHO definition of a gross beta activity of 1 Becquerel per litre was used. This is, essentially, a MAC value but it is very conservative, being equivalent to an annual dose of only 5% of that used as the limit value for members of the public. Following the accident at Chernobyl, the EC has attempted to derive unified control values for food and water. Until these are available, the gross beta activity maximum seems to offer a sensible way of protecting public water supplies.

Analyses of selected treated water following the Chernobyl accident showed (Jones and Castle, 1987) that only 4.5% of the samples exceeded the 1 Becquerel per litre limit. The amount by which the limit was exceeded was small and the length of time for which this occurred was 3–4 days. This survey also showed that the water treatment processes were able to remove an appreciable amount of the radioactivity, concentrating it in the waterworks sludges. Essentially this means that, provided that the accident is known about, water supplies can be monitored and appropriate action can be taken.

Radon-222, which has a half-life of 3.8 days, is formed by the radioactive decay of radium-226 (see Chapter C4). Although radon gas is perhaps more commonly associated with causing a radiation hazard by accumulating under the floor spaces of houses, it is a gas which is very soluble in water. Indeed some American groundwaters have been found to contain concentrations as high as 10,000 Becquerels per litre. Radon-contaminated water is potentially hazardous in two ways. The gas can be released from the water by agitation and present an air pollution problem, e.g. in the bathroom. It can also be ingested by the direct consumption of water. The latter route has been estimated to produce between 1% and 12% of the indoor radon dose. When radon is known to be a problem, it can be removed during water treatment by bubbling air through the water or by using activated carbon adsorption. Once again, therefore, it should be assumed that water, as supplied to the home, ought not to present a serious hazard, although it must be conceded that acceptable control levels have yet to be established. However, in this case in-house treatment would not be recommended as this would concentrate radioactivity within the adsorption unit and create a radiation hazard at that point.

NITRATES

Nitrogen in the form of nitrate can enter groundwaters or surface waters by a number of routes, of which the principal ones are leachate of agricultural fertilizer, domestic sewage inputs and agricultural cultivation practices. However, the most significant input is fertilizer (Croll and Hayes, 1988). In the southeast of England nitrate concentrations in rivers have been rising for several decades. These concentrations vary with the seasons with the maxima coinciding with high winter flows. The nitrate concentrations in most of these rivers and those in the east of England exceed 50 mg l^{-1} (equivalent to 11.3 mg l^{-1} measured as nitrogen) in the winter months (Croll and Hayes, 1988). Much of the nitrate stems from arable farming and there is no indication that this general trend of increasing nitrate concentrations will change unless there is a change in agricultural policies. Nitrates from fertilizers will also affect groundwaters. The aquifers in the east of England (Lincolnshire, East Anglia) are some of the worst affected. Currently, typical concentrations are 70–100 mg l^{-1} and the expectancy is that these figures will increase to 150–200 mg l^{-1} unless agricultural practices change.

Conventional water treatment processes do little to alter the nitrate concentrations in raw waters. These steadily rising levels of nitrate in raw water sources are, therefore, of some concern because of the ways in which nitrate can react within the human body. One mode of action is specific to infants (particularly those under the age of 6 months). This is the conversion of haemoglobin (which is the oxygen carrier in human blood) to methaemoglobin. This conversion is carried out by the inorganic ion nitrite, which is readily produced from nitrate within the human gut. Methaemoglobin cannot bind oxygen. Nitrate 'poisoning' of infants, therefore, results in oxygen starvation (cyanosis) which can lead to suffocation. This condition is often referred to as the 'blue baby syndrome'. There are several reasons why the susceptibility of infants is so great. The conditions in their intestinal tract are more amenable to the nitrate to nitrite conversion, their haemoglobin is more readily converted to methaemoglobin and infants consume much more fluid per unit body weight than adults. Because of all these variables, together with the possibility of a genetic, hereditary variation in susceptibility, it is difficult to define an absolutely safe level. However, a limit of 10 mg l^{-1} has been suggested as one which provides a reasonable margin of safety (Adam, 1980). This must be compared with the MAC value specified in the EC Directive of 11.3 mg l^{-1} and with lower limits in other countries (e.g. Austria, 9.0 mg l^{-1}; Switzerland, 4.5 mg l^{-1}). All these values relate to the concentrations of nitrogen in the form of nitrate, not of nitrate itself.

The impact of methaemoglobin formation is not only restricted to infants. Children and young adolescents can also suffer adverse effects from consuming water with a high nitrate content. The resulting increased levels of methaemoglobin are thought to cause impaired growth and a slowing of the conditioned reflexes (Adam, 1980). There is also some evidence, albeit not conclusive, that nitrite can pass through the placenta and cause methaemoglobin to be formed in the foetus, resulting in impaired growth.

The nitrite that is formed from nitrate can also react with other chemicals (secondary amines or N-substituted amides) to produce compounds which may be carcinogenic. However, there is no conclusive evidence for this. Forman (1987) suggests that, in Britain, nitrate in drinking water is not correlated with gastric cancer. Pocock (1985) cites both negative evidence and data which suggest that the link cannot be discounted. The latter review also shows that, in the United Kingdom, the majority of the human nitrate intake is from non-water sources.

Although there is uncertainty about the link with cancer, the role of nitrate in the formation of methaemoglobin is sufficient to warrant the control limits specified earlier. Processes are available that will remove nitrate during the treatment of raw water. However, procedures which control the inputs to source waters must also be implemented. One way of limiting the nitrate levels in boreholes is to use 'protection' zones around them where the farming activities would be modified so as to reduce nitrate losses from the land (Croll and Hayes, 1988; Knight and

Tuckwell, 1988). Essentially, this means permanent grassland rather than arable farming for the most sensitive areas. The major problem with this approach is whether farmers will accept policies which could result in their losing income. Restriction policies are easier to operate when the farm land is owned by the water company (Knight and Tuckwell, 1988). A range of operational procedures such as the blending of waters or source replacement can be employed to reduce nitrates in the treated water, but they ought not to be considered as satisfactory in the long term (Croll and Hayes, 1988). Furthermore, a range of processes can be used to remove nitrates in the treated water (Adam, 1980; Croll and Hayes, 1988), of which the most effective are ion exchange and microbial denitrification. The former technology could also be considered for in-house treatment. Achieving the EC value will be expensive: over the next 20 years; the cost will be in the region of £200 million (Croll and Hayes, 1988).

LEAD

Lead is a toxic metal (see Chapter B5). Its main pathways into the human body are from air, water or food. In general, the concentration of lead in natural waters is low (<0.01 mg l^{-1}) so that drinking water, as it leaves the treatment works, will usually conform to the MAC value specified by the EC Directive: 50 µg l^{-1} after flushing and after a 30 minute stagnation period. However, problems can occur when there are lead pipes or lead-lined tanks in the consumer's property. If the water is capable of dissolving lead, the combined effect will be to produce lead-contaminated water at the tap. The level of this contamination will be greater after periods when the water has been static in the pipes or tanks (e.g. overnight). Waters which are capable of dissolving lead are termed 'plumbosolvent'. Soft acidic waters, usually from upland catchments, are most commonly associated with this problem. This can be seen from the results of a Department of the Environment survey published in 1977 which showed that in Scotland, where soft acidic waters are common, 34% of the samples exceeded 50 µg l^{-1} and, more alarmingly, 21% exceeded 100 µg l^{-1}. A more recent survey in 1980 which was limited to Ayr (Moore, 1985) showed a 78% non-compliance with the EC Directive. Additional acidity resulting from acid rain will exacerbate these effects. Some high alkalinity waters can also be plumbosolvent. Results reported by Colling et al. (1987) showed peaks (occurring in the summer months) which were in excess of 100 µg l^{-1}.

Both types of water can be treated to reduce their plumbosolvent potential (Sheiham and Jackson, 1981). The effect caused by low alkalinity upland waters, which is due to their acidity, can be reduced by increasing the pH of the treated water to about 8.5. If necessary, this treatment can be enhanced by the addition of orthophosphate (Sheiham and Jackson, 1981). The report by Moore (1985) cites the use of a lime dosing treatment which raised the pH to 9 in Glasgow and 8.5 in Ayr. This reduced the non-compliance with the EC limit to 1% and 5% respectively. However, it must be noted that this limit was not the current value of 50 μg l^{-1} but the pre-1985 value of 100 μg l^{-1}. It is known and recognized that, when this type of treatment is used, the pH can drop in the distribution system to perhaps as low as 7.5 (Smith and Walker, 1988). High alkalinity waters that are plumbosolvent can also be treated with orthophosphate (Moore, 1985; Sheiham and Jackson, 1985). Typical results from one Water Authority show (Colling et al., 1987) that this treatment will produce water that is well below the 50 μg l^{-1} level. Although lead can originate from several other sources (e.g. air emissions), this type of remedial action by water authorities has brought about substantial improvements in blood lead levels during the period 1979-81 (Quinn, 1985).

The obvious and ultimate solution to the problem of lead in drinking water is to replace all lead pipes and/or tanks in houses. However, it has been estimated that this would cost in the region of £2,500 million (1977 costs). Also, what replacement should be used? For pipes, copper would appear to be suitable (the EC guideline value is 3,000 μg l^{-1}) but lead-based solders should not be used in joints. Also, mixed metal plumbing (part lead, part copper) should be avoided since this will increase the plumbosolvency as a result of galvanic corrosion. Plastics are another material commonly used for water supply pipes. However, some unplasticized polyvinyl chloride may contain lead-based stabilizers and these may be leached into tap water (Wong et al., 1988). This effect is most pronounced with new pipes. Other metals can also be leached from plastic pipes. For tanks, galvanized iron or copper seem to be the best alternatives (Britton and Richards, 1981). If none of these options is feasible, then flushing (i.e. clearing the pipes of water that has been static and in contact with the lead) should be encouraged (Britton and Richards, 1981). It is recommended that water from lead storage tanks is not used for drinking purposes.

MICROBIAL CONTAMINATION

The contamination of drinking water by microbes (bacteria, protozoa, viruses) is almost invariably caused by sewage and can occur either at the raw water source or during distribution. The risk is therefore one related to the spread of disease. During the treatment of raw waters, disinfection is used to kill any disease-causing organisms that may be present in the water and, when chlorine is used as the disinfectant, residual concentrations are left in the water to prevent the growth of organisms in the distribution system. The water undertakers in the United Kingdom also monitor the bacteriological quality of water in the supply system to ensure that there is conformation with the EC Drinking Water Directive. The bacteriological limits are based on indicator species rather than specific pathogens, since it is generally easier to measure indicator concentrations and the indicator species will be present in greater numbers. Although tests may be made for other microbial species, the main tests are for total coliforms, faecal coliforms and faecal streptococci. The EC Directive requires an MAC of less than 1 per 100 millilitres for each of these indicators. On this basis, therefore, drinking water should be safe.

However, mistakes do occur. In the last 50 years there have been 34 outbreaks of water-borne disease in the United Kingdom (Galbraith et al., 1987). Of these, 21 outbreaks were associated with public water supply systems, and the others with private supplies. In total, at least 11,000 people were affected, a figure which must be considered against the fact that some 250 million man-years of water were supplied during this time (say 15×10^{10} m^3). However, this should not suggest that there is scope for complacency. An examination of the data presented in the report by Galbraith et al. (1987) shows that most of the 17 outbreaks which occurred in the period 1967-86 were the result of human error. Typical examples of the causes of these outbreaks were contamination of the distribution system during engineering work and poor or inadequate chlorination. The main diseases that resulted were diarrhoea (caused by the bacterium *Campylobacter*) and viral gastro-enteritis. Although the disease is now considered to be endemic in the USA, only one case of giardiasis (a disease caused by the protozoa *Giardia lamblia*) was recorded in the United Kingdom during this period (Browning and Ives, 1987). The symptoms of this disease include diarrhoea, stomach cramps, fatigue and weight loss. These three types of disease are unpleasant but are unlikely to be serious. Indeed, in the last 20 years, no deaths have been recorded as a result of the microbiological contamination of drinking water. However, as Galbraith et al. (1987) pointed out, it is fortunate that the more serious water-borne diseases (e.g. typhoid fever) are now so uncommon in the United Kingdom that, on those occasions where sewage contamination of drinking water occurred, organisms such as *Salmonella typhi* (the bacterium causing typhoid fever) were not present in the sewage.

Although the risk from water-borne microbes is small, additional protection could be afforded by the use of in-house treatment. There are many ways of disinfecting water and the choice would most probably depend on the amount of water being used. Additional disinfection facilities for a factory site could be different from those for a block of flats and different again for an individual house. For the larger systems, chlorination or ozonolysis (swimming pool style) might be appropriate. Ultraviolet radiation could be applicable in private homes as long as the treatment units had adequate safety features to protect the users against the radiation.

Water is used within the built environment for purposes other than drinking and cooking and the microbial quality of water will have an impact on these uses. Air-conditioners and humidifiers are increasingly used in the United Kingdom. Three diseases are recognized as being associated with their use: Legionnaires' Disease (see Chapter C3); humidifier fever; and sick building syndrome (see Chapter C5). No single pathogenic organism has been found that causes either humidifier fever or sick building syndrome and the real extent of these diseases is not known. However, it is considered that the techniques for controlling Legionnaires' Disease (see Chapter C3) are also likely to be suitable for the prevention of the other two humidifier-associated diseases (Galbraith et al., 1987).

As has been mentioned earlier, swimming-pools and spas need to be considered within the building environment. Certainly they offer a water-based route for the transmission of disease. This is particularly true for spas where the water is warmer and the chlorine concentrations are lower than in swimming pools. The diseases that have been identified are swimming pool rash, swimming pool granuloma, conjunctivitis, respiratory infections and genital tract infections (Jones and Bartlett, 1985; Galbraith et al., 1987). To minimize any hazard from these, there is a need for the water quality to be monitored constantly. In addition, attention needs to be paid to the effectiveness of the disinfection procedures and the hygiene and sanitation facilities.

NON-HAZARDOUS CONTAMINATION

The non-hazardous class of contaminant includes both chemical and biological species whose existence in drinking water will cause concern or objection rather than harm. Colour is a typical example. The consumer expects colourless water. However, upland waters, particularly from a peaty or moorland location, will tend to have a natural organic colour which is harmless and which may be difficult to remove. Iron and manganese can also cause colour in water. In addition, they can stain fabrics during washing. These compounds can and should be removed during treatment. Tastes and odours are another common cause for complaint. These can be caused either by the quality of the raw water or by biological activity within the distribution mains. Tastes associated with raw water quality can be the result of chemical pollution. One such typical pollutant is phenol which may originate from an industrial discharge. Phenol itself can impart unpleasant medicinal tastes at very low concentrations (say 1 in 10^7) but, if the water is chlorinated, chlorophenols can be formed which can be detected at even lower concentrations (say 1 in 10^9). Tastes can also be imparted to raw water by the growth of algae. These are photosynthetic microbes which grow on sunlight, nitrogen and phosphorus. The tastes associated with algal growth tend to be 'fishy' or 'like cucumber'. If the treated water contains soluble organic matter, microbial growth within the distribution system may occur. This can also result in the water having an unpleasant taste ('musty' or 'mouldy'). This is exacerbated if the taste compounds react with chlorine. Some of the tastes associated with the raw water can be removed during treatment (Barker and Palmer, 1977). Some of them, together with those generated within the treatment main, would require in-house treatment if they were a serious nuisance. However, a sufficiently loud complaint to the water supply organization can often be very effective. It has also been reported (Anselme et al., 1985) that polyethylene tubing can impart odours to drinking water.

Infestations of water supply mains by chironomid larvae (bloodworms) are another source of anxiety and complaint by the consumer. The problem period for these infestations tends to be between August and November. Supply mains can also become infested by crustaceans and worms. None of these animals are known to be a public health risk. However, they are large enough to be seen by the consumer if they arrive at the tap and therefore cause concern. In addition, when they die, their decaying bodies can give rise to tastes and odours in the water. Again, the best policy is to complain. Water mains can be purged, either chemically or by scouring, and animal infestations removed.

Tap waters will have varying degrees of hardness. Hard waters might be considered only to be a problem in relation to kettles and hot-water systems. However, there is some evidence to suggest that increasing hardness (up to about 170 mg l^{-1}) can be correlated with decreasing cardiovascular mortality, particularly in males (Lacey, 1981). Sodium will also be present in most drinking waters and it is known that too much sodium in diets is associated with high blood pressure. Whether sodium in water can contribute significantly to this problem has not been established. The MAC is 150 mg l^{-1} (80 percentile value over 3 years). Most treated waters will have sodium concentrations below this value.

WATER ANALYSIS

The analyses needed to determine the quality of a water sample are becoming increasingly complex and it is certainly beyond the scope of this chapter to provide details of analytical methods. These can be found in the various standard methods. However, in general, it is not recommended that individual bodies should contemplate undertaking this complex and exacting task. The possible exception to this statement might be a large industrial concern where quality control laboratories exist and where water quality was of specific and sufficient concern to warrant the expense involved. These comments, however, should not preclude individuals from having occasional samples analysed by independent specialists. If this were required, consultant chemists, Universities or Public Health Laboratories, for example, could be approached. However, it must be stressed that these analyses cannot be done cheaply and there are, really, no 'short-cuts' for determining the quality of water.

CONCLUSIONS

Although water as supplied in the United Kingdom is essentially a safe commodity, there are a sufficient number of potential contaminants that could be hazardous to demand strict quality control. This type of control cannot be guaranteed with private supplies and, indeed, as one survey has shown (Barraclough et al., 1988), the quality of some private supply water is decidedly suspect when judged against the EC specifications (which do now apply to private supplies) and the Water Supply (Water Quality) Regulations 1989. Nevertheless, commonsense would suggest that the users of this type of supply should consider installing in-house treatment if the water quality is suspect or if there is a risk of contamination. Two points need to be made. It is difficult to judge whether there is a contamination risk. Pollution can occur unexpectedly and at times from surprising sources: a cracked sewer (Galbraith et al., 1987), the run-off of spent sheep dipping liquors (Barraclough et al., 1988) or a dead animal. It is also essential to ensure that any in-house treatment unit is properly selected to suit the requirements of the water, is properly installed and is properly maintained. Certainly concern has been expressed about the need to provide laws or some form of licensing for home treatment units (Yoo, 1987; Barraclough et al., 1988). Monitoring of private supplies is the responsibility of environmental health officers.

Public water supplies are subjected to quality control. However, whilst it is a straightforward exercise to ascertain whether any one parameter conforms to the required standard, the EC Drinking Water Directive lists 62 parameters. It is therefore necessary to have some method for judging the overall water quality. This is necessary both for internal quality control and, when required, for informing the consumer. There are various ways in which this type of assessment can be made: by defining and quantifying target levels of service and comparing the actual level of service with these targets; by using risk assessment techniques and comparing the actual risks with the acceptable risks; or by defining and quantifying water quality indices (Hayes et al., 1985). However, it is important that, whichever technique is used, the consumer can understand what the quality of the water is and how that quality may be varying. The consumer can then undertake his own risk assessment and, if necessary, modify his practices for water usage. For example, it has been shown that vending machines which dispense hot drinks (there are currently 120,000–150,000 in the United Kingdom) can be a vector for the transmission of bacterial contaminants if the supply water itself contains these contaminants (Godfree et al., 1981). The problem arises when the temperature of the water in the vending machine drops below 65–70°C, either because the unit is switched off or because of the frequency with which drinks are taken. Vending machines may be used, even when there is significant contamination of the public supply, as long as the machine dispenses the drinks at a temperature of about 70°C; in other words, there is no short-circuiting of the header tank, the heating system is compatible with the demand and a safety cut-out prevents drinks being taken if the water temperature is too low (Godfree et al., 1981).

However, the mere quantification of water quality does not help the consumer when serious accidents occur, e.g. the discharge of an aluminium-based water treatment chemical in Cornwall. It is also unlikely that in-house treatment systems would be capable of coping with every possible type of accidental contaminant. These are therefore incidents where the consumer must rely on a rapid and accurate response from the water company.

The situation in the future is unclear. As analytical techniques become more sophisticated, other contaminants may be detected and quality requirements may become more stringent. However, the production of safe drinking water involves more than having good process plant and analytical facilities. It also requires sound resource management of rivers, lakes and aquifers.

REFERENCES

Adam, J.W.H. (1980), *Health aspects of nitrate in drinking water and possible means of denitrification*, Water SA, 6, 79-84.

Aggazzotti, G. and Predieri, G. (1986), *Survey of volatile halogenated organics (VHO) in Italy*, Water Res., 20, 959-63.

Anselme, C., N'Guyen, K., Bruchet, A. and Malleviale, J. (1985), *Can polyethylene pipes impart odours in drinking water*, Environ. Technol. Lett., 6, 477-88.

Barker, M.B. and Palmer, D.J. (1977), *Persistent odour-taste removal: the use of ozone and microcoagulation or carbon*, Water SA, 3, 53-65.

Barraclough, J.F., Collinge, R. and Horan, N.J. (1988), *The quality of private water supplies in Calderdale – the implications of EC Directive on drinking water quality*, J. IWEM, 2, 487-92.

Benoit, F.M. and Jackson, R. (1987), *Trihalomethane formation in whirlpool spas*, Water Res., 21, 353-7.

Briens, P.J., Lyon, D.K. and Baggaley, R. (1989), *Operating experiences at Langsett water treatment works*, J. IWEM, 3, 50-9.

Britton, A. and Richards, W.N. (1981), *Factors influencing plumbosolvency in Scotland*, J. Inst. Water Eng. Sci., 35, 349-64.

Browning, J.R. and Ives, D.G. (1987), *Environmental health and the water distribution system: a case history of an outbreak of Giardiasis*, J. IWEM, 1, 55-60.

Castle, R.G. (1988), *Radioactivity in water supplies*, J. IWEM, 2, 275-84.

Cech, I., Holguin, A.H., Littell, A.S., Henry, J.P. and O'Connell, J. (1987), *Health significance of chlorination byproducts in drinking water: the Houston experience*, Int. J. Epidemiol., 16, 198-207.

Colling, J.H., Whincup, P.A.E. and Hayes, C.R. (1987), *The measurement of plumbosolvency propensity to guide the control of lead in tapwaters*, J. IWEM, 1, 263-9.

Council Directive on the Quality of Drinking Water for Human Consumption, 80/778/EEC OJ L229 30 August 1980.

Crane, R.I., Fielding, M., Gibson, T.M. and Steel, C.P. (1981), *A Survey of Polycyclic Aromatic Hydrocarbons Levels in British Waters*, WRc Technical Report TR 158, Water Research Centre.

Croll, N.T. and Hayes, C.R. (1988), *Nitrate and water supplies in the United Kingdom*, Environ. Pollut., 50, 163-87.

Department of the Environment (1977), *Lead in Drinking Water, a Survey in Great Britain 1975-1976*, Pollution Paper 12, HM Stationery Office, London.

Edge, J.C. and Finch, P.E. (1987), *Observations on bacterial aftergrowth in water supply distribution systems: implications for disinfection strategies*, J. IWEM, 1, 104-10.

Epstein, S.G. (1984), *Aluminium and Health*, The Aluminium Association, Washington, DC.

Fawell, J.K., Fielding, M. and Ridgway, J.W. (1987), *Health risks of chlorination – is there a problem?*, J. IWEM, 1, 61-6.

Fielding, M., Gibson, T.M., James, H.A., McLoughlin, K. and Steel, C.P. (1981), *Organic Micropollutants in Drinking Water*, WRc Technical Report TR 159, Water Research Centre.

Forman, D. (1987), *Gastric cancer, diet and nitrate exposure*, Br. Med. J., 294, 528-9.

Galbraith, N.S., Barrett, N.J. and Stanwell-Smith, R. (1987), *Water and disease after Croydon: a review of water-borne and water-associated disease in the UK 1937-86*, J. IWEM, 1, 7-21.

Godfree, A.F., Bosley, M. and Jones, F. (1981), *The use of drink vending machines with contaminated water supplies: the potential risks to public health*, J. Inst. Water Eng. Sci., 35, 80-7.

Greene, L.A. and Fadzean, C.J. (1988), *Upgrading disinfection installations in Strathclyde Region*, J. IWEM, 2, 632-7.

Hayes, C.R., Warn, A.E. and Greene, L.A. (1985), *Development of comprehensive water supply quality in Anglian Water*, J. Inst. Water Eng. Sci., 39, 539-47.

Hudson, J.A., Morris, J. and Swanwick, K.H. (1988), *Water quality management in the River Calder catchment*, J. IWEM, 2, 505-12.

Jones, F. and Bartlett, C.L.R. (1985), *Infections associated with whirlpools and spas*, J. Appl. Bact. Symp. Supp., 14, 61S-66S.

Jones, F. and Castle, R.G. (1987), *Radioactivity monitoring of the water cycle following the Chernobyl accident*, J. IWEM, 1, 205-17.

Knight, M.S. and Tuckwell, S.B. (1988), *Controlling nitrate leaching in water supply catchments*, J. IWEM, 2, 248-52.

Lacey, W.F. (1981), *Changes in Water Hardness and Cardiovascular Death Rates*, WRc Technical Report TR 171, Water Research Centre.

Lee, P.N. (1989), *Epidemiological research on Alzheimer's disease: past and present*, Environ. Technol. Lett., 10, 427-34.

Lewis, W.K., Thomas, W.M. and Barron, R.J.C. (1987), *Contamination of groundwater resources and impact on potable supplies*. In *Handbook 1987-88*, Institution of Water and Environmental Management, London, pp. 39-47.

Ministry of Agriculture, Fisheries and Food (1985), *Food Surveillance Paper 15*, HM Stationery Office, London.

Moore, M.R. (1985), *Influence of acid rain upon plumbosolvency*, Environ. Health Perspect., 63, 121-6.

Pocock, S.J. (1985), *Nitrates and gastric cancer*, Human Toxicol., 4, 471-4.

Quinn, M.J. (1985), *Factors affecting blood lead levels in the UK: results of the EEC blood lead survey, 1979-1981*, Int. J. Epidemiol., 14, 420-31.

Sheiham, I. and Jackson, P.J. (1981), *The scientific basis for the control of lead in drinking water by water treatment*, J. Inst. Water Eng. Sci., 35, 491-515.

Smith, P.G. and Walker, A.F. (1988), *A study into the cause of decline in pH during water distribution*, J. IWEM, 2, 552-8.

Sollars, C.J., Bragg, S., Simpson, A.M. and Perry, R. (1989), *Aluminium in European drinking water*, Environ. Technol. Lett., 10, 131-50.

Timmins, J.R. (1985), *Disinfection in Water Treatment and Supply*, MSc Thesis, University of Birmingham.

Vonk, M.W. (1985), *Permeation of organic compounds through pipes for drinking water*, H_2O, 18, 529-34.

Wong, M.K., Gan, L.M. and Koh, L.L. (1988), *Temperature effects on the leaching of lead from unplasticized polyvinyl chloride pipes*, Water Res., 22, 1399-403.

Yoo, R.S. (1987), *Responding to customer concern about home treatment devices*, J. Am. Water Wks Assoc., 79, (10), 34-8.

Young, T.B., Wolf, D.A. and Kanarek, M.S. (1987), *Case control study of colon cancer and drinking water trihalomethanes in Wisconsin*, Int. J. Epidemiol., 16, 190-7.

LEGIONELLA AND WATER MANAGEMENT

Michael Bailey

London School of Hygiene and Tropical Medicine

INTRODUCTION

Legionella and Legionnaires' Disease

Legionella pneumophila is a ubiquitous bacterium found throughout the world wherever there is natural fresh water. In its normal environment it is present in small numbers and presents no risk to man. However, in the last 10 years we have become increasingly aware that, when *L. pneumophila* enters building water systems, it may colonize them and grow to high concentrations within them. We know that high concentrations of Legionellae bacteria can present a risk to human health if they are inhaled, with human disease being most often associated with *L. pneumophila* serogroup 1, subtype Pontiac.

Bacteria from water systems may be inhaled if the water is sprayed into the air and an aerosol of bacteria is formed. It is now well established that this is exactly what happens in the normal operation of evaporative cooling towers and clearly in the operation of showering facilities. It is less frequently recognized that significant water spray is also a feature of running hot and cold water at normal pressure into baths and basins.

Inhaled Legionellae bacteria can cause a disease called Legionnaires' Disease which is a type of pneumonia. Legionnaires' Disease is a rare human disease which has only been recognized since the late 1970s and only arises because modern building practices bring people into contact with concentrated aerosols of the bacteria. The infection is more likely to develop in the old and infirm than in the young and healthy and is seen more often in men than women. For these reasons, early outbreaks were noticed in groups of older people and in hospital patients. As our medical detective work (epidemiology) has improved we now recognize outbreaks in the more general population. Nonetheless the number of cases per year remains small, probably accounting for 2% of all community acquired pneumonias in British hospitals. In epidemic outbreaks, as many as one in 10 may die if the cause of the illness is not recognized and properly treated. This is a small number of fatalities and illnesses. However, it must be stressed that, where they occur as a result of poor building or plant design or failures of management, these deaths and illnesses are preventable.

Pontiac Fever

Legionellae bacteria may also cause a separate illness termed Pontiac fever which is a short flu-like illness with no long-term effects. It is not known why Pontiac fever develops on the rare occasions that it does. Measures which will prevent Legionnaires' Disease will also prevent Pontiac fever.

Growth of Legionellae Bacteria in Water Systems

We have a good understanding of the features which permit and encourage the growth of Legionellae bacteria within building water systems:

- a water temperature in the range 20–50°C with an optimum between 30 and 40°C;
- stagnation or a long residence time of the water within the system (this need not be within the whole of the system but may just be in deadlegs or little-used pipework branches);
- food sources within the system either as inappropriate materials incorporated in the construction of the system or as contamination from environmental sources into stored water in the system.

Tables C3.1–3.3 show a summary of the places within building water systems (Figures C3.1 and C3.2) where problems typically arise.

HAZARD CONTROL

Guidance Available

The management of good microbiological water quality and thus of Legionella control is well understood and well documented. Guidance is published in the United Kingdom by the Department of Health and Social Security and the Welsh Office (1988), the Health and Safety Executive (1987), many professional bodies (Chartered Institute of

Table C3.1 Cooling towers

No.[a]	Description	Typical problems	Design	Installation	Operation
	Evaporative cooling tower	Becomes colonized with Legionellae bacteria Contaminates air with live Legionellae Air may be drawn into the building's ventilation system Poor quality supply water	Should be easily dismantled for cleaning Parts should be easy to clean and replace Provide good quality supply water Avoid close proximity of cooling tower outlet and building ventilation inlet Use alternative means of cooling (air cooling or air blast chillers)	Should be easily and safely accessible for inspection, cleaning and maintenance	Should be operated, cleaned and maintained according to written procedures based on published guidance Use softened water to avoid scale
1	Pond	Accumulated debris Corrosion Growth (slime) on surfaces Growth at water surface Growth of algae Foam on surface Scale	Low level drain access for cleaning Smooth uninterrupted surface Exclude light Choice of correct materials[b]	Slope to drain Good quality coating with approved material[a]	Bleed to drain Clean twice yearly Extra draining and cleaning as required
2	Distribution pipework	Growth (slime) on surfaces Corrosion Stagnation Scale	Lowest level drain point Access for cleaning Choice of correct materials[b] Correct size for good waterflow Simple runs Few bends Elimination of deadlegs	Avoid running through high temperature areas, e.g. boiler rooms Insulation against heat gain Label all pipework for easy identification	Drain completely Clean with bio-dispersant Alternate use of bypass lines and parallel pipework

		Microbial growth, fouling	Removable for cleaning	Allow room for removal	Remove and clean frequently
3	Strainer				
4, 11 12,18	Valves	Site of micro-biological colonization	Choice of correct materials[b]	Label all valves for easy identification	Alternate use of parallel valves Dismantle and clean regularly
5,6	Three-way valve, by-pass valve	Tower valved off from pipework to save energy	Label valve		Open valve when chemical treatment is added and keep open to allow circulation
7	Circulating pump	Site of micro-biological colonization	Choice of pump with approved materials[b] Easy to strip and clean	Position for easy maintenance and cleaning	Alternate use of paired pumps daily Regular checks for satisfactory operation
8	Control detector	Fouling with organic and inorganic material	Position where control valves will be most easily removabe for cleaning	Position for easy access	Maintain regularly in accordance with manufacturer's instructions
10	Condenser	Fouling with organic and inorganic material Site of micro-biological colonization	Easily dismantled for cleaning Fine tubing accessible for brush cleaning	Position for easy access and removal	Regular cleaning
13	Chemical storage	Hazards from chemicals Access for heavy drums Automatic eqipment not properly supervised and maintained	Adequate space Security for chemicals Cleaning facilities for spillages Eye-wash facilities for accidents	Hazard labelling Instructions for use On-site logbook	Training for staff including building manager's staff Instructions on site Operational details Supervision by building manager's staff

No.[a]	Description	Typical problems	Design	Installation	Operation
14	Chemical treatment pump(s)	Failure to operate due to blockage; Electrical or mechanical breakdown	Easy to dismantle and clean; Materials suitable for remote siting and long-term use with chemicals	Accessible for servicing and cleaning	Training for staff including building manager's staff; On-site operational details; Supervision by building manager's staff
15	Pond frost protection heater	Prevents proper cleaning of pond; Elevates water temperature above 20°C if thermostat malfunctions	Easily removable for pond cleaning; High temperature (18°C) cut-off	Position for easy removal	Do not run continuously
16	Sprays	Site of micro-biological colonization; Nozzles become blocked	Use approved materials[b]; Use trough and gutter as alternative		Clean regularly; Descale
17	Pack (or fill)	Site of micro-biological colonization; Fouling with inorganic material (scale); Accumulation of debris from air (leaves, insects etc.)	Easily accessible for cleaning; Small units for easy handling; Robust for frequent handling; Use approved materials[b]	Position access panels for safe, easy use	Clean regularly; Replace as necessary; Do not clean with high pressure sprays[c]
19	Ball valve	Supply water must be good quality	Use approved materials[b]	Position for easy access	Clean regularly
21	Overflow	Blockage with organic material	Easy access for cleaning	Provide drainage	Inspect regularly
22	Manual drain	Reset in error; Inadequate size; Inadequate drain capacity	Use lockable valve; Size pipework and drain to allow complete drainage in in under 15 min	Position for ease of access	Operate according to written procedures

	Component	Hazard / problem	Design requirement	Position	Maintenance
23	Automatic drain	Failure to operate Inadequate size Inadequate drain capacity	Minimize blockage	Position for easy access	Inspect regularly Record water use
24	Conductivity cell	Easily fouled Requires frequent recalibration	Easily removable for frequent maintenance Robust for frequent handling and cleaning	Position for easy access	Supervise closely Clean frequently Recalibrate regularly
25	Sampling points	Inappropriate siting	Easy to decontaminate for high quality microbiological analysis of samples	Position for easy access Site for representative samples	Sample for general microbiological quality routinely
26	Louvres	Fouled by leaves, insects, large debris, rubbish algae and scale	Use approved materials Removable for cleaning Enclosed ponds with forced draught	Position for easy access	Inspect and clean regularly
27	Fan	Accumulation of grease and dirt	Use maintenance-free fan forced draught	Position for easy access	Inspect and clean regularly
28	Drift eliminators	Site of microbiological colonization Site of algae growth Inefficient operation	Use approved materials Removable for cleaning Close fitting High efficiency	Position for easy access Fit correctly into tight housing	Inspect and clean regularly Replace when broken or badly fouled

a Number in Figure C3.1.
b Approved materials as specified in the *Water Fittings and Materials Directory* (published twice every year).
c If high pressure sprays are used, respiratory protective equipment of suitable design for airborne micro-organisms is required (Health and Safety Executive, 1987).

Table C3.2 Hot- and cold-water systems

No[a]	Description	Typical problems	Design[c]	Installation	Operation
1	Mains supply	Microbiological growth in pipework	Correct size for demand	Avoid areas in buildings (boiler-room) Insulate against heat gain Separate supply for fire services	
2	Cold-water storage	Microbiological growth Algae growth Debris Corrosion Stagnation Unsatisfactory cover Scale Warming	Correct size for demand Lipped fixed lid Access ports easy to use and hold open Access ports difficult to leave open Correct materials of con-struction[b] of tank lids and internal fittings Opposition of inlet and outlet points Low level drain point Drain size and facility to drain tank in 30 min	Provide easy access for inspection and cleaning Provide adequate lighting for inspection Insulate against heat gain Ventilate warm tank rooms	Inspect and clean regulary Exclude light from stored water Ensure access port covers in place Keep cool Monitor temperature Monitor winter use
3	Ball valve	Site of micro-biological colonization	Use approved materials	Position for easy access	Clean regularly
4	System pipework	Stagnation Water between 20-50°C Corrosion due to use of mixed metals	Avoid deadlegs Avoid proximity of hot and cold pipework Avoid mixed metals	Insulate hot and cold pipework	Monitor temperatures regularly

5	Hot-water cylinder (calorifier)	Accumulation of debris Site of microbiological colonization Accumulation of limescale Temperature stratification	Provide low level drain point of adequate size to purge debris Access panel for cleaning Return hot water to bottom circulation pump in cylinder Fit temperature sensor to drain point Insulate against heat loss	Provide easy access for flushing though low level drain point Drain size and facility to drain cylinder in 15 min	Purge bottom frequently (weekly) Inspect and clean annually
6	Pump	Site of microbiological colonization	Choice of pump with approved material[b] Easy to strip and clean Avoid paired pumps	Position for easy maintenance and cleaning	Store spare pump for quick installation
7	Blender (thermostatic mixing valve)	Keeps water temperature between 20 and 50°C	Avoid except in carefully supervised installations Use correct materials Fit close to outlet		The use of blenders makes the maintenance of good microbiological water quality very difficult
8	Tap outlet	Site of microbiological colonization	Use correct materials[b]	Outlets which will be infrequently used should be valved from the main	Drain pipework to outlets which are infrequently used Disconnect at feed pipe
9	Shower hose	Site of microbiological growth Water between 20 and 50°C stands between uses	Avoid flexible hoses Use approved materials[b] Drain hose between users	Provide water down from main to showerhead with control valve directly off main pipework	Drain when not in use

No[a]	Description	Typical problems	Design[c]	Installation	Operation
10	Showerhead	Lime scaling Site of micro-biological colonization	Use approved materials[b] Easy to remove for cleaning and descaling	Fit directly below control valve	Clean and descale regulary
–	Mixer tap	Keeps water temperature between 20 and 50°C	Avoid Use correct materials[b] Drain downstream between uses		
–	Spa bath (Jacuzzi)	Recirculated water between 20 and 50°C Becomes fouled with organic material	Use correct materials[b] Easy to dismantle and remove strainer	Access for easy cleaning Access to strainer	Maintain a free residual level of 1ppm Replenish water at least daily Remove strainer and clean daily Follow manufacturer's instructions Do not overload

a Number in Figure C3.2
b Approved materials as specified in the *Water fittings and Materials Directory* (published twice every year).
c Comply with local byelaws.

Figure C3.1 Evaporative cooling tower:

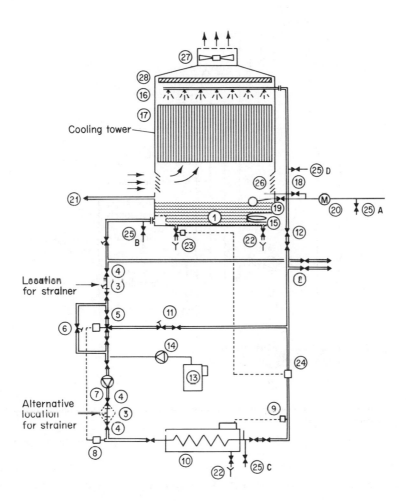

1, pond; 2, distribution pipework; 3, strainer; 4, valves; 5, three-way valve; 6, bypass valve; 7, circulating pump; 8, control detector; 9, flow monitor; 10, condenser; 11, regulating valve; 12, non-return valve; 13, chemical storage; 14, chemical treatment pump; 15, frost protection heater; 16, sprays; 17, pack; 18, quick-fill valve; 19, ball valve; 20, water meter; 21, overflow; 22, manual drain; 23, automatic drain; 24, conductivity cell; 25, sampling points (A-D); 26, louvres; 27, fan; 28, eliminators.

Redrawn with the kind permission of the Department of Health and the Welsh Office from The Control of Legionellae in Health Care Premises.

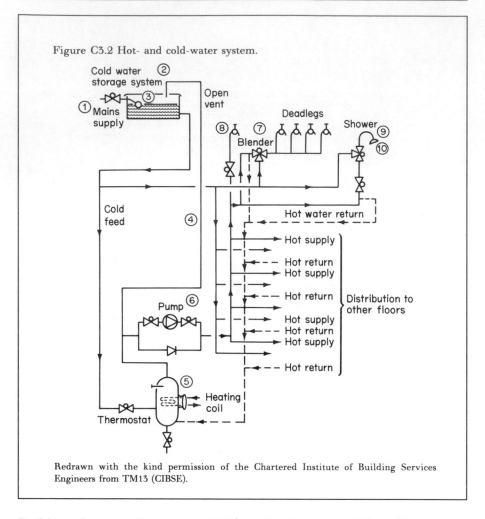

Figure C3.2 Hot- and cold-water system.

Redrawn with the kind permission of the Chartered Institute of Building Services Engineers from TM13 (CIBSE).

Building Services Engineers, 1989) and private specialists (Rosehaugh Project Services, 1989). These guidance notes all offer advice on:

- the maintenance of water temperatures either below 20°C or above 60°C in stored water and 50°C at outlets;
- the avoidance of intermediate temperatures in stored water in particular;
- the maintenance of good quality in stored water by excluding environmental contaminants;
- the exclusion from water systems of materials of construction which act as food sources;
- the matching of capacity to demand and the simplification of pipework layouts so as to eliminate stagnation and to encourage the highest possible throughput within water systems, ideally with a turnover time of no more than 8 hours.

Evaporative Cooling Systems

Evaporative cooling towers have been implicated as sources of many outbreaks of Legionnaires' Disease. In the UK, these have often arisen when towers which have been idle for months are unexpectedly activated by demand arising from sudden unseasonal warm weather.

Water in evaporative cooling systems recirculates and is continually contaminated with material washed from the air drawn into the cooling tower. This collection of dust, pollen, fungi, bacteria, insects and leaves is added to by a small but constant stream of micro-organisms delivered by the water supply. As water is evaporated from the tower, the salts and organic materials are left behind in the circulating water where they accumulate. This build-up of solids and microbiological foodstuffs can only be properly controlled by starting with good quality supply water, preferably softened (in hard water areas) and by bleeding some of the water to the drain and replenishing with good quality make-up water. With high water costs there is a temptation for managers to save money by reducing the bleed or by not using it at all. Not only does this increase the chance of microbiological growth within the system but it also makes any chemical treatment less effective and makes cleaning of the tower and pipework more difficult.

It is essential that the air intake for the ventilation system is remote from the cooling towers to avoid cross-contamination. Consideration can be given to the use of alternative means of cooling such as air coolers or airblast chillers. However, evaporative cooling towers are the most efficient for large systems as they require less roof space than alternative systems and may be considerably quieter. They cost less to install but are more expensive and demanding to maintain and operate safely. In the future new legislation may introduce mandatory requirements for evaporative cooling towers and such requirements may alter the balance of choice between wet and dry cooling systems.

Piped Water Systems

'Cold' Water

In piped water systems design and installation are frequently less than ideal, water storage arrangements are not always protected from contamination and there is frequently over capacity leading to stagnation. In cold-water storage, contamination may accumulate because of microbiological growth within the tank and it may enter the tank from the make-up water and from the air.

Contamination from outside may be dust, pollen, bacteria, fungi, bird droppings, dead birds or rodents and rubbish discarded by builders, engineers, building users or vandals. All this is easily avoided by ensuring that a lipped fitted lid is in place and is securely fixed. Such a lid is normally a requirement of the local byelaws and is specified in British Standard 6700 (1987). The lid will also inhibit the growth of algae and other organisms which require light.

The rate of microbiological growth is partly dependent on temperature. Whilst different organisms prefer different temperatures, very few will grow rapidly below 20°C. Large cold-water storage tanks must be insulated against heating from the buildings within which they are housed. Smaller domestic tanks of less than 500 litres capacity need not be insulated underneath as there is a rapid turnover of water. If tanks are sited inside or adjacent to boiler rooms or within roof spaces they will require particular attention. Cold-water mains services should not be run through hot building areas such as boiler rooms since heat pick-up from such arrangements can be enough to create and maintain a high stored water temperature. Indeed microbiological growth may be promoted within the main supply pipe itself. As with all parts of water systems, the water storage tanks and their lids must be constructed of approved materials that will not support microbiological growth themselves. It should be stressed that this includes the material of the lid which may become wet through splashes or condensation. A list of approved materials is published by the Water Byelaws Advisory Service (Water Fittings and Materials Directory, 1989).

By maintaining cold-water storage below 20°C microbiological growth can be slowed. If control of the stored water temperature is linked to a high turnover of water within the system there will be little opportunity for micro-organisms to accumulate.

'Hot' Water

In hot-water cylinders the main problem is accumulation of debris at the bottom of the cylinder (Figure C3.3). If this happens microbiological growth may be encouraged by favourable water temperatures in the cooler area below the heating element or coil. This temperature stratification, which makes it difficult to achieve a high temperature throughout the cylinder, may be overcome by regular flushing through a low level drain point, circulating the water in the cylinder and feeding the return hot water into the bottom of the cylinder.

Ventilation Systems

Ventilation systems merit attention not only because they may distribute bacteria disseminated by a cooling tower but also because they may incorporate sources of bacteria themselves. Water arises in ventilation system design in two direct ways, both by means of humidification, and in an indirect way because condensation may collect on cold surfaces (see Table C3.3).

In a typical ventilation system the air is cooled by chiller batteries. If the air contains moisture this will condense onto the chiller surface and will be collected into a driptray. These driptrays must be efficiently drained. Water standing in driptrays will stagnate and material in the water (including bacteria) may be stripped from the water surface as droplets if there is a large air movement over the surface. A further problem is said to have occurred where poor drainage arrangements permitted bleed water from a cooling tower to run from the soil stack, along the driptray drain line and into the driptray, thus feeding the driptray with Legionellae bacteria. It is therefore necessary to put an air gap into the driptray drain where it enters the soil stack. It should be stressed that the volumes of water involved in driptrays are usually too small and the temperatures too low to be suitable for substantial colonization.

The item of most concern in ventilation systems is the spray pond or air wash. Whilst these have not been implicated as sources of Legionnaires' Disease, they are frequently mismanaged and may be potent sources of both microbiological and chemical pollutants in indoor air.

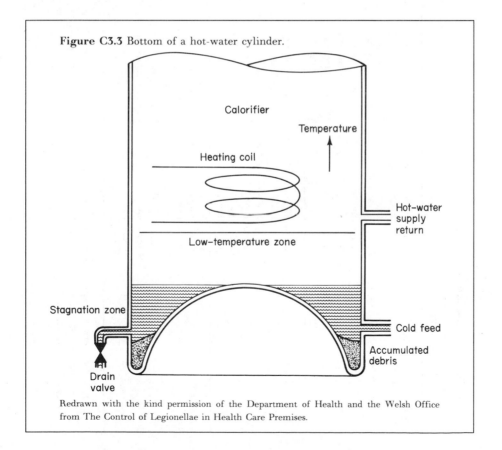

Figure C3.3 Bottom of a hot-water cylinder.

Redrawn with the kind permission of the Department of Health and the Welsh Office from The Control of Legionellae in Health Care Premises.

Table C3.3 Ventilation systems

Description	Typical problems	Design	Installation	Operation
Spray pond (air washer)	Accumulation of debris Site of microbiological colonization Corrosion Stagnation Warming	Avoid Use steam humidification Feed direct from mains supply Use approved materials Flush surfaces for easy cleaning Provide lighting for inspection	Provide easy access for frequent inspection and cleaning	Clean frequently Never add chemical treatment to water Run directly from main
Chiller driptray	Accumulation of debris and limescale Site of microbiological colonization[1] Corrosion Stagnation	Fit adequate drain Slope floor to drain Use approved materials of construction[2]	Air gap between drain and soil pipe Provide access for inspection	Inspect regularly, drain and clean
Humidifier	Accumulation of debris and limescale Site of microbiological colonization[1] Corrosion Stagnation Warming	Minimal reservoir size Fit adequate drain Slope floor to drain Use approved materials of construction[2]	Provide access for inspection	Inspect regularly, drain and clean every 2 months Do not add chemicals

[1] Approved materials as specified in the *Water Fittings and Materials Directory* (published twice every year).
[2] Never reported as source of Legionellae bacteria. They may harbour micro-organisms responsible for humidifier fever and other allergic reactions.

Spray ponds or air washes comprise a chamber in which the water is sprayed into the air from a reservoir at the bottom to humidify it. Large volumes of water are involved and there is recirculation unless the spray is fed directly from the mains and the excess water is drained away. Management of spray ponds is difficult because the reservoir inevitably accumulates material washed from the air. Since the water is sprayed directly into the air supply for the building, any bacteria will be efficiently disseminated to a 'captive audience'. Furthermore, the addition of any chemical treatment to the water will inevitably lead to the chemical being sprayed into the air supply and thus distributed into the building. The alternative approach to humidification for this application is steam humidification which should be used whenever humidification is required within ventilation systems.

Free-standing humidifiers such as spinning disc humidifiers and other small wall-mounted or free-standing humidifiers are not known to have been sources of Legionella infections in the UK, although in Australia Legionellae have reportedly been disseminated by ultrasonic humidifiers. This seems surprising since they often spray water from a stagnant reservoir. However, the water volume is small and the temperature usually low. Nonetheless care must be taken to select devices that are made of approved materials and that are readily drained and cleaned.

Microbiological growth in humidifier water can cause allergic reactions in people exposed to airborne sprays or dusts arising from bacterial cells or their byproducts. This illness is termed humidifier fever. It is an allergic illness and must not be confused with Legionnaires' Disease, which is an infection.

Decorative Water Features

Concern has been expressed about decorative water features such as fountains in shopping centres and atria. These have never been associated with Legionella infections. The water temperature is normally well below 20°C which will serve to inhibit colonization.

Nevertheless, under prudent management the features would be drained regularly and scrupulously cleaned. The addition of chemicals to decorative water features presents problems of unacceptable chemical odours and of exposing building users to chemical pollution in the air.

Spa Baths

Spa baths or jacuzzis have been identified as sources of Legionella infection in the past. They recirculate warm water and may accumulate a heavy organic load. Their use must be very carefully managed and they must be drained and cleaned daily, a procedure which demands careful supervision if it is to be consistently maintained. It is particularly important that the strainer is removed and cleaned on every occasion. In any event a free residual chlorine level of 1 ppm (part per million) should be maintained in the water at all times.

Water Softeners

Water softeners may become colonized if they are not operated in accordance with the manufacturer's recommendations. They must be backflushed (purged) once every 24 hours and disinfected once every six months.

Managing Water Systems

Avoidance of Stagnation

Water stagnation, which must be avoided in all water systems because it allows micro-organisms the opportunity to become established and to grow even where conditions are not ideal, can occur in several ways. In whole systems it occurs where there is low throughput or turnover of water because of small demand or because the storage capacity exceeds the demand by many days' capacity of water. Turnover should be at least once every 8 hours or normal washing day. The maximum residence time should be 24 hours. Stagnation will also occur locally where there are deadlegs or little-used outlets. BS 6700 recommends that outlets used less than once in 60 days should be disconnected from the system at the branch. In storage tanks stagnation may occur where inlet and outlet are not diagonally opposed (Figure C3.4). It may also occur in shower hoses and pipework to shower heads, behind washers in valves, within pumps, in oversized pipework and at the bottom of vessels which have no drainage facility. The calorifier shown in Figure C3.3 illustrates a typical incorrect solution.

The water demand of a system may be roughly estimated by calculating a maximum daily usage for each outlet and summing the results. For guidance in assessing water consumption:

- it may be assumed that each male staff member will flush a lavatory once per day and each female staff member three times per day;
- water used by urinal systems must be counted daily;
- each staff member uses 2 litres in each of three hand-washings per day;
- 25 litres of water are consumed on each occasion a shower is used;
- each use of a bath will consume an average of 250 litres;
- drinking water should not be counted if it is taken directly from the mains supply;

Figure C3.4

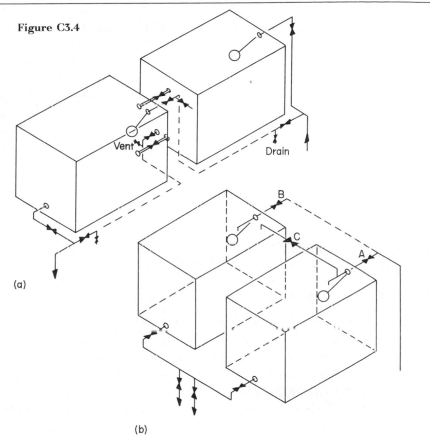

Vent

Drain

(a)

(b)

B

C

A

(a) Series connections of cisterns. The drains and vents allow drainage of pipe sections when they are not in use.

(b) Parallel connection to cisterns. Under normal operation the ball valve A is open and supplies both tanks. The ball valve B and valve C are only used for servicing.

Redrawn with the kind permission of the Department of Health and the Welsh Office from The Control of Legionellae in Health Care Premises.

- the water usage of a kitchen, dishwashers and washing machines can be considerable and will need to be estimated by the building manager on site.

The capacity of the cold-water storage and of the hot-water cylinders should be adjusted to the maximum calculated daily demand so that the equivalent throughput of only one day's supply of water is kept in the building.

Weekend Shutdowns

When managing water systems, care should be taken to avoid creating poor conditions during weekend or shutdown periods. Hot-water temperatures should be maintained at weekends. Where there is draw-off by weekend workers (now a common feature in many offices) the hot water will have to be replenished. In the past many buildings have been operated on a system of running the weekend on the hot water remaining within the calorifiers and reheating early on Monday morning. This leads to water temperatures that are ideal for rapid microbiological growth for many hours. Where water systems are unused for many days they should be drained and left empty or at least drained and refilled before being used again. This is a point of particular concern in buildings such as schools, colleges and halls of residence.

CLEANING

Design for ease of cleaning

All water systems must be designed so that they are easily cleaned and maintained. Primarily they must be accessible for all necessary procedures without risk to the operators and engineers. If they are on roof-tops, safe access must be provided together with protection against falling. Where building water systems have an inherent tendency to poor water quality which cannot be addressed by improved design, building managers and others responsible for microbiological water quality must apply treatments to the water to control and suppress microbiological growth. Typically these treatments can be divided into two classes: first the addition of chemicals to kill micro-organisms and inhibit their growth, and second the use of physical means to kill micro-organisms within the water or to remove them from the water.

Water Treatment Chemicals

The use of chemicals is both expensive and time consuming. All chemical treatments depend on regular cleaning and proper maintenance of the system since no chemicals will work effectively in a dirty system. In addition there are drawbacks because chemicals used for the suppression of micro-organisms are likely to be harmful, irritant or corrosive to operatives. Furthermore, with recent strengthening of Health and Safety at Work legislation (1974), the handling and storage of chemicals which are hazardous to health is subject to additional statutory legislation (Control of Substances Hazardous to Health Regulations, 1988). There is a further drawback to the use of chemicals in that they will inevitably be dispersed into the environment.

If cooling tower systems are treated, the correct dose of chemicals can only be calculated if the total water capacity of the system is known (Department of Health, 1989). This should be marked on the tower.

Routine use of chemicals in water distribution systems is not recommended. It is not possible to flush these systems of the chemicals thoroughly, an important point since the water may be used for drinking.

Physical Treatments

The use of physical filtration to remove micro-organisms from the water is of limited overall value because to apply high resolution filtration requires filters of large surface area associated with large pressures to move the water through the filters. Irradiation of water with ultraviolet light is another physical approach. This is effective in ideal conditions (at least 80% transmittance) but if the water is in any way turbid or if there is particulate material in it then shadowing will occur and adequate doses to the bacteria will not be achieved. These methods are also limited to organisms suspended in the water and give no residual benefit.

Pasteurization

A major physical treatment of hot water systems to control micro-biological quality is to heat the water to pasteurize it. This approach has long been recognized. Certainly Legionellae bacteria are rapidly killed at temperatures exceeding 65°C. Indeed they are killed at temperatures exceeding 55°C, but the time required for adequate killing may extend to hours at this temperature. Pasteurization has presented practical difficulties because to be effective the pasteurization temperature must be achieved for the requisite time in all parts of the system simultaneously. In addition to these problems there is the difficulty of maintaining the requisite temperature throughout the whole of the cylinder because of temperature stratification.

Attempts have been made to achieve pasteurization of water by diverting circulating water through a treatment chamber in which it can be raised to pasteurization temperature and held there for an appropriate time. Whilst this system offers improvements over merely running water at an elevated temperature through the system it still suffers from one major drawback: *L. pneumophila* grow on surfaces under the water, inside pipes, behind washers, on gaskets etc., and they grow in association with other micro-organisms in biofilms or slimes. In order for any pasteurization approach to be completely effective it must act upon the organisms and in particular the Legionellae bacteria where they are growing *in situ*.

Thermal disinfection

A comprehensive approach to pasteurization is thermal disinfection. This involves heating all the pipework by means of electrical trace heating to the pasteurization temperature and maintaining it at that temperature whilst water within the pipework is similarly heated and held at the pasteurization temperature for the requisite time. This system allows complete and effective disinfection of all pipework and water storage vessels which are normally charged with water. For total system control it has to be supplemented with a treatment programme for the outlets, in particular shower hoses and heads, whereby they are routinely disconnected, descaled and disinfected with a hypochlorite solution. This system offers the bonus of a permanent record which is readily available from the controlling thermocouples.

WATER SAMPLING

Water samples can be analysed to determine the microbiological and chemical quality of the water and the presence of specific micro-organisms including Legionellae bacteria. The interpretation of water sample analysis results requires specialist knowledge and detailed information about the sample size, type, analysis and the time of sampling and position of the sample location. In addition to water samples, slime, debris and other material from the water system can be analysed. Much of the information which can be obtained will be of little direct use to the building manager and, indeed, some of it may be misleading. Reassurance about microbiological water quality can be readily obtained by analysing samples representative of the water in the system for the presence of organisms growing at 22 and 37°C. There is a standardized test for this for drinking water (The Bacteriological Examination of Drinking Water Supplies, 1982) which may be adapted for other water systems. By utilizing this procedure the general microbiological quality can be quickly and inexpensively determined. This information must be interpreted in the light of a visual examination of the system in question and of the maintenance and operational procedures employed on the system.

Analysis of water samples for the presence of Legionellae is not generally recommended. Laboratory culture of Legionellae is difficult, expensive and lengthy (typically 14 days). The results are difficult to interpret in terms of hazard to human health but are often the source of considerable unwarranted concern and anxiety.

If the general microbiological quality of the water is good (close to the drinking water standard) then the system is clear currently of features which encourage microbiological growth. It must be remembered that water systems are dynamic and conditions may change rapidly if the management is not comprehensive.

Once the general microbiological quality has been assessed, a routine check can be made using dip slides. It is stressed that these must be used according to a strict sampling protocol and that they can only be relied upon to indicate that conditions are stable. Any change in dip-slide results should indicate the necessity for further investigation.

RECORD KEEPING

One final element of complete Legionella control lies with the need for a proper management and record keeping system. Comprehensive written operating procedures and system diagrams are essential together with on-site log books for all water systems, proper record maintenance, and the identification of a responsible person to whom all decisions are ultimately referred and to whose attention all sampling results and operational information are drawn. All aspects of the operation and management should be subject to regular independent audit.

CONCLUSIONS

* Legionnaires' Disease can be avoided by managing building water systems so that Legionellae bacteria do not have the chance to colonize them.

* Owners and managers of buildings can and should ensure good microbiological water quality by using maintenance and cleaning procedures given in existing guidelines.

* Designers and installers are responsible for specifying and creating systems which are not inherently likely to permit and encourage microbiological colonization and growth, and which are easy to maintain, and which can be readily and properly cleaned.

REFERENCES

The Bacteriological Examination of Drinking Water Supplies 1982, HM Stationery Office, London.

British Standard 6700: Specification for Design, Installation, Testing and Maintenance of Services Supplying Water for Domestic Use within Buildings and their Curtilages (1987), British Standards Institution, London.

Chartered Institute of Building Services Engineers (1987), Minimising the Risk of Legionnaires' Disease, Technical Memorandum 13.

Control of Substances Hazardous to Health Regulations (1988), HM Stationery Office, London.

Department of Health (1989), *Report of the Expert Advisory Committee on Biocides*, HM Stationery Office, London.

Department of Health and Social Security and the Welsh Office (1988), *The Control of Legionellae in Health Care Premises*, A Code of Practice, HM Stationery Office, London.

Health and Safety Executive (1987), *Legionnaires' Disease*, Environmental Hygiene Series, Guideline Note EH 48, HM Stationery Office, London.

Health and Safety at Work etc. Act (1974), HM Stationery Office, London.

Rosehaugh Project Services plc (1989) *Guidance for Designers, Installers, Maintainers and Managers of Building Water Systems with respect to Legionnaires' Disease.*

Water Fittings and Materials Directory 1989, Water Byelaws Advisory Service, 660 Ajax Avenue, Slough, Berkshire SLI 4B9.

The author gratefully acknowledges the helpful comments of Dr J. McEvoy.

APPENDIX:

SIX CASE STUDIES ON LEGIONNAIRES' DISEASE

INTRODUCTION

The case studies presented below illustrate the inter-relationship of features of design, construction, operation, management and maintenance of buildings and building water systems whereby hazardous situations may arise. Points of principle are identified for all concerned with the preservation of human health within and around buildings. The essential features of water quality management can be summarized as follows. There must be:

- a written policy setting out the building manager's approach to water quality management;
- an appointed manager with responsibility for all matters related to water quality;
- written operational procedures;
- an on-site record of all operational and maintenance activities;
- an independent audit of the building water systems and their management.

CASE 1

Background

The building was a four-star hotel which had undergone several building refurbishments during its history together with additions to allow for expansion. The management was new to the building and had inherited both the building services engineer and the resident fitter. The survey was concerned with a general audit of water quality management so that the new management team could gain reassurance or advice about the avoidance of risk of Legionnaires' Disease for residents and staff.

Site Survey

Information Available No comprehensive drawings or plans existed on site, despite recent building works. The management were largely unaware of the water services that existed. The resident fitter claimed a thorough knowledge, but his memory was less than complete and a full picture only emerged after systematic questioning.

Visual Audit The incoming cold main was traced to pumps which boosted the entire service to an attic tank room. The room was cramped with two large tanks which were connected in parallel and which were accessible only by negotiating several banks of parallel pipework. The tanks were unlidded, the water surface was dusty but the water was clear, the internal tank surfaces were corroded, and the bottom of the tank was covered in debris including a tin of pipe sealant and a pair of shoes which were splattered with paint. There was no separate drinking water supply. The hot water was supplied from calorifiers sited in the basement. These presented no particular cause for comment.

Sample Analysis and Temperature Measurements No water samples were taken because the visual examination would not have been added to by the analytical results. Water temperatures were taken at the outlets nearest and farthest from the bulk water storage for both the hot- and cold-water services. Cold-water temperatures ranged from 18°C post-flush to 24°C pre-flush. Hot-water temperatures ranged from 48°C post-flush close to the calorifiers through to 40°C post-flush far from the calorifiers to 30°C pre-flush far from the calorifiers.

Discussion

Several undesirable features emerged during the survey:

- the management did not know what it was managing;
- the cold-water storage tanks were unlidded: rubbish and debris could fall into the stored water;
- the tanks had not been cleaned for a long time;
- the cold-water storage tanks were connected in parallel with the inlet and outlet at the same end of one tank. Water in the other tank was completely stagnant;
- the water temperature measurements suggested that the hot and cold pipework was uninsulated and that the water in the pipe was either warming or cooling into the 20–50°C range which is suitable for microbiological growth;
- the hot water was being supplied at a temperature below 50°C so that the water stored in the calorifiers was always at a temperature at which microbiological growth could occur.

Recommendations

- The management was advised to commission a full set of water system drawings which should be kept on site. This would allow the opportunity to review all aspects of the water systems at the current time.
- The tanks should be drained, cleaned, repaired, repainted with a microbiologically inert paint, chlorinated and filled with fresh water.
- The cold-water storage tanks should be covered with fitted and lipped lids which should be of a microbiologically inert material and fixed in place.
- The 'stagnant' tank should be either taken out of service by disconnecting the pipework or it should be re-piped so that water flowed through the two tanks connected in series.
- The pipework should be insulated against heat loss and gain and hot- and cold-pipe services should not be run close together.
- The hot-water storage temperature should be raised to at least 55°C and preferably 60°C.

Points of Importance

* Managers cannot be complying with legally enforceable responsibilities concerning building water services if they are unaware of the details of those services.

* Elementary points such as unlidded tanks, incorrectly connected tanks, foul stored water and poor hot-water storage temperatures indicate a very low standard of management.

* Where there are many remedial actions required, they should be prioritized and staggered. In this case the actions comprised the raising of the hot-water temperature in the calorifiers (remember to warn staff and guests of the changes), reminding everyone not to drink the water, disconnecting the stagnant tank, draining and cleaning the stagnant tank and then using the stagnant tank whilst the active tank is treated.

* Where there is an undesirable but stable situation the temptation to 'stir things up' by adding chemicals should be avoided. Such action may release micro-organisms from the debris and biofilms (slimes on surfaces) and may precipitate a hazardous situation. Always drain and clear before adding chemicals.

CASE 2

Background

The building was a Victorian hospital which was used to house a ward for old people and accommodated both acute cases and long-stay patients. The management was aware of Department of Health Guidance but was concerned about the vulnerability of the patients to scalding. The survey was intended to allow advice to be given on Legionella risks associated with the shower and bath system.

Site Survey

Information Available Drawings and operational details were available on site. The hot-water system was shown to comprise two large calorifiers linked in parallel supplying hot water to a blender unit. The unit was also fed with cold water from two large Braithwaite tanks in a room above the joint boiler and calorifier room. The blended water was pumped around a ring and supplied water to showers and baths in a large bathroom facility which serviced the one remaining ward in the building.

Visual Audit The site drawings were found to be accurate. The shower units on the ring main were infrequently used. This was clear from the presence of rust running in the water when the units were turned on for temperature-measurement purposes. The calorifiers were maintained at 60°C. The cold-water storage tanks were properly lidded but were uninsulated.

Sample Analysis and Temperature Measurements No water samples were taken for analysis because immediate modification of the services would be required in any event. Water temperatures at the bottom drain points of the calorifiers were 30°C. From the bottom drain of the cold-water tanks temperatures of 22°C were measured. The single mixed supply from the ring main was measured to be between 33 and 45°C, and the temperature rose to a constant as the tap was run for some time.

Discussion

The arrangement of this hot-water system was prohibited in the Department of Health Guidance and was unacceptable because:

- the water in the ring main was deliberately maintained at a temperature which is within the optimum temperature range for the growth of Legionellae;
- unused branches to showers were full of stagnant water which, as it was connected to the system, was feeding micro-organisms into that system;
- the hot-water storage was too large for the current limited demand;
- the cold-water storage was too large and was heated by hot air rising from the boiler rooms;
- rust from corroding pipework was providing iron salts to the Legionellae and hence was encouraging their growth.

Recommendations

The managers of the building were advised that the system must be taken out of use and modified before the vulnerable population was subjected to any further potential Legionella exposure. In particular, the following recommendations were made:

- the ring main should be used for hot water only;

- the number of outlets should be reduced to a minimum, and the remainder should be disconnected at the point that they branched from the main;
- separate cold services should be run to the outlets remaining in use;
- as an interim measure cold water from a mobile tanker should be heated electrically by temporary services, thus ensuring the maintenance of patient care;
- the hot- and cold-water storage should be reduced to a capacity which would match the daily demand;
- all services, including storage tanks and calorifiers, which were to remain in use should be drained, cleaned, chlorinated and flushed with fresh water before being returned to use;
- once the calorifier was reinstated it should be regularly drained by the bottom drain point until the water drawing out reached the calorifier temperature. In this way cold water and debris would be regularly purged.

Points of Importance

* The specific advice of the Department of Health and the Health and Safety Executive cannot be ignored where it is applicable.
* Where the use of a building changes, the demand on the services may change. Reduced demand on water systems may introduce stagnation. Old systems may be designed with an over-capacity built in.
* Where the users of water systems are vulnerable to scalding, thermostatically controlled or preset mixer taps will allow finer control of water temperatures. The hot-water and cold-water services must only come together at the point of outlet. Alternatively, point-of-use water heaters may be utilized.

CASE 3

Background

The building was a residential tower block within a training establishment. The management was concerned that a trainee arriving ahead of his fellows following a long annual holiday shutdown had developed Legionnaires' Disease. The survey was conducted to investigate the possibility that the building water system was responsible for the illness and also to identify the actions necessary to prevent any possible recurrence of the health hazard.

Site Survey

Information Available Details of the building water services were available together with rough details of the floor used by the trainee in question. Each floor was served by a communal shower unit with some six cubicles. The trainee was male and the facilities on his floor (where he was the only resident at the time) were served in common with those on the floors above and below, which were designated for men. As he had gone to Germany following discharge from hospital there was no means of identifying which shower facility, let alone which outlet, he had used.

Visual Audit The calorifiers were mounted in the attic and were of an appropriate size. They had been left dormant over the holiday period and had been reheated once the building was reoccupied. There was no drain in the floor of the calorifier room. The drains from the bottom of the calorifiers were in half-inch pipework and the calorifiers held 2,000 gallons each.

Sample Analysis and Temperature Measurement Water samples were taken from the calorifiers, from the shower heads and pipes, and from the cold water make-up tank. The samples were analysed for the presence of culturable Legionellae. No Legionellae were recovered, but the general microbiological quality of the water samples was 1,000 times poorer than that permissible for drinking water. Water temperatures at the bottom of the calorifiers were measured to be 35°C.

Discussion

The water in the hot-water system in this building had been allowed to stagnate over the shutdown period and had not been drained and replaced before the building was reoccupied. Good management practice had been made effectively impossible by the absence of a drain from the calorifier room and by the restricted drainage available from the calorifiers.

Recommendations

- As an immediate step, chlorinate the pipework and outlets before re-use of the system. Remove, descale and chlorinate the shower heads properly.
- Install a permanent drain into the calorifier room. The drain should be of adequate size to allow the calorifiers to be drained in 30 minutes.
- Fit large drain-off pipes to each calorifier at the lower point so that the calorifiers can be drained in 30 minutes and the flow will be sufficient to purge the bottom of debris.
- Drain, open, inspect and clean each calorifier. Refill and heat to 70°C throughout to pasteurize the calorifiers.
- Introduce regular systems for inspection of calorifiers and descaling and chlorination of the shower heads.

Points of Importance

* Always drain water systems that are left standing when the building is unoccupied for more than a week. Drain the systems and refill before use after any period of stagnation.
* Ensure that the design of the system allows for proper management.

CASE 4

Background

The buildings were sites operated by a nationwide service industry. Each site comprised evaporative cooling towers serving computer equipment. The management were concerned to know how company maintenance procedures were being applied at the various sites across the country. The survey involved visiting a representative number of sites and observing cleaning and maintenance operations in practice. At the same time a spot water quality audit was conducted to provide an indication of the effectiveness of the existing procedures.

Site Survey

Information Available There was little on-site information about equipment, procedures or past maintenance performance. Some sites were served by in-house staff and others by outside contractors. All operatives filled in worksheets which were deposited at regional offices where they were filed by the regional engineering managers. Some cooling towers were marked with chalk or spirit pen notes which had been made during previous maintenance operations. These were not dated. The operatives were all familiar with the maintenance and cleaning procedure details in the maintenance operation manual.

Visual Audit A variety of types of cooling towers, plant rooms and methods of cleaning was revealed. The cooling towers differed in the access they permitted for cleaning. Some dismantled readily whilst others were poorly constructed with rusty catchments on access ports, making regular use impossible. Some of the cooling towers were installed so that they could not be dismantled because of lack of space or access. The plant rooms were all of similar design but the size and conditions differed. On some sites they were used as material stores, making access to the plant difficult, and all were poorly lit and had bare brick walls which were generally very grimy.

The procedures adopted by the operatives were all based on the company procedures but differed in detail. Some operatives chose to alter the amount or frequency of chemical dosing. Others chose to extend the period between cleaning operations. The manner of dosing and cleaning also differed from site to site. On some sites the computers were kept running without interruption during cleaning by isolation of first one tower and then the other.

Sample Analysis The water samples collected from the cooling towers and make-up water tanks revealed the presence of culturable detectable Legionellae in 10% of the sites, mostly in the samples from the cooling towers.

Discussion

A wide variety of conditions was found in cooling towers operated by the same company and maintained and cleaned according to a common set of detailed written instructions. This was not surprising since there was no coordinating supervision. The regional engineering managers collected the paperwork but rarely visited the sites and never when the cleaning and maintenance was in operation. The operatives were working conscientiously to achieve a satisfactory result, but they had never been told what was satisfactory nor how to recognize when they had done enough. They worked unsupervised and were told only to follow the procedures and keep the cooling capacity running. They received no feedback on their efforts. The poor lighting and dirty conditions within the plant rooms made it unlikely that a good standard of hygiene or cleanliness would be achieved. This is because the standard of the plant tends to reflect its surroundings and the standard of work tends to reflect the conditions in which it is done. The practice of isolating towers from the pipework to clean them and then reconnecting them to dirty pipework full of dirty water revealed an ignorance about the fundamental nature of the tasks being undertaken. These were to clean the whole system to remove Legionellae wherever they may be growing.

A costly manpower resource was being wasted because of lack of management and coordination, lack of training, non-provision of appropriate working conditions for the operatives and poor housing for the equipment. The management were anxious to take immediate action on the basis of the preliminary report. They were also concerned about the positive analysis results from the water samples, and demanded advice on an emergency response to the contaminated cooling towers.

Recommendations

The management were advised that the following far-reaching organizational changes were needed.

Short Term
- Initiate a review of all operational cooling towers by asking regional engineering managers to answer key questions about equipment in their region. The questions were to be about accessibility for cleaning, the proximity of cooling outlets to ventilation intakes and public areas, the colour of pond water, the presence of scum and foam, and the condition of external housings to cooling towers.
- On the basis of the review, prioritize sites for early deep cleaning.
- Devise new deep-clean procedures ensuring that towers and pipework are drained, towers are dismantled and cleaned, and the system is chlorinated before re-use.
- Provide training to all operatives and regional engineering managers in the new procedures.
- Clear all plant rooms of non-essential materials.

Medium Term
- Devise and introduce an on-site record keeping system and a system for frequent supervisory checking by regional engineering managers with signatures in the on-site book.
- Clean and paint plant rooms and upgrade lighting.

Long Term
- Introduce review procedures nationwide by central staff to ensure consistency of standards.
- Operate refresher training for all operatives and regional and central engineering staff.
- Regularly review the procedure and operational standards.

The management was advised not to prioritize those sites where positive sample analysis results had been obtained. Such prioritization would deflect resources for no clear benefit. Action should be prioritized on the basis of a combination of features including, but not led by, water analysis results. All sites, not just those visited in the survey, should be considered for priority action.

Points of Importance

* Cooling towers and their water systems cannot be cleaned if they are inaccessible or if the interiors cannot be reached.
* The conditions of the surroundings tend to be reflected in the quality of the plant and the quality of the work upon it.
* Management supervision is essential in setting up and maintaining appropriate standards.
* Training for all levels of staff is an inescapable part of good water system management.
* Records and information must be kept on site, where they must be available to the operative carrying out the procedure and to the manager overseeing the work and the standard achieved.
* Physical cleaning is the prerequisite to any further water treatment such as chlorination or the addition of other biocides.

CASE 5

Background

The building was part of a modern hospital complex and comprised evaporative cooling towers. These provided cooling for air-conditioning plant in the main hospital and for equipment in an adjacent building. The management wanted reassurance that their water quality management was adequate. The survey was to provide advice on the water quality management as applied to the evaporative cooling towers.

Site Survey

Information Available Drawings and maintenance procedures were available on site. The drawings showed details of the cooling towers and the pipework to the compressors in the main building and, on a separate circuit, the pipework to the adjacent building. The maintenance procedures and log books revealed that the same water treatment package was being applied to both systems with identical quantities of chemicals added to each by means of automatic dosing equipment.

Visual Audit It was confirmed that the capacity of the system serving the adjacent building was 10 times larger than that of the system serving the main building by virtue of the pipework differences.

Discussion

The validity of the water treatment programme was called into question since the chemical dose achieved in one system was 10 times the dose achieved in the other because of the difference in water capacity. Water treatment chemicals operate properly only at the correct dilution which must be maintained by close control. The quality of the service provided by the water treatment company supplying and administering the chemical treatments must be questioned.

Recommendations

The hospital management was advised to carry out an urgent review of the water treatment programme. In particular the following recommendations were made:

- the water treatment company should be asked for documentary evidence of their dosage calculations;
- the means of measuring the delivered dose should be checked and calibrated;
- the water quality standards expected of the water treatment programme should be properly agreed between the management and the water treatment contractor;
- a means of monitoring water quality on a regular (weekly) basis should be introduced;
- the evaporative cooling systems should be drained, cleaned, chlorinated and reinstated, with the larger system being treated as a matter of urgency.

Points of Importance

* Water treatment by chemicals must only be carried out by a reputable and competent water treatment specialist.
* Knowledge of the capacity of the system is essential for the calculation of the correct chemical dose.
* The standard to be achieved by any water management programme must be set and must be measurable by some easily determined parameter.
* The building manager must interpret the information in the maintenance log book.

CASE 6

Background

The building was a commercial office in a city centre. It contained a range of building water systems including cooling towers, hot and cold distribution systems and air washers in the ventilation ductwork. The management relied on a water treatment contractor to manage the water quality in each of the systems. For reassurance they had commissioned regular water sampling and analysis by a reputable public analyst. The survey was to review the management system.

Site Survey

Information Available Records of plant and pipework, maintenance procedures and operational details were available for inspection. Sample analysis results for a wide range of biological and chemical parameters had been kept in chronological order for the previous 30 months. Correspondence relating to action taken following the detection of Legionella cultures was also contained in the files.

Visual Audit A walk around the building confirmed a high standard of maintenance and cleaning. The staff involved were well trained and competent to perform the tasks involved in the operation and maintenance procedures.

Discussion

The technical management of the building was of a standard which did not require general adverse comment. The written procedures were comprehensive and the log books were appropriate and fully kept. There was a wealth of quantitative data produced by the analysis of frequently collected water samples. Action was swiftly taken on Legionella results but no attempt was made to interpret the other data. On several record sheets chemical parameters were highlighted as being outside normally acceptable limits. General microbiological quality was also frequently recorded as being poor, particularly in the air washers.

Recommendations

The management were advised that they were not responding appropriately to all the information which was being generated on their behalf. In order to make the information more accessible to interpretation the following recommendations were made:

- only the parameters requested by the managers should be reported by the analyst;
- the information should be compiled in graphical displays so that trends and variations from the norm would be immediately apparent;
- the advice of an independent specialist in water quality management should be sought whenever there was doubt about appropriate actions.

Points of Importance

✳ Water sample analysis must be directed towards the parameters which are of value to the water quality manager.
✳ Analysis results must be interpreted in the light of other indications of water quality such as plant conditions, operational procedures and management style and strength.
✳ Independent water quality specialists should be commissioned for the interpretation of results indicating that water quality is differing from the established norm.

RADON

Jon C.H. Miles

UK National Radiological Protection Board

INTRODUCTION

Radon-222 is a natural radioactive gas which comes from the radioactive decay of uranium via radium-226. As there are traces of uranium and radium in all soils and rocks, radon is continuously emitted from the ground. It has a radioactive half-life of 3.8 days and so may diffuse through several metres of soil before it decays, and it may move further if there are cracks in the ground or if there is groundwater movement. When it is emitted into open air it is rapidly diluted, but if it enters buildings it can sometimes reach high concentrations. People exposed to high radon concentrations for long periods are at increased risk of developing lung cancer and, because of this, limitations on radon exposures at work have been introduced under the Health and Safety at Work etc. Act 1974, and radon has been recognized as a radioactive substance for the purposes of the Building Regulations 1985 for England and Wales (Department of the Environment, 1988a)

Another isotope of radon, radon-220, is also known as thoron as it comes from the radioactive decay chain of thorium. Thoron has a half-life of 1 minute, and so does not diffuse far from its point of origin before there is significant decay. The radiation doses that people receive from thoron are on average about one-tenth of those from radon-222 (Wrixon et al., 1988).

The advice in this chapter concerns radon-222 exposures only. Three key definitions are given at the end of the chapter.

SOURCES OF RADON

There are five principal sources of radon in buildings: outside air, water supply, natural gas supply, building materials and the ground under the building. The first three sources are generally negligible in the United Kingdom. The most important source of radon in buildings is usually the ground rather than the building materials, even when local stone is used for building. This is because there is a much larger volume of soil and rock in the ground within a few metres of a building than that used in its construction. Much of the radon emitted by this soil and rock may be drawn into the building.

The average radon concentration in UK dwellings is 20 becquerels per cubic metre of air (Bq m^{-3}) (Wrixon et al., 1988), and the average level in non-residential buildings is probably similar. The range of concentrations found is from 3 to 8,000 Bq m^{-3}, the concentrations in the upper part of this range resulting in significant radiation doses to occupants.

Radon from the ground

Unless the ground is fissured or unusually permeable, the radon in a building originates from within a few metres of it. The resulting radon concentration is affected by four factors:

- *The concentration of radium in the ground* This varies by a factor of more than 10,000 from sedimentary rocks to ground containing uranium ore. The highest concentrations in the United Kingdom are found in southwest England, associated with (but not always directly above) the granite masses.

- *The permeability of the ground* This also varies very widely, the lowest values being found in unbroken rock and heavy clay. Higher permeabilities are found in sand and gravel and also in some cases where land has been backfilled.

- *Penetrations of the building* Radon enters through cracks, construction joints, gaps round service pipes and other penetrations. These gaps may be quite narrow; a long crack a millimetre wide may allow a significant amount of radon to pass through it.

- *Reduced air pressure in buildings* The air in buildings is frequently at a slightly lower pressure than outside air owing to the stack effect (caused by warm air indoors rising, as in a chimney) and to wind blowing across openings such as windows and chimneys. Extract fans can also contribute to the reduced pressure in buildings. The effect of this underpressure is to draw soil gas into buildings.

The wide variation in these four factors from area to area and building to building (and even room to room in large buildings) causes the enormous variation in indoor radon concentrations described earlier. Although it is possible to define areas where there is a risk of finding high radon concentrations, it is not possible to predict which buildings in those areas will be affected. In order to find out which buildings have high concentrations it is necessary to make measurements in each one. Because radon concentrations vary depending on the temperature and the weather, it is best to measure the average concentration over several months by leaving a passive radon detector in place (Wrixon et al., 1988).

Radon from Building Materials

Virtually all building materials contain radium and so exhale some radon. Usually such materials contribute a few becquerels per cubic metre to the average radon concentration of 20 Bq m^{-3} indoors. Building materials emit gamma rays as well as radon, and these also deliver a radiation dose to the occupants of a building. The gamma ray doses from common building materials are usually larger than doses due to the radon they exhale (Cliff et al., 1985).

Some building materials exhale more radon than normal clay bricks and concrete blocks. These include crushed granite bricks and blocks (about 10 times the emanation rate of most materials) and phosphogypsum (about 100 times normal emanation rates) (Wrixon and O'Riordan, 1980; Cliff et al., 1985). Phosphogypsum can be used in plaster and plasterboard. While it is understood that these materials from UK sources are free of phosphogypsum, some continental material is entirely phosphogypsum (NEA, 1979). Use of these materials may increase the total dose received by the occupants by between 10% and 50%, a much smaller range of variation than can be caused by radon from the ground.

Effects of Ventilation

Ventilation with fresh air will normally reduce radon concentrations (see Chapter C1). However, some means of natural and artificial ventilation can reduce the air pressure and so draw in soil gas, increasing the indoor radon concentration. A combination of well-sealed doors and windows on the ground floor with openings in upper storeys can cause a significantly reduced air pressure at ground floor level. An extract fan which is oversized or which has no compensating inlet can produce the same effect. It is therefore important that some ventilation is provided at ground-floor level and that fans and air inlets be appropriately sized.

HEALTH EFFECTS

Radon gas decays to form radioactive decay products. If these are inhaled some will be deposited in the lungs and will irradiate the lung tissues with alpha particles, and may cause lung cancer. Although it is the decay products rather than the radon which cause the damage, the health effects are roughly proportional to exposure to radon gas.

In 1556 Agricola published De Re Metallica in which he said that 'in mines in the Ore Mountains of central Europe the miners are killed by the pestilential air they breathe ... sometimes their lungs "rot away"'. The introduction of improved ventilation and lace face masks apparently improved matters in Agricola's time but 300 years later lung cancer was killing three-quarters of the miners in the same area (Harting and Hesse, 1879). It was not until 1924 that radon was suggested as the causative agent of the disease (Donaldson, 1969). In this century various epidemiological studies have been carried out in Czechoslovakia, Canada, Sweden, the USA, the United Kingdom and other countries. Reviews of these data by the International Commission on Radiological Protection (1987) and the US Committee on the Biological Effects of Ionizing Radiation (1988) have provided a reasonable consensus on the risks from radon exposure (O'Riordan, 1988). The average radon concentration in UK dwellings, 20 Bq m^{-3} (Wrixon et al., 1988), corresponds to a lifetime risk of 0.25%.

At higher concentrations, the lifetime risk is correspondingly higher. These risk estimates are based on an 80 % occupancy of a dwelling; for a workplace, where the occupancy is lower, the lifetime risk is proportionately lower. The risk estimates imply that radon may be responsible for the premature deaths of 2,000 or 3,000 people a year in the United Kingdom.

REGULATIONS AND GUIDANCE

The Ionising Radiations Regulations

The Ionising Radiations Regulations 1985 (IRR) were issued under the Health and Safety at Work etc. Act 1974. Under the IRR and the Health and Safety at Work Act, it is an offence for employers to expose their employees to radiation doses (including those from radon) above certain limits. The IRR also impose duties on employers with respect to radiation exposures of other people. Employers in radon-prone areas therefore have to take the IRR into account when commissioning building work, and in some cases have to introduce remedial measures to reduce radon levels in existing buildings. At the time of writing, Cornwall County Council is the employer with the most experience of remedial work.

The IRR are complex and provide for different levels of radon monitoring and control for different levels of employee exposure. They set an upper limit on the annual radiation dose received by workers of 50 millisieverts (mSv) a year, with lower limits for young trainees and other persons. If the concentrations of radon decay products are below levels likely to result in annual doses of 5 mSv, the detailed requirements of the IRR do not apply. For exposures between 5 and 50 mSv a year, employers must ensure that doses are kept as low as reasonably practicable and must carry out appropriate monitoring of their premises and workers, depending on the doses which may be received. If annual doses are likely to exceed 15 mSv, they must appoint a Radiation Protection Adviser. It is clearly preferable to reduce radon concentrations below the levels at which the detailed requirements of the IRR apply. As a rule of thumb, if the long-term average radon concentration in a building is below 400 Bq m^{-3}, doses to workers will normally be below 5 mSv a year. It is always possible to reduce radon concentrations below 400 Bq m^{-3} by introducing remedial measures (see the section on Existing Buildings, later). The Health and Safety Commission has issued an Approved Code of Practice on the application of the IRR to radon (1988).

The Building Regulations

The Building Regulations 1985 for England and Wales require that 'precautions shall be taken to avoid danger to health caused by substances found on or under the ground to be covered by the building' (Requirement C2). The Approved Document includes in the substances described 'any substance which is or could become . . . radioactive'. In 1988 the Department of the Environment (DoE) issued guidance recognizing that radon was such a substance and that precautions should be taken in the areas affected (Department of the Environment 1988a). The guidance provides a map defining an area which it suggests should be regarded as the area most affected (Figure C4.1). This area covers most of Cornwall and parts of Devon on and around Dartmoor. However, the guidance also suggests that to avoid future problems some precautions may be required in all of Cornwall and all of the Devon Districts of South Hams, Teignbridge, West Devon and part of Mid Devon.

Further research carried out by the National Radiological Protection Board (NRPB) has shown that there are other areas of the United Kingdom where some buildings have high radon concentrations. Much smaller numbers of buildings are affected in these areas than in Devon and Cornwall. The areas include parts of Derbyshire, Northamptonshire, Somerset, Deeside and Helmsdale. Work to define the affected areas more precisely is continuing, sponsored by the DoE, the Welsh Office, the Scottish Office and the DoE (Northern Ireland). So far, guidance on the interpretation of the building regulations for Scotland and Northern Ireland has not been issued.

Regulation 7 of the Building Regulations for England and Wales lays down that 'Any building work shall be carried out with the proper materials ...'. The Approved Document to support this Regulation

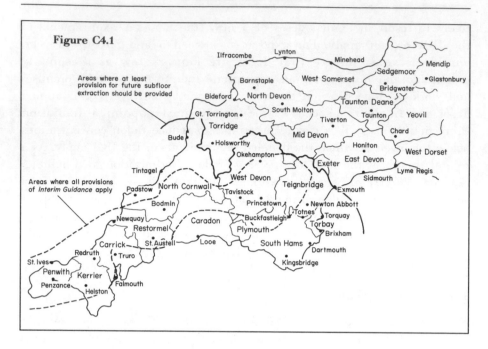

Figure C4.1

interprets this to mean, among other things, materials 'to enable the completed work to be safe and not a danger to the health and safety of persons in or about the building'. Since there is a recognized danger to health from radon, this Regulation could be taken to apply to radon from building materials. However, the amount of radon emitted by building materials commonly available in the United Kingdom is generally too small to be of concern.

The Action Level for Existing Dwellings

In January 1987 the NRPB advised the government that radon exposures in some dwellings were unacceptably high and should be reduced (NRPB, 1987a, b). This advice was revised and extended in January 1990 in the light of new evidence on the risks from radon (NPRB, 1990). The NRPB now recommends that if the concentration of radon, averaged over a year, exceeds an action level of 200 Bq m^{-3} then remedial action should be taken. At the Action Level, the lifetime risk is about 3%, i.e. about 1 in 30 people living in such houses all their lives may die of lung cancer due to radon. It is estimated that about 100,000 UK houses exceed the Action Level. The government has accepted NRPB's advice and announced that discretionary grants for remedial measures will be available in some cases. However, it is not mandatory to reduce high levels in homes; it is up to the householder to decide. The DoE currently funds a free measurement service in areas affected by radon. Any householder in these areas of England can obtain a free measurement by applying to Radon Survey, NRPB, Chilton, Didcot, Oxon OX11 0RQ. There are similar arrangements for homes in affected areas in Scotland, Wales and Northern Ireland, funded by the appropriate government departments.

PREVENTION OF HIGH RADON CONCENTRATIONS

New Buildings

In June 1988 the DoE issued Building Regulations 1985 – Part C: Radon. Interim Guidance on Construction of New Dwellings. This points out that the Building Regulations 1985 require precautions to be taken to avoid a danger to health caused by radioactive substances in the ground. Such precautions are therefore necessary in areas where high radon concentrations are most likely to occur. Although the guidance notes were developed for dwellings, the principles, and in many cases the detailed designs, can be applied to other types of building.

The guidance contains advice and drawings on precautionary measures to be taken when constructing a suspended concrete floor, an in situ concrete floor, a suspended timber floor and a stepped foundation (Figures C4.2-C4.5). The examples given are not the only solutions; alternative means of achieving the same result are also acceptable. In all designs the objective is to construct an airtight barrier across the whole site of the building, with provision for natural ventilation under a suspended floor or means of extracting soil gas from under a solid floor. Guidance on construction techniques for larger buildings has not yet been published, although the requirement to avoid a danger to health from radon is the same as for dwellings.

In applying the techniques described, it is essential that great care is taken. It is particularly important that lapping of membranes is properly executed and is clear of all service penetrations. Where possible service entries should avoid penetrating the radon-proof membrane. Where this is not possible it will be necessary to construct an airtight seal around each entry. The gap between the service pipe and the membrane should be as small as possible and should be well filled with a long-life mastic or flexible sealant. Soil gas may also enter a building inside a service pipe, for instance where a cable runs inside a pipe so, in this case, it is necessary to seal the gap between the pipe and the cable at some point. This may most conveniently be done where the cable emerges from the pipe, as long as there are no other holes in the pipe.

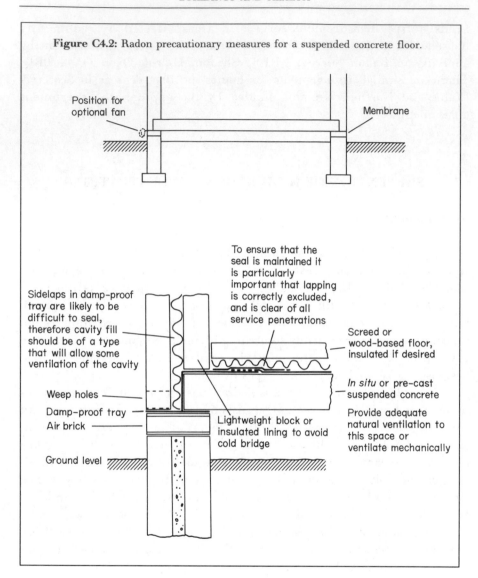

Figure C4.2: Radon precautionary measures for a suspended concrete floor.

Position for optional fan

Membrane

Sidelaps in damp-proof tray are likely to be difficult to seal, therefore cavity fill should be of a type that will allow some ventilation of the cavity

To ensure that the seal is maintained it is particularly important that lapping is correctly excluded, and is clear of all service penetrations

Screed or wood-based floor, insulated if desired

Weep holes

In situ or pre-cast suspended concrete

Damp-proof tray
Air brick

Lightweight block or insulated lining to avoid cold bridge

Provide adequate natural ventilation to this space or ventilate mechanically

Ground level

In July 1990, the Department of the Environment issued a consultation paper on, amongst other things, proposed new guidance in Part C of the Building Regulations 1985 for reducing the hazards associated with radon. It is not known when any new guidance will come into force.

Existing Buildings

In 1988 the DoE issued The Householders' Guide to Radon (Department of the Environment, 1988b), intended particularly for householders whose homes have been tested and found to have an appreciable level of radon.

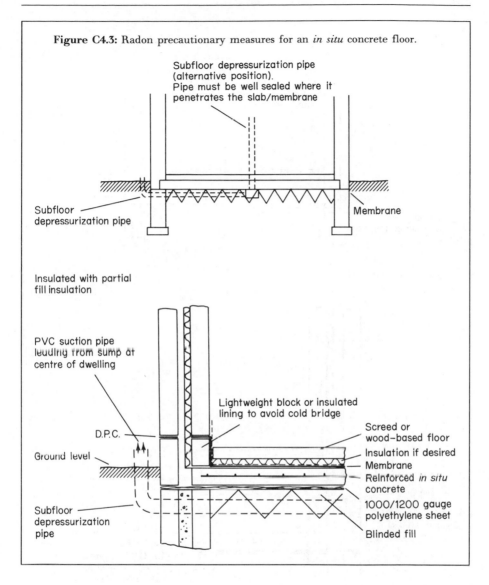

Figure C4.3: Radon precautionary measures for an *in situ* concrete floor.

Subfloor depressurization pipe
(alternative position).
Pipe must be well sealed where it
penetrates the slab/membrane

Subfloor
depressurization pipe

Membrane

Insulated with partial
fill insulation

PVC suction pipe
leading from sump at
centre of dwelling

Lightweight block or insulated
lining to avoid cold bridge

D.P.C.

Screed or
wood–based floor

Ground level

Insulation if desired

Membrane

Reinforced *in situ*
concrete

Subfloor
depressurization
pipe

1000/1200 gauge
polyethylene sheet

Blinded fill

This guide is also used by the Welsh and Scottish Offices, and a similar guide was issued by the DoE (Northern Ireland in 1989).

The Householders' Guide to Radon (1988) contains descriptions and drawings of various remedial techniques. The techniques described, though intended for dwellings, may also be applied directly to other buildings of comparable size. For larger buildings, some adaptation of the techniques may be required and this is discussed below. The Building Research Establishment intends to publish notes containing more details about remedial techniques. It is important to emphasize that remedial measures are necessary only in a minority of buildings, even in affected areas. Long-term measurements of radon should be carried out to

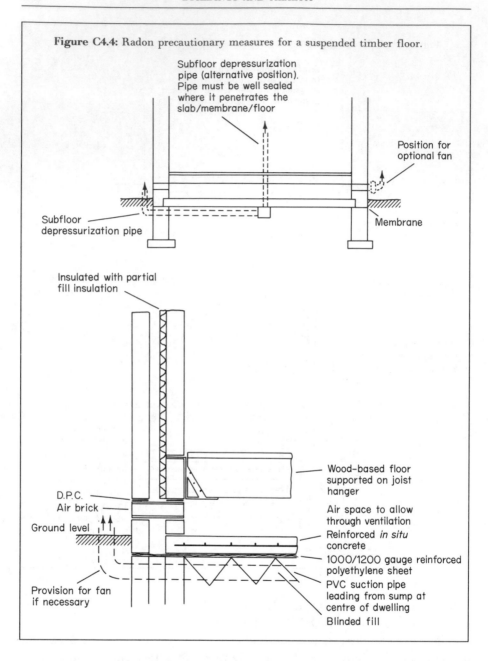

Figure C4.4: Radon precautionary measures for a suspended timber floor.

determine whether there is a significant problem before remedial measures are undertaken. Further advice on reducing radon levels may be obtained from the Building Research Establishment, Garston, Watford WD2 7JR, but if detailed technical issues are involved there may be a charge for this service.

Simple suspended floors are easier to treat than solid floors as soil gas carrying radon can be drawn off before it enters the living space. The

Householders' Guide to Radon (1988) summarizes the treatment of suspended floors as follows:

> 'You should seal suspended floors well, maintaining a high standard of work as a single large gap may seriously affect the overall result. The preferred second stage treatment is to install a fan to draw air from under the floor. If a fan is used without proper sealing, the result will probably be disappointing.'

A solid floor is likely to require a 'radon sump' to prevent entry of radon into a building. A radon sump is a small cavity dug underneath or in some cases alongside a building and filled with porous material such as

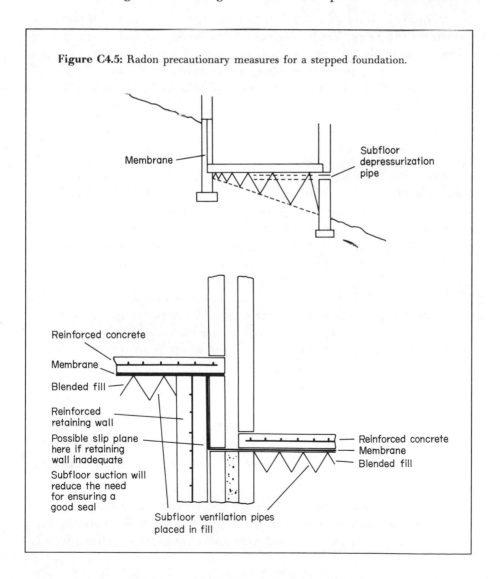

Figure C4.5: Radon precautionary measures for a stepped foundation.

coarse gravel or loose laid bricks. Soil gas is drawn out of the sump
through a pipe by a fan and dispersed in the open air. A fan of 75-100
watts power is required. The Householders' Guide to Radon (1988)
summarizes the approach:

> 'For solid floors, sealing alone is unlikely to be a sufficient
> remedy for radon problems. The recommended approach is to
> seal major cracks and gaps and then install a fan system.'

As with preventive measures for new buildings, it is essential that very
careful attention is paid to detail to ensure that the measures are
effective. Large buildings may require more than one sump to reduce the
radon to acceptable levels. The most cost-effective approach is to identify
the principal route of entry of radon, install a sump nearby and
remeasure the radon levels. Because radon levels vary so much, the re-
measurement should be carried out over several months. If high
concentrations remain, further radon sumps may be required.

A second edition of the Householder's Guide to Radon was published
in July 1990.

Extensions and Alterations

Alterations to a building can sometimes create a radon problem where
there was none before. The replacement of a ventilated suspended floor
by a solid concrete floor may leave a crack around the edge of the floor
after the concrete has contracted. Such a crack, concealed by flooring and
skirting boards, can provide a route for soil gas to enter the building. As
there is no longer ventilation under the floor, high concentrations of
radon can build up in the soil gas and be drawn into the building.
Similarly, a crack between an original building and an extension to it
can allow soil gas to enter, carrying radon. When carrying out extensions
and alterations in radon-prone areas, the objective should be the same as
when constructing new buildings: the creation of an airtight barrier with
provision for ventilation or soil gas extraction underneath.

CONCLUSIONS

* Radon in buildings can cause a health hazard in some parts of the
  country.

* Radon gas decays to form radioactive decay products. If these are
  inhaled some will be deposited in the lungs and will irradiate the lung
  tissues with alpha particles, and may cause lung cancer. Although it is

the decay products rather than the radon which cause the damage, the health effects are roughly proportional to exposure to radon gas.

* The hazard can be avoided by preventing soil gas from entering buildings. This is simpler to achieve in new buildings than existing ones. In either case, techniques are available to reduce indoor radon concentrations to acceptable levels.

REFERENCES

Agricola, G. (1556), *De Re Metallica*, (trans. H.C. Hoover and L.H. Hoover, Dover Publications, 1950).

BEIR (Committee on the Biological Effects of Ionizing Radiation) (1988), *Health Effects of Radon and other Internal Alpha Emitters*, BEIR IV, National Academy Press, Washington, DC.

Building Regulations 1985 (SI 1985 No. 1065), HM Stationery Office, London.

Cliff, K.D., Green, B.M.R. and Miles, J.C.H. (1985), *The levels of radioactive materials in some common UK building materials*, Sci. Total Environ., 45, 181-6.

Department of the Environment, (1988a) *Building Regulations 1985 – Part C: Radon. Interim Guidance on Construction of New Dwellings*, HM Stationery Office.

Department of the Environment (1988b), *The Householders' Guide to Radon*, HM Stationery Office, London.

Department of the Environment (Northern Ireland) (1989), *The Householders' Guide to Radon*, HM Stationery Office, London.

Donaldson, A.W. (1969), *The epidemiology of lung cancer among uranium miners*, Health Phys., 16, 563–9.

Harting, F.H. and Hesse, W. (1879), *Der lungenkrebs, die Bergkrankheit in den Schneeberger gruben*, Vjschr. Gerichtl. Med. Offentl. Gesuntheitswes., 30, 296–309; 31, 102-29, 31 3–37.

Health and Safely Commission (1988), *Approved Code of Practice – Part 3, Exposure to Radon*, HM Stationery Office, London.

Health and Safety at Work etc. Act 1974, HM Stationery Office, London.

International Commission on Radiological Protection (1987), *Lung cancer risk from indoor exposures to radon daughters*, ICRP Publication 50, Ann. ICRP, 17 (1).

Ionising Radiations Regulations 1985 (SI 1985 No. 1333), HM Stationery Office, London.

NEA (Nuclear Energy Agency) (1979), *Exposure to radiation from the natural radioactivity in building materials*, Organisation for Economic Co-operation and Development, Paris.

NRPB (National Radiological Protection Board) (1987a), *Exposure to Radon Daughters in Dwellings*, NRPB ASP10, HM Stationery Office, London.

NRPB (1987b), *Exposure to Radon Daughters in Dwellings*, NRPB GS6, HM Stationery Office, London.

NRPB (1990) Statement by the National Radiological Protection Board, *Limitation of exposure to radon in the home*, Documents of the NRPB, 1, No 1, HM Stationery Office, London.

O'Riordan, M.C. (1988), *Notes on radon risks in homes*, Radiol. Prot. Bull., 89, 13-14.

Wrixon, A.D. and O'Riordan, M.C. (1980), *Radiological criteria for the use of phosphogypsum as a building material.*, In Proc. Int. Symp. on Phosphogypsum, Florida.

Wrixon, A.D., Green, B.M.R., Lomas, P.R., Miles, J.C.H., Cliff, K.D., Francis, E.A., Driscoll, C.M.H., James, A.C. and O'Riordan, M.C. (1988), *Natural Radiation Exposure in UK Dwellings*, NRPB-R190, HM Stationery Office, London.

DEFINITIONS

BECQUEREL: The unit used to quantify radioactivity. 1Bq is 1 transformation per second.

SIEVERT: The unit used to quantify 'effective dose equivalent', a measure of the risk incurred by exposure to radiation.

HALF-LIFE: The time taken for the radioactivity of a radionuclide to decline by half.

BUILDING RELATED SICKNESS

David Tong and Sheena Wilson

Building Use Studies and Jones Lang Wootton

INTRODUCTION

Some people at work suffer a sickness or malaise which appears to have no specific cause, but which is in some way related to the building in which they work. It is not a specific disease, such as Legionnaires' Disease, nor an infection, nor a cancer. Sufferers experience a set of symptoms which result from sensitivity to certain conditions, in this case, a poor office environment. This malaise, and the factors which cause it, has come to be known as Sick Building Syndrome (SBS).

SBS causes widespread loss of productivity, with many sufferers reporting that their productivity is reduced by as much as 20%. Whereas Legionnaires' Disease and asbestosis are building-related health problems which affect small numbers of people very severely, SBS is sometimes experienced by over half the staff in a 'sick building' but is normally much milder in its health effects.

SBS appears to be caused by a number of factors, such as low levels of chemical pollutants, bad lighting, poor building design and inadequate management, which act cumulatively upon individual office workers and result in a typical set of symptoms. The main categories of contributing factors are shown in Figure C5.1, with more detail following later in the chapter. Although particular factors are not on their own sufficient to cause

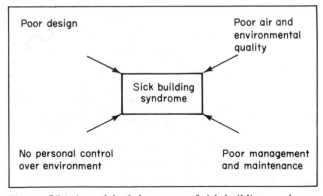

Figure C5.1 A model of the causes of sick building syndrome

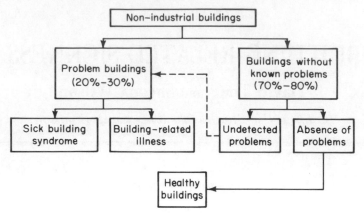

Figure C5.2 Sick building syndrome in relation to buildings (from Woods, 1988)

sickness, in combination with others they result in SBS. Figure C5.2 shows the distinction between SBS and other building-related illnesses.

The causes are difficult to identify in individual buildings without a thorough investigation. Even with such an investigation, tracing the route of causation is complicated by the fact that SBS is found in buildings which meet current environmental standards and health and safety regulations. It is considered possible that people are reacting to a 'cocktail' of chemicals each of which is at concentrations below normal sensitising thresholds. The key to solving the problem is therefore to look beyond existing regulations and to set new standards of good practice and management.

SBS poses no threat to construction site workers or to members of the public who pass by affected buildings, but is experienced solely by building occupants. The occupants most at risk are female clerical workers doing routine sedentary work. When people are doing varied work or are moving around, for example in and out of meetings, they are more tolerant of poor environmental conditions. However, if conditions are particularly poor, staff at all levels are at risk from SBS.

DEFINING SICK BUILDING SYNDROME

SBS is the chronic and concurrent experience of a characteristic set of symptoms which occur when people are at their place of work but which disappear in the evening and at weekends. The symptoms fall into four categories (Robertson et al., 1985):

Dry:	Stuffy nose, dry throat and dry skin
Allergic:	Runny or itchy nose, watering or itchy eyes
Asthma:	Chest tightness
General:	Undue lethargy, headache

These category labels do not imply cause – for example, 'dry symptoms' are not always the result of low humidity – but together, the symptoms of SBS constitute a general feeling of malaise rather than a severe illness, although in sensitive individuals particular symptoms may be severe.

Each individual may not suffer from all the symptoms, but in a building population a range of these symptoms will be evident. Experience of the symptoms may not be continuous, but one of the characteristics of the syndrome is that it is persistent and chronic rather than acute. Unlike, say, humidifier fever, it does not only occur when the individual is exposed to an environment after a period of absence. Diary studies show that SBS is not a 'Monday morning feeling'; indeed, symptoms are more likely to occur in the latter part of the working week. There does not appear to be any seasonal variation in experience of the syndrome.

There is no evidence that experience of SBS causes any long-term health effects, although this has not been investigated directly. The possibility exists that sufferers of SBS, because they are working under stressful conditions, will be more prone to typical stress effects in the long term.

A SHORT HISTORY OF SICK BUILDING SYNDROME

During the 1970s, ventilation rates in buildings declined and insulation standards rose in response to demands for energy efficiency. At the same time, new chemicals such as fire retardants and resins began to be used in building products. As evidence of the symptoms now grouped under the name SBS began to emerge, various scientists, particularly in the USA, became concerned about indoor air quality in these new so-called 'tight buildings'.

During the 1980s, medical practitioners in the United Kingdom began to investigate various illnesses caused by micro-organisms in building services. In consultations with office staff they not only found problems such as humidifier fever (which *is* caused by micro-organisms) but also discovered the unexplained occurrence of the range of symptoms now known as SBS. The work of Finnegan et al. (1984) was of critical importance in establishing the problem as worthy of further investigation. They confirmed the existence of a linked set of symptoms which occurred in some buildings and not in others.

The Office Environment Survey (OES) (Wilson and Hedge, 1987) was undertaken in the mid-1980s with the aim of measuring the extent of the SBS. It remains the only major study in the United Kingdom of the incidence of SBS. Questionnaires given to 4373 staff in 46 buildings asked about staff's experience of 10 symptoms while at work and the results established a statistical picture of the types of building most prone

Table C5.1 The incidence of building-related symptoms – percentage of staff reporting

Symptom	Most common building-related symptoms[a]	Symptons experienced at least once a week[b]
Lethargy	57	37
Stuffy nose	47	19
Dry throat	46	21
Headache	43	21
Dry eyes	27	16
Itching or watery eyes	28	18

[a] Data from OES 46 buildings studied, 4377 respondents.
[b] Data from Wilson et al. (1987) based on a sample of 484 office workers.

to SBS. The OES research study found that only 19% of the office staff surveyed reported no building-related symptoms. Some 25% experienced just one or two symptoms and 29% experienced five symptoms or more. Table C5.1 shows the symptoms most commonly reported. It also shows that, of those who experience symptoms, typically about half experience them at least once a week.

Detailed research on the various aspects of SBS still continues, particularly in the UK, Scandinavia and the USA.

INVESTIGATING 'SICK BUILDINGS'

What is a 'Sick Building'?

The general nature of SBS means that they will be reported to some degree in all buildings. Even where the incidence of symptoms has been properly surveyed there is no clear-cut line which can be drawn between sick and healthy buildings.

The OES found that, on average, three symptoms were experienced by each person surveyed. This provides a rough benchmark for assessing sickness levels in buildings, but ultimately a building can only be described as 'sick' when a systematic survey has been carried out and when those who manage the building decide that the level of complaint is unacceptable.

Initial Survey

The first stage in an investigation of a 'sick building' should be a questionnaire survey of a representative sample of the staff. This will put *ad hoc* staff complaints into perspective by establishing

- the full extent of the problem;
- the location of problems within the building;
- the relative severity of different symptoms.

An indication of the importance of proper measurement comes from the OES, which established that in only half the buildings with a high level of SBS was the office manager aware that there was a problem. Therefore it is likely that building occupants' experience of symptoms is more widespread than managers are aware of or would like to admit.

All organizations commissioning outsiders to survey staff should ensure that the firm carrying out the survey is independent. The data are likely to be sensitive and so it is essential that they are handled professionally and without bias. It is also advisable to use an organization with an existing SBS database so that symptom levels can be compared with those in other buildings. This helps to put the problem in an individual building into perspective. Poorly designed questionnaires can of course distort and exaggerate the extent of SBS.

A typical SBS investigation should involve:

- studies of the performance of building services, e.g. ventilation rates, cooling load, efficiency of dampers, fans, filters;
- studies of maintenance standards and procedures, e.g. cleanliness of plant, records kept;
- physical measures of environmental conditions, e.g. temperature, lighting and noise levels, air movement patterns;
- evaluation of design standards, e.g. building form, lighting design, colour schemes;
- evaluation of housekeeping standards, e.g. general cleanliness;
- monitoring of air quality, e.g. presence of particulate and fibrous matter, inorganic and organic gases;
- evaluation of management methods, e.g. procedures for dealing with staff complaints.

Investigations are tailored to the circumstances in particular buildings, but the range of activities listed indicates that a multidisciplinary team is required. Usually this will involve a building services engineer and an occupational hygienist. Because of the publicity that SBS has received, a number of inexperienced consultants are falsely advertising unique solutions to the problem, so the expertise of all consultants should be verified and their ability to carry out multidisciplinary analysis determined before they are given an investigative commission.

THE CAUSES OF SICK BUILDING SYNDROME

As indicated earlier, many factors lead to SBS (for a review see Sykes, 1988). Since they operate cumulatively, they should be regarded as risk factors contributing to SBS rather than outright causes. Four categories cover the range of factors involved:

- *personal factors*, e.g. stress, lack of environmental control, sedentary and repetitive work;
- *physical and environmental factors*, e.g. poor air quality, lighting, overheating, noise;
- *design factors*, e.g. low floor-to-ceiling height, large unstructured open plan areas, absence of natural light, poor lighting scheme;
- *organizational factors*, e.g. poor management and maintenance, high degree of change and uncertainty.

The following four sections, which deal with each category in turn, involve some overlap because many of the causes are interrelated. For the most part they are based on the findings of the OES.

Personal factors

The findings of the OES in this area were:

- clerical and/or secretarial staff reported 50% more symptoms than managers, and 30% more than professionals;
- the relationship between computer use and building sickness was not strong, although those who worked for more than 6 hours per day at a VDU had slightly higher sickness rates;
- women reported symptoms more frequently than men.

Staff doing routine sedentary work are the most sensitive to environmental conditions because they are continuously exposed to the same environment and because they will tend to ask more of it; they will be less accepting of bland and uncomfortable conditions than staff who have greater intrinsic job interest.

The difference in symptom rates between men and women may in part have a physiological explanation in that women tend to react more sharply to thermal conditions; they feel hot more quickly when the temperature rises and cold more quickly when the temperature falls (McIntyre, 1980). Women are also more likely to be in lower grade jobs (in the OES, only 16% of managers, compared with 80% of clerical and secretarial staff, were women) and to work in open plan offices.

The OES found that those staff who reported having little or no control over lighting, ventilation and temperature had higher sickness rates. This effect is explained by the fact that people are far more tolerant of poor environmental conditions if they have some control over them. Another finding illustrating the importance of environmental control is that staff subjected to the effects of other people's smoke or 'passive smoking' had higher sickness rates than those not exposed in this way.

Physical and environmental factors

The OES divided the buildings in the study into five main groups according to type of ventilation (Table C5.2). Although there were exceptions, air-conditioned buildings, especially those relying on water-based heating and cooling, had higher rates of sickness than buildings with either natural or mechanical ventilation systems (mechanical systems have ducted air but do not cool or humidify). The older air-conditioned buildings, i.e. those over 8 years old, especially in the rented sector, had the highest risk of SBS.

Table C5.2 Variation in the number of symptoms per person for ventilation groups

Type of Ventilation	No. of Buildings	Minimum BSS*	Maximum BSS	Average BSS	Number of People
Mechanical	7	1.25	2.55	2.18	422
Natural	11	1.55	3.40	2.49	944
All air	12	2.25	5.25	3.12	1384
Central	11	2.69	4.92	3.70	1095
Local	5	3.05	4.80	3.81	508
All buildings	46	1.25	5.25	3.11	4373

* BSS, Building Sickness Score, is the number of symptoms per person in an individual building.

This correlation with the age of the building suggests two things. Modern systems may perform better because of their improved specification, or systems may degrade over time, particularly when maintenance is ignored. As with any complex system, air-conditioning is vulnerable to failure at a number of points. The following faults have been found in air-conditioned 'sick buildings' (Woods, 1988):

- **equipment problems:** inadequate filtration, malfunctioning humidifiers;

- *maintenance problems:* dirty filters and ducts, disconnected damper linkages, disconnected exhaust fans, inadequate access to high voltage alternating current (HVAC) components;
- *load changes:* insufficient total system capacity, local shortfalls in supply when the balance in the loads changes;
- *control strategies:* over-complex control systems, abandoned automatic control systems, air supply dominated by energy efficiency rather than health criteria.

Inadequate fresh air supply and uncomfortable conditions are not unique to air-conditioned buildings. On the contrary, ventilation rates are typically lower in naturally ventilated buildings and it can be more difficult to maintain conditions at comfortable norms (Wilson et al., 1987). If the higher sickness rates in air-conditioned buildings cannot solely be explained by physical parameters, then a psychological dimension must be considered. Air-conditioned buildings tend to offer little individual control because they are designed with sealed exteriors and because temperature, air movement and ventilation – three aspects of comfort – are integrated into a single system of control.

Other aspects of air-conditioned buildings may also be important, such as the constant background system noise, and the heavy tint commonly applied to windows which reduces awareness of the outside world. In many such buildings, staff complain of claustrophobia and of being cut off from the variety and interest of external conditions.

Air quality in offices is undoubtedly a relevant issue. In the OES, staff who had the highest sickness rates also described conditions in their offices as dry, stuffy and stale. Perception of dryness and staleness may be the result of low humidity but it is known that people are poor judges of humidity. It is therefore more likely that high temperatures, low air movement and poor air quality create feelings of dryness and staleness. Studies in the United Kingdom and Denmark (Valbjorn and Skov, 1987; Wilson et al., 1987) have confirmed that these conditions are evident in buildings with high sickness rates.

A commonly suggested cause of SBS is the presence in the air of gaseous pollutants such as formaldehyde and ozone derived from building materials and office equipment. Few studies of a sick building have found pollutants at levels exceeding the current exposure limits. It is possible that a range of different pollutants may cause symptoms by creating odours and discomfort rather than having directly toxic effects (see Fanger, 1988), and there is a question of whether sensitivity to a 'cocktail' of pollutants might occur at much lower concentrations than sensitivity to the pollutants individually.

One aspect of the physical environment which is known to have effects on health and which may form part of the syndrome is noise.

Office workers tend to prefer continuous low-pitched sound at around 46 dB as this masks conversations and other irritating noise and is easy for the ear to adapt to. Long-term exposure to higher noise levels, especially if the noise is high pitched and intermittent, can become disruptive and will cause typical stress symptoms such as lethargy, headaches and allergic reactions.

Design factors

The contribution of building, interior and services design to SBS is important because once a building is constructed its elements are relatively fixed and difficult to change. Poor building services design contributes to SBS, common problems being:

- inadequate outdoor air supplied to the central air-handling units for the number and density of occupants;
- inadequate supply of air to the occupied zone because of insufficient ducting or because the 'throw' of air from the terminal point is too low;
- poorly positioned extracts, so that air short circuits in and out of the rooms without reaching the occupied zone;
- inadequate exhaust from the occupied area;
- inadequate cooling capacity.

It is not atypical to find that the positions of air outlets have not been adjusted following changes to the layout of internal partitioning. This can result in some areas getting poor air supply even though the system capacity is adequate. Another common failing is for air inlets bringing primary air into a building to be positioned near sources of pollution and contamination, such as chimneys and loading bays with traffic fumes. This is clearly a major design error.

Maintenance requirements must always be considered in the design of plant rooms and building services. If access to filters and ducts is difficult their cleaning and replacement will tend to be neglected.

Regarding building layout, the OES found that occurrences of SBS symptoms were greater in shared offices than in individual offices. Certainly the level of personal control is lower in offices designed to be open plan than in cellular offices, and shared offices are also likely to be of deeper plan than cellular offices. Working in a deep space (say over 15 m from a window) with a 'low' floor-to-ceiling height (less than 3 m) can be depressing and produce a mild form of sensory deprivation, resulting in SBS symptoms.

Interior design factors which contribute to a stressful environment include:

- dark colour schemes which create subjective warmth and reduce inter-reflected light;
- intense or high chroma colours which are visually very demanding;
- mundane lighting schemes which require uplift for visual interest.

Poor lighting can contribute to SBS – glare and flicker result in headaches and eye strain, whereas severe deficiencies in lighting will cause stress. Daylight is generally the preferred form of light in offices. Compared with many other sources daylight is more diffuse and has better modelling and colour rendering qualities. The difficulty, of course, is to avoid too much sunlight because of the problems it creates with glare and heat gain. Effective use of shading and blinds will form part of any good design scheme.

Organizational factors

An unexpected finding of the OES was that public sector buildings had higher rates of SBS than private sector buildings, whether in air-conditioned or naturally/mechanically ventilated buildings. One explanation was the type of buildings occupied by public sector organizations: in the 46-building sample, they were of a lower quality and generally older than the private sector buildings. Additionally, factors such as low staff morale and management practice may have played a part. The 1980s were a period of cut-back and restructuring in the public sector and at times staff morale was very low. In such circumstances any environmental dissatisfaction may be exacerbated by the general feelings of stress and insecurity.

In all organizations, poor management is likely to contribute to SBS in a number of ways. It is important for management to show explicitly that they recognize environmental problems where they exist. Staff with no environmental control are the worst affected by the syndrome, and their frustration and sense of helplessness are worsened if they are then confronted by a manager who refuses to acknowledge the legitimacy of their complaints. It is thus important to have an efficient system for reporting environmental problems, particularly in organizations with no specialist building manager on site. If the response to complaints is slow, staff will believe that their complaints are being ignored.

There is clear evidence (Wilson et al., 1987) that sickness rates are high in buildings with poor maintenance standards. It is clearly a management responsibility to ensure that maintenance staff are trained properly and that systems are run in an efficient organized manner, with all maintenance and changes to system operation fully documented. Wilson et al.'s study (1987) of nine buildings found that buildings where there were no staff trained to operate the HVAC system or no records of changes made to the system were prone to SBS.

Other common maintenance failings include:

- poor air supply because the system has never been commissioned properly or has become unbalanced;
- air supply terminals disconnected and not re-connected to the primary air duct;
- dirty ducts and plenums, distributing particulates in the air supply;
- dirty filters, reducing the quality and distribution of air.

CASE STUDIES

Two case studies follow this chapter to illustrate the ways in which SBS occurs and can be investigated, and show that SBS can occur in a wide variety of buildings. One case presented a sophisticated image of a high-powered sales organization, with recently refurbished offices appointed to apparently high standards. The other was a friendly but rather 'worn' back office with a large clerical work-force. Staff in the sales office complained of a subdued, gloomy and even depressing atmosphere, while for those in the other office the lighting gave a rather glaring impression.

Despite these differences, staff in both buildings suffered from SBS probably because of the features that the buildings shared. Both buildings suffered from problems with their building services which could be remedied at no great cost and would probably also bring energy savings. Both buildings were also largely open plan in design and had sealed windows. The possibility exists that in buildings designed in this way there will always be a level of SBS present unless there are other major compensating design features, such as an attractive atrium to bring life and a feeling of spaciousness to a building.

GUIDELINES FOR REDUCING THE RISK OF SBS

SBS is best controlled by exercising high standards of design and maintenance practice and management. This chapter, together with the guidance documents, standards and codes of practice listed in Appendix 1 to this chapter, provide advice on how to minimize the risk of SBS. In some buildings it will not be possible to eliminate all risk factors. For example, some city centre offices may require sealed windows to control noise and, if this is the case, other aspects of building design and management will need appropriate attention to keep the total risk loading in a building below that which may be expected to cause widespread SBS.

The following guidelines present an amalgam of views of good practice based on current knowledge of SBS.

Building Design

- Where development constraints permit, provide generous spatial proportions, with preferably a floor-to-ceiling height of at least 3 m and a depth of no more than 18 m, so that most work places will have reasonable access to views out of the building;
- explore scope for adopting climate-sensitive building structures, for example, expose the underside of the floor slab to absorb internal heat gain and stabilize temperatures;
- provide areas of visual relief and interest, e.g. light wells, atria, fountains;
- ensure that the design of plant rooms and services allows for maintenance requirements;
- explore ways in which building configuration and services design can meet user preferences for openable windows to offer user control and outside awareness.

Building Services Design, Operation and Maintenance

- Consider whether air-conditioning is necessary: if it is needed, provide adequate resources for commissioning, operation and maintenance;
- budget for commissioning, and expect to recommission periodically;
- avoid all the common failings listed in this chapter to ensure a good clean air supply;
- flush out the system regularly, before the building is occupied and at weekends;
- institute regular independent audits of building services;
- treat the Chartered Institute of Building Services Engineers recommended ventilation rates as a minimum standard.

Management

- Prioritize environmental standards in areas occupied by those doing routine sedentary work;
- establish a system for documenting and dealing with user complaints;
- ensure that an effective maintenance system is in place, with up-to-date records and manuals of system operation;
- periodically monitor environmental conditions;

- introduce smoking controls in working areas;
- ensure regular 'deep cleaning' of carpets and other absorbent surfaces which trap dirt;
- deep clean new buildings prior to occupation, to remove builders' dust and other particulates;
- ensure good standards of general housekeeping and cleanliness;
- maintain standards in all areas, and do not allow standards in clerical 'back offices' to fall.

Lighting

- Design for good daylight with careful window and shading design to avoid the need for tinted and reflective glazing and to ensure that windows do not become a glare source;
- install automatically controlled artificial lighting, with local manual override to minimize internal heat gains;
- provide local task lighting for user control;
- use high frequency fluorescent lights to avoid flicker, with high quality diffusers to avoid glare;
- provide uplighting or other kinds of decorative lighting to give visual interest.

Noise

- Use acoustically absorbent finishes;
- use laser printers, quiet typewriters and telephones that can be silenced;
- isolate or enclose clusters of noisy equipment;
- provide adequate meeting space and retreats for quiet concentrated work.

Colour

- Avoid large areas of high chroma (intense) colours;
- avoid dark warm colours which increase perceptions of heat and reduce inter-reflected light.

Chemical pollution

- Where possible, avoid building materials which emit toxic chemicals;
- in new buildings, ventilate at high rates prior to occupation to flush out chemicals from new products which emit gases at high rates;

- enclose and separately ventilate ozone-producing photocopiers and laser printers when they are used in clusters or continuously during the day. The air extract from laser printers can be filtered if there are isolated reactions from users.

CONCLUSIONS

* Some people at work suffer a sickness or malaise which appears to have no specific cause, but which is in some way related to the building in which they work. It is not a specific disease, such as Legionnaires' Disease, not an infection, nor a cancer. Sufferers experience a set of symptoms which result from sensitivity to certain conditions, in this case, a poor office environment. This malaise, and the factors which cause it, has come to be known as Sick Building Syndrome (SBS).

* Causes of SBS are not just multiple but cumulative. What increases risk is a combination of factors which add to the level of stress under which people are trying to carry out their work. None of these stress-inducing factors is new – overheating, poor lighting, unhygienic air-conditioning systems, organizational change, the difficulty of concentrating in open plan offices, and the frustration of being unable to relieve monotony or stuffiness by opening a window. They are all known to be aspects of office life which affect well-being and comfort.

* SBS is everyone's problem, but the key agents for change are the managements of organizations that occupy buildings, for it is they who will determine the overall quality of the environment in which people work.

* The control of SBS relies on qualitative judgements of design standards as well as empirical investigations of environmental parameters. Empirical investigation is essential, and will bring a great deal of valuable information to light, but other factors, particularly those relating to design, cannot be ignored despite being difficult to quantify. Investigations of SBS benefit from a multi-disciplinary approach.

* Understanding of the subject of SBS is developing, and construction professionals involved in the design and maintenance of workplace buildings should keep abreast of and take account of new guidance as it is published.

REFERENCES

Building Research Establishment (1976), *Acoustics of Rooms for Speech, Digest 192,* Building Research Establishment, Garston.

CIBSE (Chartered Institute of Building Services Engineers) (1976a), *Environmental Criteria for Design,* Guide Section A1, CIBSE, London.

CIBSE (Chartered Institute of Building Services Engineers) (1976b), *Ventilation and Air Conditioning Requirements,* Guide Section B2, CIBSE, London.

CIBSE (Chartered Institute of Building Services Engineers) (1989), *Areas for Visual Display Terminals,* Lighting Guide LG3, CIBSE, London.

Fanger, P.O. (1988), *Introduction of the olf and the decipol unit to quantify air pollution perceived by humans indoors and outdoors.* Energy and Buildings, vol. 12, pp. 1-6.

Finnegan, M.J., Pickering, C.A.C. and Burge, P.S. (1984), *The sick building syndrome: prevalence studies,* Br. Med. J., 289, 1573-5.

McIntyre, D.A. (1980), *Indoor Climate,* Applied Science Publishers, London.

Robertson, A.S., Burge, P.S., Hedge, A., Sims, J., Gill, F.S., Finnegan, M., Pickering, C.A.C. and Dalton, G. (1985), *Comparisons of health problems related to work and environmental measurements in two office buildings with different ventilation systems,* Br. Med. J., 291 , 373-6.

Sykes, J.M. (1988), *Sick Building Syndrome: A Review,* Health and Safety Executive Specialist Inspector Report No. 10, Health and Safety Executive, Bootle.

Valbjorn, O. and Skov, P. (1987), *Influence of indoor climate on the sick building syndrome prevalence,* in *Indoor Air '87* (eds B. Seifert, H. Edson, M. Fisher, H. Ruden and J. Wegner), Proceedings of the 4th International Conference on Indoor Air Quality, Berlin.

Wilson, S. and Hedge, A. (1987), *The Office Environment Survey,* Building Use Studies.

Wilson, S., O'Sullivan, P., Jones, P. and Hedge, A. (1987), *Sick Building Syndrome and Environmental Conditions: Case Studies of Nine Buildings,* Building Use Studies.

Woods, J. (1988), *Recent developments for heating, cooling and ventilating buildings: trends for assuring healthy buildings,* in *Healthy Buildings '88, vol. 1* (eds B. Berglund and T. Lindvall), Swedish Council for Building Research.

APPENDIX 1

RELEVANT GUIDANCE DOCUMENTS, STANDARDS AND CODES OF PRACTICE

The evidence associated with sick building syndrome has been reviewed in two reports:

- Building Services Research and Information Association, BTN 4 1988, Sick Building Syndrome
- Health and Safety Executive, Specialist Inspector Report No. 10 1988, Sick Building Syndrome: A Review

There are no other formal standards, guidelines or codes of practice which are directed to the control of SBS. However, much existing material is relevant in this context because it makes recommendations about design and management factors which may contribute to the risk of SBS. The list below includes the main standards, guidelines and codes of practice which now exist.

Building Regulations

Approved Document F Ventilation

American Society of Heating, Refrigerating and Air Conditioning Engineers

AHE 1988 Equipment
AHF 1989 Fundamentals
AHH 1987 HVAC Systems and Applications
AHR 1986 Refrigeration Systems and Applications
Standard 62–73 Natural and Mechanical Ventilation
Standard 62–1981R Ventilation for Acceptable Indoor Air

British Standards

BS CP 413 Ducts for Building Services (under revision)
BS476 Ceilings: Ducts, Ventilation and Fire Resistance
BS2852 Testing for Rating of Room Air Conditioners for Cooling Performance
BS3456 Room Air Conditioners
BS4533 Luminaires
BS5295 Environmental Cleanliness in Enclosed Spaces
BS5384 Selection and Use of Control Systems for HVAC Installations
BS5720 Mechanical Ventilation and Air Conditioning in Buildings
BS5925 Ventilation Principles and Designing for Natural Ventilation
BS8206 Artificial Lighting

Building Research Establishment

BR81 Credibility and Truth - a New Risk Appraisal
BR86 Summer Conditions in Naturally Ventilated Offices
BR97 Building Regulations and Health
BR129 Daylighting as a Passive Solar Energy Option
Current Paper 36/74 Ventilation in Relation to Toxic and Flammable Gases in Buildings

Current Paper 75/75 Availability of Sunshine (Sunlight Protractor BR12)
Digest 69 Durability and Application of Plastics
Digest 140 Double Glazing and Double Windows
Digest 141 Wind Environment around Tall Buildings
Digest 143 Sound Insulation – Basic Principles
Digest 162 Traffic Noise and Overheating in Offices
Digest 163 Drying-out Buildings
Digest 185 Prediction of Traffic Noise – Part 1
Digest 186 Prediction of Traffic Noise – Part 2
Digest 192 The Acoustics of Rooms for Speech
Digest 206 Ventilation Requirements
Digest 210 Principles of Natural Ventilation
Digest 226 Thermal, Visual and Acoustic Requirements in Buildings
Digest 256 Office Lighting for Good Visual Task Conditions
Digest 272 Lighting Controls and Daylight Use
Digest 278 Vibrations – Buildings and Human Response
Digest 289 Building Management Systems
Digest 293 Improving the Sound Insulation of Separating Walls and Floors
Digest 309 Estimating Daylight in Buildings – Part 1
Digest 310 Estimating Daylight in Buildings – Part 2
Digest 333 Sound Insulation of Separating Walls and Floors – Part 1, Walls
Digest 334 Sound Insulation of Separating Walls and Floors – Part 2, Floors
Digest 338 Insulation against External Noise
Inf. Paper 25/82 Formaldehyde Vapour from Urea-Formaldehyde Foam
     Insulation
Inf. Paper 6/85 Selection of Building Energy Management Systems
Inf. Paper 2/87 Hazards Associated with Redevelopment of Contaminated Land
Inf. Paper 3/87 Solar Dazzle Reflected from Sloping Glazed Facades
Inf. Paper 5/87 Lighting Controls – an Essential Element of Energy-efficient
     Lighting
Inf. Paper 9/88 Methods for Reducing High Impact Sounds in Buildings
Inf. Paper 15/88 Average Daylight Factor – a Simple Basis for Daylight Design
SO18 Solar Heating Systems for the UK – Design, Installation and Economics

Building Services Research and Information Association

BAG1	1987	Operating and Maintenance Manuals for Building Services Installations
BB108	1987	Building Services Maintenance – an Annotated Bibliography
BB110	1987	Commissioning Building Services
BLD	1989	Building Services Legislation – an Annotated Bibliography
BTM1	1988	Commissioning HVAC Systems – Division of Responsibilities
BTM2	1988	Commissioning Variable Air Volume Systems
BTN4	1986	Room Air Distribution: Design and Evaluation
BTN5	1986	Building Air Tightness and Ventilation – International Practice
BTN1	1988	Ventilation Effectiveness in Mechanical Ventilation Systems
BTN3	1988	Micro-organisms in Building Services
BTN6	1988	Fresh Air Control – Case Study in Five Commercial Buildings

Chartered Institute of Building Service Engineers

AM1	1985	Automatic Controls and their Implications for System Design

AM2	1987	Window Design
CCA	1971	Air Distribution Systems
CCC	1973	Automatic Control
CCR	1972	Refrigerating Systems
CCW	1989	Water Distribution Systems
CIL	1984	Code for Interior Lighting
CP1	1984	Refrigeration – its Role in Environmental Control
GSA1	1979	Environmental Criteria for Design
GSA4	1986	Air Infiltration and Natural Ventilation
GSA7	1986	Internal Heat Gains
GSA8	1986	Summertime Temperatures in Buildings
GSA10	1986	Moisture Transfer and Condensation
LG3	1989	Lighting: Areas for Visual Display Terminals
TM8	1983	Design Notes for Ductwork
TM17	1989	Maintenance Management for Building Services
TM18	1989	Health, Safety and Welfare

Guide Section B 2 Ventilation and Air Conditioning Requirements

The authors wish to acknowledge the help of Iain Borden of the Bartlett School of Architecture in compiling these references.

APPENDIX 2

CASE STUDIES ON SICK BUILDING SYNDROME

Two case studies are presented to illustrate approaches to the control of SBS.

CASE STUDY 1

Introduction

This case involved an investigation of a regional office owned by a national organization and built to their specification in 1973. The organization owned many office buildings and was interested in solving problems in one particular building and learning general lessons which might be applicable to their other stock. The investigation brought to light a building with many of the characteristic features of a 'sick building' as identified by research (Finnegan et al., 1984; Valbjorn and Skov, 1987; Wilson and Hedge, 1987).

Problems with environmental comfort and SBS began to emerge approximately a year before the investigation and their persistence convinced the occupier of the need for remedial action. The office comprised two large open plan floors with a small number of management offices. Along the perimeter were narrow floor-to-ceiling windows, designed to be energy efficient. The lighting was a uniform grid of ceiling-mounted fluorescents. The space was air-conditioned, with roof-top plant, and refrigeration and heating were supplied from the ground floor.

Aims of the Investigation

- To measure the nature, prevalence and distribution of staff complaints and SBS within the building by means of a staff survey;
- to measure the ambient environmental and microbiological conditions in the office so that the validity of any complaints could be assessed;
- to investigate the performance of services within the building and determine the reasons for any deviations from environmental and microbiological standards;
- to suggest remedial measures that could be taken to reduce the incidence of complaints and SBS.

Staff survey

Method The staff survey employed a self-report questionnaire. The format closely followed a questionnaire used by Building Use Studies in the Office Environment Survey (OES). This enabled comparisons to be made between the case study building and other buildings with similar or contrasting features and services. Questions about SBS measured only those symptoms which occurred when staff were in the building and which disappeared when they left.

Results The case study building had a slightly higher level of SBS (an average of 3.18 symptoms per person) than the average level measured by the OES (3.11 symptoms per person). However, the level of SBS was lower than the OES average for air-conditioned buildings (3.44 symptoms per person). The overall problem of SBS in the case study was therefore not especially severe. Nevertheless 88% of the staff experienced five or more symptoms, and so there was a strong case for remedial action.

The problem was concentrated among female clerical staff, most of whom worked on the ground floor. Professional staff occupied most of the second floor and tended to be out of the building for half of every day. The most common symptoms reported were lethargy and 'dry' symptoms. The main environmental problems reported were dryness and stuffiness. Despite the reported stuffiness, a large number of staff also reported draughts, and 49% complained of the lighting being too bright and glaring. One other notable result was that 54% of staff felt that they lacked privacy: the open plan areas had no screening to demarcate space or to offer visual privacy.

Overall the pattern of staff comment and complaint indicated that problems were concentrated among staff doing routine sedentary work who in general tend to be the most sensitive to poor environmental conditions. The type of complaints and symptoms reported indicated that the main problems lay with the heating and ventilation system, the lighting and the office layout.

Study of environmental conditions

Method Measurements of the following environmental parameters were taken in the office areas:

- air temperatures at two heights (ankle and head height) in office areas and at the air inlet and air extract points;
- relative humidity in occupied areas on the ground and first floors;
- air velocities measured at nine locations and at nine heights spaced at 25 cm intervals from floor to ceiling, and flows measured by smoke tests;
- fresh air ventilation rates in the return air ducts of the ground and first floor offices;
- noise levels – mean sound pressure levels taken in occupied areas on the ground and first floors;
- lighting – illuminance levels on desk surfaces on the ground and first floors at a range of positions both normal and parallel to the rows of luminaires, and the uniformity ratio of illuminance were measured, and the glare indices were estimated.

The central plant (air supply, extract, chillers, boilers) and air distribution systems were fully inspected. During the monitoring period the chiller plant proved unreliable and this fault was investigated. As a consequence office air temperatures were taken with the chiller plant operating and with it partially failed.

Results Staff complaints of both high and variable temperatures were borne out by physical measures. Temperatures were higher than those recommended in the CIBSE guide (CIBSE, 1976a). On the ground floor they averaged over 23°C with the chiller working and 26°C when the chiller had failed. The situation on the first floor was little better.

The relative humidity on both floors was 60% which is within the range recommended by CIBSE. This indicates that the dry symptoms were not a response to low humidity and that reports of stuffiness were not a result of high humidity. The complaints of dryness might therefore be linked with the high ambient temperatures.

The measured air velocities varied between 0.09 and 0.13 metres per second. These velocities are too low to cause draughts but may contribute to feelings of stuffiness and to the reports of dry symptoms. Moving air can create feelings of freshness by cooling the skin, but this effect would not be evident here because the velocities were low. It must also be added that if the air movement is too high it will dry the skin which is not a desirable effect. The low velocities measured in this case are unlikely to have improved perceptions of air freshness because of the high ambient temperatures - people notice the movement of cool air more than that of warm air. The draughts which were reported were adjudged to derive from two sources: smoke tests showed that there were locations where there was clashing of air streams from adjacent diffusers. Each diffuser blew air in four directions. As diffusers were 1.8 m apart and the throw of air was 1.0 m, clashing which would direct the cold incoming air down into the occupied space was possible. The second possible source of draughts was the rapid movement of people in a crowded area. The measurements taken showed that peak air velocities of up to 1.0 metre per second occurred when staff were moving around. This is annoying for people who are located next to major circulation routes. The space planning created a large number of such routes and the open plan design offered no shielding.

From measures of air changes the fresh air ventilation rate was estimated to vary between 6.7 and 9.8 litres per second per person. The CIBSE recommendations* indicate that, when the office was fully occupied and the staff were smoking, the space was under-ventilated. This finding was again consistent with stuffy conditions with odour problems, which may cause some of the symptoms reported.

Noise levels were, on average, 55–56 dB(A). These are not untypical of open plan offices but nevertheless exceed the recommendations of the Building Research Establishment (1976). They recommend 45–50 dB(A) as the maximum intrusive noise level in large offices to allow for normal conversation to take place comfortably. Twenty-seven per cent of staff were dissatisfied with noise conditions and this may be because the average measurements disguised irritating peaks in noise levels. It was unclear from the data collected whether the noise level in the building would cause headaches.

Measures of illuminance on the desk surfaces averaged about 1200 lux. Positions near walls had slightly lower levels of illuminance. These results explain the staff complaints that the lighting was too bright and the feeling that the lighting was highly uniform. The normal illuminance level recommended for staff working with VDUs is 500 lux (CIBSE, 1989).

Study of microbiological conditions

Method Samples of air, water and dust were taken for analysis from a range of sites both inside and out.

Results Counts of bacteria and fungi in the air samples taken from inside the offices were lower than those measured in samples taken outside the building, and neither level indicated any risk of contamination. Analysis of dust samples showed a typical picture of office dust, with paper fibres, synthetic fibres, human skin, insect remains and plant hairs prevalent. There were no indications that the concentrations of dust or the nature of the dusts were likely to cause health effects.

The results of the water analysis were completely satisfactory apart from water taken from the cooling tower reservoir. This was found to be heavily contaminated with the bacterium Legionella pneumophila. On discovering this, a separate investigation was begun and appropriate remedial action was taken immediately.

Recommendations made

HVAC
✳ Increase the fresh air ventilation rate;

(*CIBSE (1976a) recommend a range of air supply rates from 8 to 25 litres per second per person. The selected rate will vary according to the degree of smoking, the nature of the work and the density of occupants. It should be noted that in CIBSE (1976b) a recommendation of 16 litres per second per person is made where the occupants are sedentary and there is some smoking.)

* re-time the start-up sequence of the air-conditioning plant to ensure temperature of 20°C at the start of the day;
* investigate further the reliability and capacity of the chilling plant;
* examine and modify the air distribution of each diffuser;
* divide the first floor core area into two control zones to provide a better tailored environment;
* draught-proof the sources of air infiltration.

Lighting
* Reduce the illuminance and heat gain from the lighting by removing alternate luminaires in a chequer board array;
* retain all perimeter luminaires to 'wash' the walls with light and create visual uplift and interest;
* consider the installation of low brightness diffusers to reduce complaints of glare if the reduction in illumination does not reduce complaints;
* consider the installation of high frequency fluorescents to reduce perceptible and imperceptible flicker if the above measures do not reduce complaints.

Microbiological
* Instigate immediate remedial action to eliminate Legionella pneumophila;
* no other action was suggested other than to ensure that cleaning regimes are supported with regular deep cleans to prevent dust build-up.

Office Layout
* Review space planning philosophy, which currently produces large clusters of desks, to determine whether greater privacy is possible;
* replan the office to reduce the number of main circulation routes;
* consider the provision of screening around selected workplaces to enhance feelings of privacy and to reduce draughts.

CASE STUDY 2

Background

This case is of particular interest because it demonstrates that SBS can occur in buildings that appear to many observers to be of a high quality. The building had been totally refurbished only a year before the investigation. It had new furniture and fittings of a high standard, and a fan coil air conditioning system had been installed. Nevertheless, shortly after the occupying organization moved in from nearby offices, complaints of discomfort and sickness arose and were noted by the Personnel Department. The other interesting feature about this building was that the occupier was a private sector sales-oriented company, where the staff were highly motivated. Indeed, one of the reasons for the investigation was that staff were concerned that SBS was reducing their productivity.

The building was on five storeys, with each floor having 300 square metres of usable office space. One hundred and thirteen staff occupied the building, concentrated on the three middle floors. The average density of occupation varied between the three floors at 5.7–12.8 square metres per person. The occupied areas were lit solely by uplighting with no ceiling-mounted luminaires.

Aims of the Investigation

An investigation was instigated after an initial walk-through evaluation of the offices and discussions with key managers. This preliminary work identified a number of problem areas and the investigation was set up with the following main aims:

- to measure the nature, prevalence and distribution of staff complaints and sick building symptoms within the building by means of a staff survey;
- to evaluate the performance of the air-conditioning system, and in particular to determine whether the design and operation of the system was able to handle heat loads in the building;
- to evaluate environmental conditions and air quality through monitoring of temperature, humidity, air movement and filtration;
- to assess the adequacy of illumination levels on work surfaces.

Staff survey

Method The same as in case study 1.

Results Staff dissatisfaction was exceedingly high by comparison with the OES data. The OES average sickness rate measured in buildings serviced by fan coil units was 3.8 symptoms per person (Wilson and Hedge, 1987): in the case study building, the average was 5.26 symptoms per person.

It was particularly noteworthy that senior as well as junior staff and males as well as females suffered extensively from SBS. This differs from the usual pattern and illustrates the point that in very sick buildings the problems affect all types of staff. The symptoms of lethargy, dry and itchy eyes, sore throats and blocked nose were all experienced by over 50% of the staff and the incidence was spread evenly across all floors.

Most staff were doing sedentary work but it was not routine, and 44% of staff described their work as highly stressful. This compares with only 20% in the OES. Most of the staff believed that working conditions reduced their productivity, with 36% saying that this reduction was by 20% or more. This is likely to represent an overestimate, but it does indicate a high level of concern on the part of the staff.

In terms of environmental conditions the following problems were noted:

- the majority of staff rated environmental conditions as hot and stuffy in summer with dry and stale air all year;
- over 71% of staff were very dissatisfied with the lighting: this is an extremely high score by comparison with data from other studies carried out by Building Use Studies.

Staff also complained of a drab interior colour scheme and a gloomy depressing atmosphere. Many of the interior fittings were of dark woods with deep maroon fabrics. All the windows were tinted to prevent glare but this created a dull uniform source of external light.

Evaluation of the air-conditioning system and environmental conditions

Method Evaluation of the air-conditioning system included studies of drawings and documentation, detailed inspection and performance measurements of central plant (air supply, extract, chillers, boilers), distribution systems and terminal units (fan coil units and radiators), calculation of cooling loads, and discussion with designers, suppliers and operators. The filters in the main plant room and most fan coils were checked. Detailed calculations were made of cooling requirements across the building including measurements of heat gains from equipment. Point-in-time measures of temperature and humidity were taken on all floors on 10 occasions.

Results The HVAC system was of a high standard, and the plant rooms were clean and well maintained. The humidifier relied on steam which carries some health and safety advantages, and the operating manual for the HVAC was commendably comprehensive.

The average fresh air supply rate was 17 litres per second per person but this generosity of air supply disguised other problems. The air was supplied and extracted at floor level and had little chance of circulating into the occupied zone. This created stagnant air with deficient mixing of the cool supply air with warm room air. The result was stale stuffy conditions.

These conditions were further exacerbated by deficiencies in the cooling system. Faults were fourfold:

- the performance of the fan coil units was below the stated capacity set out in performance charts provided by the manufacturers;
- all the filters examined were dirty, and this reduced air movement through the coils which in turn affected the ability of the fan coil units to cool the air as well as clean it;
- several settings and controls on the air-conditioning system needed changing – the current settings were adding to cooling requirements as well as wasting energy;
- the system, as then operating, did not have sufficient capacity to deal with cooling loads in the building. While peak cooling loads in the building were found to be 135 kW, the current cooling capability was 50 kW. As a result space temperatures frequently reached 25°C.

At a minimum, the HVAC system needed tuning. A more radical proposal was that the air circulation, which was very sluggish, should be improved by re-positioning return air ducts from the floor to the ceiling. This option, on first inspection of the ceiling void, appeared feasible but needed to be fully costed.

Lighting survey

Method The lighting survey involved examination of the uplighting luminaires and measurements of illumination levels at all work-stations and at the level of the luminaires. In addition energy consumption by the lighting was calculated. Tests were carried out to establish the contribution made to overall illuminance in a typical office by the various sources – windows, uplighters and task lights. An assessment was made of the relative light outputs of existing uplighters with both original and new lamps, and of a new uplighter using a high pressure sodium lamp.

Results Measurements of illumination levels showed that the lighting was performing badly. While the recommended level of light for office work is 500 lux, average readings at work-stations were 224 lux. The principal problem was that a large number of lamps in the uplighters had partially expired. This was because a previous problem with switching control prevented them from being automatically turned off at night and staff failed to recognize that replacement was required. It was recommended that these lamps were replaced. Luminance levels could have been improved further by the installation of high pressure sodium lamps with a higher efficacy and longer life. If these improvements did not raise illuminance levels sufficiently, then consideration would have to be given to a supplementary ceiling-mounted fluorescent scheme.

There were other deficiencies: the ceiling, at a height of 2.3 m, was really too low for an uplighting scheme; the colour and reflectance of the interior finishes were totally inappropriate for a lighting scheme which depended on reflected light; the heavy tint of the windows virtually eliminated natural light so that it made no contribution to illumination on the working plane. Any change in these elements would have been extremely costly.

Particle measurements

Method Dust samples were taken on every floor from fan coil filters. These were analysed by optical microscopy.

Results No asbestos or man-made mineral fibres were found in the samples taken. The main particulates were typical organic matter found in offices, as described in case study 1. However, there were large amounts of building dusts in some samples which were thought to result from the refurbishment work which had been completed only recently. This high level of building dusts may create sensations of dryness and cause irritation of the eye and upper respiratory tract.

Options Measurements of environmental conditions illustrated that staff complaints were justified. Two strategies were available to improve conditions:

- nil cost or even financially beneficial remedial action (for example re-setting controls to reduce heat gain which may also save energy);

- medium-cost options of around £50,000 such as replacement of the lighting scheme and re-positioning of the air extract in office areas.

The client was made aware that there were also more fundamental deficiencies in the way that the building was fitted out which could not be remedied other than at very high cost. This meant that staff dissatisfaction could only be reduced and not eradicated.

CHAPTER C6

ALLERGY

Morris Greenberg

Mount Sinai Medical Center, New York

WHAT IS AN ALLERGY?

'Allergy' is commonly defined as a hypersensitivity to a substance that causes the body to react to any contact with it; but the term is used loosely and consequently gives rise to considerable confusion.

A *true* allergic response to a substance can be defined as signs and symptoms of disease produced by specific immunological mechanisms initiated by that substance. However the term is also used increasingly and more widely to describe signs and symptoms of disease for which there is no specific immunological mechanism, but where an individual simply feels better for avoiding the substance and becomes ill again on re-exposure to it (Mumby, 1985). Debate on this issue of definition continues in the medical profession.

There are two distinguishable elements to the true allergic process. In the first phase the foreign material enters the body and is recognized, and the body produces an antibody to it. This stage is silent in terms of disease, but laboratory tests are able to detect the response. The second stage comprises repeated exposures, varying from several occasions to frequent heavy exposures over decades, which may occur without complaint until suddenly the apparent tolerance breaks down and signs and symptoms of allergic disease appear.

Over the years our understanding of the complex processes in allergic disease has evolved so that, while the above simple description holds in general, a complex system of intermediary cells present in the blood and tissues and various constituents of body fluids have been identified that are required to take part in the causation of true allergic disease. The quantity of a substance and the frequency and duration of exposure required to elicit antibody production, and subsequently allergic disease, vary with the innate properties of that substance, the point of entry into the body (inhalation seems to be the most powerful route) and the individual's capacity to respond. Certain individuals are hypersusceptible to becoming allergic to commonly occurring materials (e.g. pollen, fungi, house mites, domestic animals) and they are referred to as 'atopic'. These individuals are also found to be more susceptible to becoming sensitized and allergic to a range of materials met at work.

There is a mistaken belief that the non-atopic person is not at risk of allergy. In practice, although atopic subjects as a group respond more quickly and to lower levels of exposure, the non-atopic group will respond, although a longer time may be required and a different pattern of response may be elicited. The importance of distinguishing true allergy from 'allergy' in its wider, non-restrictive sense, apart from treatment, relates to the advice given to persons with true allergy. Where there is risk of exposure to a known material with a record for causing allergy, then greater care to avoid exposure is indicated. However, when disease results from other mechanisms, there is no reason for asymptomatic atopic persons to be considered at greater risk. Estimates of the prevalence of atopy vary between 25 and 50% according to geographical and age factors, so blanket restrictions would discriminate against a substantial proportion of the population (Greenberg et al., 1970).

The management of hazardous materials cannot be achieved by the employment only of survivors but by the principles of substitution, containment, local exhaust ventilation and finally personal protection. Once an individual has developed allergy, only extremely efficient personal protection can be expected to work, as response may be to amounts of the material that are below the limit of chemical detection.

In the remainder of this chapter, 'allergy' is used to cover both true allergy and the wider, less-restrictive meaning.

SIGNS AND SYMPTOMS OF ALLERGIC DISEASE

Any organ or tissue of the body can be the site of an allergic response. Commonly, complaints are referred to eyes, nose, throat, chest and skin. Only the most troublesome site may be complained of although an examination and further questioning may indicate more extensive involvement.

It must be remembered that there is a limited repertoire of disturbances of structure and function at these sites which is shared with several other disease mechanisms that can be described broadly as chemical, physical and pharmacological. The common complaints are:

- *eyes:* itching, redness, soreness, swelling of the lids, weeping;
- *nose:* itching, soreness, blocked, running, sneezing;
- *chest:* discomfort, tightness, wheeze, breathlessness, cough;
- *skin:* itching, redness, whealing, blistering, scaling, oozing.

The terms 'hay fever', 'asthma' and 'dermatitis' are commonly applied to various groups of these signs and symptoms but they do not necessarily mean any specific external cause, or indeed any external cause, or specific mechanism.

In addition to these site-specific complaints, more generalized complaints may be made, such as loss of energy, and aches and pains in muscles, bones and joints in the absence of swelling. Loss of appetite severe enough to be accompanied by weight loss and a feeling of feverishness with raised body temperature may also occur.

Several time sequences may be recognized between an exposure and the allergic response. Exposure may be followed by an 'immediate' complaint, i.e. any of the signs and symptoms listed above appear within seconds or minutes. The response may be delayed for several hours after exposure which, if the period of exposure is brief, is likely to be misleading when the cause is being searched for. An individual exposure may elicit an immediate response which remits promptly on cessation of exposure, to be followed by a separate, delayed response. When cessation of exposure is followed promptly by relief from complaint this may readily prompt an association with cause. Unfortunately, whilst in the majority of instances cessation of exposure promptly leads to loss of symptoms, in a proportion complaints may continue for hours and even years in a fluctuating manner. While the signs and symptoms listed might at first sight seem no more than a nuisance, when the lungs and airways are affected the effects can be temporarily disabling or permanent, progressive and fatal. There is also the possibility of death during an acute episode.

'ALLERGY' AND CONSTRUCTION

Using the term 'allergy' in the non-restrictive mode to cover the whole gamut of mechanisms that elicit more or less the same pattern of complaints and similar long-term health consequences, what are the sources of the responsible agents? Two sources are the materials used in construction, and the environment created by the construction. Broadly speaking, residents mainly suffer from environmental causes whereas construction workers are mainly at risk from materials. An exception to this general rule is the do-it-yourself (DIY) householder who can sensitize himself by heavy exposure in 'construction' work and suffer subsequently from exposure to residual traces. (An example of this is the householder who treated extensive areas of woodwork with polyurethane varnish and subsequently coughed and wheezed at night for months on end.) In general, however, adequate data for evaluating the burden of 'allergy' for construction workers or for householders are not available.

CONSTRUCTION MATERIALS WITH 'ALLERGIC' POTENTIAL

A wide range of construction materials have an 'allergic' potential, including adhesives, concrete and mortar mixtures, cleaners for brickwork and stone, decorative and protective treatments for concrete, brickwork, metals, timber and timber-based products, floor treatments and finishes, formwork and mould treatments, grouting material, insulants, and sealants. All these may contain chemical compounds that on skin contact or on inhalation of vapour, droplet or fine dust forms can lead to 'allergic' complaints in unprotected workers. Any attempt to produce a comprehensive list of substances with 'allergic' potential would be herculean and rapidly obsolete with technological change. However, it is the responsibility of the manufacturer, importer or supplier of substances to provide, to each person they supply, adequate safety information to ensure that substances will be safe when used, stored or transported. These legal obligations are in practice normally discharged by providing a comprehensive safety data sheet of potential hazards and safety precautions.

The active chemical responsible for disease can be of varying degrees of complexity ranging from the simplest inorganic material (e.g. chrome ions present in concrete, causing dermatitis) to organic materials (e.g. polyisocyanates, causing respiratory disease). In unprotected workers, the potential of an agent to cause respiratory or skin disease is largely dependent upon the site of maximum contact, rather than on an intrinsic property of the agent to aggress the respiratory system or the skin. Nevertheless, certain agents such as polyisocyanates are more commonly associated with respiratory effects, chrome more commonly with skin effects, and formaldehyde with both. Some products aim to prevent disease by using reactive agents of low volatility. However, if they are viscous they may be heated before decanting, which can have dire effects, and products intended for safe use by roller application may end up being sprayed to speed up the work.

The safety of a product could be tied in with the conditions of recommended use, but in the real world of construction this might be naive. Even when recommendations rise above the inadequate *'Avoid contact — do not use in inadequately ventilated areas'*, it is reasonably foreseeable that, in the absence of competent supervision, precautions may go by default. The requirements for impermeable protective clothing and high efficiency respiratory protection may not be practicable on a construction site — unlike a factory where they remain in the province of a specialist. In addition, when sales of the product are through conventional trade and DIY outlets, it is possible that products sold to the general public and to the non-specialist may be mis-used.

THE INDOOR ENVIRONMENT AND 'ALLERGY'

Temperature, relative humidity and air speed are among the indoor environmental factors that, acting directly, can produce complaints relating to eyes, nose, throat, chest and skin, or exacerbate pre-existing conditions in individuals. Construction materials can contribute to these complaints. Simple dusts, both discrete particulate and fibrous, have produced eye, nose, throat chest and skin complaints. On occasion, there appears to be an interaction with indoor climatic conditions, as with the seasonal skin complaints of office workers at visual display units attributed to the combined effects of dust, low relative humidity and static electricity charges. Mineral fibre has also been associated with episodes of eye, respiratory and skin complaints when insulation material inappropriately placed in forced air ventilation ducting has been disturbed by air currents. Volatile well-perceived chemicals such as solvents used in paints and wood treatments, and formaldehyde released from resins, may provoke complaints of an 'allergic' and more general nature.

Construction workers tend not to complain about climatic conditions, dusts or volatile agents, either because they accept discomfort as their lot, or because as survivors they are tolerant, or occasionally because they are adequately protected. Residents as a general rule are more likely to complain when they experience physical discomfort or perceive there to be a loss of amenity, even with faint traces of solvents and other pungent materials, but materials rarely give rise to skin problems for residents.

More important than building materials in the cause or exacerbation of 'allergic' complaints are the irritant gases and fumes arising from domestic activities such as heating, cooking and smoking. The increase in domestic insulation and reduction of air exchange in the pursuit of fuel economy and energy efficiency has led to an increased importance of the role of indoor air pollution, supplanting the general environment as the predominant atmospheric hazard (see Chapter C1). Residents may complain seasonally of dryness and itching of the skin as a result of the low relative humidity associated with central heating in winter.

In addition to the above conditions is a range of domestic flora and fauna responsible for 'allergic' and truly allergic disease. At the macroscopic level there are domestic pets (cats, dogs, hamsters) whose dejecta permeate the household and sensitize the susceptible. Obviously, construction professionals cannot be held responsible or be expected to remedy this situation. At the microscopic level there are house mites, sporing fungi and yeasts and, less commonly, amoebae that can colonize a building and its equipment and cause allergic and other diseases. House mites, fungi and yeasts are potent sensitizers, constituting the common allergens to which the atopic person more readily becomes allergic. They flourish in an environment of high relative humidity and low ventilation. Fragments of these organisms or their decayed material or their metabolites, becoming airborne, can be inhaled and cause disease. Stagnant water forms a good site for the growth of organisms and their subsequent death to produce an organic 'soup'. This material as well as spores and fragments of organisms can become airborne by convection or by active dispersal by ventilation. Episodes of respiratory complaints and more general symptoms may be chronic or episodic, depending on a variety of conditions. This is a field where architects and building services engineers can contribute to the prevention of human disease, by designing buildings where environmental conditions do not encourage the proliferation of microbiological agents and where constraints on ventilation do not lead to the build-up of toxic and irritant fuel combustion products. The principles of indoor environmental control have been established, as have those of energy conservation (see Chapters C1, C3 and D3).

Consideration of the bases for human health disturbance can lead to an optimum trade-off between the ventilation requirements for health and the measures required to conserve energy. Even in a civil engineering context it is necessary for engineers to consider biological principles in design. In a concrete box girder, failure to prevent the accumulation during construction of detritus which will serve as a substrate for micro-organisms, and the presence of a damp unventilated environment for their proliferation can lead to premature weakening of the fabric with a severely reduced lifetime for the structure.

CONCLUSIONS

∗ Any organ or tissue of the body can be the site of an allergic response. Complaints can be site-specific or of a more general nature, but clearly not all complaints of sore eyes, sneezing, tight chest or blistering skin are allergic reactions.

∗ Adequate data for evaluating the burden of 'allergy' for construction workers or for householders are not available. That a problem exists may be deduced for the former from experience in other industrial groups, and for the latter from clinical experience.

∗ For construction workers probably the commonest problem is 'dermatitis'. Contact with wet concrete with its alkaline effect and its potential for chrome sensitization, and the vigorous use of abrasives and organic solvents for skin cleansing, are probably major contributors.

∗ Unless adequately controlled, *in situ* polymerization and the use of polymer formulations by workers would be expected to lead to skin and respiratory sensitization. If the installation of urea formaldehyde foam cavity insulation is not undertaken in accordance with appropriate standards, residents may complain of skin and respiratory discomfort as well as general discomfort.

* Residents may complain seasonally of dryness and itching of the skin as a result of the low relative humidity associated with central heating in winter.

* Unlike the situation with construction workers, materials rarely give rise to skin problems for residents.

* However, ineptly installed mineral fibre insulation in ventilation trunking has given rise to irritation of eyes, nose, throat and chest.

* For the householder, the major respiratory health hazards to initiate disease or exacerbate existing disease result from irritant gases and fumes generated by cooking, heating and smoking, from microscopic flora and fauna encouraged by indoor climatic conditions, and from dejecta from domestic pets.

* Measures are available to the industry to prevent or ameliorate many of these complaints.

REFERENCES

Mumby, K., (1985), *The Food Allergy Plan*, Unwin Paperbacks, London.

Greenberg, M., Milne, J.F. and Watts, B. (1970), Br. Med. J., 2, 629-33.

Woods, B. and Calnan, C.D. (1976), *Toxic Wood*, British Journal of Dermatology 95, Supplement 13, 1-97.

Control of Substances Hazardous to Health Regulations (1988), HM Stationery Office, London.

World Health Organisation (WHO) (1988), *Indoor Air Pollutants: exposure and health effects*. Report of a WHO meeting, June 1982, WHO Copenhagen.

PESTS

Peter L G Bateman
Rentokil Ltd.

'Take heede how thou laiest the bane for the rats, lest thou poison
thy servant, thy selfe and thy brats'.

THOMAS TUSSER, 1580,
Five Hundred Pointes of Good Husbandrie

INTRODUCTION

A pest is defined as a troublesome or destructive animal, one that
annoys especially by imposing itself when not wanted, and as any
organism that injures or irritates man. In buildings, pests spread
dangerous contamination, cause expensive depreciation, can ruin a
reputation, and are prohibited by legislation. When a contractor has to
pay £125,000 compensation for failing to protect a site worker from the
rats that gave him Weil's Disease, or an international hotel undergoing
a multi-million pound refurbishment is heavily fined for having
cockroaches, it can be seen that the problem of pests in buildings
deserves serious attention.

In the context of buildings, pests fall into six categories:

1 Those that can literally eat the occupants out of house and home or
   destroy the building fabric, including woodworm, rodents, textile pests
   such as clothes moths and carpet beetles, or pigeons and starlings
   which foul structures and block gutters and downpipes.
2 Those that spread illnesses or carry bacteria from filth to food,
   including flies, cockroaches, mice and rats, which pollute the indoor
   environment and threaten those who live in it. Mould spores or mites
   attracted to the nests or droppings of pests or circulated in air-
   conditioning may indirectly cause other illnesses.
3 Parasitical pests such as fleas, bed bugs and lice that are introduced by
   cats, dirty clothing or secondhand bedding and furniture, and biting
   flies that breed in neglected guttering and stagnant water.
4 Stored-product insects that destroy stored commodities, such as the
   wide range of moth, mite and beetle species that thrives in
   warehouses, silos and factories and may also breed in old birds' nests

or buildings, including scavengers such as hide, mealworm and spider beetles.

5 Seasonal nuisances that may be unacceptable for various reasons, such as booklice, woodlice, wasps, flying ants, spiders and silverfish. Some of them, although harmless themselves, may be indications of some defect that needs to be corrected. Silverfish for instance, often indicate a source of rising damp, condensation or leaking plumbing that needs to be put right.

6 Occasional wanderers from outdoors, such as earwigs, crane flies, maybugs or ground beetles.

These are some examples which indicate the nature of the problems these pests can cause:

- 'bird-fancier's lung' and other illnesses can be caught from dried pigeon droppings inhaled during cleaning or demolition;
- wet droppings on walkways, ledges and staircases have caused numerous accidents;
- women in a multi-million pound computer block near Guildford were being bitten by fleas that were traced to a dead starling in the intake of the air-conditioning system;
- mice in a Ministry of Defence office destroyed secret blueprints of a mine;
- flies in a canteen kitchen sent half the workers home with food poisoning;
- booklice in a damp storage room made documents impossible to handle;
- firebrats invaded a computer on its voyage from Japan – it had to be fumigated before it could be used;
- lifts were brought to a standstill by rats jamming the cable drum in the shaft;
- buildings have been destroyed by fire-raising mice;
- pigeons have blocked downpipes, guttering and hopperheads with their nests and droppings have caused dry rot outbreaks;
- flocks of starlings have brought chaos to the Forth Road Bridge and bombarded Southampton Docks with an estimated 4 tons of droppings a night, obliterating the dockside cranes which the dockers refused to operate;
- dust mites in offices contribute to Sick Building Syndrome, according to Dr Leinster at the 1990 British Occupational Hygiene Conference;
- shoppers complain about pigeons fouling shop fronts and pavements;
- there were mice on the top floor of the new Stock Exchange

before it was occupied for trading (the Financial Times called it the power of the small infestor).

Having pests is also bad public relations. Loss of business from closure of premises, or from bad publicity because of prosecution for infestation can be considerable.

These are just a few examples of why there is a need to pest-proof buildings as far as is possible and, where appropriate, to use the services of a competent specialist pest control contractor to prevent such problems arising.

The truly pest-proof building has yet to be designed, basically because if people can enter and leave it, so can insects, mites, rodents and birds, but sound design, good construction and reliable maintenance can considerably reduce the risks arising from infestation.

Although the health hazard no longer matches that posed by The Black Death, the cost of damage by pests in modern sophisticated buildings runs into many millions of pounds and far exceeds the price of available prevention. The disturbance caused by refurbishment work often results in displaced mice, fleas, or cockroaches seeking their creature comforts elsewhere. Their new home may still be in the same building, but may be the one next door or in the next block.

LEGISLATION

There are a number of laws against continued operation of unhygienic or infested premises.

Under the Prevention of Damage by Pests Act 1949 occupiers of premises have a legal duty to report to their local authority if rats or mice are present on their land 'in substantial numbers'. Where the premises are used for a business including manufacturing, storing, transporting or selling food, then the occupier must report any infestation to the local authority where the infestation involves a 'risk of substantial loss of or damage to food'. The local authority may give whatever directions it considers appropriate to control the infestation. Where food is involved the Act relates to mites and insects as well as to rodents.

The Food Hygiene Regulations 1970 (incorporated under the Food Act 1984 and adopted under the Food Safety Act 1990) are intended to secure the hygiene of food preparation and sale. They make provision for the cleanliness of premises and persons dealing with food, the design and maintenance of food premises, temperatures for food storage and disposal of waste. The new Food Safety Act 1990 requires food premises to be registered with the local authority and permits food authorities to provide food hygiene training. The Act curtails Crown Immunity for Government buildings (including hospitals and prisons).

The Public Health Act 1936 and the Housing Act 1961 empower local authorities to take action against health hazards attributable to pests. They also impose obligations on local authorities to prevent infestation in buildings for which they are responsible in the districts which they control.

A warning has been issued to construction workers by a Health and Safety Executive medical adviser to avoid inhaling the spore-laden dust from dried pigeon droppings. The Health and Safety at Work etc Act places a duty on employers to safeguard the health, safety and welfare of their staff and of anyone else visiting their premises. Employees also have a legal duty to use protective clothing issued to them and not to interfere with items introduced to protect health and safety.

The Animals (Cruel Poisons) Act 1962 states that where a satisfactory humane alternative exists a ban may be imposed on the use of poisons for killing rats and mice which cause symptoms of pain and suffering. Restrictions have been imposed on certain substances, eg strychnine, by the Animals (Cruel Poisons) Regulations 1963, The Food and Environment Protection Act 1985 makes it a criminal offence to use as a pesticide any substance that has not been specifically cleared for the purpose under the Control of Pesticide Regulations 1986. These Regulations also require that all those whose business involves applying pesticides must be trained to a proper level of competence.

More recently, the Control of Substances Hazardous to Health Regulations 1988 (introduced under the Health and Safety at Work Act) require formal assessment and control of hazards arising out of potential exposure to pesticide chemicals used by businesses. The Health and Safety Commission has published an Approved Code of Practice under these Regulations specifically in the context of fumigation operations.

Fines imposed can now be substantial, and unhygienic food premises, processes or equipment posing a risk of injury to health can be closed down by Environmental Health Officers. Breaches of the criminal provisions of the Food Safety Act 1990 can result in up to two years imprisonment and/or an unlimited fine being imposed on culpable individuals in addition to the fines levied on the companies which they work for.

The Wildlife and Countryside Act 1981 is relevant in a different way, in that it gives protection to various birds, mammals and plants. In particular, disturbance of bats is largely prohibited and there are substantial penalties for causing bat deaths. The Act incorporates formal legislation on protection of birds, and provides lists of birds whose numbers may be controlled in prescribed circumstances.

CONTAMINATION: HEALTH HAZARDS FROM PESTS IN BUILDINGS

The diseases pests can transmit are summarised in Table C7.1. The main types and sources of contamination are:

Table C7.1 Some Diseases Transmissible To Man From Pests Found In Buildings

VECTOR	PATHOGEN	ILLNESS
Brown Rat and House Mouse	Leptospira icterohaemorrhagiae	Weil's Disease
	Trichinella spiralis	Trichinosis
	Salmonella spp.	Salmonella Food Poisoning
	Yersinia pestis	Plague
	Salmonella spp.	Food Poisoning
	Streptobacillus moniliformis	Rat Bite Fever
	Erisepelothrix rhusiopathiae	Erysipelis
	Rickettsia typhus	Murine Typhus
	Rickettsia prowazeki	Scrub Typhus
	Rickettsia Uzari	Rickettsial Pox
Cockroach	Shigella alkalescens	Dysentery
	Shigella paradysenteriae	Summer diarrhoea
Bacteria	Pseudomonas aeruginosa	Infections of: urinary tract, upper respiratory tract, wounds and burns.
	Staphylococcus aureus	Boils
	Streptococcus faecalis	Faecal contamination
	Escherichia coli	Urogenital/ intestinal infections
	Salmonella spp. including	Typhoid, other enteric fevers,
	S.typhi & S. typhimurium	gastroenteritis
	Mycobacterium lepraemurium	Leprosy
	Klebsiella pneumoniae	Pneumonia
	Serratia marcesens	Upper resp.tract infection
	Proteus vulgaris	Gastroenteric infection
	Yersinia pestis	Plague
Fungi	Aspergillus fumigatus	Aspergillosis
Protozoa	Entamoeba histolytica	Dysentery
Helminths (worms)	Enterobius vermicularis	Pin/thread worm
	Trichuris trichiura	Whipworm
	Ascaris lumbricoides	Roundworms
	Ancylostoma duodenale, Necator americanus	Hookworms
Viruses	Hepatitis	Jaundice
	Poliomyelitis	Polio
Pharaohs Ant	Salmonella	Food Poisoning Pseudomonas Infections of urinary or respiratory tract or wounds
	Staphylococcus aureus	Generalised infections including sore throats
	Streptococcus spp. Clostridium spp.	Food poisoning

- Flies, cockroaches, ants, mice, sparrows etc., pollute food and spread diseases including several forms of food poisoning and gastro-enteritis. Dead insects, rodent hairs and droppings are unwanted ingredients, making food unacceptable for consumption. Dead birds or rodents in water storage tanks or air-conditioning ducting are also sources of problems.
- The average house mouse sheds 80 droppings every 24 hours and because its bladder is ineffective, it constantly contaminates all food, cooking equipment, work surfaces and storage areas.
- A house fly carries about one and a half million germs on its body, legs and hind gut as it commutes from filth to food. Cholera, diphtheria, ophthalmia, and dysentery, are all fly-borne diseases.
- House dust mites cause allergic reactions in some people, severe cases developing Kawasaki Disease which has proved fatal in young children. Mites are also implicated in Sick Building Syndrome.
- In tropical climates, buildings are also invaded by typhus-carrying lice, malarial mosquitoes or vectors such as ticks, which spread other fatal diseases.
- In Europe, the Pharaohs ant has been found to carry 19 pathogenic organisms around British hospitals; and the cockroach has been associated with 40 disease or wound infection organisms inside buildings.
- Salmonella, pseudomonas, staphylococcus, streptococcus, polio virus, E.coli, are just a few of the organisms carried by these pests.
- Others spread by rodents include trichinosis, Weil's Disease (ten deaths last year in the UK), and numerous livestock diseases.
- Histoplasmosis and aspergillosis are associated with bird droppings. Feral pigeons at feed warehouses in Liverpool were responsible for transmitting the 1984 outbreaks of Fowl Pest to Britain's poultry flocks, and sparrows infesting a canteen were implicated in a food poisoning outbreak.
- Ornithosis (a 'flu-like illness) can be carried by starlings to man.

PRINCIPLES OF CONTROL

Pest control is based on three types of action: exclusion, restriction and destruction.

Exclusion Much can be done to build-out pests at the design stage of a project and some detailed guidance is given in the next section.

Restriction Most modern construction materials and methods can make a building relatively impervious to pest attack and again detailed guidance on active construction and maintenance measures is given in the next section.

Destruction Some public health pests are dealt with by local authority Environmental Health Departments without charge, but this is usually a 'fire brigade' service, dealing with complaints as they arise. Only certain pests are covered and there is seldom the long term protection of a contract. DIY products are available for very limited infestations, e.g. household insecticides in sprays or puffer packs, rodenticides as ready-to-use baits and traps. These may be adequate as 'first aid' measures but for limited infestations only, and it must be remembered that contamination of food with pesticide residues is as unacceptable as contamination by the pests themselves. Most premises need continual monitoring, regular inspections and treatments whenever necessary to prevent infestations building up. This is the role of the pest control servicing company as a contractor (see the section later on the use of pest control contractors).

GUIDELINES FOR DESIGN, CONSTRUCTION AND MAINTENANCE

Keeping buildings and their occupants in good health requires effort by all those responsible for the design, construction, maintenance and provision of specialist cleaning and pest control services. The following notes provide guidelines for positive action that can be taken in design and planning, at the construction stage, and in operation and maintenance to protect a building from pests. It is recognised that not all suggestions can be applied to all projects since they may be incompatible with other requirements.

Overall Project Design

- Buildings such as food factories, catering premises, pharmaceutical warehouses, hospitals and hotels are clearly vulnerable to infestation. Risks become higher if buildings are sited in areas likely to be already populated by pests. A refuse tip, canal or railway bank, livestock farm or slaughterhouse close by may be significant as a reservoir of possible trouble.
- Any refuse compound associated with a development should be sited well away from main buildings and constructed on a smooth-rendered concrete base with ground drains. Any incinerators must be capable of dealing with the quantity and type of refuse to be burned.

- For high risk buildings, consider fitting an electronic mouse detector system.

Building Design

- Good foundations will normally stop rats from getting in to buildings but if they do not rest on bedrock they should extend vertically below ground at least about 900 mm or have an L-shaped curtain wall about 600 mm deep with a 300 mm projection from the building. On piled foundations the reinforced concrete beam spanning the piles should be about 900 mm deep below ground level to stop rodents.
- To protect against mice, no external or other cavity wall should have any holes larger than 5 mm in diameter.
- Rats and mice will climb up rough exterior surfaces so it is best to eliminate such finishes and to avoid projecting quoins, buttresses or ledges which might give a foothold or provide access to any higher points of entry that are unlikely to be as well proofed as those on the ground floor.
- All stairs, ladders and platforms should be designed for easy cleaning.
- Pre-fabricated building panels usually provide more opportunity for infestation to develop than do solid brick or concrete walls; certain partition or cladding materials such as strawboard, hardboard or blockboard offer little resistance to gnawing rodents and may, especially if damp, encourage moulds, booklice and fungus beetles. Strawboard should certainly be avoided in any damp situations such as kitchens or bathrooms.
- Suspended ceilings are helpful in hiding horizontal pipework and services, but access for inspection for pests and maintenance must be built in. Structural walkways should always be provided in large premises. Suspended ceilings should be of metal lattice incorporating cleanable panels. Aluminium backed and faced fibre-board has proved successful in many food factories. Flush-fitting ventilation grilles should be fitted. Solid ceilings should be well-insulated to avoid condensation and mould growth, and should be smooth, fire resistant, light coloured, coved at wall joints and easy to clean.
- Cavity closers should be included at the top of all cavity walls and there should be no gaps between joists and rafters. This will keep out birds and rodents (including squirrels which are an increasing problem in roofs). Adequate ventilation must of course still be provided but any gaps or holes into the roof for this purpose must be proofed with mesh.

- Lift shafts, dumb waiters, and refuse chutes and their garbage hoppers should as far as possible be of smooth internal construction and proofed against rodents. Floor cavities should be sealed where they enter lift shafts.
- Floor joists should be built in or fitted on to joist hangers and all internal partitioning wall and ceiling cavities be sealed off.
- Pipes, ducts or cables passing through walls should fit tightly or be built into fire stops. Joists where pipes or ducts pass through floors and walls should be protected by metal flanges and to allow for heat expansion, and hot water pipes should be carried in sleeves through vertical or horizontal partitions. The base of elevators, conveyors and production machinery should be surrounded with a 600 mm high smooth metal fence and conveyor ends should have tight-fitting doors.
- Wherever drains, hoists, fan vents, conveyors, pipes, cable conduits or ducts pass between buildings through walls or foundations they should be close-fitting to prevent any infestation spreading from one building to another.
- Any external meter boxes must have well fitting doors and all pipes or wires adequately sealed. Standard conical or rectangular metal rat guards should be fitted to soil pipes and rainwater downpipes, projecting about 230 mm from the pipes and built into the walls at the point where they touch it. Tops of open pipes should be fitted with balloon guards. Mesh fitted over rainwater goods will keep out nest debris.
- Fire escapes should be enclosed.
- Fine grilles should be fitted over air intakes.

In high risk buildings, such as food premises or those containing high-value equipment:

- Wall surfaces are best smooth, impervious, non-flaking and light-coloured and must be capable of being thoroughly cleaned and, if necessary, disinfected. Suitable wall surfaces include resin-bonded fibre glass, ceramic-faced blocks, glazed tiles with water-resistant grouting and rubberized paint on hard plaster or sealed brickwork. Some paints incorporate a fungicidal additive but absorbent emulsion paint should not be used. Plastic sheeting can be heat formed to fit corners and angles. Stainless steel splashbacks are recommended behind sinks and working surfaces.
- Floors should be durable, non-absorbent, anti-slip, without crevices and capable of being effectively cleaned. Where appropriate they must be resistant to acids, grease and salts, and suitable floor coverings may be epoxy resin, granolithic, welded

anti-slip, vinyl sheet and anti-slip ceramic or quarry tiles. Wooden floors are unacceptable. If concrete is used, it must be steel-float finished and sealed with, for example, an epoxy sealant to stop it generating dust. Floors should slope sufficiently for liquids to drain to trapped gulleys — one in sixty is the minimum recommended.

- Coving can be used at wall/floor junctions and wall/ceiling junctions to help cleaning operations and minimise the risk of accumulated debris and dirt that can harbour insects or mites.

- Hollows behind skirtings, architraves and mouldings should be filled in or designed out to minimise pest harbourage and any dry linings sealed. Plaster should be taken right down to floor level behind skirtings and right up to the ceiling behind coving.

- Round section legs, struts or supports at least 250 mm high are to be preferred over square section, to avoid dust and food scraps collecting and to make cleaning easier.

- The base of H-section columns should be surrounded with concrete to ease cleaning.

- Pipework, cables and fittings should be built in solid or so sited away from walls that they can be easily cleaned all round. Spaces beneath fittings should either be large enough for easy cleaning or filled solid.

- Flexible connections are recommended for gas fittings. All electrical switches should be flush-fitting.

- External doors should be fitted with metal kick plates not less than 300 mm high and the metal plates should also fit jambs and door linings.

- In retail premises, raised 'gondola' type counters in sales and serving areas will avoid the dead spaces above the plinth of enclosed counters.

- As with entry points, it is important that within a building all partitions and internal walls and floors are sealed around electrical conduits, plumbing, heating pipes, trunking or service ducts that pass through them.

- The many pests attracted to light can be countered by installing ultra-violet electronic fly killing units in which flies are electrocuted by a suspended or wall-mounted device which attracts them (and wasps) to its ultra-violet light, kills them as they touch the live inner grid and drops them into a catch tray.

Doors and Windows

- All doors should close on a level threshold, have smooth, non-absorbent surfaces, be tight-fitting and self-closing.

- BS 2911 recommends any letter plates be at least 760 mm above ground level to prevent them becoming 'rat flaps'.
- Frames should avoid acute angles. Right-angled joints between frames and walls should be beaded or filled to form continuous surfaces. Architraves should be avoided.
- All woodwork should be well-seasoned, properly knotted, stopped, primed and given three coats of polyurethane paint.
- Finger-plates are useful where hand contact is expected.
- Many food factories use polypropylene or toughened rubber doors as they require little maintenance and are easy to keep clean.
- Roller shutter doors must fit tightly and despatch bays be protected by plastic strip curtain doors. Nylon bristle-strip is remarkably versatile for pest-proofing conventional doors.
- Doors of bin rooms below refuse chutes should be self-closing, flush fitted and of metal construction.
- Window ledges or other essential projections should slope at 45 degrees to discourage birds from perching and roosting on them.
- Exclusion of the highly mobile adult fly can be achieved by screening windows with a PVC covered fibre-glass mesh. These should be easily removable for regular cleaning and any necessary repairs. Mesh screens need to be no more than 2 mm mesh to exclude flies and 5 mm to exclude mice.

During Construction

- During new building work, demolition or extensive renovation, all redundant pipes and ducts should be removed or filled. Drains and sewers not in use must be sealed and disused drains and sewers excavated and removed, and the holes filled with consolidated hard rubble. If they cannot be removed, open pipes should be filled with concrete.
- Hardcore contaminated with decayed wood should not be used — there are several cases of new buildings suffering from built-in dry rot or wharf-borers originating from this source.
- Known ant nests should be eliminated from site before construction.
- Panels used in construction should have all expansion joints filled with mastic and covered by metal angle or cover strip. Fillings of felt or similar soft materials should be avoided and all airbricks or ventilation grilles should be cased through cavities.
- All structural and joinery timber should be pre-treated with timber preservatives to meet the specification relating to its end usage. This is an industrial process carried out by authorised timber merchants using vacuum pressure impregnation plants to

apply water-based preservatives. These become chemically fixed within the vulnerable sapwood and provide permanent built-in protection against wood-boring insects and fungal decay. There will then be no need for any subsequent spray treatment.

Operation and maintenance

- Good housekeeping, stock control and correct storage of in-gredients, packaging materials and finished goods will minimise the chances of infestation developing undetected. Detailed cleaning will reduce the risk of food residues accumulating under or around food mixers, automatic machinery, under sinks or in the crevices of store rooms. Specialised items such as silos and ventilation ducting should be cleaned by properly equipped pest control or hygiene contractors.
- Suppliers should be checked for adequate pest control provision and neighbours should co-operate in eliminating infestation from the district.
- Cleaning schedules and methods need to be compatible with pest control activities, especially if high pressure water jets or steam jets are used. Some pest control contractors also provide specialist cleaning services so that co-ordination is assured.
- Ideally, refuse should be sorted (wet, dry, combustible, non-combustible, edible, inedible) segregated and labelled for appropriate disposal.
- Any refuse compound, with lidded skips or bins, should be hosed down, cleaned and sprayed with an approved insecticide by a reputable contractor after each refuse collection. Maintenance should provide for specialist occasional cleaning of refuse chutes by a contractor who will use special rotary head brushes and spray heads. The area around incinerators should be cleaned daily. Pallets should be inspected and cleaned regularly.
- Many pests are attracted to water so any dripping taps should be repaired promptly, access denied to water storage tanks and cisterns, condensation avoided, obsolete plumbing removed and all gratings, grease traps, and drainage gulleys kept clean.
- Warehouses should be well-lit and well ventilated, and all incoming ingredients and packaging separated from outgoing product. A strip of white paint at the edges of a warehouse floor helps to show up any sign of infestation.
- Stacks of goods should not be built against walls or into corners. A 600 mm wide space should be kept between stacks and different types of goods should be well separated.
- Lift shafts must be thoroughly cleaned and kept free of rubbish; lift machinery should be regularly dismantled and cleaned.

- Pipe lagging must be kept in sound condition to prevent it being used as harbourage by insects.
- To combat flies indoors, where staining must be avoided, a colourless, oil-based preparation with a synthetic pyrethroid such as permethrin as the active ingredient can be sprayed on to walls, ceilings, light fittings and other favoured resting sites. The number of treatments will depend on the conditions that prevail; high temperatures, greasy fumes and dust will degrade the insecticide faster than lower temperatures and minimal airborne deposition. Sometimes flies can breed all the year round inside warm premises where all residues are difficult to locate and here spray treatments will be required throughout the year.
- Effective inspection, repair and maintenance of drains will reduce the risk of rats entering from sewers. Coarse wire wool embedded in cement will fill most entry holes in walls.
- All production machinery, especially in food factories, must be stripped, inspected and cleaned regularly, and dust removed from all structural and working surfaces.
- Door seals, window closures and screens must be inspected regularly, and cleaned if necessary.
- Temperatures should be kept as low as comfort and working processes permit as insects thrive in warmth and humidity.
- Staff facilities such as cloakrooms, lockers, toilets, canteens and changing rooms should not be neglected – they can be reservoirs of cross-infestation. Maintenance stores are often the most untidy.
- All air-conditioning filters, grilles and ducting should be cleaned regularly.

CONTROL MEASURES

Apart from thorough pest proofing of premises by good design and sound construction, and prevention of infestation by scrupulous cleaning, sound stock and efficient waste disposal, it may still be necessary to have pesticides applied after detection and monitoring or expert inspection have confirmed the need for them. The active ingredients currently in use and approved under the Control of Pesticides Regulations 1986 are described in the Appendix to this chapter.

Materials Safety Data Sheets are available from pest control contractors working on commercial or industrial premises, covering the concentration, flammability, toxicity, hazard classification and any special precautions for each formulation. These will be needed as part of the risk assessments undertaken by premises managers under the Control of Substances Hazardous to Health Regulations 1988. The definition of substances hazardous to health includes biological contaminants as well as chemicals, so an accumulation of pigeon droppings or the presence of legionella in the hot water system, or pathogenic bacteria spread by insect or rodent pests could all lead to prosecution.

Formulations will vary according to the surface to which they need to be applied, the species of pest, the nature of the premises, and any special precautions that need to be taken in each case. A water-based formulation is needed for bare brickwork; a wettable powder for plastered surfaces; an oil-based spray for tiled surfaces; a gel for fuse boxes or vulnerable electrical equipment; a dust for blowing into floor or wall cavities; a mist or fog for space spraying – all incorporating the same insecticide, or each needing a different insecticide. Traps and sticky boards may still be used as a last resort against rodents and cage traps against pigeons, but care must be taken not to cause unnecessary suffering.

Today, the emphasis is very much on proofing premises against pests; preventive measures such as good housekeeping, waste disposal, stock control and cleaning; with detection and monitoring devices placed within buildings so that chemical pesticides are only used when and where pests are present. These devices include sex pheromone traps for various species of moths that are pests of stored commodities, sticky but non-toxic traps left in place overnight when cockroaches are active, and even a sophisticated electronic mouse detector called Mouse Alert based on infra-red intruder alarm technology.

Safer pesticides include insect growth regulators such as methoprene to eliminate colonies of Pharaohs ants from highrise housing estates, aggregation pheromones to attract cockroaches to insecticidal bait, and sex attractant for flies, to ensure that they linger longer at the insecticide incorporating it. Non-chemical devices such as ultra-violet electronic fly killers are constantly being improved and tamper-resistant plastic bait boxes are available for mouse control.

Pest control technology is adapting to meet the needs of the building industry and estate management as well as to changes in the incidence of pest species and such problems as insecticide resistance. This takes considerable investment in research, in assessing new techniques and materials and in re-equipping and training pest control staff with the appropriate items and information. The graduate biologist is now commonplace within a pest control service, backed by chemists, zoologists and a wide range of specialists in trouble-shooting and problem solving.

USE OF PEST CONTROL CONTRACTORS

More and more food manufacturers, distributors, retailers and caterers have become aware of the need to prevent contamination of ingredients, equipment, preparation surfaces and finished products by insects, birds, mites and rodents. Although scrupulous cleaning, waste disposal and improved construction of buildings can reduce the risk of serious infestations, it is still necessary to supplement such preventive methods with other physical or chemical pest control techniques. The application of insecticides in close proximity to food immediately involves the need to prevent undesirable contamination by pesticide residues, and employing a specialist contractor will enable a building owner to take advantage of the sophisticated equipment, technology and materials now available. Those companies in membership of the British Pest Control Association abide by its own Code of Practice and the best have their own safety and technical training programmes, thorough supervision, quality control and R & D support, and can call on additional resources of manpower quickly and effectively. Good pest control must of course be paid for; but bad pest control is far more expensive and can be disastrous.

A well trained pest control surveyor will be able to identify and trace the extent of a pest infestation, write detailed instructions for appropriate treatments including the selection of the best pesticide formulation and minimum effective dosage, rate of application and any special precautions to be taken. The service teams are trained in the correct use and maintenance of equipment, the preparation and safe application of the pesticide and the proper recording and reporting of baits laid, areas sprayed and all treatments carried out. Leading contractors also now place greater emphasis on detection and monitoring techniques to minimise the use of chemicals and to maximise their effectiveness.

The pest control contract

Many factors need to be considered in using contractors for pest control. It is important that an accurate record of visits is kept and advisable that a 'pest book' is maintained on the premises under the control of management. It should be signed by the contractor and a representative of management at each visit. The following information should be included:

- the results of the initial survey;
- the work carried out as a result of the survey;
- the degree of infestation found and the type of pests involved, with particulars of any vulnerable or high risk areas;
- details of each treatment carried out and the pesticides used;
- references to any ultra-violet flykiller units and the basis of their maintenance;
- the recommendations made by the contractor on each visit and the action taken;

- a record of any special or emergency visits made by the contractor;
- records of all reported sightings by staff, of pests on the premises.

A QUESTION OF BALANCE

In the recent past, some concern has been expressed about the chronic effects of low doses of certain timber treatments. Under the COSHH Regulations such matters will often be resolved by the need to question every step of a proposed treatment. For instance, is it necessary to use a particular formulation? Is there an alternative way to treat the problem? If there is still a need to use it, then appropriate safety precautions must be observed. Such an approach is not new to the professional; indeed it is the only way he can stay in business.

Permethrin has replaced lindane as the preferred active chemical, which replaced dieldrin, which replaced DDT, which replaced sodium fluoride, in just over 50 years. Most complaints about timber treatment are caused not by the active ingredient but by temporary reactions to the solvents by those who were inadequately protected, did not read the label, or were victims of unsafe working practices. Water based preservatives and paste formulations overcome the problem of solvents. Other pesticides are not exposed because they are encapsulated.

The argument of risks balanced against benefits, and the tendency to confuse toxicity with hazard, will no doubt be debated elsewhere. Let one plea suffice, and that is for genuinely objective, scientific and independent assessment by those qualified to do so to determine who is protecting whom against what. The environment, including the built environment, can be a dangerous place if it is left without protection from some of its natural elements.

The rat is an unacceptable part of the environment, as are 'natural' mouse droppings, mould spores and weevils that occur in unprotected premises. If a building has dry rot, it needs treating by the most effective methods and material available, consistent with safety. The British Pest Control Association devises its codes of practice, negotiates with the Health & Safety Executive, runs residential training courses and ensures that pest control is conducted with a proper degree of professionalism.

SAFETY PRECAUTIONS FOR DIY

Much small-scale pest control is undertaken in domestic and office buildings on a DIY basis. Some essential precautions need to be taken.

1 Before using any insecticide, wood preservative or rodenticide, read the instructions on the label and follow them exactly.

2 Store all pest control chemicals where children cannot possibly reach them.

3 If possible, avoid transferring pesticides from their original containers. If it is done, return any unused residues to the proper container and do not leave any in unlabelled jars or tins.

4 Before using an aerosol spray can, make sure the hole in the release button is pointing in the right direction.

5 Any splashes of pesticide on skin should be washed off quickly and, after pesticides have been used, hands should be washed before food is eaten.

6 Avoid inhaling vapour or fumes from sprays and do not allow pets or domestic animals to have access to baits, liquids or powders.

7 Do not spray insecticides or wood preservatives near naked flames, or smoke while applying them, because many are carried in inflammable solvents. Open windows and doors to improve ventilation.

8 Dispose of residues carefully by washing them down an outside drain with plenty of water. Never throw a spray can on a fire or puncture the can but place the empty unit in a dustbin.

9 Burn or deeply bury the bodies of rats or mice killed by rodenticides and only handle them with gloves on.

10 Never apply insecticidal chemicals directly to the fur of cats or dogs unless they are specified for the purpose. Proprietary brands of veterinary flea powder or insecticide specially formulated for veterinary use are available.

11 Pest control chemicals are selected for their insecticidal or rodenticidal efficiency and their low toxicity to man and other animals. However, where food is prepared or stored, take care not to spray utensils, working surfaces or the food itself. Some chemicals have an aromatic odour which can taint foodstuffs.

12 If in doubt, call in a professional pest control company.

CONCLUSIONS AND OVERALL GUIDELINES

* Most buildings are vulnerable to damage or contamination by pest infestation.

* Designers and specifiers, surveyors, facilities managers and building services engineers need to have a greater appreciation of the need to eliminate pests.

* The occupiers of buildings have legal obligations to keep them free from infestation, and pest control contractors have legal obligations to do their work safely as well as efficiently.

* An infested building is a potential health hazard and may be unsafe. It will certainly be unpopular.

* Using the design guidelines in this chapter together with an awareness of pests can reduce or eliminate the risk of infestation, especially when followed up by responsible maintenance.

* Pest control is increasingly a complex scientific discipline subject to increasing legislation and is most effectively entrusted to specialist pest control contractors who in turn are increasingly providing more comprehensive services to higher standards.

* Consultations between specifiers and pest controllers at an early stage of any development enable potential problems to be avoided, safeguards to be established and preventive measures installed which can make future monitoring and detection of pests more effective and may eliminate them altogether.

* Most pest control clients do not have problems, but need the attention of the pest controllers to keep them that way.

* The price of freedom from pests is eternal vigilance, but the cost of pest control is a great deal less than the cost of having an infestation.

* Free surveys and advice are available from most major pest control companies and a list of member companies is available from The British Pest Control Association.

BIBLIOGRAPHY

A–Z of Household Pests, The British Pest Control Association, Derby.

Bateman, P.L.G., *Household Pests*, Blandford Books, 1979.

Building Research Establishment, *Reducing the Risk of Pest Infestations*, Digest No. 238.

Busvine, J.R., *Insects and Hygiene*, Methuen.

Cornwell, P.B., *Pest Control in Buildings*, Rentokil Library Series, Rentokil Book Department, Felcourt, East Grinstead, West Sussex RH19 2JY.

Hickin, N., *Pest Animals In Buildings – A World Review*, Longman 1985.

Hickin, N., *The Conservation of Building Timbers*, Rentokil Library Series.

Keeping Pests Out of Business Premises, Rentokil Pest Control.

Lucas, C., *Hygiene In Buildings*, Rentokil Library Series.

Mallis, A., *Handbook of Pest Control*, Franzak & Foster, Cleveland, Ohio, USA.

Sprenger, R. A., *Hygiene For Management*, Highland Publications, 4th ed., 1989.

APPENDIX 2

ACTIVE INGREDIENTS IN RODENTICIDES AND INSECTICIDES

Rodenticides

Alphachloralose: For mice indoors only. A hypothermic agent inducing a quick painless death normally close to the bait. Cereal or paste formulations available for professional use; available as Alphakil for DIY use. Not effective at ambient temperatures above about 65°C. Rapidly metabolised so does not accumulate in the body and mode of action provides good degree of safety.

Bromadiolone: Probably the most effective second generation anticoagulant. Effective against both rats and mice. May be used outdoors or indoors. Has both acute (quick acting) and chronic (slow acting) effects so can kill after one feed and death occurs in 2–7 days. Effective against warfarin-resistant rodents. Available as a contact dust or in grain or paste baits for both professional and DIY use. (Rodine 'C' or Rentokil Mouse Control System complete with bait boxes and paste tube.) Specific antidote is vitamin K.

Brodifacoum: Similar in action to bromadiolone but may only be used indoors. Only a single feed is needed. Vitamin K is the specific antidote.

Calciferol: Based on an overdose of vitamin D2 inducing hypercalcaemia. Mice need to feed on grain or seed baits for 1–3 days, die in 5–8 days.

Chlorophacinone: An indane-dione anticoagulant for use in baits against rats.

Needs 5 days consecutive feed by the rat but said to be less toxic to cats, dogs and pigs than other anticoagulants.

Coumatetralyl: Another hydroxycoumarin anticoagulant requiring repeated takes of bait. Also available as a contact dust. Marketed as 'Racumin'.

Difenacoum: Another hydroxycoumarin type anticoagulant but effective only after repeated feeding over 4 or 5 days. Vitamin K is the antidote. Available for DIY use as Neosorexa.

Fluoracetamide (1081): A highly toxic organic fluoride recommended by MAFF only for use in sewers against brown rats. No longer manufactured so supplies probably no longer available. No antidote. Acutely poisonous to all mammals.

Warfarin: The original anti-coagulant, inducing death by internal bleeding but without apparent symptoms of pain. Requires repeated feeding over about 5 days. More effective against rats than against mice and now ineffective in some areas because of genetic tolerance to it developed by both rats and mice.

Insecticides

Actellic: Pirimiphos methyl, a broad spectrum organo-phosphorus compound available to kill crawling insects and fly larvae as a dusting powder or as a liquid or encapsulated for a slow release effect. Also used in domestic aerosols. Contact, stomach and fumigant action. Breaks down rapidly in contact with moisture.

Alphacypermethrin: For both flying and crawling insects. Good retention on porous surfaces. Good performance at low dosage. Available for professional use as Fendona.

Azamethiphos: Used primarily against flies in animal houses (agricultural or zoos) in conjunction with a synthetic sex pheromone, 'Muscamone' (a-tricosene) to improve its attraction to flies.

Bendiocarb: Good general purpose carbamate insecticide against crawling insects. Formulated as dusting powder, wettable powder or liquid sprays. Rapidly metabolised and excreted by mammals. Useful against ants and cockroaches. Marketed as Ficam.

Boric Acid: Boric Acid powder. An inorganic insecticidal dust. Slow acting but very persistent insecticidal action when blown into cavities and gaps used as harbourages by cockroaches. Also used in a gel bait against Pharaohs ants.

Carbaryl: A carbamate introduced by Union Carbide as Sevin. Very effective against wasps and ants and safe enough for use in domestic situations including parasites of pets. Available as a wettable powder or dusting powder.

Carbon Dioxide: Occasionally used as a fumigant to control rodents in buildings where other gases would taint food. Development of a lightweight portable fumigation 'bubble' by Rentokil may lead to its greater use as an effective (and 'organic') fumigant against insect infestations in stored commodities, books, costumes or other artefacts. Also used as a propellant for pressurised cylinders of pyrethroid insecticide ('Pestigas'). Professional use only.

Chlorpyrifos-methyl: An organo-phosphorous compound effective against stored product insects, mosquito adults and larvae and other household insect pests. Contact, stomach and fumigant action but low mammalian toxicity. Straight chlorpyrifos ('Dursban') useful for cockroaches but of limited value against other insects.

Diazinon: A versatile organo-phosphorous compound effective against cockroaches, ants, flies and other insects, and against lice and mites. Highly volatile but rapidly broken down in the body and excreted. Readily absorbed through the skin and too readily inhaled in confined spaces. Wide range of formulations available.

Dichlorvos: The organo-phosphorous vapourising insecticide used in slow-release resin strips for killing flies indoors. Veterinary uses against animal fleas ('Nuvan') and often incorporated with other insecticide for its 'flushing' action. Effective against flies, moths, ants, cockroaches, bedbugs, fleas and mosquitoes. Non-persistent.

Dieldrin: One of the most widely used of the organochlorine insecticides that succeeded DDT. Now phased out, restricted or banned. Very persistent, highly stable, readily absorbed through the skin and accumulates in body fat. Highly toxic to fish.

Fenitrothion: Widely used organo-phosphorous compound, not readily absorbed through the skin and does not accumulate in the human body. Dusts, wettable powder, oil-based and emulsion formulations available. Contact action against crawling insects including cockroaches. Also in domestic and garden sprays.

Iodofenphos: Similar properties to fenitrothion and widely used against mosquitoes, flies, cockroaches, mites and stored product pests.

Lindane: Successfully used in public health, structural and agricultural pest control for 40 years this gamma isomer hexachlorocyclohexane (Gamma BHC) is the organo-chlorine chemical that replaced DDT and Dieldrin. It is now itself being replaced by less persistent and less volatile materials such as permethrin but is still accepted for a wide range of uses where food is not exposed. Originally introduced by ICI as Gammexane. Some insects now resistant to it.

For many years lindane has been the preferred active ingredient of woodworm-killing fluids because of its persistence and stability within treated timbers at 1.2%. It is also used in pharmaceutical lotions and shampoos for the control of headlice in children at 2% concentration.

A range of formulations made it widely available for crop protection, control of disease-carrying insects and for mothproofing fabrics.

Malathion: One of the earliest organo-phosphorous insecticides (1950) gained wide acceptance for agriculture and horticulture and as an effective killer of mites and the treatment of stored grain. More recent formulations removed the unacceptable odour. It has moderate persistence and is not readily absorbed through the skin but has largely been replaced for indoor use by fenitrothion.

Methyl Bromide: Bromomethane. A specialist fumigant when used as a gas. Highly insecticidal and non-corrosive and non-flammable but degrades rubber. Supplied for professional fumigators only. Used for infested mills, warehouses, ships' holds, palleted products or cargoes. Buildings or parcels to be treated must be sealed gas-tight. Full respirators are worn by operators as the gas is highly toxic to man.

Methoprene: 'Pharorid'. A synthetic insect growth regulator or juvenile hormone used against Pharaohs ants, which sterilises the queen ants and stops the larvae developing. Very target specific.

Paradichlorobenzene: Replaced naphthalene moth balls to protect stored clothes from clothes moth and carpet beetles. Colourless crystals slowly give off a heavy vapour that smells strongly. Stable, non-corrosive and non-staining but largely non-effective. Toxic to man at above 300 ppm.

Pentachlorophenol: PCP or 'Penta'. The most effective fungicide yet available to prevent fungal decay of structural timbers by dry rot and wet rot. Used since 1936 for timber preservation, usually at 5% active ingredient. Organic zinc and boron products are beginning to replace it in the face of concern arising from misuse or unsafe working practices that have allegedly caused injury to workers. PCP is irritating to the skin and mucous membranes, especially to the eyes so protective clothing must be worn when using it.

Permethrin: A popular synthetic pyrethroid especially effective for fly control but also being used for crawling insects, textile pests and as a replacement for lindane in woodworm killers. Low mammalian toxicity.

Phosphine: Fumigant gas derived from pellets of aluminium phosphide ('Phostoxin'). Formulated with a fire suppressant (ammonia carbamate). Suitable for professional use only. Useful against stored product pests including grain pests and for infested museum specimens or fabrics.

Pirimiphos-methyl: (see Actellic)

Pyrethrins: The active extracts of the natural insecticide pyrethrum.

Pyrethroids: Synthetic products with the properties of pyrethrins extended to give longer persistence, thus broadening the spectrum of use. Effective primarily against flying insects because of quick 'knock-down' effect but more persistent formulations now also work against crawling insects and textile pests. Derivatives include resmethrin, permethrin and cypermethrin.

PESTICIDES USED IN INDOOR AND OUTDOOR AMENITY AREAS

Kenneth Fletcher

Consultant

INTRODUCTION

There are two environments of concern here: that external to a building but necessarily associated with it; and internal amenity areas with planting and ornamental features integrated into the building's design.

External Environment

In this context, the external environment consists of areas such as driveways and paths, gardens and lawns, children's playgrounds, and even playing fields and games courts, all associated with buildings. The combination of factors to be considered for the safe use of chemicals in this environment is not found elsewhere, with the following likely to be involved:

- communal unsupervised access by many house-holders or other occupants, their children and their pets;
- access by the public;
- limited means of closing an area;
- an area large by domestic standards but small compared with, say, a public park;
- maintenance by persons whose skill and knowledge may not be high.

Contrast such areas with a domestic garden where access is limited and is largely controlled and supervised. In a domestic garden, any chemicals used are those available in small packages on the retail market and formulated for safe use in (relatively) unskilled hands. Far more dangerous chemicals are used in large quantities on farms and in public parks, but restriction of access and professional use provide the means for ensuring safety.

Ornamental Environment within a Building

Many aspects of internal amenity areas within buildings also differ from those more usually encountered.

- The environment is generally artificial. Not only does this mean the use of a growing medium other than soil but, more importantly, there will be an absence of rain and direct sunlight. In these circumstances chemicals will tend to be more persistent since they will be neither washed into soil nor destroyed by light or ultraviolet radiation.
- Exposure to any chemicals present will be almost entirely by inhalation; actual contact will be infrequent.
- Exposure may be prolonged for receptionists, for example, for whom this may be a working environment.
- Children and animals are less likely to be a significant part of the population at risk.
- Although maintenance of the amenity will probably be in the hands of specialist contractors, it cannot be assumed that they are in any way aware of health risks.

It must be appreciated that there is no such thing as a 'safe' chemical, since any chemical wrongly used is potentially harmful. The dangers in their use lie both in their intrinsic hazard, some being far more hazardous than others, and in their method of use. In the situations being considered where there is unlimited access, no supervision, the possibility of unskilled use and possibly a large area, it follows that the need for chemicals should be minimized and, where this is unavoidable, formulations with low toxicity should be employed.

TYPES OF CHEMICAL

Formulations

Chemicals are sold in a number of different formulations, the most common being:

- crystals, powder, or a concentrated solution for dissolving in water to use as a spray or in a watering can;
- in the case of water-insoluble materials, a very fine powder or a solution in a solvent which can be diluted in water to form an emulsion or suspension;
- as powder or granules for direct application without dilution.

With regard to safety each of these has advantages and drawbacks. All concentrated material is potentially dangerous, but the formulations for direct application are usually more dilute and thus safer. Moreover they can be applied accurately. Granules, however, may remain on the surface for a long period and are accessible to animals or children, and poisoning has occurred as a result. Sprays usually offer no threat once they have been applied apart occasionally from contact irritation or allergy. If they are applied carelessly, for example in windy conditions, they may fall outside the intended area and cause damage. An accumulation of spray, for example by puddling, is also potentially dangerous. Factors such as these can influence the design of amenity areas and the use of chemicals in them and examples are given below.

Fertilizers

Amenity areas do not usually contain plants requiring a high input of nutrients. Trees and shrubs are very undemanding in this respect, given reasonably fertile soil to start with, and should not require any chemical feeding, whereas lawns may need fertilizing from time to time since they are constantly mowed. Fortunately, fertilizers are generally of low toxicity and should present no problems at the point of application. It must be remembered, however, that fertilizers are soluble; they may not necessarily be retained completely by soil and can be washed out by rain. Where appropriate, fertilizer should be applied as a solution to the area rather than in granular form to ensure that chemicals are not present on the surface over a period.

Herbicides

Unfortunately weeds tend to grow almost everywhere and have to be controlled. Hand or mechanical weeding is usually impracticable or uneconomic and is also rather inefficient. In many areas herbicides will thus have to be used for weed control. They can be divided into several different types.

- *Short-acting total herbicides* generally kill or severely restrict all kinds of plant life and they are used where weed growth is already well established in areas not containing desired plants. Although there are some compounds of low toxicity, most of them are of high toxicity and should preferably be avoided or used with considerable care.

- *Short-acting selective herbicides* have the property of killing weed species in grass (or cereal crops) while leaving the grass unharmed. In amenity areas their only use would probably be on lawns. They are mostly of low toxicity (some members of the group are believed to have shown serious harmful effects, and therefore the use of these particular chemicals is no longer permitted).

- *Long-acting herbicides* suppress the growth of weed seedlings for a long period (up to a year) after a single application. In appropriate circumstances some can be applied to desired species without damage, but this use requires considerable technical knowledge. They are not very efficient at controlling established weeds. They are generally of low toxicity.

- *Growth-inhibitors* can be used where ground cover is needed in areas which are difficult to mow or otherwise control. They are for professional use, since training and experience are required to ensure safe use.

Other types of herbicide exist but they are of specialist interest and are unlikely to be used in the circumstances under discussion.

Fungicides

As with insecticides (see below), it is not likely that fungicides will find much application in amenity areas. As the name suggests, their role is the control of disease-causing fungi such as mildews and rots. There are several plants which seem to suffer frequently from disease; roses are an example and attempts to grow these successfully are almost inevitably accompanied by the use of fungicides (and insecticides). However, there are plenty of possibly more appropriate trees and shrubs which do not have this drawback. Although they possess some differences in spectrum of activity amongst themselves, fungicides are broadly similar in their properties and in general are of moderately low toxicity.

Algicides

Algae form a group of plants which grow in water ranging in size from microscopic to large. They require light for growth and where this is available they can become a nuisance, fouling water supplies or ornamental ponds. Algicides can be used to control them, either non-specific, in which case they kill other plants as well, or specific to algae for use in, say, ponds containing desirable species.

Wood Preservatives

Materials used for the preservation of wood have been covered in other chapters. There are no further considerations peculiar to amenity areas.

Insecticides

In the context under consideration it is not likely that insects will prove much of a problem. As with herbicides, insecticides may vary in their use or application. Virtually all are used as sprays or, in the case of those acting systemically, by watering into the soil. There are two main types:

- *Non-persistent insecticides* are designed to kill quickly on contact or by ingestion and then be broken down within a few days. Each may have its own spectrum of activity, i.e. one will have an action against caterpillars, whereas another will be particularly effective against aphids. It is worth noting in this context that there are compounds that kill aphids which do little harm to beneficial insects such as bees or ladybirds.

- **Persistent insecticides** remain active at the point of application for a lengthy period (up to or exceeding a year). Their main use is in public health operations for control of flies or mosquitos. Since they may have undesirable side-effects their use is greatly restricted.

The toxicity of insecticides varies widely from extremely toxic to fairly non-toxic. Many of the members of this group can be harmful to other wildlife, such as fish, and such effects must always be considered.

Rodenticides

In any place where food or refuse is present, rats in particular, but also mice, are a potential problem. Not only can they cause a great deal of structural damage and spread disease, but the mere presence of these animals is a source of revulsion to most people. Their eradication and control is difficult and undoubtedly a matter for specialists. Rodenticides are poisons which require the rats to ingest bait several times to produce an effect, and they are very toxic to rats, humans and pets. Their use is far better avoided by suitable design of buildings, particularly drainage and surrounds – see Chapter C7.

Molluscicides

Molluscicides are chemicals used to kill slugs and snails. By far the commonest is based on metaldehyde and is usually formulated as pellets for scattering on the ground around plants. Metaldehyde is quite toxic; dogs have been killed by eating the pellets, and other species must be at risk although modern formulations contain a repellant. There are also liquid formulations that are less effective but less accessible in use and therefore preferable for use in public areas.

NAMING OF CHEMICALS

A confusing variety of names are applied to pesticides.

- **The official chemical name** (which in fact is really a formula) of the active ingredient which describes the structure of the chemical according to an agreed international convention: thus a widely used herbicide is NN'–dimethyl-44'–dipyridylium dichloride.

- **The agreed standard or trivial name:** most chemical names are too unwieldy or technical for everyday use, and so a much easier one is invented and approved. Thus the above chemical is usually known as paraquat (strictly paraquat dichloride). This name is internationally observed and can be used irrespective of the manufacturer.

- *The trade name:* this describes a particular formulation of the pesticide chemical. It usually contains other ingredients and is specific to one manufacturer. For example, a 20% solution of paraquat in water containing a wetting agent and other ingredients manufactured by ICI is called 'Gramoxone'. As a 2% solid formulation with other constituents it becomes 'Weedol'. Thus it is quite possible for closely similar formulations of identical chemicals to have entirely different trade names if made by different manufacturers.

- *Group names:* most pesticides come in families, i.e. they can be grouped, with each group containing members with similar chemical structures which usually perform similar functions. Familiar examples are the organophosphorus insecticides, each of which contains in its chemical structure the element phosphorus combined in a similar way. Although they may have similar basic structures it must not be assumed that members of a group can substitute for one another; two compounds may both be insecticides but may be effective against totally different ranges of insects. Toxicity may also vary widely. Some such as parathion (not used in the UK) are very dangerous, and others such as malathion are relatively safe. However, even malathion requires manufacture by a competent, reputable company and proper storage to ensure it does not break down to more dangerous material.

Examples of typical groups of chemicals for different uses are as follows.

- *Herbicides:*   Immediate acting: paraquat, potassium chlorate, glyphosphate (slower acting but less toxic). Long-term: simazine, atrazine, diuron. Selective: the 'hormone' weedkillers, 2:4D, mecoprop
- *Insecticides:*   Synthetic pyrethroids; permethrin, cypermethrin. Organophosphorus: malathion. Organochlorine (semi-persistent): gamma-hexa-chlorocyclohexane (gamma-BCH).
- *Fungicides:*   Benomyl, triforin and many others
- *Molluscicides:*   Metaldehyde, methiocarb

It cannot be emphasized too strongly that these are illustrative examples only and that, before using any pesticide, its suitability for the particular purpose must be established. Usually the label or sales literature with the product will make this apparent, but if there is any doubt then advice should be sought from a suitable source such as a competent consultant, the Ministry of Agriculture Pesticide Advisory Service or the British Agrochemicals Association.

CONSIDERATIONS FOR THE DESIGN AND UPKEEP OF EXTERNAL AMENITY AREAS

The basis for the safe application of chemicals in amenity areas in the circumstances of random access with little control, as outlined above, must be to use them as little as possible and to design to this end. Chemicals are dangerous, and in the present context if an accident can happen it almost inevitably will, sooner or later. With this in mind, each component of possible areas is examined below to assess the necessity and role of the types of chemicals listed above.

Pathways and Drives

The use for chemicals on pathways and drives is in the control of weeds. A well-constructed tarmac-surfaced drive or road on an adequate foundation will not harbour weeds for many years; when deterioration occurs, remaking will probably be undertaken. Paths and walkways intended primarily for pedestrian traffic are a different matter. These can have many different types of surface, impervious such as tarmac or concrete or permeable such as gravel, paving or ornamental stone, or brick. Since the foundation is probably fairly light, weeds will grow, especially on rough surfaces like gravel. There is a danger in using herbicides on impermeable surfaces, which has resulted in many poisonings of animals. Sprays used for weed control form puddles in depressions on tarmac or paving which are then drunk from by animals. The spray concentrating on the surface may also be an irritant. The corollary is that if impermeable surfaces are to be used (and these probably require least maintenance), they must be smoothly constructed with sufficient camber to allow fast drainage. Rough surfaces will attract weed growth but are permeable so that the problem of puddling does not arise. Long-acting herbicides of low toxicity can be used on these to suppress the weed. Probably the most difficult design is the combination path, for example stone slabs set in a mosaic of gravel. Attractive though these paths are, weed control in the gravel is accompanied by residual spray on the slabs and, from the point of view of weed control by chemicals, they are best avoided. Maintenance should aim to control weeds before germination rather than allowing them to attain vigorous growth, necessitating the use of the more toxic total herbicides.

Trees, Shrubs and Cultivated Areas

Those responsible for designing an amenity area must be clear about what is needed. If the aim is to approximate to a garden in the horticultural sense, not only will this be labour intensive but it will almost certainly imply the frequent use of pesticides. However, there are many trees and shrubs not significantly affected by insects or disease and, by using these in preference to others, a very pleasant environment can be created in which pesticides have a very limited role or none at all. Most hardy shrubs are trouble free in this respect; roses should be avoided. Flowering cherries can be martyrs to aphids; ornamental crab-apples are equally effective with fewer drawbacks. Any professional horticulturalist should be able to advise on suitable species; there is a very wide range available which regrettably seems to be much under-used in this application.

Lawns

The above remarks apply equally to grassed areas. The production of a lawn of bowling green quality is difficult and needs treatment with chemicals more or less continually. A grassed space functioning as a pleasing background, picnic area or playing ground does not need a high specification. Weeds are easily tolerated, disease is usually not significant and maintenance is confined to regular cutting and occasional spiking and raking. Apart from an application of fertilizer from time to time there should be no other need for chemicals.

Playgrounds and Games Courts

Playgrounds and games courts present the same problems as pathways, and considerations similar to those outlined above apply. However, it is assumed that premises large enough to include such amenities will be maintained by professional staff or contractors.

Refuse Disposal

Most premises require an area for the storage of refuse prior to collection. It is essential that this should be rodent proof, which implies brick or concrete construction with a solid roof and a solid self-closing door. There is a similar though lesser problem with litter disposal in the surroundings. Waste food and its containers or wrappings, always found after picnics, undoubtedly attract vermin. These can be discouraged by the use of litter bins. The common construction of mesh and plastic bag is of little use as it is too vulnerable to many kinds of animal. A metal bin with spring-loaded lid is preferable. The aim of these precautions is to prevent the need for rodenticides; their use should be taken as a failure of design.

Storage of Chemicals

The need to store chemicals should only arise if large areas are involved.

Small areas should need little use of chemicals, and when these are necessary they should be bought in quantities sufficient only for the immediate purpose. Storing chemicals in places where there is potential uncontrollable access is hazardous. If storage has to take place, possibly because of the scale of use, then it must be done in a suitable building constructed of brick or other permanent material. Within the building there should be provision for storage in a lockable cupboard; open shelving is not suitable. The Health and Safety Executive has issued guidelines on the storage of pesticides.

INDOOR AMENITY AREAS

Ornamental features containing plants and water effects may be incorporated in large buildings such as office and apartment blocks and department stores. These can be substantial projects resembling conservatories, possibly having elaborate ponds and fountains or water curtains. They are artificially maintained, usually by external specialist contractors. The health hazards associated with these constructions include those encountered in outside areas plus some peculiar to the special environment.

Plants

Indoor plants can suffer the same disease and insect attack as those outside. The control of these is similar. However, to avoid as far as possible the use of chemicals many firms use biological agents such as predatory insects or disease organisms for control, and this practice is to be encouraged. When this is ineffective chemicals must be used, and here it is better to use a systemic agent applied by watering into the growing medium rather than a spray. It is worth noting that these plantings contain a wide variety of ornamental species including many exotic varieties, and allergy to the dust or pollen from these is to be expected.

Water

Water constantly recirculated in a light, warm environment will grow many undesirable organisms – algae, bacteria, microscopic animals – unless it is treated. This treatment usually takes the form of filtration and sterilization by chlorine or other chemicals, but additional agents like algicides may also have to be used. It is not generally appreciated that running water, particularly that allowed to fall onto a solid surface as in a fountain or waterfall, generates an aerosol or mist which is injected into the surrounding atmosphere and can be inhaled.

From the nature of these constructions and their use, it is apparent that any health risk arises through inhalation of contaminated air. It is most unlikely that chemicals will be used in these circumstances in quantities sufficient to pose any significant risk, particularly if systemic pesticide formulations are employed. However, the combination of pesticides and possibly allergens from plants and water in places in which people may work all day does imply that ventilation should be thorough. This is also the case if air from the area is circulated to other parts of the building. It is sound practice for work involving the use of chemicals to be done when the premises are unoccupied, preferably in the evening to allow time for contaminants in the atmosphere to disperse.

It follows from this that a contractor using pesticides approved for agricultural use for maintenance of amenity areas must have a certificate of competence recognized by the appropriate Minister. If other pesticides are used no such certificate is required. However, although pesticides approved for general use are safer than those for agriculture, their unskilled use may still cause problems.

A recent piece of legislation, The Control of Substances Hazardous to Health Regulations (1988), will reinforce the above. These regulations (the responsibility of the Secretary of State for Employment with administration by the Health and Safety Executive) refer particularly to chemicals in the workplace. Under their provisions, an employer using chemicals must make an assessment of the likely hazards of his chemicals and take all necessary steps to ensure the safety of employees or others who may be affected by his activities. Compliance will be in the hands of inspectors of the Health and Safety Executive who have the power to force improvement of a practice or order its cessation. It is probable, for example, that the highly undesirable spraying of pesticides in occupied premises would be judged unacceptable under these regulations.

CONCLUSIONS

* There is no such thing as a 'safe' chemical, since any chemical wrongly used is potentially harmful. The dangers in their use lie both in their intrinsic hazard, some being far more hazardous than others, and in their method of use. In the situations being considered where there is unlimited access, no supervision, the possibility of unskilled use and possibly a large area, it follows that the need for chemicals should be minimized and, where this is unavoidable, formulations with low toxicity should be employed.

* Wherever possible, the use of horticultural chemicals in amenity areas should be avoided, by designing out the need for them. In small outdoor amenity areas there should be little or no need for the application of pesticides, and appropriate selection of plant material and design of the area is sufficient to avoid their use.

* In larger or specialist areas some pesticides may be necessary, and in larger amenity areas within buildings some use of chemicals is almost inevitable. Maintenance of these areas should be in the hands of specialist firms or appropriately qualified staff.

* The competence of staff and/or contractors with regard to safe use of chemicals within the areas should be investigated before their employment. In particular they should be encouraged to use chemicals of low toxicity.

* Before using any pesticide, its suitability for the particular purpose must be established. Usually the label or sales literature with the product will make this apparent, but if there is any doubt then advice should be sought from a suitable source such as a competent consultant, the Ministry of Agriculture Pesticide Advisory Service or the British Agrochemicals Association. Appropriate regulations, and instructions for use provided with a product, should be strictly adhered to.

BIBLIOGRAPHICAL REFERENCES

Amenity Pesticides, British Agrochemicals Association Handbook, BAA, 4 Lincoln Road, Peterborough PE1 2RP.

Chemical Safety Series, Storage of Approved Pesticides, Guidance for Farmers and other Professional Users, CS19, Health and Safety Executive, HM Stationery Office, London.

Code of Practice for the Agricultural and Commercial Horticultural Use of Pesticides, Ministry of Agriculture, Fisheries and Food, HM Stationery Office, London.

The Control of Pesticides Regulations (1986) implementing Part III of The Food and Environment Protection Act (1985), HM Stationery Office, London.

The Control of Substances Hazardous to Health Regulations (1988), HM Stationery Office, London.

CONTAMINATED LAND: RISKS TO HEALTH AND BUILDING INTEGRITY

Ian F. Viney and John F. Rees

INTRODUCTION

Dealing with contaminated land is now becoming an increasingly important part of civil engineering and building development, whether that development be construction of new buildings, roads or public parks. As the area of land available for redevelopment diminishes, and planning restrictions on agricultural and green belt land are more rigorously interpreted, there are growing pressures to build on sites hitherto considered unsuitable or too difficult because of poor ground conditions and chemical contamination. Emphasis is now placed on urban and inner city renewal where large tracts of land have lain unused since the decline of traditional industries.

'Contaminated land' is a non-specific term used here to describe land containing substances that, when present in sufficient quantities or concentrations, are likely to cause harm to man, the environment or materials used in construction. It covers a wide range of occurrences from sites with small easily identified surface deposits to those containing extensive areas of unidentified chemical wastes. The redevelopment of such sites without giving due consideration to the risks involved can present specific problems such as hazards to human health during the phases of ground preparation, construction and occupancy, risk to animal and plant life, and special construction hazards associated with the presence of aggressive ground conditions or poor stability. Failure to take account of potential hazards can lead to significant problems during or after re-use and may put at risk not only the workforce directly involved in development but also the people who will live or work on a reclaimed site.

Recognition of chemically contaminated land as a specific hazard to redevelopment as distinct from a general problem of dereliction has only occurred relatively recently. Little information is available on the long-term effectiveness of reclamation techniques, and knowledge and experience of problems following development is somewhat deficient. An increasing number of problems is now arising, both during and after development of contaminated sites, highlighting the need for adequate assessment of the associated hazards and the design of appropriate remedial measures. Many of these problems are linked to the fact that contamination is often literally covered up, with little consideration for the hazards this may cause, or simply dug up and moved to become a problem elsewhere.

So far the United Kingdom has largely escaped major pollution incidents on contaminated land causing extensive loss of life. However, incidents of properties exploding owing to the presence of landfill-derived methane gas and of the discovery of toxic cyanide wastes on school playing areas are causes of major concern. There is a pressing need for the best possible reclamation means to be adopted if a legacy of potential environmental disasters is not to be built up for future generations.

This chapter provides a brief introduction to the problems of contaminated land, gives a broad overview of the principal hazards, introduces the methods of dealing with contaminated sites, including the need for thorough site investigation and remedial treatment, and briefly reviews current legislation and guidelines. Since the engineering difficulties associated with such sites are largely well understood, the chapter concentrates on chemical hazards.

SOURCES OF CONTAMINATION AND THEIR ASSOCIATED HAZARDS

The first problem facing a developer is the identification of the existence of a potential hazard. This is difficult because, although the most heavily contaminated sites are often those where contamination is visible, in many older industrial areas contaminated materials may be concealed beneath later development. Inner city sites, where gasworks, waste tips and old production centres have been located, can conceal particularly difficult problems for development, but the problem may also be widespread in more rural areas as a result of waste disposal, uncontrolled use of pesticides and fertilizers, or mining and mineral extraction.

Examples of land which may become contaminated as a result of man's activities include:

- landfills and waste disposal sites;
- gasworks and coal carbonization plants;
- oil refineries, petroleum storage and distribution sites;
- scrap metal yards;
- sewage works and sites where sewage sludge has been applied to land;
- railway land;

- chemical plants, including pharmaceutical, acid, alkali, paint, dyestuff and explosives manufacturing plants;
- power stations;
- tanneries;
- paper and printing works;
- industries making or using wood preservatives;
- smelters, foundries, steelworks and metal-finishing plants;
- mining and extractive industries;
- dockyards and filled dock basins.

In addition to these examples, there are areas where natural conditions may present a threat to buildings or health, including naturally occurring high sulphate concentrations which can be detrimental to building materials, methane gas emissions from buried peat or coal strata, or emissions of the radioactive gas radon (see Chapter C4). This chapter concentrates on man-made contamination, although the same principles often apply when natural contamination is present in significant concentrations.

The Scale of the Problem

The extent of contaminated land left as a legacy of this country's industrial heritage is largely unknown; however, new areas are being discovered all the time as pressure for land redevelopment intensifies.

Overall, little has been done in the United Kingdom to seek out and identify problem contaminated sites, and this has resulted in insufficient knowledge of the location of contaminated sites or of developed sites which are polluted. Only limited programmes to identify or discover polluted sites that are current or potential hazards have been undertaken. Surveys undertaken by the Welsh Office identified approximately 750 potentially contaminated sites in Wales which are available for redevelopment (Welsh Office, 1988), and detailed surveys have also been undertaken in Cheshire. Recent estimates undertaken by the Department of the Environment (DoE) have indicated that the stock of contaminated land may amount to 35,000 hectares (Bottomley 1989). Evidence presented to the House of Commons Environment Committee (1990) disagrees with these estimates, however, suggesting that 50,000–100,000 contaminated sites may exist occupying more than 50,000 hectares.

Estimating the amount of contaminated land is particularly difficult because whereas the extent of dereliction can be appreciated visually, the extent of chemical contamination often cannot. In addition, contamination may be masked by seemingly innocuous or naturally occurring material and may also be distributed far more widely than the immediate boundaries of a former industrial site or waste tip. Industries often used adjacent land to

Table C9.1: Main categories of chemical contamination*

CONTAMINANT CATEGORIES	MOST LIKELY OCCURRENCE
1 Heavy metals, e.g. cadmium, lead, arsenic and mercury, which are hazardous to health	Metal mines, iron and steelworks, foundries, smelters, electroplating, anodizing and galvanizing works, engineering works, scrap yards and where catalysts, paints etc. are used; the use of pesticides and disposal of industrial and domestic wastes
2 Other metals, e.g. copper, which inhibit plant growth and are classed as phytotoxic	
3 Combustible substances, e.g. coal and coke dust, heavy tar deposits and sulphur, which present a fire risk	Gasworks, power stations, railway land, colliery and coke works etc.
4 Flammable, toxic and explosive gases, e.g. methane, carbon dioxide, hydrogen sulphide	Landfills, filled dock basins, gypsum wastes
5 Substances aggressive to building materials, e.g. sulphates, chlorides and acids	Made ground, including slags from blast furnaces, chemical and municipal waste tips
6 Organic contamination, e.g. oily and tarry substances, phenols and solvents, which may be toxic and contaminate water supplies, these compounds may also be volatile and present odour problems	Gasworks, tar works, refineries, chemical works, chemical and municipal waste tips, drum recycling plants, wood treatment plants
7 Asbestos	Asbestos was used in significant quantities in a large range of commercial, retail and industrial buildings which means that all demolition sites should be suspected of this contamination
8 Radioactive materials	Sites where radioactive materials have been processed
9 Biologically active materials	Sewage works, waste tips, sites where sewage is added to land, tanneries
* Adapted from ICRCL (1987)	

dump wastes, and contaminants often escape from the boundaries of a site via air or water. A particularly pertinent example is the emission of landfill gas and its migration from landfills towards surrounding development which is currently a major source of concern. A survey undertaken by HM Inspectorate of Pollution during 1987–8 revealed 1390 active and closed landfills that pose a potential risk from gas. Of these, approximately 750 lie within 250 m of housing and industry and represent the greatest risk (HM Inspectorate of Pollution, 1989).

The House of Commons Environment Committee 1990 has recommended that local authorities be obliged to compile registers of contaminated land using common methodology. The Government is now encouraging the compilation of these registers based on historical usage of the land with the aim of aiding their identification for development purposes.

Sources and Hazards

The main categories of contaminants are summarized in Table C9.1. There are many potential sources of such contamination which require consideration, including,

- accidental leakage and spillage from pipes and tanks during plant operation;
- the storage and disposal of raw materials, byproducts and waste materials;
- the disposal of unwanted wastes and residues on or adjacent to a site by disposal to properly designated landfills, dumps or tips;
- the deposition of airborne particles from stack or volatile exhaust emissions;
- the uncontrolled demolition of industrial plants, which may contain contaminating materials such as asbestos lagging, chemically impregnated brickwork, tars in pipes and underground tanks etc;
- further dispersion of contaminants as a result of soil disturbance, or leaching and drainage of the more soluble and mobile contaminants into surface water and groundwater.

If a contaminated site is redeveloped without recognition of the hazards from these sources, and without implementation of remedial measures then there is a high probability that one or more of the following consequences may occur:

- an immediate or long-term threat to the health and safety of those involved in reclamation or redevelopment, and to those working or living on or near the developed site;

- decreased safety of a development owing to the effect of aggressive chemicals, fire and explosion or physical settlement;
- other detrimental effects, such as contamination of groundwater and air pollution as a result of disturbance of contaminated soil, or difficulties in establishing vegetation;
- problems are remedied;
- reduced value of the land, expensive emergency action or abandonment of the proposed redevelopment.

Risks to Human Health

Risks to human health from contaminated land can arise in a number of ways.

Ingestion Both chronic (long-term) and acute (short-term) health effects may occur as a result of direct or indirect ingestion. Many contaminants may present a risk via direct accidental ingestion of soil or dirt. Although acute health effects are relatively unlikely, children may be at risk from sucking or placing non-food items in the mouth, particularly in the rare cases of children suffering from pica, a habitual tendency to ingest non-food items. Indirect ingestion may occur as a result of the consumption of food plants grown in contaminated soils which may be coated with particles of soil and dust or may have accumulated contaminants in their edible parts.

Where water supplies pass through soil containing organic compounds, particularly phenols, these may migrate through plastic water pipes and taint the water, even when present in low concentrations (see Chapter C2).

Inhalation The inhalation of either gaseous or particulate matter may also result in health risks. The Chapters in Section B of this book cover the hazards from inhalation of dusts, lead, asbestos, gases and solvents.

Skin contact Contaminants such as tars, oils and corrosive substances may cause irritation to the skin through direct contact with contaminated soil. Some of these contaminants may be carcinogenic in the event of long-term exposure, but this is unlikely.

Pathogenic micro-organisms may present a hazard at sewage works, on land where sewage sludge has been deposited, and at sites where clinical wastes have been dumped. Although the disease-producing organisms present in sewage are greatly reduced by the sewage treatment process, and many pathogens are killed by exposure to light, air, moisture, cold, heat etc., and release into the environment can render them non-infective, not all are easily destroyed, and there is always the possibility of activity being retained. Caution should therefore be exercised during the investigation and reclamation of such sites.

Radioactive materials Radioactive wastes are controlled under the Radioactive Substances Act 1960. Although not usually encountered on licensed landfill sites, they may be present on some development sites. A number of industrial processes have involved the processing of metals containing radioactive elements and, although disposal of radioactive materials is now closely controlled, some may remain in derelict buildings, contaminated land or waste spoil. Radioactive materials can enter food chains and water supplies, and in some cases can concentrate in particular organs of the body, resulting in risks of carcinogenic and teratogenic effects.

Contamination of water supplies and groundwater Leachates from landfills may contaminate both surface water and groundwater, and disturbance of sites during construction work may release contaminants into water courses and aquifers. The use of cover systems where contamination is left buried in the ground may result in lateral or vertical migration of the more soluble mobile contaminants.

Phytotoxicity

Phytotoxicity (the prevention or inhibition of plant growth, an effect which varies between species) may occur as a result of contamination, although it is often not easily recognized because other factors such as soil nutrient status, waterlogging or low oxygen levels have similar effects. The main phytotoxic elements are boron, copper, nickel and zinc, which are required in trace quantities for plant growth but which are toxic at elevated levels. Oils, coal tars, phenols and sulphates also exhibit phytotoxic effects at concentrations which are non-toxic to humans. Methane, carbon dioxide and other gases may give rise to phytotoxic effects by causing the displacement of the oxygen content of the soil in the root zone.

Chemical Attack on Building Materials and Services

Sulphates may attack concrete by converting tricalcium aluminate in the cement into high-sulphate calcium sulpho-aluminate and precipitating magnesium hydroxide and gypsum in the pores of the concrete matrix. This exerts mechanical pressure which can lead to weakening of the structure. Where sulphide is present, further sulphate production may occur as a result of microbial action or aerial oxidation. Sulphate attack on building materials may be enhanced in the presence of acid conditions.

In addition, acids, oily and tarry substances and other organic compounds may accelerate the corrosion of metals in soils and have detrimental effects on plastics, rubber and other polymeric materials used in pipework and service conduits or as seals and protective coatings for concrete and metals.

Combustion

Fires may occur below ground if material of a suitable calorific value is present. Materials such as coal and coke particles, oil, tar, pitch, rubber, plastic and domestic wastes are all combustible. If heated by, for example, contact with buried power cables, careless disposal of hot ashes or bonfires on the surface, underground materials may ignite and burn in an uncontrolled manner. Fires below ground may also result in major ground cavitation and subsidence which can affect the structural integrity of buildings.

Odours

Odours can be generated by the release of toxic or flammable gases from landfills and in land contaminated with organic compounds such as coal tars. Even if the hazards associated with the causes of the odours can be dealt with, the nuisance caused by odours may be difficult to control and may affect the choice of end-use for a site.

Particular Hazards associated with Landfills and Tips

Former landfill sites and tips can present particular problems for redevelopment. Consideration of gas generation from such sites requires particular attention because it has now become a major cause for concern. Flammable gases such as methane arising from the degradation of organic materials may form explosive mixtures if they accumulate in a confined space such as beneath or within buildings or in service ducts. Gas production depends on many factors, is likely to continue over at least 15 years, and may take 50 years or more to stabilize.

Landfill gas (LFG) consists predominantly of a mixture of methane and carbon dioxide, although other toxic trace components may be present, with the ratio of methane to carbon dioxide determining its properties. Methane is explosive at concentrations of 5%–15% in air and is flammable at high concentrations. Since there is a risk of stratified layers of gas accumulating in non-ventilated spaces, mixtures of LFG and air should always be regarded as potentially explosive and flammable. The production of LFG is therefore particularly hazardous when the intention is to construct new buildings on or near a site.

Since LFG is a potentially highly mobile gas, even if its rate of production is not high (as is often the case in tips over 10 years old), it may slowly collect in buildings above or alongside landfills. In porous strata, LFG may affect buildings some distance away and lateral diffusion may be exacerbated by covering a site with low-permeability materials such as clay, concrete foundations, roads and car parks etc. Although methane and carbon dioxide are odourless as pure gases, LFG, with its content of other trace organic compounds, is normally particularly odorous and this is often a good indication of its presence. Occasionally, in passing through soils and rock, the trace odorous compounds are removed, thus generating a gas mixture which is essentially odour free yet still potentially explosive.

In addition to chemical contamination, damage to building structures as a result of settlement and consolidation of infilled materials may occur, but such difficulties are outside the scope of this book.

DEVELOPMENT CONTROLS AND RESPONSIBILITIES

Legislative Framework

The UK approach to contaminated land operates almost exclusively in the context of land redevelopment, to promote the re-use of land for beneficial purposes although substantial changes in this approach are anticipated following the publication of the House of Commons Environment Committee Report (1990) on contaminated land, the Environmental Protection Bill, and the establishment of the National Rivers Authority (NRA). Local authorities and those responsible for contaminated land are encouraged to adopt a systematic approach to assessing hazards in relation to redevelopment use. They have a number of statutory powers which although not specifically focused on contaminated land may be used to address some of the problems which may be experienced during redevelopment. Other factors such as control of waste disposal and application of building regulations are also relevant.

Town and Country Planning Act 1971

This Act as amended gives Local authorities powers to control the development of land which might be contaminated, through refusal of, or conditions imposed on, planning applications. This and other planning legislation is being re-enacted in the form of the Town and Country Planning Act 1990.

Even before a planning application is made, informal discussion between developers and local authorities is encouraged. DoE Circular 21/87 (DoE, 1987) places the onus on a developer to assess whether or not land is suitable for a particular purpose, to demonstrate this when applying for planning permission and to accept responsibility for the safe and secure occupancy of the development. If an authority believes that land may be contaminated, this can be brought to the attention of a developer at this stage, enabling an applicant to undertake an adequate site investigation or design a reclamation scheme accordingly. If a proposal is unsatisfactory, planning permission may be refused on grounds including those of contamination. Alternatively, permission may be granted without conditions relating to contamination if the authority is satisfied that none is required (DoE, 1987).

There is no legal requirement on application for planning permission for a developer to disclose that a site is contaminated if the pertinent question has not been asked; rather the system relies on the diligence of the planning authorities. (See, however, Environmental Assessment below.) The proposed contaminated land registers should contribute significantly to the identification of potential problems associated with the development of contaminated sites.

In response to concern about the safety of landfill sites that might be generating methane gas, DoE published Circular 17/89 (DoE, 1989). This gives advice on the consideration of planning applications for development close to or on existing landfills and warns that permission should not be granted unless reliable arrangements can be made to manage migrating gas and minimize risks.

Under Section 52 of the Town and Country Planning Act 1971 restrictions may be placed on developments to prevent pollution being caused or aggravated by reclamation or construction works.

Control of Pollution Act 1974 and Control of Pollution (Special Waste) Regulations 1980

These measures provide the principal legislation controlling the disposal of waste. The Control of Pollution Act 1974 made it an offence to dispose of controlled wastes on a site which does not have a waste disposal licence for the receipt of such wastes, but fly tipping remains a serious problem which is impossible to quantify. It also made it an offence for any person to cause or permit any poisonous, noxious or polluting matter to enter any stream or controlled waters unless authorized, an offence now contained in the Water Act 1989.

The Control of Pollution (Special Waste) Regulations 1980 provided further levels of control of wastes which are 'dangerous to life'. These 'special wastes' may only be disposed following a process of pre-notification to the receiving waste disposal authority and the transfer of a special waste consignment note, but the ultimate fate of wastes covered by these regulations is determined by specific landfill site licences issued under the Control of Pollution Act.

The Environmental Protection Bill 1990 will replace the Control of

Pollution Act waste provisions and will impose a further 'duty of care' on waste producers and handlers of waste to ensure proper management.

Public Health Act 1936

This Act imposes a duty on a local authority to inspect its area for statutory nuisances, which could include effects associated with contaminated land, and provides local authorities with powers to abate or prevent recurrence of the nuisance. Statutory nuisances will be streamlined by the Environmental Protection Bill.

Government Guidelines

There are currently no statutory limits in the United Kingdom regarding contamination concentrations on a site to be redeveloped. Instead, a number of recommended guidelines relating to acceptable concentrations of contaminants for different end-uses of land have been published.

The potential problems of contaminated land were first formally recognized by the UK government in 1976 with the establishment of the Interdepartmental Committee on the Redevelopment of Contaminated Land (ICRCL) within the DoE. This committee has produced a series of guidance notes for sites such as landfills (ICRCL, 1988), gasworks (ICRCL, 1986b), sewage works and farms (ICRCL, 1983a) and scrapyards (ICRCL, 1986c), together with reviews of particular hazards associated with asbestos (ICRCL, 1985) and fire (ICRCL, 1986).

The policy of determining acceptable and unacceptable levels of contaminants has developed by consideration of the sensitivity of a proposed end-use of a site and relating this to appropriate action and trigger concentrations for specific contaminants. ICRCL guidelines provide a framework of recommendations, but leave much open to professional judgement, and cover only a limited range of common contaminants. There are substantial deficiencies relating to many organic and inorganic compounds, chlorinated compounds, ammonia and pesticides. Thus, those assessing sites are often required to consult the values developed by the former Greater London Council (Kelly, 1980) for uncontaminated and contaminated soils, and more comprehensive European guidelines as secondary sources. Useful guidance has also been provided by the Building Research Establishment (1981) on protection required for concrete in sulphate-bearing soil.

Other Relevant Issues

Local authorities may also control the development of polluted sites by using powers under the Building Regulations 1985, the purpose of which is to ensure the health, safety and welfare of persons in or about the buildings, or those who may be affected by them or matters concerned with them.

The Building Regulations 1985 require that, where buildings are to be constructed on contaminated land, the foundations are capable of resisting any attack by sulphate or other deleterious material, that the land is reasonably free of faecal or offensive animal or vegetable matter, and that precautions are taken to avoid danger to health caused by substances in or on the ground immediately covered by buildings. The Regulations do not cover the ground around buildings and therefore do not address directly the possibility of migration of contaminants, especially gases.

The Occupiers Liability Act 1957 imposes a specific statutory duty on the occupier of a property to take such care as is reasonable to see that visitors are safe in using premises for the purposes for which they are invited or permitted to be there.

The Health and Safety at Work Act etc 1974 places a duty on every employer to ensure, as far as is reasonably practicable, the health, safety and welfare of all its employees. This is particularly relevant to those employed in the investigation or reclamation of contaminated sites. The Act also requires employers to conduct their undertakings in such a way that other persons, such as visitors or members of the public, are not put at risk. The Health and Safety Executive is responsible for the enforcement of the Act and can be informally consulted.

The Control of Substances Hazardous to Health (COSHH) Regulations 1989 have now been incorporated into the Health and Safety at Work Act introducing a new legal framework. These regulations lay down the requirements to employers for a step by step approach to assessing the risks to health associated with exposure to hazardous substances and the establishment of safe working practices to prevent or control those risks.

The European Commission Directive EEC 85/337 on the assessment of the impact of certain public and private projects on the environment has now been incorporated into the UK legislative framework as the Town and County Planning (Assessment of Environmental Effects) Regulations 1988. This requires that projects which are likely to have significant effects on the environment by virtue *inter alia* of their nature, size or location shall be subject to an assessment of those effects. Guidance on the provisions of the Regulations is provided in DoE Circular 15/88 (DoE, 1988a).

Future Legislation and EEC Influences

Relatively high concentrations of contaminants are acceptable on UK sites in comparison with European countries such as the Federal Republic of Germany and the Netherlands. However, EEC legislation is increasingly influencing the United Kingdom and will continue to do so. The DoE is currently reviewing the status of land reclamation in the United Kingdom and these findings are likely to lead to a much tighter control of standards. There is a pressing need for national criteria in terms of acceptable levels of contamination, and for the scope of the ICRCL guidelines to be expanded.

The recent House of Commons Environment Committee Report on Contaminated Land (House of Commons, 1990) contained wide ranging criticism of the basis of contaminated land regulation, technical guidance and remedial techniques being used in the UK.

One particular weakness of the present law is that there is no method to ensure that information on contaminated sites is retained in an accessible form, or that vendors make such information known when selling a site. Instead, the sale and purchase of land is based on the legal principle of *caveat emptor* or 'buyer beware'. It is therefore possible for a developer to purchase a contaminated site without being aware of its history. It has been proposed that the rule of *caveat emptor* be abolished but this has been opposed by the Law Commission Conveyancing Standing Committee and the situation is currently uncertain.

Increasing public concern over the disposal and transport of toxic wastes, and the increasing cost of landfill, are also likely to have repercussions on land reclamation by reducing the types of waste that can be disposed of at licensed tips. This is likely to focus more attention on the use of wholly destructive techniques for the eradication of soil contamination problems in line with the general approach taken in the Netherlands, Denmark and the Federal Republic of Germany.

The National Rivers Authority (NRA), whose role is to protect the aquatic environment and preserve water quality, can be expected to play an increasing role in controlling the reclamation and development of contaminated land. The House of Commons Environment Committee (1990) has advocated the NRA taking pre-emptive action on contaminated land that could be a source of pollution, but the NRA currently has limited powers of enforcement. The powers of the NRA under the Water Act 1989 could theoretically be used in connection with contaminated land; however, evidence presented to the Committee highlighted the practical difficulties associated with their implementation. The NRA therefore continues to rely on the planning authorities to impose precautions necessary to prevent or avoid exacerbation of ground water pollution during reclamation including restrictions on the type of foundations which may be used, the levels of contamination with may remain on a site, and the imposition of water quality monitoring programmes during and after redevelopment. Greater regard for water quality issues and statutory consultation with the NRA is recommended as part of the planning process.

TACKLING THE PROBLEM

Where a site is known or suspected to be contaminated to such an extent that a proposed development could be adversely affected, a site investigation is normally required to identify the hazards before a planning application is determined. Should remedial action be required to protect buildings, services, future users or occupiers, then planning permission may be granted subject to conditions specifying the measures to be carried out.

ICRCL guidelines advocate a systematic approach to redeveloping a potentially contaminated site. The overall approach can be summarized as:

- review data on the site's history;
- design and undertake an appropriate site investigation to determine whether a potential contamination problem exists and to assess any hazards;
- select the most appropriate use for the site and decide what, if any, remedial action is required;

and is shown diagrammatically in Figure C9.1.

A list of organizations offering consultancy services for the investigation of chemically contaminated land and its analysis can be obtained from the Professional Affairs Department, Royal Society of Chemistry. The assessment of contaminated sites in the United Kingdom is now covered in a draft British Standard (British Standards Institution, 1988), a document which should contribute greatly to the unification of methods used for site investigation.

Reviewing Site History and Identifying Hazards

Information on the history of a site can be obtained from a wide range of sources, including maps, the ordnance survey, trade information, photographic records and technical papers. Many authorities and large organizations such as British Gas or British Rail often have useful information available, and the Health and Safety Executive may provide information on previous work history. Recollections of former employees and local residents can often provide extremely valuable insights into a site's history. Collation of this type of information can help by indicating the type of contaminant likely to be present, and the location of any process likely to have resulted in contamination.

Before a sampling strategy is finalized, the site should normally be visited to observe conditions such as underground voids, cables, gas mains, distribution and type of vegetation, presence of unusual surface

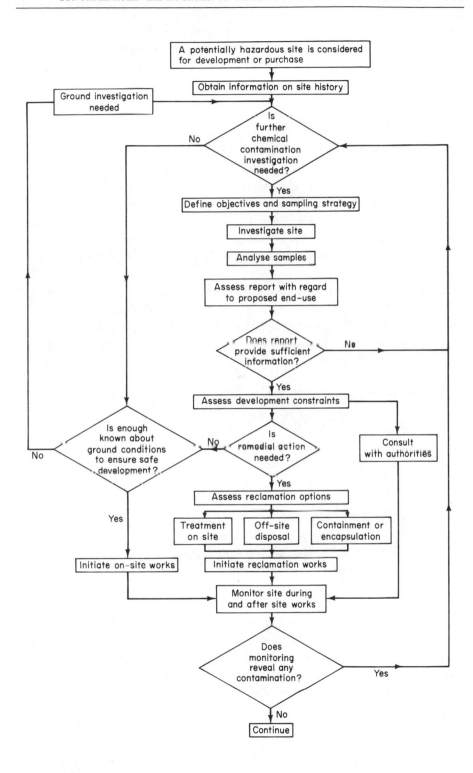

Figure C9.1: Sequence for development of a contaminated site

materials, unusual odours or fumes, the presence of any obstructions such as mass or reinforced concrete or buried tanks, and to secure information on any particular safety aspects which may affect site investigation teams or future workers on the site.

Site Investigation

The investigation of sites to determine the suitability of the ground for civil engineering and building works is common practice, but in many cases site investigations only determine the requirements for foundation design, and neglect consideration of chemical contamination. Financial savings from an inadequate investigation of a contaminated site will soon disappear if a planning application is rejected or because contamination requiring expensive remedial action is only found during or after redevelopment.

The investigation of a chemically contaminated site is a specialist skill requiring considerable expertise and experience, and there are now many competent organizations providing chemical site investigation and consulting services. The main objectives of a chemical site investigation are (ICRCL, 1987; British Standards Institution, 1988) cost-effectively to:

- determine the contaminants present in the soil, water or gaseous phase;
- determine their lateral and vertical distribution across the site and their concentration both on and below the surface;
- provide adequate data for the design of remedial action if required.

The selection of the most appropriate sampling strategy is a matter of experience, and should be undertaken to provide a statistically valid sampling framework across the site whilst assessing areas most likely to be contaminated and locating the most contaminated areas. The use of trial pits excavated with a mechanical excavator on a regularly spaced sampling grid is usually preferred to boreholes. This approach offers a greater opportunity for observing general subsurface conditions and is less likely to result in cross-contamination of samples. However, boreholes may have to be used if samples are required from depths greater than those which can be reached by an excavator. Samples of soil and water are normally taken from discrete depth intervals or according to soil horizons and site conditions.

Comprehensive analysis of all samples collected during a site investigation is costly and may be time consuming. Instead, it is usually preferable to undertake a phased assessment of samples, commencing with the most common contaminants of concern to the proposed end-use.

Special requirements for landfills and tip sites

The DoE recently published an important technical memorandum on the monitoring and control of landfill gas which also provides guidance on the survey and investigation of sites where gas is being produced (DoE, 1988b). This is a key document to be consulted when considering any redevelopment on or adjacent to restored landfills. A revised version is currently under consideration.

Where redevelopment of a landfill site is to occur, a systematic investigation to determine gas concentrations, distribution and emission rates over a realistic period is advocated. This usually commences with sampling from confined spaces, drains, and cracks and discontinuities in the ground surface. The monitoring of methane or other potentially hazardous gases can then be undertaken in appropriate areas by the use of monitoring probes (Crowhurst, 1987). These should normally be capped, particularly in older sites where gas production is slow, to ensure that representative gas samples can be obtained. Monitoring should be undertaken over a reasonable period of at least six months to assess emissions under changing environmental conditions, and should also address the potential for gas to migrate laterally and vertically from a site.

In addition to conventional monitoring of gas, a range of proprietary tests has been developed to measure LFG production and yield and to provide more accurate and rapid prediction of its rate, duration and potential future yield (Biotreatment, undated).

Data assessment

Realistic data assessment is obviously only possible if the requirements of a site investigation are clear from the outset, enabling suitable data to be obtained. Careful assessment of the significance of contamination and the importance of risks disclosed by the site investigation is necessary. Some contaminants, such as methane or asbestos, present an obvious hazard at low concentrations, but the environmental significance of many contaminants is not well understood. In the United Kingdom indirect methods based on 'threshold trigger' and 'action target' concentrations have been adopted (Figure C9.2). However, these are currently limited in scope and application, and considerable experience is required to determine the significance of the levels of contamination found and the potential hazards. Bewley (1990) argues for an urgent review of analytical methodologies and an extension of current guidelines.

The significance of any hazard on a given site is taken to depend primarily on the intended site use, since this is the determining factor as to who or what may be at risk, and ICRCL guidelines provide guidance on this issue. Examples of acceptable levels of contaminants for particular end-uses are given in Table C9.2. If the level of contamination is less than the threshold trigger value for a particular contaminant and a particular end-use, then the ground can be treated as if it were un-contaminated with that chemical. If the levels are greater than those quoted for the action target value, then some form of remedial work is required. Between these two sets of values, contamination may present a risk, and professional judgement is required to decide whether that risk justifies remedial action or not. The concept of trigger concentrations is discussed more fully in the 'Gasworks Report'(1987).

The most sensitive end uses for a site are generally considered to be housing with gardens or allotments where occupants may be in direct, prolonged contact with soils through gardening, play, or the growth and consumption of food crops. A 'hard' end use comprising industrial or commercial building is the least sensitive as it is assumed that regular exposure to contaminated materials will not occur. Defining contaminated land in relation to end use in this way has been criticised in the House of Commons Environment Committee Report (1990) because 'it may be underestimating a genuine environmental problem and misdirecting effort and resources'. The report advocates emphasis on land which is a hazard irrespective of end use.

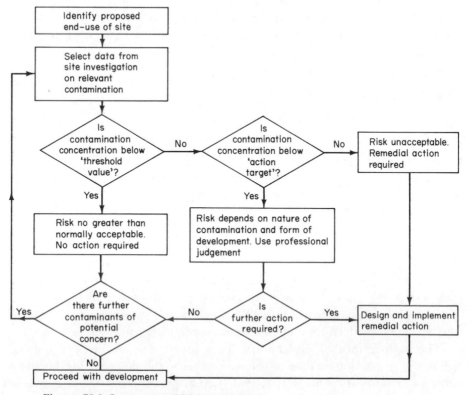

Figure C9.2: Interpreting ICRCL guidelines.

Table C9.2: Examples of tentative trigger concentrations for selected organic and inorganic contaminants

CONTAMINANT	PLANNED USES	TRIGGER CONCENTRATION (mg kg^{-1})	
		THRESHOLD	ACTION*
Lead	Domestic gardens, allotments	500	
	Parks, playing fields, open spaces	2000	
Mercury	Domestic gardens, allotments	1	
	Parks, playing fields, open spaces	20	
Free cyanide	Domestic gardens, allotments	25	500
	Landscaped areas, buildings, hard cover	100	500
Polyaromatic hydrocarbons	Domestic gardens, allotments	50	500
	Play areas, landscaped areas, buildings, hard cover	1000	10 000

* No trigger concentrations for 'Action' are specified by ICRCL guidelines for lead or mercury. *Source*: ICRCL, 1987.

GRANTS AND FUNDING FOR REMEDIAL MEASURES

Reclamation of contaminated land can incur considerable expenditure and the high costs often act as a barrier to redevelopment. There are a number of grants from UK central government which may be available to help bring sites into beneficial use. These are administered through DoE regional offices in England and Northern Ireland and through the Welsh and Scottish Development Agencies from whom current details can be obtained. Urban Development Corporations have been set up by the Government with the objective of regenerating a number of designated areas; they can offer assistance to potential developers and act for local planning authorities in that area.

Derelict Land Grant Derelict Land Grant is available to both local authorities and private developers for the reclamation of land which is incapable of beneficial use without treatment. The grant is payable at different rates in Assisted Areas, Derelict Land Clearance Areas, National Parks, and conservation areas.

City Grant and Urban Programme City Grant was introduced in May 1988 to replace the former Urban Development Grant and provides financial assistance towards reclamation and development costs for schemes costing £200,000 or more. The Urban Programme assists selected urban local authorities with schemes which will improve the economic, environmental or social problems of inner cities.

Other sources Other grants and incentives may include Regional Development Grants and selective Financial Assistance and Enterprise and Simplified Planning Zones. The European Regional Development Fund enables EC funds to be used to correct regional imbalances in unemployment and regenerate declining industrial areas. Derelict land reclamation is eligible when the reclaimed area will provide land for industrial sites.

OPTIONS FOR REMEDIAL ACTION

Once assessment has confirmed that a site is contaminated, and changes in the land-use to minimize risks to the most sensitive targets are not feasible, some form of remedial action will be required to limit any nuisance or hazard, and enable the land to be re-used safely.

In the United Kingdom the emphasis has been placed on providing safe conditions at a site's surface, but these are somewhat short-term solutions and in many cases have given little consideration to the protection of groundwater, the prevention of mobile contaminants such as methane migrating from a site into surrounding strata, or protection of services and appropriate selection of building materials for a potentially aggressive subsurface environment. Where remedial action is required, there is all too often a tendency to propose 'blanket' remedial measures such as the use of cover systems or the removal of contaminated materials to a tip without considering their suitability or undertaking a full technical or economic evaluation of the alternatives.

The primary objective in undertaking remedial action is to ensure that risks to public health, the environment and building integrity are either eliminated or reduced to acceptable levels. This can be achieved by one or a combination of three broad strategies: complete removal, destruction of contaminants, or ensuring that alternative measures are designed to remain effective in the long term. The choice between these strategies and combinations of them will depend on the nature and extent of contamination, the intended end-use of the site, and the funding and time available.

Disposal to a licensed tip

Large-scale removal of contaminated material has been widely used in the past, yet issues relating to the disposal of contaminated spoils are increasingly becoming a major constraint. The method has the inherent disadvantage that it simply transfers a problem elsewhere to become a burden on future generations, In addition, further hazards and nuisance can be associated with the transport of contaminated materials through urban areas and, where contaminants have penetrated to considerable depths or large volumes of wastes are present, removal of materials may be precluded on economic grounds.

Few landfill sites are licensed to accept toxic materials which are on the restricted list for disposal and long transport distances to suitably licensed tips are often required. Where disposal of wastes is permitted, restrictions on the rates at which licensed tips are able to accept such wastes can limit disposal and have severe repercussions on the development programme. The need to import fill material adds still more to the cost of such a project, and there can be practical problems in ensuring that imported material is indeed 'clean'. Certification of the satisfactory chemical composition of the imported fill should be provided, particularly when waste spoil is imported. Owing to the environmental and economic implications associated with the excavation and disposal of contaminated materials on a significant scale, this method should only be considered as a last resort.

Encapsulation or fixation

Soil cover reclamation, where contaminated material is concealed beneath an uncontaminated soil material which acts as a barrier to pollutants, is the method currently in favour in the United Kingdom, and represents a form of encapsulation and the physical segregation of the chemical contamination from the building and human environment. If designed adequately, this can be a cheap and competent alternative. However, this method leaves potentially hazardous contaminants on the site, albeit below a cover layer. Mobile or gaseous contaminants may either rise up through the cover layer to disrupt or harm the users of the site or migrate off site to contaminate surrounding areas. The design life of such a system must therefore be considered to be finite. Work by Cairney (1987) has led to an understanding of the design criteria required for a soil cover system.

Treatment and destructive techniques

On-site treatment, which may include physical, chemical or biological treatment undertaken *in situ* or following excavation of contaminated material, can provide a permanent remedial alternative. The alternatives are:

- physical regrading of a site to average out concentrations of contaminants, which can be successful in some circumstances;

- addition of alkali in the form of limestone or slaked lime to counteract the effects of low pH and to immobilize sulphate;
- wholly destructive techniques to eradicate chemical contamination, interest in which is increasing;
- biological treatment, which has the most proven record, has been applied successfully in the United Kingdom, the Federal Republic of Germany and the USA. It is a technique based on enhancing the activities of naturally occurring organisms which already exist in low numbers in the soil and can be applied to the treatment of a wide range of organic contaminants such as tars, phenols, oils etc.

Biological treatment involves the selection of indigenous groups of micro-organisms that can metabolize the toxic compounds from a site. These are grown in large numbers and reintroduced into the soil, and the soil physical environment is optimized to enable the bacteria to break down toxic compounds to simple harmless molecules such as water and carbon dioxide. Following successful treatment, detailed analysis of the site is undertaken by an independent authority to validate the treatment and to provide certification of the condition of the land for a prospective purchaser.

The technique is not a panacea for land de-contamination. However, there is considerable scope for its more selective application in combination with other more conventional reclamation methods to offer an overall solution to problem sites or to minimize the requirement for removal of materials to a distant tip. The significant advantages of the technique are that it is wholly destructive and can be highly cost effective compared with the alternatives (Bewley et al 1989).

There is considerable interest, particularly in other European countries, in other forms of treatment including soil washing, air stripping, thermal degradation and stabilization, which in some cases can be undertaken using specially designed mobile plants on the site itself. These methods have not generally been applied to full scale commercial projects in the United Kingdom up to now, but attention is likely to be increasingly focused upon them in the future.

Other Considerations

Planting Special consideration may also be required if plants are to be grown on a redeveloped site. Where good quality top soil is in short supply, the most suitable plant species for revegetating a site are those with shallow roots, such as grass, which are more resistant to many forms of contamination. If trees are to be planted, the ground may need to be prepared by excavating contaminated material and backfilling with clean top soil (ICRCL, 1987).

Fire A further matter of potential concern is the presence of combustible materials which may ignite and smoulder underground and put buildings at risk. If an underground fire is detected in time, it may be controlled by excavating combustible material ahead of the burning area and damping down the remains. A large fire is very difficult to control and will often have to be left to burn out, the only solution being to dispose of potential combustible materials before redevelopment begins (ICRCL, 1987).

LONG-TERM EFFECTIVENESS AND MONITORING

Remedial measures should be designed to be both durable in the sense that they continue to perform in the desired manner for the length of time required and robust in the sense that they can withstand foreseeable events such as flooding. If the treatment is to be considered permanent, it must be designed to last at least for the lifetime of a building constructed on a treated site, which in the case of housing may be hundreds of years. This is difficult to ensure as we have little experience on which to base designs and few data are available on the effectiveness of reclamation methods. There are a limited number of sites more than a few years old reclaimed with full recognition of contaminant problems and few on which long-term monitoring or evaluation has been carried out. Actions that remove contamination or render it harmless through a destructive process provide an ultimate solution if carried out properly, and the question of long-term effectiveness does not apply. Other methods offer a solution of finite or uncertain duration. It is therefore necessary that the requirement for maintenance and monitoring also be recognized in the design of reclamation works.

Deficiencies of current methods

In general, treatment systems based on cover systems are vulnerable to loss of effectiveness with time, particularly if they are designed for aesthetic reasons with little consideration of their design requirements. The United Kingdom has so far escaped pollution incidents of the severity of Love Canal in the United States, which became synonymous with hazardous waste problems. The site was used for tipping chlorinated wastes until 1953 and was subsequently capped and sold. Development proceeded for residential housing and a school, but in the late 1970s leachates began to appear in the basement of properties. This led to the relocation of 2500 people and a bill for $30 million for the US government. There is now growing evidence of a number of reclamation schemes in the United Kingdom which may not have taken a sufficiently long-term view of potential environmental or health risks. For instance, a recent survey undertaken for the Welsh Office (Richards, Moorehead and Laing Ltd, 1988) on sites reclaimed following contamination by manufacturing or waste disposal activities has indicated that some may still be posing environmental hazards. This has been one of the few genuine attempts to monitor sites after reclamation.

Examples of failure included a site containing drums of phenols and tars which was reclaimed using a cover of limestone shale. Leachate has now been found to be escaping and killing vegetation. On another site, elevated levels of metals were found in soils and vegetation because no break layer was provided in the soil cover, and a further example was a site where zinc levels in a nearby stream had doubled following reclamation and high levels of zinc were apparent in pasture grazed by sheep. There have been other examples elsewhere in the United Kingdom of contaminants accumulating in food or edible plants where housing developments have been sited on reclaimed sites. To a large extent, evidence is only just emerging of failures due to inadequate remedial measures.

Unless the methods used for reclamation in the United Kingdom are improved and standardized, it is possible that considerable difficulties similar to the current great alarm regarding the problems of LFG, the foundations of which have been laid down over the last 20 years of inadequate management, will become apparent.

Requirements for monitoring

Routine monitoring of redeveloped contaminated sites together with provision for programmed maintenance where appropriate, particularly on sites reclaimed using soil cover systems, would contribute greatly to identification of any relevant changes and ensure that unacceptable risks do not occur in the future. ICRCL guidelines state that monitoring of sites following reclamation may be desirable, but in practice the requirement is seldom applied.

It would be in the interests of improved and unified standards if all reclamation projects employing cover systems were monitored not only for migration of contaminants off site but also to ensure that contaminants are not rising through the cover. Monitoring in its simplest form may involve visual observations such as noting any evidence of vegetation die-back, and may be extended to include monitoring of the physical properties of a soil cover or presence of specific contaminants. Where the status of the subsurface gas environment has been identified as being potentially hazardous, monitoring probes for gas should be installed within and surrounding the site. Probes should be located in high-permeability strata and adjacent to buildings and other sensitive areas, and monitoring will be required through a range of atmospheric conditions over a prolonged period of time.

BUILDING ON CONTAMINATED LAND

Where construction is to proceed on a reclaimed site, further measures over and above those required to safeguard future users or occupiers may be required to ensure the integrity of the buildings and other structures. In addition to any geotechnical difficulties, protection must be provided against chemical contaminants which may either be detrimental to building materials or present a risk of explosion or fire. Consideration should also be given to safeguarding workers on site who may be involved in site investigation, reclamation or redevelopment works. New guidance on the development of contaminated land has recently been published (Institution of Environmental Health Officers, 1989).

Protection of Site Workers

During the redevelopment of contaminated sites the hazard to workers is often overlooked despite the fact that they may be the most exposed target group and may be involved in the installation of measures for the protection of future users. The greatest area of concern here is the risk to workers from direct contact with contaminated materials. The main routes of exposure are via skin contact, hand to mouth contact such as when eating or smoking cigarettes contaminated by dirty hands, and inhalation of dusts, vapours and gases. As a general principle, precautions are required to minimize exposure of the work-force by taking appropriate protective measures. Protection for workers can be provided in the form of clothing, hygiene and safety equipment, and does not necessarily mean expensive items. Specialist advice from an occupational hygienist should be obtained if particularly hazardous conditions are likely to be encountered during site works. Guidance on many of these hazards is given in other Chapters.

Protection of Buildings and other Structures

Hazards of concern here include direct chemical attack on materials such as concrete and plastic pipes and indirect effects such as damage to building structures as a result of settlement and risks associated with the accumulation of flammable gases within confined spaces.

Construction materials and services Building materials may be in direct contact with contaminated soils over long periods of exposure which may result in a range of detrimental effects. The extent of damage will vary according to the specific conditions on site such as concentration of the contaminant, porosity of the soil and water content, and may go undetected for a considerable period. All building materials used below ground may be at risk.

Concrete is the most widely used construction material for subsurface applications. When well compacted, with adequate cement content, it has good resistance to chemical attack, although fresh concrete may be more vulnerable. The adverse effect of sulphates on concrete made with Ordinary Portland Cement is well documented, and the Building Research Establishment provides guidance on the protection of concrete in sulphate-bearing soils. In general, stringent quality control of concrete production and placing, and specification of sulphate-resisting cement can overcome sulphate problems at concentrations of total sulphate in soils of up to 2%. Above this level, additional protection in the form of a protective coating such as heavy duty polyethylene sheeting is required.

Plastics are being increasingly used in building components, and service pipes, tanks and membranes may be particularly at risk. Plastic water pipes can be affected by the presence of organic contaminants which may either weaken the plastic, leading to stress corrosion, cracking and failure, or migrate through the pipes resulting in contamination of the water. Plastic pipes should not generally be provided on sites containing organic contaminants unless service runs can be adequately safeguarded by locally excavating contaminated material and providing clean backfill. Plastics are resistant to many other types of chemical attack and it should be possible to identify types which are resistant to the prevailing conditions.

Clay bricks are among the most durable of building materials and are likely to be unaffected by chemicals. The mortar may be susceptible to attack but this can often be overcome by using sulphate-resisting cement.

Metals in contact with contaminated soils may be susceptible to biological corrosion, particularly in the presence of high sulphate levels where cast iron may be corroded by sulphate-reducing bacteria. Copper and galvanized steel may be corroded in acid soils and some made grounds. Under such conditions, metals may require protective coating with materials such as bitumen or resins.

Rubber is most likely to be found in the form of pipe-sealing rings, although it is also a component of sealants. The types available differ greatly, and it is important that types to suit the prevalent conditions are purchased.

Bitumens and asphalts are fairly resistant to attack, although organic contaminants may cause them to soften.

Preventing gas ingress Recent advice issued by the DoE has highlighted the potential hazards associated with building on or adjacent to active and former landfill sites and resulted in recommendations that landfill sites be used for agricultural or open space until wastes have stabilized (DoE, 1988b). Supermarkets, warehouses and factories have been successfully developed on restored sites by the adoption of necessary safeguards, but there are examples of developments running into difficulties by failing to take account of the relevant factors. It is generally recommended that housing with gardens should not be located on or close to actively gassing sites because, while a house can be made gas-tight, it is more difficult to ensure the integrity of sheds, greenhouses and outhouses.

Problems are not only apparent on domestic refuse and industrial waste sites. Sites which have taken so-called 'inert' wastes are also a serious cause for concern because these often include packaging materials, cardboard, wood etc. which can be slowly degraded to yield methane.

It is not possible to design measures to limit the hazards associated with the redevelopment of landfill sites until adequate data on the extent of the problem have been obtained. Remedial measures are site specific depending on rates of gas emissions, gas composition and the proposals for development. Nonetheless, in broad terms hard development of landfill sites is only permitted using designs which will ensure the safety of buildings and occupants. Building design must be such as to overcome potential subsidence, gas ingress and detrimental effects on construction materials.

On actively gassing landfills, measures must be designed to withstand the effects of gas by preventing gas reaching and entering buildings, and providing adequate ventilation/dilution at critical locations within buildings to prevent accumulation to dangerous levels. It is essential to ensure that the measures are durable and remain effective until gas emissions have ceased or are negligible.

On some sites, interceptor trenches can be used to prevent gas reaching buildings; however, buildings must be designed to prevent gas entry by sealing effectively and taking measures to prevent the accumulation of LFG in confined spaces. There are many potential points for gas to enter a building, making it difficult to ensure a gas-tight seal. Generally, floors should be cast as a single slab, with no jointing, and gas-tight plastic membranes should be provided either within or beneath the slab to reduce gas ingress. Entry points for services should be at the side of a building, not through the floor slab, and care should be taken to seal them. At sites where there is steady high methane production, the provision of an airspace beneath the floor slab is desirable. A positive path to vent any gas from this space should be provided, possibly by mechanical means. Where methane concentrations are lower, it may be sufficient to cast floor slabs on coarse aggregate and install perforated pipes to vent naturally or via a pumped system.

It is seldom sufficient to rely solely on preventing gas ingress; further measures are often required to monitor the accumulation of any gas within or beneath buildings and vent it where necessary. These may take the form of alarm systems to warn of potentially dangerous gas levels, and extraction systems which actively vent buildings. Gas detection equipment is required to ensure that a safe environment exists and to ensure that gas control measures are working satisfactorily.

HM Inspectorate of Pollution recommends that buildings should be evacuated if the methane concentration exceeds 20% of the lower explosive limit (LEL) of 5% gas in air. At concentrations below 20% LEL continuous monitoring should be undertaken until gas control measures have been demonstrated to be effective (DoE, 1988b). A further hazard is associated with carbon dioxide which is a highly toxic and asphyxiant gas. Carbon dioxide has a long-term occupational exposure limit (OEL) of 0.5% and gives cause for concern in excess of 0.25% (Health and Safety Executive, 1988). Since carbon dioxide usually coexists in similar proportions to methane, the standards for methane will normally ensure that carbon dioxide also remains at safe levels.

Where a land development involves covering large areas of a site with impermeable materials such as concrete, further measures may be required to prevent the lateral migration of gases from presenting a hazard to adjacent developments. At shallow landfills, the use of simple interceptor trenches 1–2 m wide filled with coarse aggregate may suffice. Alternatively, it may be necessary to vent such a system with passive or active venting systems depending on the rate of gas production. Other methods involve the use of an impermeable barrier which can be achieved, for instance, by injecting bentonite grout (a liquid clay) into the ground. The effectiveness of such a system can seldom be guaranteed and, where methane migration is likely to be a serious problem, more extensive systems involving pumping from gas collection boreholes and flaring off the gas may be required. Further measures may also be required to vent areas of hardstanding such as car parks.

Gas recovery Considerable interest is now focusing on the commercial utilization of gas from landfills and there are more than 20 schemes in the United Kingdom where gas is being recovered for direct use in kilns, boilers and furnaces or in power generation. If the quantities of gas are sufficiently large and of suitable quality, these schemes have commercial potential for utilization as a valuable source of energy. A commercial gas recovery scheme can be an environmental credit since it reduces gas pressure in a site and alleviates many of the problems associated with gas migration. However, it is important to ensure that gas control systems are operating even when gas is not being utilized. Gas is usually collected and pumped to nearby consumers on adjacent land. Where buildings are required on a landfill as part of the commercial scheme these should be safeguarded against the ingress of gas and monitored for its presence as detailed above.

SUMMARY AND CONCLUSIONS

* The growing emphasis on the redevelopment of land which has become contaminated as a result of previous use for waste disposal or industrial purposes has concentrated attention on the hazards associated with such sites and the application of remedial techniques to enable their safe and reliable re-use. The redevelopment of these sites need not be an insurmountable problem provided that consideration of the presence of contamination is made at an early stage of the development process and the necessary steps are taken to ensure that future users or occupiers are protected against hazards which can be foreseen, avoided or eradicated. Prospective developers have a moral duty to adopt the best possible reclamation means if a legacy of potential disasters is not to be built up for the future. Guidance on the approach that should be taken has recently been published by the Institute of Environmental Health Officers (1989).

* The first issue facing those involved in developing such sites is in recognizing when a potential problem exists, but advice on the location of such sites can be obtained from regional offices of the DoE, Welsh Office, local planning authorities and HM Inspectorate of Pollution. Alternatively, it may prove necessary to appoint a specialist consultant to review the history of a site, determine the likelihood of the presence of contamination and, where necessary, undertake a site investigation.

* The hazards associated with contaminated land may include threats to the health and safety of future users or occupiers of the land, harm to animal and plant life, detrimental effects on building materials and services, and risks to the surrounding environment from contaminant migration. These differ from site to site and their significance depends to a considerable extent on the proposed end-use of the land.

* Whenever the previous history of a site, its adjacent property or other indications suggest that contamination has occurred, prospective developers should investigate the site to check whether it is suitable for its intended use. Local planning authorities should therefore be consulted at an early stage whenever it is proposed to develop contaminated sites.

* The most effective way of developing contaminated land is often to choose an end-use tolerant of the contamination present, but where this is impractical remedial action may be required to render the site safe for its intended use. There are currently no absolute standards by which contaminated land can be assessed, therefore specialist expertise is needed to determine the existence of potential hazards and to design appropriate remedial measures.

* Interest is now focusing on the application of wholly destructive techniques to eradicate contamination problems permanently, or the use of controlled encapsulation techniques to isolate contaminated materials. The retention of contaminated materials on site, albeit beneath a cover system, offers a solution of finite duration and such measures must be designed to be effective over a long time period and at least for the lifetime of any buildings constructed on the treated site.

* In general the current UK approach of leaving contamination in the ground and covering it can be regarded as cosmetic and designed solely to enable the short-term re-use of land rather than a permanent resolution of contamination problems. This policy of ensuring that the surface of a site is suitable for its intended end-use shows little concern for the contamination of groundwater (Chapter C2). Water is the primary agent of the movement of many contaminants, and it is essential that its likely movement and the effect that it will have on contaminant dispersal is carefully considered at the design stage, particularly when using cover systems. The protection of groundwater which may be used for drinking purposes is of prime importance, and assessment of the implications of disturbing the water table and affecting the mobility of contamination is of considerable significance.

* In the Netherlands and the United States solutions to protect groundwater and prevent migration of contaminants from problem sites include sealing the base of sites and installation of vertical barriers to prevent lateral migration, but UK experience of these methods is somewhat limited and they are not widely applied.

* Where buildings are to be constructed on a contaminated site, the provisions of the Building Regulations 1985 will apply and advice on design appropriate to the site can be obtained from the Building Control Section of the local planning authority or from the Building Research Establishment.

* Consideration should also be given to the safety of those working on the site during investigation, reclamation or redevelopment. Where potential hazards are present, the Health and Safety Executive or the local Environmental Health Department should be consulted.

APPENDIX:

FOUR CASE STUDIES

CASE STUDY 1:

The reclamation of a Lancashire gasworks by the application of microbial techniques to eradicate contamination

INTRODUCTION

The Greenbank Gasworks site occupies approximately 10 hectares to the east of Blackburn, between the outer ring road and the Leeds-Liverpool Canal. The site housed a fully operational gasworks from the beginning of the century until 1977 when it was dismantled following the introduction of North Sea gas to replace the coal gasification process. Blackburn Borough Council purchased the site in 1983 with the intention of reclaiming and restoring it by making full use of the government Derelict Land Grant scheme. Industrial development was planned since the area formed a natural extension to a substantial existing industrial area.

Although the site was known to be contaminated with the waste products from gas production, the full extent and nature of the pollution was not known when the site was purchased. A series of ground investigations had found the site to consist of between 0.7 and 5.5 m of loosely compacted fill material, some of which was soaked or stained with tar. The fill was highly variable, consisting of soil, gravel, ash, cinders, rubble, slate, spent oxide, tar, bitumen, wire, rope, clinker etc. Soft to firm laminated clays were present beneath large areas of the site, underlain by gravel overlying boulder clay.

SITE INVESTIGATION

A firm of consulting engineers was appointed in 1985 to advise on the contamination of the site. The primary objective of this main investigation was to assess the constraints to development imposed by the contamination present. The area was divided into a 25 m grid and trial pits were excavated at the intersections. Approximately 150 trial pits were excavated and samples were recovered at regular depth intervals for analysis for a range of common contaminants.

The chemical investigation indicated that over half of the site was contaminated, mostly below 0.25 m depth, with concentrations of phenols, coal tar, sulphate, cyanide and heavy metals that exceeded the recommended standards for redevelopment as defined within the Interdepartmental Committee on the Redevelopment of Contaminated Land (ICRCL) guidelines (1987). Contaminants were distributed in specific areas of the site, reflecting the products of different processes that had taken place. Coal tar was associated with former tar storage areas and free tar was found at depths of up to 4 m. Phenol contamination, at concentrations which could permeate through plastic water pipes to taint water supplies, was widespread. In other areas, cyanide wastes and potentially combustible sulphurous materials were associated with the presence of 'blue billy' or spent oxides arising from the former gas purification process. Toxic metals, such as lead and arsenic, also occurred in some locations and sulphate concentrations in many areas were above the recommended Building Research Establishment (1981) guidelines for concrete in contact with sulphate-bearing soils.

In addition to chemical contamination, the uncompacted fill was considered to require consolidation before even low load-bearing foundations could be constructed, whereas piling would be necessary for any development requiring high load-bearing capacity. The spent oxide present on the surface of the site was considered to be a fire hazard if allowed to dry out and would necessitate the use of soil cover, even for a car park.

WHY MICROBIAL TREATMENT?

The nature of the contamination and the volume of polluted material on the site represented severe physical and financial problems for development. Initially, two options for dealing with the contamination were considered by the Borough Council.

- *Cover on site* was discounted because of the area and volume of contaminated material and the volume of clean material needed to cover it. A further factor was the risk to groundwater and the possible contamination of nearby water courses.
- *Removal from site* Detailed discussions with the waste disposal authority indicated that disposal would not be a viable option because the nearest suitably licensed tips were 40 kilometres away and the restriction regarding the rates at which the material could be accepted would have serious repercussions on a development programme. A further problem was that similar volumes of clean material would have to be imported to restore the ground to original levels.

Following discussions with the Department of the Environment (DoE) and Biotreatment Ltd, a novel approach to reclamation of the site was adopted which involved an on-site programme integrating microbial treatment with conventional engineering to reduce the levels of contaminants to post-treatment targets in accordance with ICRCL guidelines. This approach provided both a cost-effective and environmentally acceptable solution.

The distribution of contamination was first defined more closely by further investigation in which trenches were excavated across the most contaminated areas. From the results of these investigations it was apparent that contamination could be divided (Figure C9.3) into biodegradable material comprising coal tar and phenols and non-biodegradable material comprising heavy metals and complex cyanide. The scheme, developed on a design and construct basis, overcame the severe cost and environmental penalties associated with the more conventional alternatives and offered a permanent solution to the pollution problems. Microbial processes alone can rarely resolve all the problems associated with contaminated land, and this was the case at Blackburn where encapsulation techniques to deal with non-biodegradable materials and conventional engineering were an integrated part of the successful reclamation. Key elements of the programme involved;

- the microbial treatment of 30,000 cubic metres of waste contaminated with organic materials;
- on-site encapsulation of 13,500 cubic metres of inorganic contaminants;
- installation of a pollution control cut-off and treatment system for surface water;
- conventional civil engineering works including foundation removal, general landscaping to finished contours and regrading to allow redevelopment to proceed;
- quality assurance through independent validation to define the final status of the site.

DEVELOPMENT OF THE TECHNOLOGY

The microbial technology applied at Blackburn is based on the acceleration of natural degradation processes to which pollutants are exposed in the natural environment. Soil micro-organisms, capable of degrading many toxic wastes, are

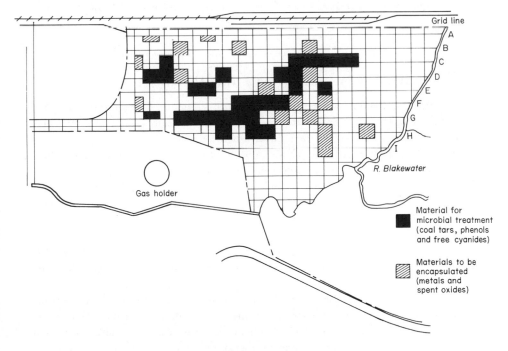

Figure C9.3: Blackburn gasworks site-plan showing contaminated areas

normally present in low numbers in contaminated soils. However, soil conditions are rarely suitable for their growth and so pollutants persist. The technology involves the selection of indigenous groups of organisms that can metabolize the toxic compounds present. These are grown in large numbers and reintroduced into contaminated soils under controlled conditions, together with supplementary reagents. Optimum conditions for the growth of the selected natural microbes are determined and the soil environment is modified accordingly, thus allowing the bacteria to break down the toxic compounds to simple harmless molecules such as water and carbon dioxide. Once pollutant degradation is complete, the bacteria return to natural levels.

The initial stages of the project at Blackburn involved the isolation of naturally occurring micro-organisms from samples of polluted material followed by a laboratory programme to determine the conditions which would most rapidly accelerate the natural biodegradation process. Field trials were then undertaken on site to optimize physical conditions and test various combinations of microbes and chemical reagents.

During the first eight weeks of a trial period, decreases in coal-tar concentrations from 12,500 to 7,600 milligrams per kilogram and phenols from 530 to 70 milligrams per kilogram were obtained. Statistically significant reductions in the concentrations of individual polynuclear aromatic hydrocarbon (PAH) constituents were achieved including potentially carcinogenic compounds such as benzo[a]pyrene (Bewley et al., 1989). No reduction in the concentration of toxic compounds was observed in control treatments where microbes were applied. The laboratory and field studies provided extensive data on the reduction of individual PAH and phenol species and unequivocal evidence that micro-organisms, nutrients etc. were required to reduce contaminant concentrations.

SAFETY MEASURES DURING RECLAMATION WORKS

Following discussion with the Health and Safety Executive and the Environmental Health Department, specific safety measures were implemented during reclamation works to safeguard all operatives.

The site was divided into 'clean' and 'dirty' areas so that all personnel working on the site passed through a decontamination unit prior to leaving the main site area and entering the compound. Machines were washed down before leaving the site. All operators were made aware of the potential hazards, and good standards of hygiene were maintained by prohibiting smoking, eating and drinking on the main site area.

Protective clothing in the form of synthetic boots, gloves, washdown overalls, face visors and barrier creams were made available and used as appropriate. In addition, monitoring of gas and vapours in trench excavations and manholes was enforced during their construction. Regular checking of the site and 'wetting down' was undertaken as necessary to ensure that contaminants did not dry out and create a dust problem that could affect the site and surrounding area. No such problems were encountered during operations.

FULL-SCALE RECLAMATION

The full-scale works in which the optimized microbial techniques were integrated with more conventional engineering practices commenced in August 1986. Before any earthworks were undertaken, the site was cleared of all vegetation and an integrated drainage scheme incorporating a pollution cut-off was installed as a permanent feature to prevent the escape of any contaminated groundwater into the nearby River Blakewater. This was undertaken after discussions with Northwest Water.

Leachate and site run-off was collected and stored in a lagoon, facilitating analysis and further treatment if required prior to disposal to sewer. The overall approach of biological treatment and retention of some encapsulated waste on site meant that the project required a waste disposal site licence.

The non-biodegradable materials were encapsulated on site into a purpose-built clay-lined coffin. This was situated beneath the proposed path of a road embankment, thereby minimizing the area of land which would be restricted for further development. Extensive earthworks, including foundation removal and general landscaping to finished contours, were also undertaken to improve the site and prepare it so that development could proceed using conventional techniques.

The organically contaminated materials were excavated and screened to remove large objects such as contaminated bricks, concrete etc., which were crushed where possible and incorporated back into the screened material for treatment. The processed material was then spread out in layers to form large treatment beds of approximately 750 mm depth in appropriate areas of the site. Processing provided a homogeneous material with a large surface area to encourage microbial activity. Each layer of the treatment beds was sprayed with a mixture of micro-organisms, chemicals and nutrients from an agricultural boom sprayer. Good mixing and aeration were then ensured by passing conventional agricultural equipment over the beds. During excavations, numerous tar tanks containing liquid tar and tar soaked rubble were encountered. These were characterized and treated on site.

Monitoring of the concentration of pollutants was undertaken until analytical data indicated that target concentrations had been met. An independent validation was then carried out by Lancashire County Analysts following which the soil in the beds could be placed and compacted to Department of Trade specifications in the original excavation or elsewhere on site.

The results (Table C9.3) show the efficacy of the treatment process. These data represent the results of analysis of samples taken from parallel grid lines at 25 m spacing across the site. Concentrations of PAHs were reduced from a mean of 22,000 milligrams per kilogram and a maximum of 295,000 milligrams per kilogram to a mean of 150 milligrams per kilogram and a maximum of 710 milligrams per kilogram, substantially below the target concentration of 10,000 milligrams per kilogram. Similarly, phenols originally present at a mean concentration of 205 milligrams per kilogram and a maximum of 9,000 milligrams per kilogram were reduced to a mean of 3.2 milligrams per kilogram. Furthermore, analytical data indicated that all species of PAHs and phenols were substantially reduced. Independent validation provided unequivocal data on the status of the site and demonstrated the effectiveness of the reclamation programme. Development of the site is now proceeding with the main infrastructure completed.

DISCUSSION AND CONCLUSIONS

The reclamation of the Greenbank Gasworks site represented a cost saving of 15%–20% over disposal to landfill.

The 2 year contract for on-site treatment at Blackburn compared favourably with the time required for conventional methods owing to restrictions on the rate at which suitably licensed local tips could accept the heavily contaminated soils. Since this project was the first of its kind, a significant proportion of the contract involved research and development work, and the actual site works were undertaken in approximately 1 year. The 2 year period for reclamation of Greenbank is therefore likely to be atypical of the time required for similar projects of this nature. Indeed, decontamination of a further gasworks in the United Kingdom has been undertaken in a 62 week programme with a substantial area of the site handed over after only 16 weeks, and

Table C9.3: Concentrations of polyaromatic hydrocarbons and total phenols across the Greenbank gasworks site before and after site remediation

Grid line[b]	Volume (m³)	POLYAROMATIC HYDROCARBONS[a]		PHENOLS	
		Before reclamation estimated mean[c]	After validation mean	Before reclamation mean	After validation mean
C	5,060	11,500	171	22	<4
D	5,060	19,600	249	27	<4
E	750	3,700	243	29	<3
F	3,940	11,100	144	37	<2
G	10,100	36,900	110	470	<3
H	560	9,900	76	52	<4
Total	25,470	22,000	148	205	<3

All values are expressed in milligrams per kilogram.
[a] Total PAHs determined as the 16 priority pollutants specified by the Environmental Protection Agency.
[b] See Fig. 1 for location.
[c] The values of PAHs given before treatment are estimates which have been extrapolated from toluene extract data in the initial site investigations. Study by BioTreatment has found PAH concentrations to account for 27.9% toluene extract in samples from the Greenbank site with a correlation of 0.83 (significant at the 99.8% level).

decontamination of a chemical works site has recently been completed in five months.

CASE STUDY 2:

Reclamation of a gasworks site using soil cover

INTRODUCTION

The reclamation of the Redheugh gasworks site for the 1990 Gateshead Garden Festival has been well documented (Cairney, 1987; Barford, 1988) and represents a good example of a site reclaimed using a well designed soil cover system.

The 8.3 hectare site facing the River Tyne and Dunsden Staiths in Gateshead was used for town gas generation for over a century. Prior to the decision in 1984 that Gateshead was to host the 1990 Garden Festival, the Borough Council had acquired the site from British Gas with the intention of reclaiming it. Detailed site surveys had been commissioned in 1980 to assess the degree of contamination present as a result of town gas production. These revealed more than 2 m thickness of contaminated wastes in which there was a near-surface perched groundwater table. Soil and water samples showed considerable variability, but potentially hazardous levels of cyanides, phenols, coal tars, arsenic, sulphides and sulphates were widespread and required specific treatment to overcome their respective problems.

WHY SOIL COVER?

The decision to reclaim the site using soil cover reclamation was undertaken because of the excessive costs and difficulties associated with removing approximately 190,000 cubic metres of contaminated materials. In addition, the identification of an artesian aquifer just below the original clay-floored valley raised the possibility of a risk of flooding of the lower levels of the site if soil loads were removed.

The potential attraction of the economic and promotional aspects of the Garden Festival concept and priority access to Derelict Land Grant allocations was obvious.

DEVELOPMENT OF A SOIL COVER SYSTEM

Once a soil cover was chosen, the problem was to identify the most sensitive elements of the proposed development. Although planning had not been completed, it was decided that the site should not house domestic gardens, allotments or any deeper rooted vegetation. However, in order to introduce sufficient safeguards, a design requirement based on housing with gardens was selected. The council later decided that the site should be redeveloped for leisure/recreation/tourism; however, the recommended standards remain relevant.

In 1983 the Council appointed an advisor for the specifications for a soil cover system which would contain contamination *in situ* without danger of migration to the surface or to adjoining sites. Given the range of potential end-uses, the building foundations and their associated buried services were identified as the most sensitive elements since houses might have to be occupied for a century or more. A design based on protecting housing foundations for 100 years was chosen.

RECLAMATION OF THE SITE

Monitoring of the perched water table had indicated that the groundwater could reach the existing surface of the Redheugh site in wetter periods and might be able to rise through any soil cover laid on the site. Thus the initial reclamation activity was to construct rubble-filled drains to ensure that groundwater could not rise above the present surface level of the site and to reduce infiltration of any percolating water into the contaminated soil. During this period, concrete areas were broken up and various underground vats of tars and other liquids were emptied by specialist contractors and taken to suitable licensed tips.

Earlier meteorological analysis had indicated that in a 100 year period the site could expect to suffer a 100 day drought which would so dry out exposed sandy soils that suctions equivalent to 1,000 cm of water would occur and could carry contaminants to the surface of a soil cover. The Bloemen model (Cairney, 1987) was then used to quantify the volumes of soil water that could rise up by capillary flow through different types of soil. Two locally available types of soil, a sandy silt and silty gravelly sand, were identified and their characteristics were modelled at various cover depths. This indicated that material with a high proportion of clay and silt gave the higher upward migration rates of soil water and was therefore the least suitable of the materials readily available.

This information alone is insufficient to determine the effectiveness of the different soil covers and it was necessary to consider the chemical quality of the rising soil water. This was undertaken by identifying the highest value for each analysed chemical parameter in the groundwater samples obtained during the site investigation and estimating the soil covers mathematically against a water containing these worst qualities. Obviously, the method introduces a significant safety margin, because design water quality represents a worst case, but it guards against poor groundwater quality in unexplored areas of the site.

Having obtained the data, the thinnest possible soil cover that would be needed to protect the site was selected after consideration of ICRCL guidelines. The availability of local materials determined that a soil cover of 75 cm Blaydon sand over 75 cm dolomitic gravel should be used with a 50 cm thick layer of silty gravelly sand placed beneath foundations to ensure that the reclamation was safe.

The final stage of the design was to ensure that all soil and top soil could be laid over those points of the site where plant growth might be required without adversely affecting the long-term efficacy of the soil cover layer. This was undertaken by applying established methods of checking particle grading curves of the cover material against those of the overlying soils (US Bureau of

Reclamation, 1974) and designing a further layer of medium sand whose particular sizes would prevent any top soil material from being washed down to clog the pore spaces in the soil blanket. If this had not been done, as the soil silted up, its suction characteristics would have increased to the point where much greater upward movement of the polluted soil water was possible.

A final consideration was that testing of the possible soil cover materials (to establish their suction, water content and hydraulic conducting properties) took place at the bulk density values likely to give the greatest site bearing capacities, and when the soil cover was laid on the site it was necessary to ensure that these densities were achieved in practice.

This approach of designing a soil cover system from first principles to include drainage, a capillary break layer and adequate top soil offers a reliable and durable solution. However, the retention of contaminated materials on site, albeit beneath a cover layer, leaves it subject to failure.

CASE STUDY 3:

Design of a motorway service station on a landfill site

INTRODUCTION

A series of motorway service stations is being planned for the M25, the London orbital motorway. One such site is at Thurrock, just north of the Dartford Tunnel crossing of the Thames, where Esso Petroleum Ltd have developed a site under licence for the Department of Transport. The 40 acre site comprises an old quarry which has been infilled with industrial refuse to depths of 20 m and is actively producing landfill gas. The development comprises a motel and amenity building, fuel forecourt and parking area for 670 cars, 80 trucks and 35 coaches. This study is reproduced in abridged form from a paper presented by D L Jones et al (1988) with the kind permission of L G Mouchel and Partners and Esso Petroleum Co Ltd.

PROJECT ORGANISATION

Safety has been the overriding concern of the developer. The challenging geotechnical problems including control of landfill gas, leachate and excessive settlement, all of which have a significant impact on public safety, require the establishment of a specialist design team. The team was structured to comprise several overlapping layers of specialists in the relevant areas of expertise. Specialists were charged with checking each other's work so as to ensure that the best and safest solutions were used.

The major design effort and control of field constructions was entrusted to L. G. Mouchel & Partners, a firm of consulting civil engineers. Aspinwall & Co Ltd were appointed as landfill gas subconsultants. The consultants' work was periodically reviewed for safety considerations by Esso Engineering (Europe) Ltd and Dames & Moore, reporting directly to the client. Biotreatment Ltd, acting on behalf of Dames & Moore, provided input on rates and future yields of landfill gas production for the site. Further assessment and control was provided by W S Atkins appointed on behalf of the Department of Transport.

DESIGN OBJECTIVES

Design objectives related principally to reducing the potential for future settlement and the minimization of risks associated with landfill gas.

Long-term settlement of the order of 500–1000 mm was predicted in the deep areas of fill, and the effect of these settlements would be potentially dangerous in terms of disruption of services, roads, parking areas and building forecourts. It was therefore necessary to consider means of reducing and evening out the settlement to an acceptable level, both in terms of building material tolerances and with a view to long-term maintenance.

The design was also required to render the buildings and public areas free from any risk associated with potential emissions of landfill gas. Imposing restrictions on the public in a widely used multipurpose facility was not considered feasible except in the refuelling area and restaurants. The development was required to be capable of being used in the same manner as a motorway service area on a green field site. The migration control system needed to eliminate odours in public areas, provide total protection from risk associated with landfill gas and cope with the worst predictable landfill gas production rates.

SITE HISTORY

Through a series of desk and field studies it was established that the area previously consisted of a gently domed hill made up of natural deposits of sand and gravel overlying chalk. The sand and gravel were extracted between 1940 and 1970, and the underlying chalk was quarried progressively after removal of the granular deposits. Extraction was complete in 1974, and the site was left as a series of water-filled lakes and random mounds of overburden.

Reclamation of this area began in the 1970s with the construction of the London orbital motorway (M25) to the west of the site and the shaping of a recreational lake to the east. The remaining space was used for land filling with industrial wastes between 1978 and 1984. The final restoration profile was similar to the ground levels pertaining prior to mineral extraction at the site, and the waste was covered by up to 2 m of inert fill.

SITE INVESTIGATION

Thicknesses of waste between 4 and 20 m were predicted in the desk study and were proved in the subsequent field work. The major problems highlighted by this first investigation included:

- substantial volumes of landfill gas that were being generated by recent landfilled refuse;
- the potential for large ground settlements;

- contamination of the ground by heavy metals and possibly asbestos;
- the potential for combustion in the ground.

Between 1984 and 1987 the site capping of about 2 m of clay and rubble was completed but otherwise the land remained untouched. In early 1987 a second investigation was undertaken to establish design parameters for foundations, gas control systems and settlement reduction techniques.

A general layout was determined taking into account the planning and infrastructure requirements for a motorway service station in the United Kingdom. The investigation used a grid of boreholes with gas-monitoring installations to provide data on gas concentrations and pressures both vertically and laterally throughout the site. It was recognized at this stage that only two settlement reduction techniques were likely to be effective in significantly reducing the long-term settlements on site. These were dynamic compaction and preloading by earth embankments. Whichever technique (or combination) was used, a large reduction in the permeability of the wastes and unquantifiable changes in gas production were anticipated. Thus, whilst carrying out pumping trials before compaction would provide useful baseline data by which later trials could be assessed, they would not provide appropriate data by which to design the gas migration control system.

In the absence of government guidelines for assessment of gas production rates, and bearing in mind the wide variations that occur in 'apparent' gas production as assessed by pumping trials, it was decided to design the control system on the basis of the worst foreseeable landfill gas production rate. Prediction of the future potential for gas production and assessment of the size of the pumping requirements for the control system were made using three methods:

- measurement of the calorific value of the wastes;
- measurement of the cellulose-to-lignin ratio of the waste;
- comparison with other sites.

The three methods led to the formulation of a maximum foreseeable landfill gas generation rate of 1000 cubic metres per hour, and this flow was used in the design pipework for the migration control system.

Supplementary investigations included the installation of settlement gauges, gas-pumping trials, and false colour infrared and thermographic aerial photography.

DESIGN

The gas control system was designed to achieve the following objectives:

- to eliminate the risk of explosion, flammability, toxicity, asphyxiation and odours due to the presence of landfill gas at the site;
- to exclude methane completely from all buildings, accessible services, ducts and enclosed spaces;

- to use a set of control systems which are the simplest and require the least maintenance to achieve the above two objectives;
- to design sufficient gas control methods to facilitate successful operation throughout the remaining gas-producing lifetime of the site for all possible gas emission rates;
- to prevent unnecessary air ingress in order to minimize risks of underground combustion.

In order to achieve these objectives the following principles were applied to the detailed gas control system.

- Two levels of control should exist; the area supporting any buildings or similar structures should have more stringent controls than the remainder of the site (i.e parking and landscaped areas).
- To prevent gas entry, buildings should have a vented void space beneath all floors and special service entries, in addition to an active gas extraction system in the surrounding fill. Permanent continuous gas monitors with an alarm system should be installed to demonstrate that the system is excluding gas in accordance with the design criteria.
- The car parking and other hardstanding areas should have a collection system which can control gas emissions over the entire surface area. In practice this means that a system should be maintained to prevent a sustained positive pressure of gas beneath the low permeability layer.
- There should be sufficient gas control of the landscaped, picnic and other vegetated areas to prevent significant surface gas emissions, to keep all vegetation healthy and to prevent any detectable odour from the gas.

The control of settlement was managed through the application of a range of techniques. The refuse within the quarry varied in depth from approximately 8 m to 20 m. Thus, apart from large overall settlements, significant differential settlements were expected. Unless the settlement was controlled, this could have serious consequences for the gas-sealing layers and pipework.

To assist in minimizing settlement, the whole of the site was dynamically compacted using a 15 tonne weight to achieve an energy capacity of 250 tonne metres per square metre. This technique, although not affecting settlement by organic degradation, significantly reduced the void ratio of the fill. The induced settlement was of the order of 1 m. A further advantage of the technique is that a stiffened surface crust is formed which tends to even out settlements.

Dynamic compaction reduces but does not eliminate settlements. Areas of particular concern were at the quarry cliff lines where large depth changes occur over relatively short horizontal distances. In these localities, polypropylene geogrids were placed at the top and bottom of the clay layer to provide a soil reinforcement capable of accommodating large strains. In addition, the gas barrier system contained a non-woven geotextile separator and a high density polyethylene membrane. These also are able to withstand a degree of strain without rupture. It was therefore considered that the combination of systems would greatly assist in reducing both total and differential settlement and so would maintain the integrity and safety of the gas collection system.

Constant monitoring of settlement was programmed both during the construction phase but also post construction to monitor the effectiveness of dynamic compaction. Measurements were taken of the ground surface as well as at depth using the installed settlement gauges.

Gas was controlled through a pumped system. As a general rule in migration control schemes, the control system is located between the source of the gas (the landfill) and the area to be protected (the development). This has led to the use of lines of vertical wells around the perimeter of landfills to protect developments and existing structures on the ground adjacent to the landfill. At Thurrock, the source of gas *is* a landfill, not adjacent to it. Thus it was considered most appropriate to locate the primary control system in the horizontal plane close to the surface of the waste and below an engineered capping layer.

A back-up vertical well system was also designed in two specific areas. The first was a ring of walls around the main service building which are not intended to be pumped except under exceptional circumstances but will be operated for short periods on a regular basis as a maintenance routine. The second ring of wells was placed around the refuelling area where, in order to mitigate settlement, the waste was entirely excavated and replaced by clay and sand fill. The wells form a vertical barrier around the edge of the waste, protecting an area of 'clean' land adjacent to the landfill.

It must be emphasized that whilst the preferred primary migration control method for the site has been described as a horizontal system, it is not like the horizontal systems used in many other landfills. The granular collection blanket and pipework is laid at the top surface of the waste rather than in trenches within the body of the waste. The system will be operated to extract only as much gas as is necessary to maintain a negative pressure barrier at the interface of the waste and the development.

GAS CONTROL BY AREA

The amenity building has been subject to the highest level of control. This comprised the use of two permeability contrasts below the structure. Pumped extraction from horizontal pipework laid in a granular blanket below the clay capping layer provided the primary protection. A ventilated subfloor void provided secondary protection, with a membrane incorporated in the concrete floor slab. Gas monitors were installed in the subfloor void and in confined areas within the amenity building, all linked to a staged alarm system which activates a series of procedures relating to the level of gas detected.

The refuelling area, consisting of petrol and diesel forecourts and payment kiosk, is in an area with only approximately 8 m of fill. Consequently, a philosophy of isolation was adopted. This consisted of complete removal of all refuse down to the underlying chalk. The base and sides of the excavation were then lined with clay and the remaining hole was infilled with a silty fine sand. A clay capping was placed over the sand fill. As a further back-up, a vertical well system connected to an independent ring main also surrounds the fuel area.

A single level of control is applied to the parking and recreation areas and uses the permeability contrast of a granular collection layer overlain by clay capping, coupled with gas extraction from horizontal pipework laid in the granular layer.

During construction, the site capping 1.5 m thick was stripped and stockpiled prior to dynamic compaction operations. A 500 mm granular blanket was laid and dynamic compaction was undertaken. The compaction reduced the thickness of this blanket which was then made up to a minimum thickness of 200 mm. Following this, a further 200 mm of granular material was laid, thus forming a transmission layer through which gas could flow. The transmission layer was overlain with a non-woven geotextile to act as a separator between the granular layer and a clay seal. The clay seal consisted of a 500 mm layer of plastic clay compacted wet of optimum to minimize the risk of shear cracks during compaction. This layer forms the main gas barrier within the works. After compaction, the clay was covered with a polyethylene membrane, the function of which is to assist in retaining moisture within the clay and to act as a second methane barrier.

A thin blinding layer of sand was placed over the plastics layer and the inert site capping, previously removed, was returned to a depth of typically around 800 mm. Pavement construction layers, which vary between 500 and 1000 mm, were then placed over the returned capping. A typical section is shown in Figure C9.4.

GAS COLLECTION AND DISPOSAL

Gas collection is by a system of perforated collector pipes within the transmission layer connected to an imperforate ring main lying above the clay seal. The perforated collector pipes are 110 mm in diameter and are placed at the top of trenches within the transmission layer. The trenches are to ensure that efficient collection points exist rather than relying wholly on the granular layers placed during and after compaction. It is considered that compaction may well reduce material permeability within the upper layers.

The collector pipes are of polyethylene and are specifically designed for use within landfill gas collection systems. They are flexible and can accommodate large vertical strains. To alleviate horizontal strains due to settlement, a simple sliding joint mechanism is employed at every connection leading to the ring main. An advantage of this system is that, should breakages occur in the pipe, they are not detrimental to the through flow of gas as alternative paths exist within the transmission layer. Thus, once installed, the need to penetrate the sealing layers for maintenance purposes should be entirely eliminated.

The ring main was placed above the clay seal, thus allowing access for maintenance without disruption of the sealing layers. The ring main is made of high density polyethylene 250 mm diameter and capable of withstanding a pressure of 6 bar. The pipe is relatively flexible and can endure reasonable horizontal and vertical strains. However, to allow for substantial movement due to vertical settlement of the landfill, expansion loops in the form of S bends were incorporated within the design. The expansion loop is contained within a trench backfilled with expanded polystyrene to minimise the lateral 'earth' pressures which could inhibit the expansion of the pipe. The ring main contains a valve at every connection point with the collector pipes. It is thus possible

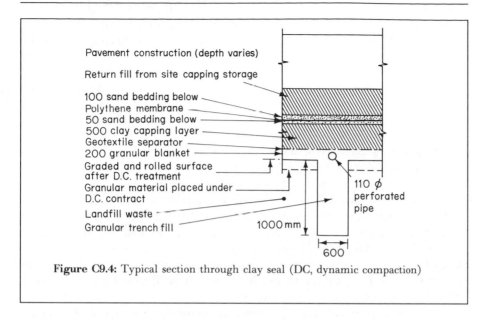

Pavement construction (depth varies)

Return fill from site capping storage

100 sand bedding below
Polythene membrane
50 sand bedding below
500 clay capping layer
Geotextile separator
200 granular blanket
Graded and rolled surface
after D.C. treatment
Granular material placed under
D.C. contract
Landfill waste
Granular trench fill

110 ϕ
perforated
pipe

1000 mm

600

Figure C9.4: Typical section through clay seal (DC, dynamic compaction)

both to isolate and/or to regulate gas flow within any section of pipe to allow for changing circumstances or for maintenance purposes. A gas take-off point is also provided at every valve to allow gas samples to be taken and so that the pressure in the main can be monitored.

At present it is not intended to utilise the gas but merely to dispose of it safely by flaring or other means. It may be that once the system is operational this aspect will be reviewed in the light of data on gas quality and flow rates, and further consideration may be given to energy production. It is anticipated, however, that the actual amount of gas extracted will be substantially less than the maximum foreseeable rate of 1000 cubic metres per hour, and that the calorific value of the gas will be lower than that typical of large domestic waste sites.

Once operational, the pumping rates from the collector system will be adjusted to achieve a slightly negative pressure with respect to atmospheric in the granular collection blanket. The pressure in the blanket will be monitored by a series of pressure transducers/transmitters spread throughout the site which will be linked to a central control panel in the gas disposal centre. Regular checks will also be made of the gas flow and composition at various points within the ring main. The information obtained will provide data to enable the gas flow to be controlled at any point within the collection system.

SAFETY RATIONALE

In the course of the design period there have been a series of technical review meetings with the whole design team which have served to optimize the design. Of paramount importance has been the safety rationale in which design proposals have been critically questioned to ensure that the highest design safety standards are maintained. The following gives a brief indication of the thinking which has ensured for various aspects of the scheme.

The clay seal prevents upward migration of gas and inhibits air from entering the system. However, clay can shrink and crack, so rendering the barrier ineffective. As the clay is placed wet of optimum, shear cracks during compaction are minimized. Also, the provision of an overlying layer of plastic maintains moisture so that shrinkage cracking is inhibited. However, the layer acts as a second line of defence should local failure of the clay occur. A third line of defence exists in the form of the returned site cover material and pavement construction which will provide approximately 2 m of cover over the clay.

The provision of collector pipes within the transmission layer ensures that minimum flow distances occur before a collector pipe is reached. Any local blockage within the perforated pipework is not significant as flow will readily occur within the granular layer and bypass any blockage.

The ring main contains valves which can either control or isolate gas flow. By closing appropriate valves, complete sections can be isolated, but owing to the presence of the transmission layer and the network of pipes, alternative routes for gas flow always exist. Sampling points occur at regular intervals along the main. Thus, if air ingress occurs, it can readily be detected, the area can be isolated and remedial action can be taken.

Extraction is from a central gas disposal centre. If the disposal is rendered totally inoperative through plant breakdown, a mobile extraction system can be operable on site within a few hours of failure.

Excessive settlement will cause distress to any installed sealing system and pipework. This has been minimized by dynamic compaction, the extensive use of geotextiles in sensitive areas and expansion joins within all pipework. Preventive maintenance is the key, however. Monitoring of surface profiles will be undertaken which, combined with subsurface measurements of settlement within the fill mass, will enable appropriate measures to be taken before significant distress occurs.

The fuel forecourt is isolated from gas by removal and replacement of all refuse beneath this area. However, a ring main around this zone and a separate system of vertical wells is also provided to give added protection. For the amenity building, where greater depths of fill occur, replacement is not feasible. Here, as previously described, a high level of control occurs incorporating barrier systems, back-up vertical wells and force-vented voids. A high level of monitoring is also to be installed in all structures and appropriate safety level checks maintained.

CASE STUDY 4:

**Landfill gas generation and migration problems at a Salford landfill
and the design and installation of a gas migration control system**

INTRODUCTION

The Lumns Lane landfill site is located in a valley in Salford, bordered on the south side by British Coal disposal activities. Colliery spoil is being deposited on the side and valley bottom and the area is being levelled. Previously, colliery spoil had also been placed on the northern edge of the valley in the area laying south of Bolton Road but the depth and extent of the area was unknown. An area of housing is located alongside this colliery spoil next to Bolton Road, some 150 m from the landfill.

The municipal solid waste (MSW) landfill is located on the northern side of the valley. Prior to its establishment a synthetic membrane was installed between the coal spoil and the prospective landfill to prevent water ingress into the placed MSW.

A 2 m passive venting trench was installed on the periphery of the site in addition to 15 gas-monitoring points 2 m deep. Monitoring data showed that methane concentrations were undetectable immediately to the rear of the Bolton Road housing in the colliery spoil some 120–150 m from the landfill, but rose rapidly towards the landfill only to decrease again in the vicinity of the venting trench.

Attention was drawn to prospective problems when burning of weeds ignited a source of gas on the colliery spoil area between the landfill and the housing on Bolton Road. There was obvious concern for the possibility of methane ingress into the domestic properties in Bolton Road, a situation which required detailed examination and assessment to determine the need for and type of gas control.

In considering the mitigation of landfill gas migration problems, it is obviously important to establish rates of gas production, the geological or other paths of gas transmission, and the source or sources of gas production. Where there is cause for any doubt relating to the source of gas, then clearly it is important that this is unequivocally resolved, particularly for the design and establishment of an appropriate control scheme.

There is often confusion regarding the source of gas, particularly as methane can arise in large volumes from MSW landfills but also from coal deposits and as such represents a safety issue for British Coal. At the Lumns Lane site there was obviously a need to establish whether or not the gas was being generated from the landfill or from the colliery spoil and to use these data as the basis for designing a remedial scheme.

DESK STUDIES

Initially a site investigation was undertaken to address the following objectives:

- determine the extent and depth of the original ground behind the houses;
- determine the depth of colliery waste at its deepest point;
- check the temperature gradients in the colliery wastes;
- assess the mode of methane generation;
- ascertain the possibility of deep strata migration below Bolton Road;
- enable the design of a gas migration control scheme.

The investigation commenced with a search of the scientific literature for possible mechanisms of methane production from coal wastes was undertaken to determine whether the colliery spoil could be the source of methane problems at Lumns Lane.

The first database to be searched was the National Technical Information Service. Approximately 7,000 references to methane generation, production and evolution were found. Cross-referencing these with colliery spoil or wastes failed to produce a single reference. A further two databases were examined using a similar search strategy, the United States Department of Energy 'Energy' database and the 'Compendex Plus' database collated by Engineering Information Inc. Neither of these databases appeared to contain any information relating methane production to colliery spoil types.

British Coal were contacted to ascertain whether they had information on the generation of methane from colliery spoil tips. The headquarters of British Coals's Technical Department at Bretby, Burton-on-Trent, was visited. They were unaware of any incidences of methane being present in colliery spoil and they were unable to suggest a mechanism by which methane could be produced from colliery spoil.

Contact was then made with the Coal Research Establishment, Stoke Orchard, Cheltenham, Gloucestershire. This facility had undertaken an examination of the evolution of volatiles from coals during heating. Carbon dioxide was shown to evolve at 50°C and ethane, propane and other straight-chain hydrocarbons evolved at temperatures above 70°C. No evidence was found for the production of methane.

A computer model was then used to estimate the volumes of gas that might be produced from the refuse in the landfill. This indicated that in excess of 10,000,000 m³ could be expected to be generated from the landfill refuse on site until at least 2005 and possibly beyond. Clearly, these data indicated the long-term implications inherent in the situation.

SITE INVESTIGATION BOREHOLES

In order to investigate the geological strata and the dip of the original valley before it was filled with colliery shales, two boreholes 6 inches in diameter were sunk into the colliery spoil adjacent to the properties on Bolton Road, as shown on the location plan (Figure C9.5).

The first borehole LUM021 was sunk to a depth of 10.3 m below ground level (bgl) and showed fill and colliery wastes to a depth of 4.3 m bgl where a 2.1 m layer of stiff brown clay was found overlying dense brown sand, the sand being proved for 4.0 m before the hole was terminated.

The second borehole LUM022 was sited 20 m further into the tip and was sunk to a depth of 10.6m. Fill and colliery wastes were evident to a depth of 7.3 m bgl underlain by dense brown sand. The sand was again proved for a depth of 3.3 m before termination of the hole.

Both holes were screened with 4 inch perforated well casing. The annulus was filled with gravel, the top was sealed with cement grout and end caps were fitted to facilitate future methane monitoring. During their construction, both

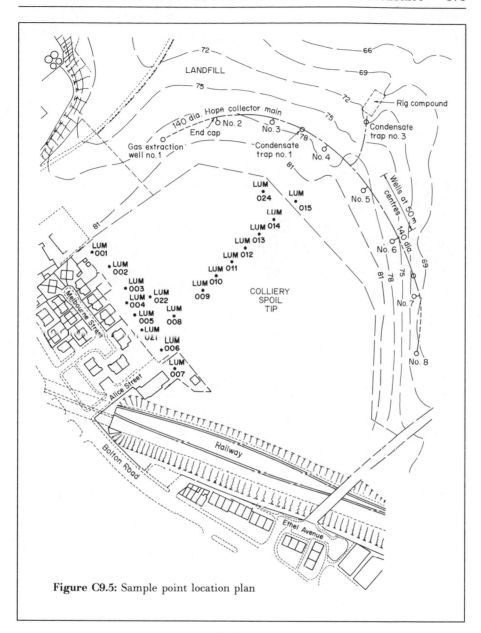

Figure C9.5: Sample point location plan

holes were monitored for methane at varying depths and concentrations of less than 1% of the lower explosive limit (LEL) were recorded.* Further monitoring of these holes was carried out on an on-going basis, and the results are shown in Table C9.4.

Further deep boreholes were sunk in the positions shown in Figure C9.5 to

---

* Methane in air is explosive when present at concentrations between 5 and 15%. Thus 5 % by volume represents the LEL.

Table C9.4: Methane concentration measured in trial pits and boreholes at Lumns Lane

Monitoring date	SAMPLE POINT NUMBER								
	001	002	003	005	006	007	008	009	010
Aug 1	0	0	0	0	0	0	0	28	28
Aug 5	0	0	0	0	0	0	0	30	30
Aug 12	0	0	0	0	0	0	0	0	22
Aug 16	0	0	0	0	0	0	0	0	28
Aug 17	0	32	24	–	0	0	1	–	–
Aug 18	0	30	24	–	0	0	0	–	–
Aug 19	0	24	18	–	0	0	3	–	–
Aug 22	0	24	0	–	0	0	0	–	–
Aug 24	0	28	16	–	0	0	21	–	–
Aug 26	0	0	0	0	0	0	0	35	36
Aug 30	0	0	0	0	0	0	0	36	36
Sep 2	0	0	0	0	0	0	0	36	37
Sep 5	0	0	0	0	0	0	0	0	0
Sep 9	0	0	0	0	0	0	0	34	32
Sep 12	0	0	0	0	0	0	0	30	32
Sep 15	0	0	0	0	0	0	0	35	33
Sep 20	0	0	0	0	0	0	0	24	28
Sep 22	0	0	0	0	0	0	0	29	26
Sep 26	0	0	0	0	0	0	0	30	27
Sep 30	0	0	0	0	0	0	0	31	28
Oct 4	0	0	0	0	0	0	0	33	37
Oct 7	0	0	0	0	0	0	0	32	35
Oct 11	0	0	0	0	0	0	0	34	38
Oct 13	0	0	0	0	0	0	0	36	42
Oct 17	0	0	0	0	0	0	0	36	42
Oct 21	0	0	0	0	0	0	0	37	39

All methane concentrations are expressed in percentages of methane.

establish the depth of the colliery shales and the original valley profile in more detail. Borehole LUM024 was sunk adjacent to the boundary fence to a depth of 27.0 m bgl. Fill and colliery wastes were evident to 22.90 m bgl underlain by dense brown sand similar to that found in the two shallower boreholes.

In order to prevent the risk of spontaneous combustion, the borehole was continually purged with nitrogen; this maintained an oxygen-deficient atmosphere but meant that methane monitoring was not possible during constructions. On completion of the borehole at 27.0 m bgl the hole was part backfilled and a 4 inch perforated casing was installed in the shales for future monitoring purposes.

				SAMPLE POINT NUMBER					
011	012	013	014	015	021	022	024	023 Sand	023 Shale
36	34	37	34	0	0	0	—		
37	33	38	—	0	0	0	—		
30	—	—	—	0	0	0	—	0	0
37	36	45	—	47	0	0	—	3	22
30	34	35	42	41	0	—	27	17	22
37	35	37	44	42	0	—	29	10	16
34	42	40	54	51	0	—	34	Sealed	13
35	44	40	48	36	0	0	34		
34	43	40	45	40	0	0	32	25	28
42	41	45	45	45	0	0	32		
43	40	43	44	42	0	0	31	17	17
43	41	44	42	43	0	0	33	—	21
8	38	32	44	42	0	0	34	—	19
38	38	42	42	42	0	0	31	—	21
37	36	42	43	44	0	0	36	—	23
40	34	36	36	27	0	0	36	—	25
34	31	38	38	38	0	0	32	—	25
33	31	41	40	43	0	0	34	—	24
31	34	40	41	43	0	0	34	—	21
30	31	40	40	39	0	0	29	—	26
34	34	35	42	39	0	0	35	—	23
34	35	41	43	37	0	0	38	—	26
31	33	46	47	46	0	0	38	0	26
35	37	47	50	50	0	0	41	0	26
41	43	49	50	47	0	0	43	0	26
45	43	52	54	0	0	0	42	1	27

The second borehole LUM023 was sunk in a similar manner, with nitrogen purging, to a depth of 21.0 m bgl. Colliery shales were evident to a depth of 17.0 m bgl, where brown silty sands were encountered and proved to 21.0 m bgl. Two perforated standpipes 3 inches in diameter were installed in the completed borehole, one being sealed in the underlying sands and the other in the colliery shales, to enable future monitoring of methane levels.

Temperature measurements were taken however, to determine the temperature gradient within the tipped shales. Temperatures varied from 16.5°C at 6.0 m depth to a maximum of 31.5°C at 23.0 m depth in borehole LUM023. These temperatures were not consistent with thermogenic gas generation from the colliery spoils.

SITE INVESTIGATION TRIAL PITS ADJACENT TO BOLTON ROAD/ALICE STREET

A series of 10 trial pits was excavated to a maximum depth of 3.5 m bgl along the boundary of the tip. In some places it was evident that the gardens had been extended beyond the original fence line onto the tip itself. The trial pit locations therefore had to be altered slightly to take account of these extensions.

In all the trial pits, clay was encountered at between 1.0 and 3.0 m depth apart from trial pit 3 where shales were found to 3.5 m bgl, which was the maximum depth reached by the machine. All the trial pits showed fill or shale in varying thicknesses and seemed to indicate that the shales are 'thinning out' but extend beyond the fence line and into the gardens. Further investigations within the garden areas would be required to determine the full extent of the shales.

The results from the various trial pits and boreholes indicate that the shales extend from the boundary adjacent to the properties on Bolton Road towards the landfill site with a gradient of approximately 1:3. The maximum depth of shales found was 22.9 m bgl as the original valley appears to follow this line.

Both the colliery shales and the underlying sands are permeable mediums through which methane gas may migrate, the shales probably being more permeable than the sands.

METHANE MONITORING

Monitoring of methane levels was undertaken on a regular basis in all available sampling positions. The results are shown in Table C9.4.

External factors such as barometric pressure were monitored and correlations were drawn between detected methane levels and barometric pressures. In general, an increase in methane levels was observed with a decrease in barometric pressure. This was particularly apparent in monitoring points at an increasing distance from the landfill. These findings are consistent with previous observations that methane migration from landfills is influenced by the prevailing barometric pressure.

CONFIRMATION OF METHANE SOURCE

The literature search described earlier suggested that the methane detected in the spoil tip did not originate from the colliery waste. The possibility thus existed that the methane detected in the colliery spoil arose in the landfill and migrated into the waste tip. If this was the case, then the gas from the waste tip should contain trace components also detected in the landfill gas.

Samples of gas were taken from boreholes LUM023 situated halfway across the shale tip and LUM024 which was adjacent to the landfill. All samples were collected in pressurized gas vessels which were filled and evacuated five times before the final sample was collected. Control samples of air were also taken. These samples were analysed by mass spectrometry.

Particular attention was given to identifying traces of chlorinated organics in the gas samples. The major conclusions of this analysis were:

- the compositions of the samples from the colliery spoil and the landfill were very similar;
- the landfill gas samples were more complex than the colliery spoil samples;
- trichlorofluoromethane was detected in all samples except the control, indicating a common source;
- the ratio of dichloroethanes and trichloroethanes to dichloroethanes and trichloroethanes was 3.1 and 2.4 for samples taken from LUM024 and LUM023 respectively. The ratio for the landfill gas sample was 0.3.

Although chlorinated organics were detected in the control sample, the specific presence of trichlorofluoromethane in the field samples indicated a common source. Qualitative interpretation of the chlorinated organic 'fingerprints' was complicated by their presence in the control blank.

Coal contains between 0.4 and 0.9 % by weight of chlorine. Some 40% 60% of this chlorine is emitted as hydrogen chloride (HCl) when coal is heated. No other chlorine-containing volatiles are detected during HCl evolution. This suggests that the volatile chlorinated organics detected in the colliery spoil samples did not arise from the coal waste. It appeared that the gas arising in the colliery spoil was not generated in situ. The most likely source was the landfill as evidenced by the common contaminant trichlorofluoromethane. The effect of gas migration through the colliery spoil on the qualitative gas trace contaminants was unknown.

GAS PUMPING

While the laboratory work was being undertaken to determine the source of the gas, the monitoring of gas concentrations in the boreholes and trial pits was being undertaken in conjunction with pumping tests to determine rates of gas production for various wells. Pumping tests were undertaken with a mobile pumping rig and flarestack capable of pumping up to 500 m³ of gas per hour. The pumping test was also used to demonstrate the effective reduction in gas concentrations in the coal spoil when suction was applied to wells on the landfill periphery.

REMEDIAL ACTIONS AND RECOMMENDATIONS

It was evident from the results of this investigation that landfill gas was migrating off site, both the shales and the underlying dense sands being permeable media through which the gas could migrate.

The immediate areas of risk were the properties adjacent to Bolton Road, where some methane, although in fairly low concentration was detected. Some control of the gas was achieved by the continual pumping and flaring from within the tip itself, the concentrations of methane detected rising quickly when this operation ceased.

The abundance of vegetation with no evidence of 'die off' on the shale plateau indicated that the landfill gas was moving horizontally rather than vertically through the shales and was not simply venting to atmosphere through them. There was some evidence of migration through the underlying sands but it was difficult to interpret the data and draw conclusions.

The results shown in Table C9.4 indicated decreasing levels of methane across the plateau towards the houses in Bolton Road. This situation could change if the pumping operation on the site ceased, and higher concentrations of methane would be detectable over a wider area.

There are several solutions for the effective control of methane migration, the simplest being the installation of a perimeter cut-off system. This can take the form of a passive venting trench excavated through the shales and into the underlying clay. Although this forms a physical barrier, it has disadvantages. Firstly, it was not fully known to what extent methane migration may take place in the underlying sands, especially if there was an accumulation of gas, and therefore an increase in pressure, within the landfill site itself. Secondly, all passive venting systems pose the danger of accidental ignition caused by the careless discard of cigarettes or matches for example. Coupled with this are the potential odour problems which could be a considerable nuisance to the residents of Bolton Road. A further problem with this system was the installation. Several of the properties adjacent to the colliery spoil had extended their gardens over the colliery shale, thus making excavation to the underlying clay impossible without considerable disruption.

The investigation was restricted to the identification of methane production and movement in the area of the colliery shales. It was also considered likely that methane migration was occurring in other areas of the site. This, coupled with the long-term potential for gas production, suggested that a migration control scheme in the form of forced gas extraction to deal with the problem at source would be the most appropriate and reliable solution. This form of remedial scheme consists of a series of deep wells, placed to form overlapping radii of influence to intercept the gas, connected to a suitable pump unit, the extracted gas being flared to atmosphere.

GAS MIGRATION CONTROL SCHEME

A permanent gas migration control was established through the provision of a pumped well system. This was designed to prevent further gas leaving the landfill across the boundary and also to withdraw gas already in the coal spoil area.

Six vertical gas wells were installed within the landfill mass, some 10 m in from the edge. The wells were placed to a depth of some 28 m to the full depth of the landfill and at 50 m centres in accordance with the Department of Environment Waste Management Paper No.27 (1988). The wells were connected to an electrically driven pump unit and the gas was safely disposed of through a flarestack on site.

REFERENCES

Barford, J. (1988), *Gateshead Garden Festival Site*, In Land Rec. '88, University College Durham, July 1988.

Beckett, M.J. and Simms, D.L. (1988), *Assessing contaminated land: UK policy and practice*, in *Contaminated Soil* (eds J.W. Assink and W.J. Van den Brink), Martinus Nijhoff, Dordrecht, pp. 285–94.

Bewley, R.J.F. (1990), *Setting standards for the restoration of contaminated land*, Chemistry and Industry, 4 June 1990.

Bewley, R.J.F., Ellis B., Theile P., Viney I. and Rees J.F. (1989), *Microbial Clean-up of Contaminated Soil*, Chemistry and Industry, 4 Dec 1989, pp.778–783.

Bottomley MP, V. (1989), In symposium address, SCI Water and Environment Group Symposium: Cleaning Contaminated Soil, 29 June 1989, London.

British Standards Institution (1988), *Draft for Development: Code of Practice for the Identification of Potentially Contaminated Land and its Investigation*, DD:175.

Building Research Establishment (1981), *Concrete in Sulphate-bearing Ground and Groundwaters*, Digest 250, BRE, Garston, June.

Cairney, T. (1987), *Reclaiming Contaminated Land*, Blackie, Edinburgh.

Crowhurst, D. (1987), *Measurement of Gas Emissions from Contaminated Land*, Building Research Establishment Report.

Department of the Environment (1987), *Landfilling Wastes: a Technical Memorandum, Waste Management Paper 26*, HM Stationery Office, London.

Department of the Environment (1987), *Development of Contaminated Land*, Welsh Office Circular 22/87.

Department of the Environment (1988A), *Environmental Assessment*, DOE Circular 15/88.

Department of the Environment (1988B), *The Control of Landfill Gas: a Technical Memorandum on the Control of Landfill Gas Including a Code of Practice*, Waste Management Paper 27.

Department of the Environment (1989), *Gasworks Report (1987) Problems Arising from the Redevelopment of Gasworks and Similar Sites*, DOE Circular 17/89. 2nd edn, HM Stationery Office, London.

Environmental Protection Bill (as amended by Standing Committee M), HM Stationery Office, London.

Health and Safety Executive (1988), *Occupational Exposure Limits*, Guidance Note EH40/88.

HM Inspectorate of Pollution (1989), *First Annual Report 1987–1988*.

House of Commons Environment Committee (1989), *Toxic Waste*, Second Report, HM Stationery Office, London.

House of Commons Environment Committee (1990), *Contaminated Land*, HM Stationery Office, London.

ICRCL (1983A) (Interdepartmental Committee on the Redevelopment of Contaminated Land), *Notes on the Redevelopment of Sewage Works and Farms*, ICRCL 23/ 79, 2nd edn.

ICRCL (1986B), *Notes on the fire hazards on contaminated land*, ICRCL 61/84, 2nd edn.

ICRCL (1985), *Asbestos on Contaminated Sites*, ICRCL 64/85.

ICRCL (1988), *Notes on the redevelopment of landfill sites*, ICRCL 17/78, 7th edn.

ICRCL (1986B), *Notes on the redevelopment of gasworks sites*, ICRCL 18/79, 5th edn.

ICRCL (1986C), *Notes on the redevelopment of scrapyards and similar sites*, ICRCL 42/80, 2nd edn.

ICRCL (1987), *Guidance on the assessment and redevelopment of contaminated land*, ICRCL 59/83, 2nd edn.

Institute of Environmental Health Officers (1989), *Contaminated Land - Development of Contaminated Land – Professional Guidance*.

Jones D.L., Crowcroft, P. and Pritchard, B.N. (1988), *Design of a motorway service station on a landfill site*, in Proc. GRCDA 11th International Landfill Gas Symposium, Houston, Texas.

Kelly, R.T. (1980), *Site investigation and materials problems*, presented at the Conference on Reclamation of Contaminated Land, Society of the Chemical Industry, Eastbourne.

Richards, Moorehead and Laing Ltd (1988), *An Assessment of the Effectiveness of the Methods and Systems used to Reclaim Contaminated Sites in Wales*, Welsh Office, ref. 1148.

Welsh Office (1988) *Survey of Contaminated Land in Wales*.

ACKNOWLEDGEMENTS

The authors gratefully acknowledge the assistance of Tom Cairney of the Faculty of Construction, Liverpool Polytechnic, and David L. Jones, Principal Geotechnical Engineer, L G Mouchel & Partners, in the preparation of the case studies presented in this chapter.

Section D

The Wider Environmental Impact

ENVIRONMENTAL ASSESSMENT AND MANAGEMENT

Paul Tomlinson

Ove Arup & Partners

INTRODUCTION

In recent years there has been a dramatic rise in the public awareness of environmental issues and, today, the public recognise that the local, national and global environments are being adversely affected by man Hitherto public environmental concern has been directed towards large projects such as the Sizewell B power station or localised issues such as opencast coal mining. With environmental issues being linked to a general increased awareness of health issues, quality of life concerns are emerging and are bringing about the emergence of the 'green consumer'.

While green consumerism has been expressed in terms of domestic products, similar attitudes have emerged within other sectors, not least the construction sector, with a new genre – the 'green building'. Indeed, with the Government placing greater emphasis upon the 'polluter pays' principle and a requirement for the utilities to achieve market rates of return, the construction industry and property developers will be placed under greater pressure to produce buildings having lower demands on the environment. As buildings are designed within a competitive environment, 'green' buildings will only emerge if a market for such buildings develops or regulation is increased. It is also important to recognise the pressure for change being generated by the Directives from the European Community, for example the Construction Products Directive, referred to in Chapter A3. The focus of these pressures is towards sustainable development, where economic and environmental policies are fully integrated. Such sustainable development will require a change in consumption patterns towards more acceptable products.

As previous chapters reveal, environmental issues may emerge at the individual, community, national or global scale and occur either within or outside a building. Indeed, concerns may be linked in future to the extraction, manufacturing or waste disposal aspects of materials used by the construction industry. Clearly, as a major consumer of resources, the construction industry is linked to environmental issues at local, national and global scales. The building industry, consequently, is affected by the increased attention devoted to environmental subjects as a result of legislation (particularly from the European Community), use of materials, eg. tropical hardwoods or CFCs, and the wider understanding of the potential for adverse environmental consequences from man's actions. A useful review of these pressures is provided by Richard Lorch Associates (1989).

With that background, the purpose of this chapter is to:

- review the evolution of environmental assessment and environmental health assessment;
- identify environmental effects;
- discuss the question of uncertainty;
- examine the role of audits;
- consider the information and training needs for environmental management;
- present a view on the integration of environmental management into the decision-making process for building projects.

While it is impossible within the confines of a single chapter to present answers to any specific environmental management problems, it is hoped that this chapter will contribute to a greater awareness of the issues and the decision-making context in which those problems should be assessed and managed.

EVOLUTION OF ENVIRONMENTAL IMPACT ASSESSMENT (EIA)

Since the 1960s, problems of assessing major development projects have become apparent in line with increasing environmental awareness. For example, a proposal to build a third London airport during the mid-1960s established a precedent for the broadening of project appraisal. A special commission (the Roskill Commission) was established to identify the most suitable site for the airport. The Commission's assessment concentrated on social and economic consequences and attempts were made to ascertain the relative costs and nature of effects upon various social groups. In effect, the appraisal attempted to widen the scope of traditional cost-benefit analysis to those impacts not easily reduced to monetary or welfare measurements. This approach, however, stimulated considerable public disquiet regarding the monetary valuation of certain features, such as a Norman church.

Objectives and Constraints

As flaws in cost-benefit analysis (CBA) became more apparent, an approach which became known as Environmental Impact Assessment began to emerge. It was in the United States that the term Environmental Impact Assessment was first legally defined by the 1969 National Environmental Policy Act. The key part of this act was Section 102(c) which brought about the need for Environmental Impact Statements (EIS), the text resulting from the EIA process. At this point, it is important to note that the term Environmental Assessment (EA) and Environmental Statement, rather than EIA and EIS are the legal terms used in the UK, although they are frequently interchanged. Care must, however, be taken with overseas terminology, since EA often refers to an initial study, with EIA meaning a detailed investigation. This paper adopts the term EA in preference to EIA.

EA was first conceived as an 'add on' component to CBA designed to incorporate all those potential impacts that had proved troublesome. As a consequence, early practitioners used EA as a means of collecting information, but often failed to comprehend the environmental context in which the development was proposed. EA evolved, however, into a comprehensive approach to project evaluation, in which environmental considerations are given increased importance in the decision-making process alongside economic and technical considerations.

Ideally, the EA process should seek to:

- produce decisions that are considered competent;
- produce fair decisions;
- allow consultation and participation by affected parties;
- accomplish goals at least cost.

In theory, public interest is best served by a decision-making process that reflects the best scientific understanding about the affected environment. EA is a planning instrument designed to enhance environmental and natural resource decisions by improving the scientific and technological basis of such decisions. It should also allow the political process to deal with the issues of scarcity and conflicting interest. In reality EA operates in a context where:

- scientific uncertainty surrounds the consequences of projects;
- natural resources and environmental quality are scarce in an economic sense;
- conflict occurs among the users of the resources, with some interests having a more powerful influence on the allocation of resources than others;

- substantial environmental risk or hazard, particularly low
  probability, high consequence events exist;
- the distribution of costs and benefits is unequal.

Environmental assessment first emerged in the UK in Scotland as a result of the exploitation of North Sea oil and gas. Such studies, however, tended to be descriptive rather than analytical with little standardisation of the treatment of project-induced effects. Nevertheless, continued experience with environmental assessment has helped form the view that it makes a broadly positive contribution to both the project proponent and regulatory authorities.

European Community Directive on Environmental Assessment

Since 1973, the European Community has pursued Environmental Assessment as an instrument of environmental policy, before a Directive on 'the assessment of the environmental effects of certain public and private projects' was proposed in 1977. A much watered-down Directive was formally adopted in June 1985 (European Community, 1985).

From the outset, the purpose of the Directive was to instigate a process which includes the provision of information, consultation processes and a systematic approach to the making of a project authorization decision. In order to avoid unfavourable competitive influences on economic development within the Community, the Directive sought to harmonise the development control and environmental standards between Member States. In particular, it sought to harmonise:

- the types of projects subject to environmental assessment;
- the main obligations on developers;
- the content of the assessment.

In seeking to achieve such harmonisation, the Directive proposed the following:

- a general requirement to ensure that planning permission for
  certain projects is only granted after an appropriate prior
  assessment of the likely significant environmental consequences
  has been completed;
- cooperation between planning authorities and developers in
  providing environmental information;
- a general requirement to consult all statutory bodies with
  responsibility for environmental issues and other Member Sates
  about the trans-frontier effects of a project;
- a requirement to inform the public of the issues relating to

particular projects and to provide an opportunity for their views to be made known.

While several major development projects are subject to a mandatory EA requirement, the majority only need an EA when project circumstances so require, such as when a sensitive area like a Site of Special Scientific Interest may be affected. There are, however, a series of indicative guidance thresholds and criteria that affect the construction industry (DoE, 1989). For example, new urban development on sites not previously intensively developed may require an EA where the site is more than 5 hectares, a significant number of dwellings are in close proximity or more than 1,000 square metres (gross) of commercial space is being provided. Special recognition of conservation area designations and the built heritage can also affect the need for an EA. While the regulatory requirements may not always be such as to require an EA to be undertaken, in practice many developers fully accept the benefits to be gained by the voluntary submission of an Environmental Statement.

Environmental Health Impact Assessment

Among the pressures for the wider application of environmental assessment are those associated with human health. The World Health Organisation (WHO) have recognised that EA is a key tool in the area of preventative health care and have, therefore, promoted the concept of Environmental Health Impact Assessment (EHIA) (Giroult, 1988). EHIA can be defined as an assessment of the consequences of a proposed action having either a direct or indirect affect on those attributes having a strong link to human health. Such attributes are not *per se* agents of disease; however they may facilitate human contact with biological, chemical and physical agents and they exert a health effect in a number of ways – see Table D1.1. In this context, the handling of hazardous substances, timber preservatives, air-conditioning and water systems of buildings may generate health concerns. There is, however, a need to generate parameters which adequately define the relationship between the internal environment and health effects. This is particularly the case when considering parameters to define the internal environment / comfort / ambience and the effect of low level chronic exposure to organic compounds.

TOTAL ASSESSMENT

Within the construction industry and property development sector, there is a need to consider the health and environmental consequences that

Table D1.1 Potential Consequences of Environmental Health Factors
Contact with Agents of Disease: Exposure to agents of communicable diseases. Intensive exposure to toxic materials or agents causing immediate acute disease. Low level exposure to toxic material or agents which may cause acute or chronic disease over extended periods.
Exposure to agents with potential for inducing genetic change
Lowering Resistance to Infection
Subclinical Irritation, Nuisance and Discomfort
Aggravation of Existing Disease
Improvement of Conditions Compatible with the Achievement of Physical and Social Well-being
(Adapted from Giroult, 1988)

arise during site preparation, construction, installation, occupation and demolition of buildings. For example, an environmental assessment could embrace land contamination concerns, work place exposure to airborne pathogens and hazardous materials as well as the disposal of wastes. In such an assessment, changes in human exposure patterns and intensity must be systematically considered for the separate risk groups. Environmental health issues and wider quality of life issues are rarely 'black and white', but are expressed in terms of degree of risk and amount of confidence one can place on the understanding of the system being investigated. Both EA and EHIA consequently need to draw upon the perceptions of an assessment philosophy mainly derived from the nuclear industry, namely risk assessment – see Chapter A2.

While formal risk assessment emerges with high levels of quantification, another assessment philosophy is also emerging to join the family of assessment studies. Social Impact Assessment focuses upon the social and cultural environments and key issues in quality of life concerns. As people spend some 90% of their lives inside buildings, the health and social aspects should be considered. Technology assessment represents a further assessment technique which, as its name implies, seeks to examine incipient technological development and potential consequences to forewarn of effects and modify the introduction and diffusion of the technological development. These assessment procedures are not separate, but overlap, covering a set of conceptual, methodological, organisational and consequential aspects (Cope and Hills, 1988). There are a number of ways in which such assessment studies can improve the efficiency of decision-making, but to be effective they should be implemented at an early stage of project planning and design. Assessments must be an integral component in the design of projects, rather than something utilised after the technical studies are complete. There should be a continuous feedback between the environmental technical and financial studies. Compressed timescales for the assessment process, however, ultimately defeats the objective of the exercise, since only a cursory examination of the issues may be possible.

Cost and Time

This trend towards a prior assessment of man's actions, adopting the 'prevention is better than cure' philosophy is not without cost. It must, however, be a mark of democracy that actions are evaluated to identify all the benefits and costs prior to a decision being taken. It is difficult, if not impossible, to draw conclusions regarding the average time and cost associated with an environmental assessment. The main reason for this difficulty is that costs and time are associated not just with the type of project, but also its location. Other factors such as the extent to which information is readily available and the expertise required during the assessment are also important. Finally, the point in time and the way in which the assessment is undertaken is important. For example, whether an assessment is undertaken as part of engineering/economic feasibility studies early in project or programme planning, or as an additional study initiated separately from and after other studies have been completed, affects costs and time schedules (Kennedy, 1988).

Costs of a formal Environmental Assessment in the UK can vary from £20,000 to over £50,000 and require anything from two to six months to complete. Looking at the time and costs in isolation, however, can be misleading. Expressing the cost of an assessment as a percentage of the total project costs can provide a different perspective. Similarly, an extended period preparing an assessment need not cause delay if integrated with other planning and feasibility studies. Also, time invested up-front may then avoid crisis management costs or public inquiry costs at a later date.

While a formal procedure exists for environmental assessment as part of the development consent process, it is unlikely that regulations could easily extend this requirement to aspects of building design. Nevertheless, increasing European Community controls on aspects of the construction industry (see Richard Lorch and Associates (1989) and Chapter A3) will result in a move towards some assessment requirements, whether these are formal or informal in nature. The environmentally aware developer will foresee these developments and seek to establish corporate environmental assessment procedures in order to minimise the costs associated with the disparate studies. The costs to business of environmental degradation should also be recognised, and comprise the imponderable costs associated with quality of life issues, corporate image and difficulties in recruiting staff. Such costs may turn out to be greater than those associated with environmental assessment and the 'prevention rather than cure' philosophy.

Environmental Assessment and the Decision-making Process

The environmental responsibility of organisations commences as soon as a project is conceived. At this stage, environmental questions relate to the broad objectives set for the project, such as whether the project is correctly located and sized. Project location may well be influenced by land values and rental charges, but location is also critical to a project's potential to cause environmental damage. A decision to seek a greenfield site for a 'parkland' development could well encounter a series of environmental constraints. Such constraints could comprise: green belt policy, sites of archaeological, historic or ecological value, areas of high landscape value, increased urbanisation, induced development, new urban infrastructure. Alternatively, an urban location could encounter other environmental constraints such as loss of public open space, land contamination, urban congestion, noise and air pollution. A building situated in a polluted or noisy area is likely to influence the need for air-conditioning, while an exposed site is likely to experience increased energy consumption. Floor space targets may well influence the gross site area subject to development and hence site related environmental effects, as well as the human and material resources needed to service the project with the consequent indirect environmental effects on transportation, etc.

The adoption of an environmental assessment and management philosophy in the construction industry will require recognition that issues apparently unconnected with the environment can play a part in restricting the range of environmental options available elsewhere in the decision-making process. As major projects are not subject to a single decision point, it is important that higher level decisions are made with awareness of the potential loss of flexibility they may impose on later lower-level decisions for reducing the adverse and improving the positive environmental aspects of a project. Frequently, environmental assessment is regarded as a final stage regulatory exercise to be overcome in pursuit of planning permission, and this attitude inevitably restricts the ability of the assessment to modify the environmental consequences of a project. Indeed, it can be argued that the proponent fails to gain the full benefits of the assessment process through this approach. What is needed is for environmental assessment to play a role at all stages in the decision-making process from inception, feasibility studies, design, planning, construction and operation.

While it is suggested that higher level decisions should be made with awareness of their implications for lower order decisions, the inability to isolate causes of environmental change and to assign them to particular policies has been a principal factor restricting the development of policy appraisal techniques. Unless the environmental effects of policy decisions can be identified and isolated from other causes of change, it is impossible to assess either their effects or effectiveness in protecting environmental quality (Wathern et al, 1988). Although similarities exist between project-based and policy appraisal, policy decisions can give rise to effects occurring over extended geographic areas and timescales. For example, corporate policy decisions concerning the development site selection criteria could well prove to be a key factor ultimately affecting the environmental consequences of individual projects. Policy decisions on building styles could also affect the energy efficiency of buildings and their use of resources. Policy decisions on areas not obviously connected with environmental concerns also require careful appraisal, since indirect long term effects can emerge. For example, the development of information technologies assists in the relaxation of locational constraints upon commercial activities. It could then induce change in office and factory building requirements, with decentralisation and new flexible building forms affecting not just the spatial distribution of employment, but also work patterns and environmental pressures. New locational criteria may then be expressed in terms of pressures on:

- the price of accommodation;
- environmental and cultural attractions;
- accessibility.

A further example of where a lack of consideration of the environmental dimension in high level decisions can foreclose options later is in the way architectural design influences selection of building materials. The design concept, for example, could involve the specification of high quality hardwoods or facing stone. These materials may originate from a rain forest or a National Park. They may also have adverse health risks associated with their manufacture or use. Consequently, when building materials are being ordered, flexibility in the selection of environmentally acceptable products may not exist if the architectural design does not recognise environmental and health concerns.

THE ENVIRONMENTAL ASSESSMENT PROCESS

A formal environmental assessment process is unlikely to be imposed upon the construction industry. There is, nevertheless, a responsibility upon all involved in this business sector to incorporate voluntary environmental assessment processes into the planning and design of new buildings. As indicated earlier, there is a need to apply the practice of environmental assessment at the policy, plan and project design levels. Regardless of the decision-making level, a series of activities comprise the environmental assessment process, although the boundaries between the individual activities are more conceptual than real. The activities are:

1 *Screening:* an activity designed to determine whether an environmental assessment is required;

2 *Scoping:* establishing the terms of reference for the study in which the broad range of issues to be studied are defined;

3 *Identification of environmental effects:* this activity is interlinked with scoping, but involves the fine tuning in the definition of issues to be studied;

4 *Information assembly:* information on the project and host environment;

5 *Forecasting:* techniques seeking to estimate the magnitude and probability of a potential environmental effect;.

6 *Evaluation of significance:* the process of determining the importance of predicted effects and selecting a preferred solution;

7 *Communication:* the presentation of the assessment results to the decision maker and non-experts.

Screening

It is unlikely that all policies, plans and projects ought to be subject to some form of environmental assessment. While the thresholds have been established for the application of formal environmental assessments in support of planning applications, it is suggested that there ought to be an industry-wide code of practice for environmental assessment. Such a code of practice could encompass thresholds and criteria which would stimulate an examination of the environmental implications of the proposals. Such thresholds and criteria might address the following issues:

- size of heating/ventilation systems;
- use of contaminated or greenfield sites;

- use of hazardous materials;
- floorspace.

As consideration of the environmental variables becomes an automatic component of decision-making in the building design and construction industry, so the need for formal or voluntary environmental assessment procedures that are somewhat apart from design and construction activities could diminish.

Scoping

While threshold criteria may stimulate the need for a formal or informal environmental assessment, it is appropriate that the scope of the issues to be addressed is carefully circumscribed. In the case of some proposed projects, such as out-of-town developments, external environmental concerns relating to urban sprawl and traffic generation may be issues to consider. In other situations, concerns may relate to specific aspects of the internal building environment.

Identification of Environmental Effects

The earlier chapters of this book have suggested that the potential for interactions between the construction industry, property developer and the environment extends across a wide variety of issues. The environmental consequences of a project can be expressed in different ways:

- as a direct effect quickly emerging following the introduction of development change, and expressed in physical, socio-economic and socio-cultural dimensions;
- as indirect effects, which only emerge after a long time period, such as in the case of human exposure to asbestos;
- the change to a valued landscape as a result of the incremental development;
- the largely uncharted psychological effects of working in an unpleasant environment.

These effects may be revealed at various spatial scales from the individual construction worker or building user to the wider community and ultimately to the global environmental system.

The internal function of a building can be a key to the physical health of its occupants as well as their general well-being as influenced by the building aesthetics. Equally, the external functioning of a building can give rise to positive and negative effects. These may include local wind turbulence or opportunities for crime due to the creation of dark recesses. In addition, hard landscapes can do much to bring about a sense of loss of security and comfort where visual and amenity effects have been ignored in the desire for a functional building. It is increasingly recognised that opportunities exist to enhance the ecological value of developments, provided an open minded attitude is taken in building design.

At a wider scale, introduction of a major building can influence the economic and social functioning of its neighbourhood. Indeed, urban regeneration frequently seeks to exploit this very attribute. However, the incremental nature of such investment can result in concerns moving from a particular building towards the structure, operation and appearance of an urban community. One need only review the conflicts arising from development in London Docklands to uncover the social tensions property development can stimulate. The Royal Art Commission for Scotland, in its 1988 Annual Report, highlighted the view that only those developments which do not destroy the scale of the historic centres of cities and towns should be permitted, while encouraging investment and prosperity necessary to maintain those centres. Major property development must consequently be sympathetic not simply to the architectural setting of the project, but also to its environmental and social context.

There is a current tendency for every problem area to be espoused as either an environmental or green issue. There is a need to choose those which truly affect the environment, cover those which are peripheral, and discard the remainder. It is suggested that attention ought to be confined to those areas which concern the environmental (and health) aspects of the internal working spaces and can also be seen to minimise deleterious effects on the external environment. The following classification of environmental issues may be suggested:

Truly Environmental and Green

- Energy conservation (or consumption) and its effect on CO_2 production which causes the greenhouse effect. Other gases, such as methane, also contribute to the greenhouse effect.
- Energy use in producing building materials. This relates to item (i), but is currently of secondary importance compared to energy consumption over the life of the building in use. (See Chapter D3).
- The use of CFCs (and halons) (which are generally agreed to be the cause of ozone depletion in the upper atmosphere and also add to the greenhouse effect) in thermal insulation, refrigerants and fire extinguishers (see Chapter D2). (Note that the use of the proposed, less efficient, refrigerant alternatives will increase the amount of CO_2 entering the atmosphere.)

- The use of solar gain as part energy conservation. This could be included under the generic heading of 'Renewables'.
- Material recycling of detritus from day to day operations within the built environment. The major elements are:
    1. Paper
    2. Catering waste – organic and non-organic
    3. Plastics
    4. Glass
    5. Industrial waste – metallic and plastic
    6. Chemical waste and effluents
    7. Timber
- Material recycling from demolished buildings has to be addressed, but could perhaps be consigned to a longer term policy review.
- The use of tropical hardwoods (or the destruction of the rain forests) – which is more of an architectural than engineering problem. (This may be an overplayed area as many rain forests are being destroyed for short term ranching where timber may not be extracted at all – only burnt, creating more CO_2.)
- Deleterious materials such as PCBs (often used in the past as insulants in transformers).

Peripheral Issues

These are largely concerned with the criteria for a comfortable and healthy working environment and extend beyond the normal specified parameters. They include:

- Air quality – engineering
    1. Fresh air rates
    2. Air change rates
    3. Temperature
    4. Humidity
    5. Infiltration
    6. Filtration
- Air quality – pollution and hazardous materials
    1. Tobacco smoke
    2. Volatiles and organic vapours
    3. Fibres and dusts
    4. Micro-organisms
- Lighting
- Noise and acoustics – modern office equipment
- Glazing – colour and outside awareness
- Finishes – colours and reflectances

Medical and Miscellaneous

This group of problems is often included in the environmental and green issue debate, but should be excluded – there may be some overlap with the health aspects of the working environment, but many are clearly medical and should be defined as such. They comprise:

- *Legionnaires' Disease:* proper maintenance should prevent its occurrence either internally or externally. (See Chapter C3.)
- *Sick building syndrome (SBS):* this is recognized by the World Health Organization (WHO) as a medical condition, but they cannot specify a cure. (A variety of environmental hazards may contribute to SBS but the condition itself need not be considered. (See Chapter C5.)
- *Radon effects:* this naturally-occurring gas is a health hazard in some geographical areas and can be dissipated by suitable design of new buildings, or ventilation procedures in existing buildings. (See Chapter C4.)
- *Methane produced organically:* a different type of risk to radon, but also treated by good design practice. (It should also be noted that methane is a very potent greenhouse gas whose industrial production and release should be inhibited.)
- Possible hazards from high voltage overhead cables (a potential problem area currently being re-examined).

Methods for Identifying Environmental Effects

A variety of methods have been developed assist in the identification of environmental effects of development projects. Beanlands (1983) defined the term 'Method' as any specified orderly approach to the assembly, analysis and interpretation of information.

Checklists are one method frequently used for the identification of effects, although a variety of different types exist, ranging from a simple list of factors to a highly structured approach involving importance weighting and impact scaling. A simple checklist prepared for environmental health impact assessment is presented in Table D1.2. As with checklists, a variety of matrices are available (Chase, 1976), the most famous of which is the Leopold matrix (Leopold et al, 1971). The Leopold matrix is a numeric matrix containing 100 project actions and 88 environmental characteristics giving rise to 8800 possible interactions. A section of a matrix is presented in Figure D1.1.

Networks and systems diagrams are a further group of methods which seek to explore the indirect effects of projects. Methods have evolved from the early inventive approaches, to sophisticated weighting and ranking methods such as the Environmental Evaluation System and the Water Resources Assessment Method, to systems theory methods (Environment Canada 1982, IIASA 1979). Finally, methods have moved from highly quantified approaches to those which are transparent, easily understood and produce scientifically valid assessments. Beanlands (1983) detailed the following issues linked with the development of EA methods:

- *Simplified complexity:* reduction of the complex and scientifically challenging need to predict with useful accuracy to the presentation of interactions between human and ecological systems by filling in cells in a matrix or classifying effects by symbols, etc., is a major oversimplification of reality;

Table D1.2 Checklist for Use in Environmental Health Impact Assessment

Disease Agents

Biological:	Parasites, helminths, protozoa, bacteria, mycobacteria, Rickettsia, viruses.
Physical:	Noise, vibration, inert dust, ionizing radiation, non-ionizing radiation, excessive temperature or humidity.
Chemical:	Toxic chemicals, heavy metals, organics, inorganics, fermentable organics.

Environmental Health Factors

Primary:	Urban air pollution, indoor air pollution, improper solid waste disposal, improper liquid waste disposal, lack of proper drainage, toxic wastes, radioactive leakage, noise level, unstable structures (accidents).
Secondary:	Increase of vector population resulting from increase in food supply, habitat, or reproduction sites.

Exposure pathway of Toxic Chemicals

Food, drinking water, air breathed, skin contact.

Exposed populations for hazardous industrial plants: workers, their families, surrounding population, consumers of products.

Risk Groups

Infants, children of pre-school age, pregnant women, elderly people, handicapped people, persons suffering from specific chronic diseases, persons with specific genetic defects, workers in hazardous plants.

(Source: Giroult, 1988)

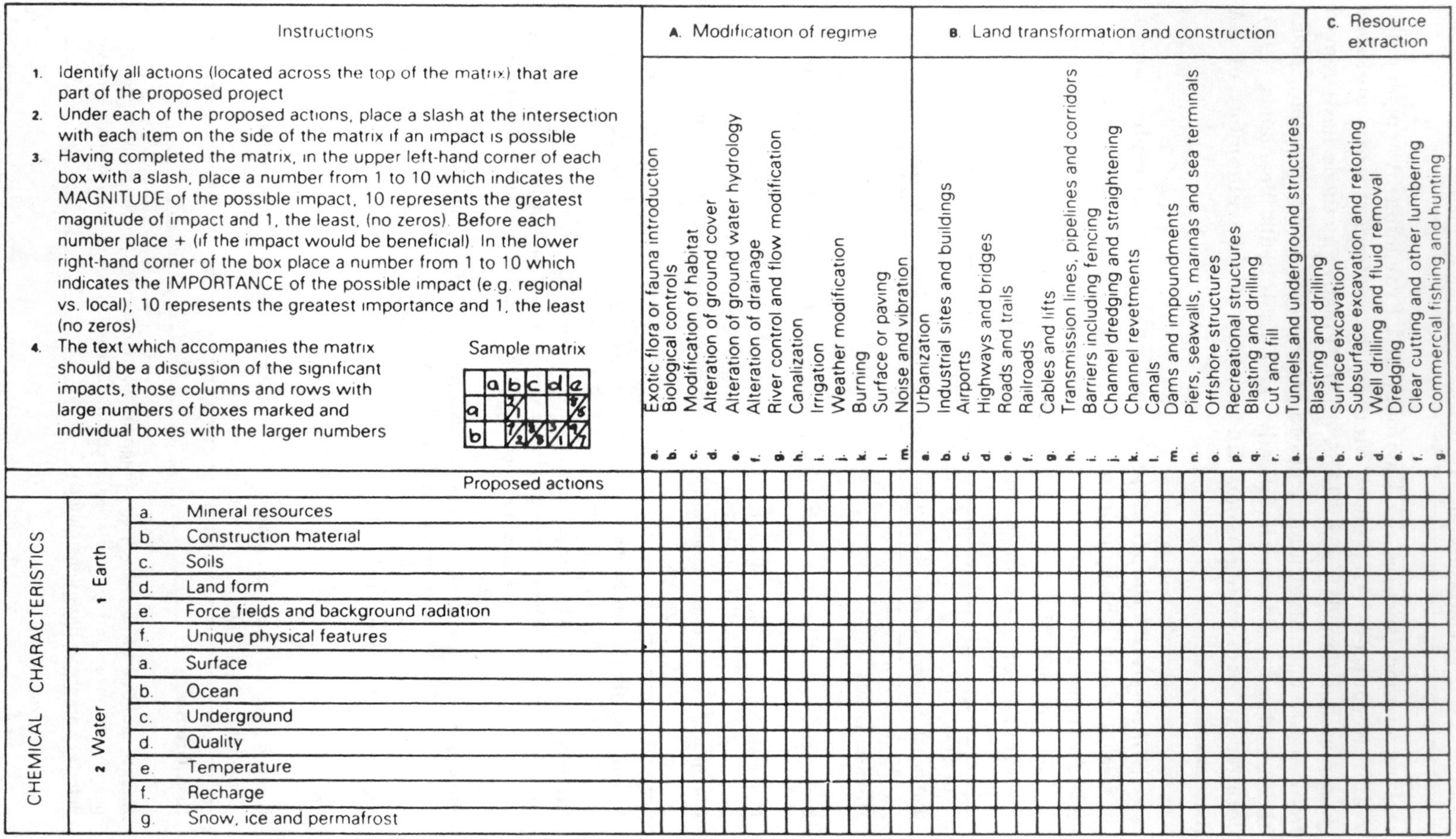

Instructions

1. Identify all actions (located across the top of the matrix) that are part of the proposed project

2. Under each of the proposed actions, place a slash at the intersection with each item on the side of the matrix if an impact is possible

3. Having completed the matrix, in the upper left-hand corner of each box with a slash, place a number from 1 to 10 which indicates the MAGNITUDE of the possible impact, 10 represents the greatest magnitude of impact and 1, the least, (no zeros). Before each number place + (if the impact would be beneficial) In the lower right-hand corner of the box place a number from 1 to 10 which indicates the IMPORTANCE of the possible impact (e.g. regional vs. local); 10 represents the greatest importance and 1, the least (no zeros)

4. The text which accompanies the matrix should be a discussion of the significant impacts, those columns and rows with large numbers of boxes marked and individual boxes with the larger numbers

Sample matrix

A. Modification of regime
- a. Exotic flora or fauna introduction
- b. Biological controls
- c. Modification of habitat
- d. Alteration of ground cover
- e. Alteration of ground water hydrology
- f. Alteration of drainage
- g. River control and flow modification
- h. Canalization
- i. Irrigation
- j. Weather modification
- k. Burning
- l. Surface or paving
- m. Noise and vibration

B. Land transformation and construction
- a. Urbanization
- b. Industrial sites and buildings
- c. Airports
- d. Highways and bridges
- e. Roads and trails
- f. Railroads
- g. Cables and lifts
- h. Transmission lines, pipelines and corridors
- i. Barriers including fencing
- j. Channel dredging and straightening
- k. Channel revetments
- l. Canals
- m. Dams and impoundments
- n. Piers, seawalls, marinas and sea terminals
- o. Offshore structures
- p. Recreational structures
- q. Blasting and drilling
- r. Cut and fill
- s. Tunnels and underground structures

C. Resource extraction
- a. Blasting and drilling
- b. Surface excavation
- c. Subsurface excavation and retorting
- d. Well drilling and fluid removal
- e. Dredging
- f. Clear cutting and other lumbering
- g. Commercial fishing and hunting

Proposed actions

CHEMICAL CHARACTERISTICS

1 Earth
- a. Mineral resources
- b. Construction material
- c. Soils
- d. Land form
- e. Force fields and background radiation
- f. Unique physical features

2 Water
- a. Surface
- b. Ocean
- c. Underground
- d. Quality
- e. Temperature
- f. Recharge
- g. Snow, ice and permafrost

Figure D1.1: Section of the Leopold Matrix

- *Unwarranted sophistication:* EA methods may provide a false sense of sophistication and scientific validity as a consequence of the manipulation of figures or letters masking the weak assumptions and data inputs;
- *Numbers versus data:* the excessive use of numbers gives rise to an implied assumption that data exists to support value judgements on the relative importance of parameters. The mathematical manipulation of such numbers is often in error if such numbers are not based on measurements;
- *Second generation information:* methods which seek to translate data into ranking, weighting schemes or indices not only generate new numbers, but may also mask the original data possibly leading to incorrect interpretations.

Despite the development of numerous methods such as checklists, matrices and networks, there is no one universal method which can be applied in all situations. Methods do not act like cook books, in that a successful EA is not achieved by simply meeting the requirements of a particular method. One reason for employing a method is that it attempts to provide a mechanism by which environmental effects are systematically identified or evaluated on a common basis. Methods have clear limitations, as the results achieved are dependent upon the quality and quantity of information available, as well as the assumptions upon which they are based. A fuller description of environmental assessment methods is presented by Clark et al (1984).

While a variety of methods can assist with the identification of environmental effects, little work has been undertaken on the development of methods specifically orientated towards buildings. An outline network for buildings is presented in Figures D1.2 and D1.3. There is clearly scope for the development of methods to aid the identification and evaluation of environmental effects associated with buildings. One pioneering attempt to develop an assessment method for new office designs has been proposed by the Building Research Establishment (Baldwin, et al, 1990). The main objectives of the method are to:

- provide recognition for buildings which are friendlier to the global environment than normal practice and so help stimulate a market;
- improve the internal environmental quality and occupation health;
- raise awareness of the role of energy use in causing environmental change;
- reduce the long term effect of buildings on the global environment;

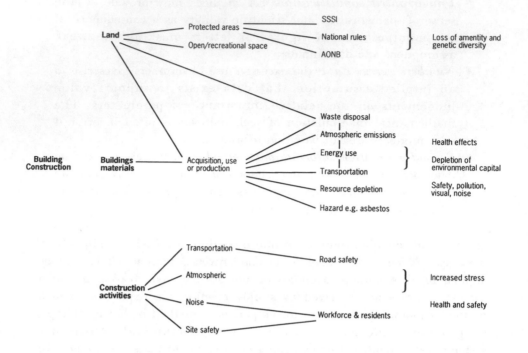

Figure D1.2: Network diagram for building construction

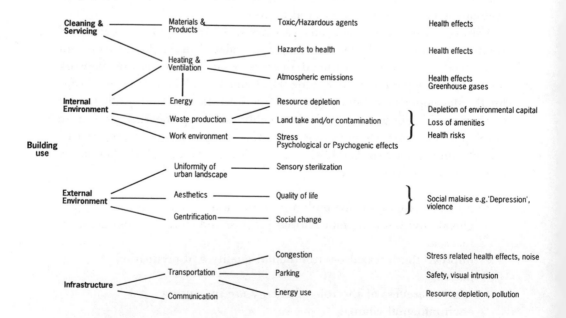

Figure D1.3: Network diagram for building use

- provide a common set of targets and standards;
- encourage designers to achieve environmentally sensitive buildings.

The assessment method is undertaken at the design stage and involves the identification of those aspects where the proposed design meets or falls short of a set of target requirements.

Information Assembly

The application of environmental assessment to the building industry would stimulate a considerable need for information and it is helpful to consider the nature of these needs, for example:

- *field data:* eg. baseline water quality, or soil survey data;
- *modelling:* eg. the dispersion of contamination;
- *laboratory study:* eg. testing of effluents or the health implications of buildings;
- *literature survey:* eg. on material properties;
- *comparative analysis:* effects of similar projects in analogous locations.

The time required for data collection is often one of the major constraints in scheduling an environmental assessment, particularly when the assessment is dependent upon the provision of information from statutory bodies, voluntary organisations and field surveys. Information collection could be particularly lengthy if details on the origin of hardwoods, for example, were not available and it were necessary to contact suppliers. In contrast, the timescale set by project proponents may be too short for meaningful information and data to be collected on existing environmental conditions and the environmental properties of the proposed building materials.

For some situations, little or no information exists, such as new hazards or where there are few events with low or unobservable long term effects. In other situations, it is necessary to extrapolate from parallel situations. Identification of such risks stimulates a search for information and usually scientific and public controversy. Paradoxically, a source of uncertainty is the continuous production of new information from scientific research. New data usually leads to a more complete understanding of the nature and consequences of a risk, but it may also overturn established views. During a period of scientific research, public anxiety may be generated and a public perception of the risk established which may then be difficult to modify when more information becomes available. An example of a narrow rather than comprehensive application of established scientific information in the anticipation and management of a risk is that of radon. The distribution of radium in rocks and soil has long been known, as has the fact that radon is a cause of lung cancer; yet only recently has the exposure of the general population to radon in confined spaces in homes and other buildings been investigated and found to be significant. Forecasting used in EA is consequently an exercise in reducing uncertainties.

Forecasting

Forecasting reduces uncertainties which are generated by:

- a poor understanding of the physics, chemistry and biology of the processes involved with a lack of knowledge to build an adequate predictive model;
- fundamental errors in problem and system representation in that the important variables involved or system processes are not or cannot be known so precise projections cannot be made;
- random external variables, for which probability distributions may be constructed or where the processes are inherently probabilistic or so complex that it is not feasible to construct and solve predictive models (Duinker, 1989, Malvern and Paterson, 1989).

As the health implications of buildings may emerge as a major issue, epidemiological studies may be a key component within environmental assessment where the forecasts of low-level environmental exposure to chemicals must be made. While epidemiology may be valuable in revealing any potential effects of chemicals on human health, as with other assessment disciplines, it is often of uncertain or limited use because of uncontrollable factors. Among the most important of these are sample size, securing an unexposed control group, memory bias in reporting exposure data, and problems relating to latency period where symptoms do not appear until years after exposure. Also, the numerous factors associated with life style, such as smoking, eating habits, use of alcohol or drugs, and differences among ages and sexes, are important considerations (Fowle and Grima, 1989). Given such methodological difficulties it is helpful to establish a framework by which such studies can be judged. One such framework has been proposed by Landrigan (1983) to aid the evaluation of causal associations between chemical exposure and health effects:

- the nature and extent of the exposure must be documented and so the exposed and control/unexposed populations must be precisely defined;

- the health effects must be assessed as unequivocally as possible;
- alternative explanations for the association must be controlled for the exposed and control populations;
- the relationship between exposure and the health effect must be evaluated for practical and statistical significance, with particular attention paid to the detection of dose-response relationships.

In cases of exposure to environmental hazards, it is vital to recognise that exposure to mixtures of chemicals or microbiological risks occur. Such chemical mixtures may give rise to additive, synergistic or antagonistic consequences. In order to aid the evaluation of hazards, a coding system has been proposed by the Clark University Hazard Assessment Group (1983), (see Table D1.3). Such a system could be adapted to building materials and extended to encompass the wider environmental implications of material extraction, use and disposal.

Where the topic under investigation has a potential effect upon human health, further techniques become appropriate such as fault-tree analysis, epidemiology, microbiological studies, toxicological experimentation and statistical analysis. Several techniques may be used for a single issue. For example, to determine whether human exposure to a contaminant could occur, it is necessary to demonstrate that chemical pollutants could be present in an area where people were likely to come in contact with them. Hydrologists and meteorologists may be needed to plot the movement of the agents in surface water, groundwater and air. The route of entry into the body (ingestion, inhalation, absorption through the skin) must be forecast, since not all chemicals are absorbed equally effectively by all routes and many are not absorbed at all by one or other of the routes (Frank, et al, 1989). Once exposure is established, estimates of daily dose and duration of exposure or body burden should be made. Clearly this can be a difficult task, depending on the quality of the data available.

Once individual predictions have been made, then the importance of each effect should be considered. The attributes considered should include:

- *Scope:* the extent of the effects over the space and time;
- *Level:* the level at which the effects of an interaction impinge upon the environment;
- *Directness:* whether the interaction has direct or indirect effect;
- *Cumulative:* the effects of the project combined with those of other operations in the area;
- *Probability of occurrence*
- *Direction, positive or negative*
- *Magnitude*
- *Timescales and duration*
- *Synergism.*

Table D1.3 Hazard Descriptor Definitions

Technology Descriptor

1. **Intentionality** - Degree to which technology is intended to harm using a categorical scale;
3 - not intended to harm living organisms;
6 - intended to harm non-human living organisms;
9 - intended to harm humans.

Release Descriptors

2. **Spatial Extent** - Maximum distance over which a single event has significant impact, using a logarithmic scale, $1 < s < 9$, where $s = \log_{10} d + 1$ rounded to the nearest positive integer and d is the distance in metres.

3. **Concentration** - Released energy or materials.

4. **Persistence** - Time over which a release is a significant threat to humans.

5. **Recurrence Measures** - The mean time interval between releases above a minimum significant level.

Exposure Descriptors

6. **Population at Risk** - Number of people potentially exposed to the hazard.

7. **Delay** - Delay time between exposure to the hazard release and the occurrence of consequences.

Consequence Descriptors

8. **Annual Human Mortality** - Average annual deaths to the hazard in question.

9. **Maximum Human Mortality** - Maximum credible number of deaths in a single event.

10. **Future Generation** - Number of future generations at risk for the hazard in question, using a categorical scale;
3 - hazard affects the exposed generation only
6 - hazard affects children of the exposed generation, no others
9 - hazard affects more than one future generation.

11. **Non-human Mortality** - maximum potential non-human mortality, using a categorical scale;
3 - no potential non-human mortality;
6 - significant potential mortality;
9 - potential species extinction.

12. **Actual Non-human Mortality** - Measures non-human mortality that has actually been experienced on a categorical scale;
3 - no species extinction.
6 - significant mortality.
9 - species extinction occurred.

(Source: Clark University Hazard Assessment Group, 1983)

Evaluation of Significance

While the environmental implications of a major development can be wide ranging, the significance of the issues will vary. Given that the resources which can be devoted to environmental affairs will be limited, it is important that those resources are concentrated on the environmental effects that are potentially the most damaging. While resources are devoted to the creation of good internal air quality, since this can be reflected in a happy and healthy staff, investment in avoiding tomorrow's problems will be difficult without codes of practice or regulations. Significance may then be seen in terms of the financial imperative rather than longer term global concerns. Equally, in addressing external environmental concerns resources ought not to be concentrated upon minor air quality issues associated with a heating system if the company does not adopt ozone friendly products or does not restrict its use of vehicles with large capacity petrol engines. It is important, therefore, that the assessment of significance recognises the various opportunities a developer has to manage direct and indirect, internal and external, environmental consequences at the individual, local community, national and global scales. While it might be tempting totally to disregard small scale effects, recognition should be taken of any cumulative consequences that might arise.

While uncertainty causes difficulties in the generation of environmental predictions, it is important that the assessment process makes some attempt to determine the significance of the potential effect. The following questions should be considered in evaluating the significance of potential effects.

- Which risk groups will be affected and in what way?
- Is the effect reversible or irreversible, repairable or non-repairable?
- does the effect occur over the long or short term, is it continuous or temporary and increase or decrease with time?
- Is it local, regional, national or global in extent?
- Would the effect be controversial?
- Would a precedence be established?
- Are environmental and health standards and objectives being threatened?
- Are mitigating measures available and how costly are they?

Communication

All decisions based on forecasts within an EA carry some degree of uncertainty, but elements of this uncertainty may be isolated and made less uncertain or characterised by research. Decision-makers should be able to specify, in general terms, the types of error in specific performance indicators they could accept. Decision-makers are, however, rarely fully aware of all the possibilities of changing a development and altering related conditions and events in order to improve the response of an environmental performance indicator. Discussions with analysts should seek to explore where:

- control is possible;
- effectiveness of control is reasonably certain;
- control resources would be most efficiently applied;
- control should be aimed at changing the probability of occurrence or magnitude of an event to below a critical level.

Reduction of uncertainty

In order to reduce uncertainty and assist the decision-making process, it is necessary to produce broad, scientifically-supported assessments that specify the risks associated with each alternative. This frequently involves cross-sectoral information which is difficult to integrate into a useful format for decision-makers and the public (Malvern and Paterson, 1989). Decision-makers are accustomed to judging the acceptability of a project using traditional techniques, such as cost benefit analysis, which tends to mask many of the risks and adverse effects. To overcome this problem it is important that an environmental report adequately discusses trade-offs, conflicts and the acceptability of environmental risk. Trade-offs among the costs, benefits and risks of alternatives should be described before the conflicts among various individuals or groups are considered. Such conflicts may arise as a result of different perceptions of risk or different personal values, or because of an inequitable distribution of costs, benefits and risks (Byer, 1989).

Clearly the acceptability of risk is a key component of the decision-making process. An extreme approach is to operate a zero risk principle, where no involuntary risk is accepted. This is, however, impractical. Even if a risk could be eliminated, it might simply be substituted by other risks or require expenditures better spent elsewhere. A practical alternative is a comparative analysis to identify the lowest achievable risk or the best available technology (BAT) to control a risk. Basing decisions on scenarios such as worst-case has its appeal, though this tends to focus attention solely on the risk/adverse attitudes of society (Byer, 1989). Other options are for postponement of a decision until specific uncertainties are resolved. Alternatively, the development could be permitted as proposed with a requirement for monitoring of the uncertain relationships, taking further action if monitoring suggests that undesirable effects are occurring. The solution hinges on what is a reasonable and acceptable risk? In a technological society, it is reasonable, however, to expect the legal and administrative procedures for assessing environmental risk to become more elaborate reflecting greater understanding of risks (Grima, 1989). In this context, EA must expand its theoretical and operational framework to explicitly include risk assessment. In short, an EA must aim to provide the decision-maker with answers to the following questions:

- What is the problem?
- Who/what will be affected?
- How will they/it be affected?
- What can be done (alternatives)?
- What are the costs?
- What are the consequences of being wrong?
- What is the recommendation?

After recognising the problem of uncertainty, one potential solution is to adopt techniques of decision analysis which provide a quantitative framework for making decisions when uncertainty exists. Their approach is based upon two assumptions. First, incomplete data, and second, that the decision maker will be influenced by the probability of events with known consequences. A main tool in decision analysis is the decision tree which results from different actions, (see Figure D1.4). Not all uncertainty can be handled or addressed through decision analysis, however, since in some situations there is no clear view of the relative importance of the various issues. The challenge, therefore, is not so much to insist on a removal of uncertainty, but to confront it and cope with it by improving the provision of information and addressing distributive implications of risk decisions on various sectors of the community.

MITIGATION, MONITORING AND AUDITS

When issues have been identified during the environmental assessment process and the significance of the effects determined, it is then necessary to identify mitigation and monitoring programmes. While solutions to potential environmental issues exist, there is frequently a financial consideration. Consequently, cost-benefit analysis can emerge as a valuable tool in the identification of the most cost-effective mitigation measure. In the case of issues where no reasonable alternative may exist, monitoring is an appropriate strategy. Monitoring programmes can be established to provide an early warning system – for example, a regular inspection programme for the heating and ventilation plant. Other monitoring programmes may involve the tracing of the origins and destinations of materials used in buildings to emerge as wastes for disposal. With the envisaged introduction of new regulations on waste disposal under the Environmental Protection Bill, there will be a duty of care placed upon producers of wastes. It is proposed that this responsibility will not simply cease when a transportation firm removes the wastes, but will extend ultimately through to the disposal site. The environmental monitoring requirements on businesses are therefore likely to be extended – see Chapter A3.

Linked to monitoring is the practice of environmental auditing, a

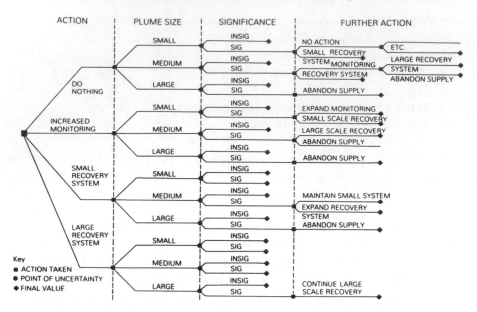

Figure D1.4: Example decision tree for groundwater contamination
(source: De Jongh, 1988)

subject now gaining increased attention. The term 'audit' has been transferred from the language of finance to environmental science, since it effectively portrays a concept of examination and assessment of performance.

A *performance audit* seeks to review the environmental performance of procedures, plant and personnel. Companies are increasingly adopting performance audit systems as businesses recognise the complexity of environmental regulations and appreciate the economic consequences of their environmental liabilities. Essentially these audits are concerned with determining whether actions to deal with environmental responsibilities and the awareness of personnel of such actions are satisfactory. McIntyre (1983) identified the following advantages of such audits:

- more efficient allocation of resources by modifying operating practices and manpower planning;
- appraising compliance practices and problems in a systematic and consistent manner providing accurate information to assist with insurance underwriting;
- reducing legal costs;
- enhancing relationships with regulatory agencies;
- enhancing corporate image;
- evaluating new development projects;
- responding to new regulations in a consistent and structured manner.

In determining the need for a performance audit, project managers ought to consider the following questions:

- What financial and business penalties exist for inadequate environmental management?
- How significant is public opinion to the business?
- Are competitors gaining a market advantage?
- Can an environmental strategy produce financial benefits?
- Are financial institutions expressing environmental concerns?

A performance audit would include some or all of the following topics:

- corporate policy and environmental management systems;
- awareness of regulations and responsibilities;
- plant design and operation;
- maintenance programmes;
- control of raw materials and residuals;
- occupational health and safety;
- incident reporting procedures;
- product safety during manufacture, use and disposal;
- transportation policy;
- energy conservation;
- environmental awareness of personnel;
- contractor selection and supervision;
- external communication;
- visual appearance of the facility.

It is suggested that performance audits could provide valuable insights into the management of building design, construction and use. Through the process of checking, it should be possible to improve predictive capabilities and refine the assessment process. Although up-front costs will be associated with audits, they can be expected to lead to savings by the better specification of the assessment and ultimately improvements to building design and operation.

Environmental assessments and audits could stimulate the development of corporate environmental policies and environmental management plans for individual development projects. Clearly, this would be unnecessary for some buildings, so this approach should be restricted to large scale development projects. For the smaller buildings, however, it may be possible to devise a simple environmental management guide which draws together consideration of both the internal building environment and the external environment in terms of material flows into and out of the building. Ideally designs will evolve so that a building and its associated management systems are so structured

that the environmentally acceptable path is always the simplest
management path. In this way environmental problems may be designed
out or mitigated to a level where the effects are not significant.

INFORMATION AND TRAINING NEEDS

Should environmental assessment principles be incorporated into the
design and functioning of buildings, this will stimulate a need for a
major improvement in flows of health and environmental information on
building products and the construction of buildings. Manufacturers of
building products will need to provide information not simply upon the
technical characteristics of their materials, but an environmental
specification may also be required. This could comprise information
regarding the source of raw materials and the generation of
environmental damage during their extraction, manufacture or disposal
of waste products and their acoustic and thermal effectiveness. A code of
practice on product labelling plus an independent audit system would
seem to be beneficial.

The need to assemble information on the environmental and health
implications of construction materials, building construction and use is
likely to be a major task requiring a wide variety of inter-disciplinary
research. Among the topics that could be addressed are:

- improved site selection criteria;
- environmental health labelling for building products;
- alternative, energy-efficient building designs and fuel sources;
- resource use minimisation techniques;
- waste reduction techniques;
- environmental assessment techniques and procedures;
- codes of practice.

The BRE identified the following four categories of issues where the
available information is inadequate for their inclusion within the
assessment method (Baldwin, et al, 1990). These are:

Issues where insufficient information is available

- The fuel used by the fuel industries during extraction and
  distribution and the effect upon carbon dioxide emissions;
- release of greenhouse gases during fuel extraction, processing and
  distribution;
- the energy content and associated carbon dioxide emissions of
  building materials;

- energy used during construction and transportation of people and materials to the site;
- energy consequences of site selection;
- CFCs in packaging materials used during construction;
- environmental consequences of obtaining and processing building materials;
- energy used during maintenance, refurbishment and demolition;
- use of alternative energy sources;
- sick building syndrome;
- pollutant release during fire or demolition;
- use of recycled products for construction.

Issues where doubt exists on whether environmental effects occur

- Internal environment parameters such as temperature, noise, negative ions etc;
- organic gases and vapour from building materials;
- wood preservatives;
- ventilation effectiveness;
- lighting levels and other aspects of lighting such as glare;
- sunlight reflection from building facade;
- airborne particulates and organisms.

Issues where suitable criteria for assessment remain to be developed

- External appearance, aesthetics;
- noise generated by the building;
- ease of maintenance;
- habitat destruction and other environmental aspects of site selection;
- use of contaminated land.

Issues which it is not possible to assess satisfactorily at the design stage

- Building management control procedures;
- building monitoring equipment;
- radon emissions into the building.

The production and assimilation of the environmental specification of materials will require individuals who are able to use such information and make the appropriate decisions among competing materials. Since no material is likely to be totally environmentally benign, trade-offs between competing environmental interests as well as finance and building aesthetics will be needed. Where the decision maker has only partial information or a restricted appreciation of the environmental trade-offs, then sub-optimal decisions could be made.

Further environmental benefits accrue when developers adopt a more pro-active stance towards environmental management. This could involve R & D by development companies, consulting engineers, research institutes and universities in anticipation of future EC legislation and resource constraints. For example, increases in the real cost of water, energy, transport and waste disposal seem inevitable as a result of both Government policy and resource limitations. Now is the time to research environmentally sustainable solutions, and for the lessons of the 1974 oil crisis not to be forgotten.

At present there are numerous seminars on environmental issues targeted at businesses. While these seek to establish new policy directions and create awareness, there is an apparent need for low budget environmental awareness training courses. Individuals and businesses who consider that environmental concerns are relevant to their activities need to be reached through such awareness training.

Finally, there is a need for improved environmental training of engineers, architects and planners. In particular, consulting engineers and architects ought to consider in-house awareness training for their staff leading toward the establishment of corporate environmental policies. If clients increasingly seek consultants with environmental capabilities, then there is clearly a marketing advantage for such consultants to establish strong reputations in environmental affairs on a par with that of their architectural, engineering and design capabilities.

It is important that environmental concerns are seen not just to exist 'elsewhere', such as in the rainforest, but to be immediate and local to the individual's input to the design and functioning of a building. If the problem is left to someone else, it is almost certain that it will remain unsolved. The nature of the environmental imperative is potentially so serious that it is up to everyone to consider what positive contribution he or she can make.

CONCLUSIONS

* The building industry is increasingly recognising that its actions have various effects upon the physical and human environment. These consequences may be expressed at local, national or global scales and can directly or indirectly effect human health. Recognition of these concerns and greater regulation has brought about a need for the application of environmental assessment and management in the construction industry. A structured approach is considered essential in order to avoid resources being expended on issues of marginal significance.

* Many of the environmental implications of buildings arise as a result of policy or strategic decisions, but lower level tactical decisions are also important. It is necessary, therefore, that assessment protocols are established to allow the ramifications of policy decisions to be evaluated. Not all policies or projects will require the adoption of an environmental assessment process; indeed, through improved awareness on behalf of the engineers and architects, buildings will be constructed that are more environmentally benign. Nevertheless, in the case of large projects, internal environmental assessments may be a useful additional tool.

* Environmental assessment techniques and practice has evolved as a means of examining the environmental implications of development projects with the introduction of legal requirements for major projects. To date, however, such assessments have tended to focus upon the external physical environmental effects of projects, with little attention being devoted to the building materials and internal environmental issues primarily related to health. Consequently, many of the methods and predictive techniques developed for environmental assessment are not specifically directed to the needs of the building industry.

* The introduction of environmental awareness into the construction industry will stimulate the need for greater dissemination of information regarding the environmental performance of building materials. This could easily extend into a paperchase unless attempts are made to focus upon only the significant environmental issues. The lack of knowledge is a fundamental constraint to many aspects of the environmental assessment process, introducing uncertainty into the decision-making process. In this regard there is a need for research into the effects of low level exposure to pollutants within buildings.

* Linked with environmental assessment is the subject of performance audits which help provide information to refine the assessment and management process. Fundamental to both the assessment and audit tools is the need for businesses to establish corporate environmental policies and to clearly assign environmental responsibilities to their staff. Without corporate policies, it is argued, the assessment and audit processes will fail to be fully integrated into the decision-making process.

REFERENCES

Baldwin, R., et al, (1990), *BREEAM 1/90 – An Environmental Assessment for New Office Designs*, Building Research Establishment Report, Watford.

Beanlands, G., (1983), *Do EIA Methods have a Future?*, Paper Presented at the Symposium on *Environmental Impact Assessment: Current Status and Future Directions*, Crete, 10–17 April 1983, Organised by CEMP, University of Aberdeen.

Byer, P.H., (1989), *Elements of Risk Management*, in Fowle, C.D., Grima, A.P., and Munn R.E., (Eds.), *Information Needs for Risk Management*, Environmental Monograph No. 8, Institute for Environmental Studies, University of Toronto, Canada, pp 9–18.

Chase, G.H., (1976), *Matrix Techniques in the Evaluation of Environmental Impacts*, in Blisset, M., (Ed.), *Environmental Impact Assessment*, Engineering Foundation, Austin Texas, pp 131–152.

Clark, B.D., et al, (1984), *Perspectives on Environmental Impact Assessment*, D. Reidel, Dordrecht.

Clark University Hazard Assessment Group, (1983), *Methods for Analyzing and Comparing Technological Hazards: Definitions and Factors Structures*, Report 3, Centre for Technology: Environmental and Development, Clark University, Worcester, Mass.

Cope, D. and Hills, P., (1988), *Total Assessment: Myth or Reality?*, in Clarke, M., and Herington, J., (Eds.), *The Role of Environmental Impact Assessment in the Planning Process*, Mansell Publishing Limited, London, pp 174–193.

DoE, (1989), *Environmental Assessment: A Guide to the Procedures*, Department of the Environment, London.

Duinker, P.N., (1989), *Give and Take: The Role of Regulatory Decision-Makers in Risk Analysis for Environmental Impact Assessment*, in Grima, A.P., Fowle, C.D., and Munn, R.E., (Eds.), *Risk Perspectives on Environmental Impact Assessment*, Environmental Monograph No. 9, Institute for Environmental Studies, University of Toronto, Canada, pp 113–127.

Environment Canada, (1982), *Review and Evaluation of Adaptive Environmental Assessment and Management*, Environment Canada, Ottawa.

European Community, (1985), *Council Directive 85/337/EEC on the Assessment of the Effects of Certain Public and Private Projects on the Environment*, OJ No. L 175, 5 July 1985.

Fowle, C.D. and Grima, A.P., (1989), *Conclusions and Directions*, in Fowle, C.D., Grima, A.P., and Munn, R.E., (Eds.), *Information Needs for Risk Management*, Environmental Monograph No. 8, Institute for Environmental Studies, University of Toronto, Canada, pp 303–312.

Frank, J.W. et al, (1988), *Information Needs in Epidemiology: Detecting the Health Effects of Environmental Chemicals Exposure*, in Fowle, C.D., Grima, A.P., and Munn, R.E., (Eds.), *Information Needs for Risk Management*, Environmental Monograph No. 8, Institute for Environmental Studies, University of Toronto, Canada, pp 129–144.

Giroult, E., (1988), *WHO Interest in Environmental Health Impact Assessment*, in Wathern, P., (Ed.), *Environmental Impact Assessment: Theory and Practice*, Unwin Hyman, London, pp 257–271.

Herington, J., (1988), *Environmental Values in a Changing Planning System*, in Clark, M., and Herington, J., (Eds.), *The Role of Environmental Impact Assessment in the Planning Process*, Mansell Publishing Limited, London, pp 140–162.

IIASA, (1979), *Expect the Unexpected – An Adaptive Approach to Environmental Management*, International Institute for Applied Systems Analysis, Laxenburg, Austria.

Kennedy, W.V., (1988), *Environmental Impact Assessment and Bilateral Development Aid: An Overview*, in Wathern, P., (Ed.), *Environmental Impact Assessment*, Unwin Hyman, London, pp 272–285.

Landrigan, P.J. (1983), *Epidemiologic Approaches with Exposures to Waste Chemicals*, Environmental Health Perspectives, 48: pp 3 97.

Leopold, C.B. et al, (1971), *A Procedure for Evaluating Environmental Impact*, Geological Survey Circular, No. 645, US Geological Survey, Washington, DC.

Malvern, R.J. and Paterson, W.M., (1989), *Managing Uncertainty in Environmental Assessment: A Project Proponent Perspective*, in Grima, A.P., Fowle, C.D., and Munn, R.E., (Eds.), *Risk Perspectives on Environmental Impact Assessment*, Environmental Monograph No. 9, Institute for Environmental Studies, University of Toronto, Canada, pp 129–149.

McIntyre, S.T., (1983), *Environmental Auditing – A Timely and Effective Tool*, Journal of Air Pollution Control Association, 33, pp 909–913.

Richard Lorch Associates, (1989), *What Are You Doing About the Environment?* Richard Lorch Associates, London.

Tomlinson, P., (1986), *Environmental Assessment in the UK: Implementation of the EEC Directive*, Town Planning Review, 57(4), pp 458–486.

Tomlinson, P. and Atkinson, S., (1987), *Environmental Audits: Proposed Terminology*, Environmental Monitoring and Assessment, 8(3), pp 187–198.

Tomlinson, P., (1989), *Environmental Statements: Guidance for Review and Audit*, The Planner, 75(28), pp 12–15.

Royal Fine Art Commission for Scotland, (1989), *Twelfth Report*, HM Stationery Office, London.

Wathern, P. et al, (1988), *Assessing the Environmental Impacts of Policy*, in Clark, M. and Herington, J., (Eds.), *The Role of Environmental Impact Assessment in the Planning Process*, Mansell Publishing Limited, London, pp 103–123.

CHLOROFLUOROCARBONS (CFCs)

Steve Curwell and Chris March

Leeds Polytechnic and University of Salford

INTRODUCTION

Chlorofluorocarbons (CFCs), a group of stable man-made gases that have been in widespread use are destroying the atmospheric ozone layer which shields the earth from incoming ultraviolet radiation. Research into ozone depletion indicates that it could cause a decline in crop yield of certain species, effect aquatic organisms deleteriously, exacerbate smog in certain areas, accelerate degradation of some plastics and paints, increase the number of cases of skin cancer and it may also increase the incidence of some virus infections.[1]

CFCs are used in buildings in insulants and refrigerants – their main uses in construction – and in aerosol foam sprays and fire protection equipment, the most commonly used being CFC11 and CFC12. Their success in building applications has been largely due to their non-flammability, low toxicity, cost-effectiveness and high stability. This high stability means that they can be contained and used for many years without breaking down; but it is this very property that in turn causes problems in the stratosphere because the CFCs take a long time to break down and lead to ozone depletion. The gases there now will take many decades to disappear, so any further discharges exacerbate the problem further.

In addition to their impact on the ozone layer, CFC11 and CFC12 are some 17,500 and 20,000 times respectively more potent as a `greenhouse gas' than CO_2. Whilst CO_2 is present in the atmosphere in much greater quantities than CFCs, because of this high potency and because CFCs persist much longer than CO_2 before being broken down, major reductions in CFC discharges into the atmosphere will eventually have a considerable impact on the greenhouse effect. This is an important point to appreciate, since much of the publicity given to CFCs has only been in association with depletion of the ozone layer, and not its effect as a greenhouse gas. However, because depletion of the ozone layer is of great concern, the emphasis in this chapter is on the ozone layer issue rather than the greenhouse effect, since by demonstrating the need for elimination of CFCs to protect the ozone layer, it follows that a reduction in greenhouse gases from this source would occur automatically.

The chapter first deals with the reasons for using CFCs in buildings (a subject covered in some depth in Reference 3), and then reviews the political position since that introduces the different CFCs that are of concern, and determines the extent to which each individual CFC is deemed to remain acceptable. The balance of the chapter then deals with where CFCs are found in buildings, and the possible alternatives that could replace them.

WHY USE CFCs?

Before it was realised that CFCs were associated with the depletions of the ozone layer, they were used with widespread acceptance in many applications (not just building applications) due to their unique combination of properties – non-flammability, low toxicity, cost effectiveness, high stability, better thermal properties than air and, in those insulation products formed with a closed cell structure, improved vapour resistance.

The most obvious and useful of these properties is the improved thermal performance: to provide the same thermal insulation value, foam material containing CFCs will require a significantly reduced thickness Ordinary expanded polystyrene or mineral wool would need to be used at almost twice the thickness than if foamed polyurethane rigid board was used, for example, in cavity wall construction*. The wall cavity can be constructed so that when filled or partially filled with mineral wool, the wall will still meet the thermal requirements of the new Building Regulations. The use of foamed polyurethane will also satisfy the requirements but, for the same thickness of insulant, it will provide a better standard of insulation than mineral fibre, or for the same standard of insulation will allow the width of the cavity to be reduced.

THE POLITICAL POSITION

There has been a dramatic change in attitude politically in recent years, demonstrated by a number of international agreements. The key events have been the signing of the Montreal Protocol, the production of the statement called the Helsinki Declaration, and a recent meeting in London to review the Montreal Protocol.

Montreal Protocol

In September 1987, the world's prime consumers and manufacturers of CFCs signed an agreement in Montreal – called the Montreal Protocol[2] –

---

* It is important to appreciate that extruded polystyrene is CFC-blown but expanded polystyrene is CFC-free.

designed to reduce emissions into the atmosphere. The protocol deals primarily with all fully halogenated CFCs and Halons of commercial significance which are listed in the Annex to the protocol in two separate groups. Each CFC and Halon is given a number signifying 'ozone depletion potential', thereby providing a relative scale of danger to the earth's ozone layer on the basis of the larger the number, the greater the risk. The two groups are listed below in Table D2.1:

Table D2.1 The main CFCs and their Potential for Ozone Depletion

GROUP		SUBSTANCE	OZONE DEPLETION POTENTIAL
Group I	CFC11	Trichlorofluoromethane	1.0
	CFC12	Dichlorodifomethane	1.0
	CFC13	Chlorotrifluoromethane	
	CFC113	Trichlorotrifluoromethane	0.8
	CFC114	Dichlorotetrafluoroethane	1.0
	CFC115	Chloropentafluoroethane	0.6
Group II	Halon 2111	Bromochlorodifluoromethane	3.0
	Halon 1301	Bromotrifluoromethane	10.0
	Halon 2402	Dibromotetrafluoroethane	6.2

There are many CFCs available, not included in the protocol, the most common being as listed in Table D2.2.

Table D2.2 Other common CFCs and their Potential for Ozone Depletion

SUBSTANCE		OZONE DEPLETION POTENTIAL
CFC22	Chlorodifluoromethane	0.05
CFC123	Dichlorotrifluoroethane	< 0.02
CFC132b	Dichlorodifluoroethane	< 0.05
CFC134a	Tetrafluoroethane	0
CFC142b	Chlorodifluoroethane	0.05

The protocol requires signatories to freeze consumption of Group I substances at 1986 levels by 1990, to reduce consumption by 20% by 1994, and to reduce it by a further 30% by 1999. Production, on the other hand, is allowed to increase to 110% of 1986 levels by 1990, followed by a decrease to 90% of 1986 levels by 1994 and to 65% by 1999. The difference between consumption and production figures was agreed to make allowance for developing and low-consumer countries who, it is argued, need to increase slightly their consumption of CFCs as their economy develops. For Group II substances there is a freeze on consumption and production at 1986 levels commencing three years after the protocol came into force in January 1989. This has more recently been updated in Helsinki.

The Helsinki Declaration

On 2 May 1989, the governments of the 50 countries represented at the first meeting of the parties to the Vienna Convention and the Montreal Protocol produced a statement which included decisions to:

'AGREE to phase out the production and the consumption of CFCs controlled by the Montreal Protocol as soon as possible but not later than the year 2000 and for that purpose to tighten the timetable agreed upon in the Montreal Protocol taking due account of the special situation of developing countries.

AGREE to phase out halons and control and reduce other ozone-depleting substances which contribute significantly to ozone depletion as soon as feasible.

AGREE to commit themselves, in proportion to their means and resources, to accelerate the development of environmentally acceptable substituting chemicals, products and technologies.'

The Revised Montreal Protocol: London, June 1990

On 29 June 1990, the Montreal Protocol was revised at a meeting in London, with the agreed changes due to come into force on 1 January 1993.

At the time of going to press, there is still some uncertainty about the interpretation of all the details. However in summary, the following controls were agreed:

- Consumption of the five controlled CFCs covered in the original protocol will be cut by 50% by 1995, 85% by 1997 and 100% by 2000. Also a further 10 CFCs not controlled in the original protocol are now also to be phased out by 2000.
- Consumption of the Halons 1211, 1301 and 2402 are to be cut by 50% by the year 2000. These reductions are measured against 1989 consumption figures.
- Some new substances have been included, notably methyl chloroform and carbon tetrachloride.
- There is to be no ban on HCFCs, so-called transitional

substances, despite some reservations about that position by some of the parties to the Protocol. The meeting adopted a non-binding resolution which called for their use to be ended by 2020 if possible and 2040 at the latest.

WHERE CFCs ARE USED IN BUILDINGS

The two main applications of materials containing CFCs in buildings in the UK are as insulants and refrigerants. There is a further smaller usage in aerosol foam sprays and in fire protection equipment.

Insulation

The insulation materials using CFCs in their manufacture are extruded polystyrene and polyurethane, polyisocyanate and phenolic rigid foam boards. There is also a limited amount of sprayed *in situ* polyurethane foam used to either upgrade existing buildings or insulate tanks and other storage vessels. These materials represent about 9% of the total UK insulation market. The remainder comprising 80% mineral fibre, 9% expanded polystyrene, 1% ureaformaldehyde and 1% by other means.

It is known that approximately 26,000 tonnes of foamed plastic containing CFCs was used in UK buildings in 1987. The amount of CFCs contained in rigid polyurethane varies depending upon its density and there is more in the extruded polystyrene material. It is suggested by the authors that something in the order of 3,000 tonnes is consumed currently in the manufacture of these materials for construction purposes. The main uses of materials containing CFCs are listed in Table D2.3.

To place the use of CFC-containing insulation in buildings in context, a typical domestic house, 5 m x 8 m in plan area with 25mm partial fill cavity wall insulation, uses approximately 0.1 tonnes of insulation material; on the other hand, a supermarket 100m x 50m in plan constructed with laminated polyurethane panels uses approximately 10 tonnes.

Refrigeration

If a CFC is used as a refrigerant, the number remains the same, but is prefixed by the letter R – eg. CFC11 becomes R11.

A variety of CFCs are used in refrigeration. The five controlled substances in Annex 1 of the Montreal Protocol (see above) are all used as refrigerants in vapour controlled systems, ie R11, R12, R113, R114 and R115. Other CFCs not restricted by the Protocol but used in refrigerants include R22, R13 and R502. The total market for refrigerants accounts for approximately one third of the total world usage of CFCs. The air-conditioning industry is currently investigating the use of alternatives.

Table D2.3 The main uses of materials containing CFCs

	VOLUME M³	TONNES
	OF MATERIALS CONTAINING CFCs	
Extruded Polystyrene:		
Flat roofs, terraces and balconies	15,000	480
Pitched roofs	5,000	160
Walls (linings and cavity fill)	65,000	2,000
Polyurethane/Polyisocyanate:		
Roofs		9,625
Walls		7,000
Floors		875
Plant and pipework		1,000
Phenolic:		
Pipe sections	37,500	1,320
Dry lining buildings	7,000	240
Other building and panels	5,500	200

These figures are approximate, based on information obtained in 1987 from a variety of sources. Polyurethane foam used for pipe insulation also uses CFCs, but the usage is small in relation to the total market.

Ninety-eight percent of CFCs currently used are the refrigerants R11, R12, R22 and R502 (see Figure D2.1). R502 is used primarily for refrigerants in supermarket frozen food and dairy display cases and comprises mainly 50% CFC115, a controlled substance and 50% Hydro-CFC22, an uncontrolled substance. R22 is considered less hazardous in

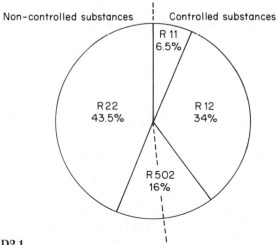

Figure D2.1

terms of depletion of the ozone layer but cannot necessarily be used as a substitute for one of the others.

Aerosol Sprayed Foam Insulation

The use of spray foams (applied using aerosol cans) for sealing and insulation in the UK is small compared with Europe, probably due to differing construction practice. In the UK, window and door frames are usually built into a wall during the bricklaying operation, thereby leaving small gaps between brickwork and frame, which can be bridged by sealant. Elsewhere, spaces are left in the wall into which the frame is eventually fixed. In this case, the gap between the two components may be larger and is often sealed using spray foams. These cans have been readily available in builders' merchants and DIY outlets, and trends in insulation may lead to increasing use of these foams. However, non-CFC foams are now available.

Fire Protection Equipment

Use of CFCs, particularly Halons 1301 and 1211, in fire protection equipment takes advantage of the non-flammability of the material. It is well suited for use in computer suites where systems are designed to flood the whole area with CFC gas in the event of fire, thereby smothering the fire by excluding oxygen. However, losses of the CFC gas can occur due to false alarms and poor maintenance. Use in extinguishers is thought to be a very small proportion of total consumption, with domestic production and imports of Halon 1301 and Halon 1211 being approximately 600 and 1200 metric tons per annum respectively.[3]

WHAT ARE THE ALTERNATIVES?

Five main strategies can be adopted to reduce the consumption of CFCs by the construction industry:

* selection of alternative insulation materials;
* development of alternative 'blowing agents' for foamed insulation products;
* design of buildings to reduce the need for air-conditioning plant;
* development of alternative refrigerants for air-conditioning systems;
* development of collection equipment and procedures to reduce leakage and loss in both the manufacture of foam products and refrigeration plant.

The last option assumes continued but more efficient use of CFCs, which may be necessary, at least in the short term, in the refrigeration and air-conditioning sectors. Because of the difficulties in conversion of existing equipment, more efficient maintenance offers the greatest potential in these sectors and this option is explored later in the chapter.

Alternative Insulation Materials

The main insulation applications in UK buildings are:
1 Cavity wall insulation.
2 Timber-framed wall insulation.
3 Pitched roof insulation:
     (a) horizontal ceiling, (b) sloping ceiling.
4 Flat roof insulation:
     (a) warm roof construction, (b) inverted roof construction.
5 Ground floor and basement insulation.
6 Internal wall lining.
7 External wall lining.
8 Lightweight roof and wall cladding systems.
9 Building services insulation:
     (a) pipes and tanks, (b) ductwork, (c) refrigeration and air-conditioning plant.

In the majority of cases there are alternatives to materials manufactured using controlled CFCs, which provide acceptable technical solutions, and details are given in Reference 3.

It would be relatively simple to cease the use of foamed insulants in applications 1, 2, 3, 4a, 6 and 9 without any serious technical difficulties and, for some applications (2, 3 and 6) it is preferable to use non-combustible materials, which means the majority of foam insulants are less suitable.

The main difficulties arise with the remaining applications (4b, 5 and 7) where the waterproof characteristic of foam insulants is a major advantage. With the inverted form of flat roof construction, the insulation is fixed outside the waterproof membrane and so waterproof insulation, extruded polystyrene, is used. Similarly waterproof material is necessary for work below ground level in basements, and would be an advantage in external wall linings. The only feasible alternative for these applications is cellular glass at approximately three times the cost. Composite panels, composed of steel, aluminium, GRP and GRC with foamed insulant applied to the underside or within the panel, are resistant to the interstitial condensation problems that often afflict alternative forms of lightweight cladding. There is no obvious alternative without considerable changes in design and construction practice, and manufacture.

Alternative Blowing Agents for Foam Insulation

The major manufacturers of CFCs are concentrating their efforts on CFC123, not controlled by the Protocol, which could be used as a replacement for CFC11 as a blowing agent and also for CFC12.[5] Butane and carbon dioxide are also being investigated.

A German company has claimed to have developed a rigid polyurethane board with similar thermal properties to those currently in use, but using compressed air. The innovation, it appears, is to increase the number of bubbles in the foam by reducing their diameter. It remains to be seen how this material's other properties match specifiers' needs.

Experiments have been conducted using CFC22 in the manufacture of expanded polystyrene, but these have proved unsuccessful. The most likely solution appears to be by using CFC142b or a mixture of CFC 142b and 22. In both cases the thermal performance is expected to be similar to those blown with CFC11. In Scandinavia, industry is currently using non-halogenated CFCs mixed with a flammable gas, but the thermal insulation is some 20% less than if using CFCs 11, 12, or 22. A major advantage of the material is thereby lost.

Alternative Refrigerants

The refrigeration industry has taken the initiative in seeking alternatives for the CFCs used in refrigerants and in air-conditioning plant. A one day conference organised by the National Economic Development Office and the Institute of Refrigeration held in May 1988 looked at both long and short term substitutes and the methods by which the requirements of the Montreal Protocol could be met. The CIBSE policy on CFCs, February 1990, indicates the industry's concern and determination to act.

Work is currently taking place to find a replacement for R11, which is likely to be R123. Testing has already started on equipment using R11, and it is estimated that if these tests are successful, the replacement will be commercially available in 1993. Long term research is also being carried out on a R502 replacement, but it is estimated that this will take another eight years.[5]

Converting existing systems using R12 is more problematic. It had been thought that the equipment could be converted to use R22, R500 or R502. However, it has been found that, in changing from R12 to R22, new equipment is usually needed and that R500 has not been a suitable option.

Thus it is only possible to satisfy the longer term requirements of the Protocol by considering the use of non-controlled refrigerants. The thirteen largest producers of CFCs have chosen to concentrate their resources on R134a[54] which will eventually replace R12 refrigerant. This will be available in the UK by 1991.[5]

Waste of Refrigerants

Poor maintenance of air-conditioning systems is a major factor in the loss of CFCs. Large amounts of refrigerant are lost through leakage and the need to replace contaminated refrigerants. Whereas a domestic refrigerator contains about 100 grams of refrigerant, a large industrial unit may contain 80 tonnes. It has been estimated that in the commercial and industrial sectors, 75% and 50% respectively of the refrigerant used were accounted for by servicing.[6]

It is clear that since refrigerants (not just in buildings) account for some 30% of world usage of CFCs, a major saving could be made if improved maintenance were carried out.

Many companies are now taking initiatives in this direction. In many maintenance contracts, clauses have been introduced stating that the CFCs must not be released, and several of the chemical companies now provide recovery systems to recycle the refrigerants. However, steps must be taken to improve this situation even further, and tighter controls introduced. Superior automatic detection equipment is needed in larger building installations to indicate leakage at an early stage which, when combined with proper maintenance procedures, could reduce losses to a relatively low level. Careful commissioning of systems to prevent serious losses at first charge is essential.

The development of improved leak detection equipment, maintenance procedures and log book recordings needs to be initiated immediately. Maintenance is often difficult to carry out due to lack of appropriate access, and not all tanks and pumps can be readily or easily drained permitting collection of the refrigerants. Where this is a problem, alterations to existing equipment should also be carried out, but this may be difficult to do without releasing the CFCs already in the system. It has been suggested that domestic refrigerators should carry a surcharge to the consumer over and above the normal sales price. This surcharge could be collected and placed in a central fund which would eventually be used to pay for the collection and recycling of the CFC refrigerant. Such a system could also be considered for larger building plant.

ISSUES AND RECOMMENDATIONS FOR THE FUTURE

In new buildings the need for air-conditioning should be questioned and the possibility explored of building forms that are naturally lit and ventilated. Designers should consider methods to prevent deep sun penetration to the interior of the building and more carefully consider what the percentage of external glazing to total area of external wall should be, although such changes require client acceptance. If the earth's surface temperature warms up as a result of the greenhouse effect, whilst this should mean a reduction in some parts of the world in the demand for space heating, thereby using less energy, there is likely to be a need for improved cooling. This makes these design issues even more important.

The question should be asked whether insulation standards can be satisfied without using materials containing CFCs. In Use of CFCs in Buildings[5] it was demonstrated that there are suitable alternatives for the vast majority of building applications. However, there are difficulties with metal cladding systems, as new technical solutions will be required. There is no reason why these cannot be achieved but there will be cost implications.

New blowing agents are being developed, but can we afford to wait, bearing in mind that CFCs currently used in insulation application are some 20,000 times more potent than CO_2 as greenhouse gases? CIBSE (the Chartered Institution of Building Services Engineers)[7] and the RIBA (the Royal Institute of British Architects)[8] have recommended to their members that they should not specify insulation materials containing CFCs. These professional bodies have also recommended, and the authors support them, that refrigeration should be avoided if natural or mechanical ventilation is a feasible alternative. If refrigeration is necessary, then plant using R22 should be used until such time as hydrofluorocarbon substitutes are available, although there is now serious concern that even this will be unacceptable as far as depletion of the ozone layer is concerned.

CIBSE and RIBA further recommend that access for maintenance of refrigeration plant be made large enough to permit ease of both the checking for leaks and draining of refrigerant and that the installation of leak detection alarms should be considered. In any case only competent maintenance contractors should carry out maintenance work. Another suggestion (not by CIBSE) is that an odour could be introduced into the refrigerant to assist in detecting whether a leak has occurred.

Refrigerants in refurbished or decommissioned plant should be collected and sent for recycling.

CIBSE also advised that their members should avoid specifying halon gas fire control systems as these can only be tested by releasing the gas directly into the atmosphere. New test procedures are being developed using other gases in order to minimise halon releases.

The current reliance on voluntary codes in the UK can be contrasted with recent developments in the USA. In December 1989 the 'Revenue Reconciliation Act 1989' came into force in the USA. The Act imposes excise duty on producers and importers of ozone depleting chemicals as well as upon manufacturers of products containing these substances. The chemicals include CFCs 11, 12, 113, 114, 115 and Halons 1211, 1301, 2402. The tax begins at a base figure of $1.37/pound weight in 1990, increasing to $2.64 by 1994 and thereafter by the addition of 45 cents/year. The exact levy is also related to the ozone depletion potential of individual chemicals. The Act will impose significant costs on manufacturers and is certain to provide additional incentives to explore new materials and solutions.

REFERENCES

1 Miller, A.S. et al, *The sky is the limit – strategies for protecting the ozone layer*, World Resources Institute, November 1986.

2 UNEP, *Montreal Protocol on Substances that Deplete the Ozone Layer*, Final Act 1987.

3 Curwell, S.R. et al, *Use of CFCs in Buildings*, Fernsheer Ltd, London, December 1988.

4 New Scientist, 26 May 1988.

5 Information provided by ICI.

6 Crowhurst, R.J., *National and International Controls (EEC implementation of the Montreal Protocol: situation to date*, paper at the NEDC/Institute of Refrigeration one-day conference, 18 May 1988.

7 CIBSE *Preliminary Policy on Chlorofluorocarbons*, CIBSE Technical Board, June 1989.

8 *The Initial RIBA Policy Statement on Global Warming and Ozone Depletion*, RIBA, May 1990.

BIBLIOGRAPHY

Ackroyd, K., *Safety Aspects of Chloroflurocarbon Refrigerants*, Paper presented to the Institute of Refrigeration, 6 December 1979, London.

Bertram, Stephen, *R.502 : A Second Look*, Refrigeration, Air-Conditioning and Heat Recovery, March 1988 – pp.19–20.

British Rigid Urethane Foam Manufacturers' Association Ltd (BRUFMA), *CFC Emissions and Rigid Urethane Foams:* Submission by the Executive Committee of BRUFMA to the House of Commons Environment Committee, 15 January 1988.

Building Research Establishment, *Cellular Plastics for Building*, Digest no.224, BRE 1981.

Butler, D.J., *CFCs and the Building Industry*, BRE Information Paper IP23/89 1989.

Charnas, Dan, *Blowing Agents: Regulatory Issues Cloud Horizon*, Plastics Technology, July 1987 – pp.83–85.

Curwell, S.R. and March, C.G., *Hazardous Building Materials: A Guide to the Selection of Alternatives*, E. and F.N. Spon, London, 1986.

Downing, R., *Development of Chlorofluorocarbon Refrigerants*, ASHRAE Transactions, Symposium Paper KC-84-08, No.3, pp.481–491, 1984.

Elastongran UK Ltd, *Combating The Effects of Chlorofluorocarbons On The Ozone Layer*, BASF Group, Derby, England, 1987.

Encyclopaedia of Polymer Science and Engineering, 2nd Ed., John Wiley and Sons, USA, 1988.

Friends of the Earth, *Evidence to the House of Lords Select Committee on the European Communities investigation of The Ozone Layer* – Implementing the Montreal Protocol, 1988.

House Of Lords Select Committee On The European Communities, *The Ozone Layer – Implementing the Montreal Protocol*, 1988.

IAL Consultants Ltd., *The Market for Thermal Insulation Products in Selected European Countries Vol.1*, London, 1988.

Imperial Chemical Industries plc, *Arcton Refrigerants Cool the World*, ICI, Runcorn, England.

Litchfield, M.H and Longstaff, E., *The Toxicological Evaluation of Chlorofluorocarbon 22 (CFC 22)*, Fd. Chem. Toxic Vol.22, No.6, pp.465–475, 1983.

Johnston, K., *Into the Void – A Report on CFC's and the Ozone Layer*, Friends of the Earth, London 1987.

Junior Liaison Organisation, *What are you doing about the Environment?* November 1989, London.

Norton, Francis J., *Diffusion of Chlorofluorocarbon Gases in Polymer Films and Foams*, J. of Cellular Plastics – September/October 1982 - pp.300–315.

Environmental Protection Agency, *Preliminary Estimates of the Officer of Air & Radiation*, October 1986.

Refrigerants and the Environment: Consequences of the Montreal Protocol, Proceedings of the one-day conference, 18 May 1988.

Sporon-Fielder, Axel, *Removal of TDI and Recovery of CFC: Practical Experience with an Activated Carbon Filter System Installed at a Soft Foam Producer*, Cellular Polymers – Vol.5, pp.369–386, 1986.

U.N Environmental Programme, *Flexible and Rigid Foams*, Technical Options Report, June 1989.

U.N Environmental Programme, *Refrigeration, Air-Conditioning and Heat Pumps*, Technical Options Report, June 1989.

Vasquez, Analia, and Williams, Roberto J.J., *Effect of Process Variables on the Foaming of Phenolic Resins*, Cellular Polymers, Vol.5, pp.123–140, 1985.

Woods, George, *The ICI Polyurethanes Book*, John Wiley and Sons, London.

Working Group of Legal and Technical experts for the Preparation of a Protocol on Chlorofluorocarbons to the Vienna Convention for the Protection of the Ozone Layer, *Conclusions of the Scientific Working Group*, April 1987.

Zwolinski, Leon M. and Dwyer, Frank J., *Dual blowing agents lower cost of polystyrene foams*, Plastics Engineering, June 1986 pp.45–48.

THE GREENHOUSE EFFECT, AND ENERGY CONSERVATION IN THE CONSTRUCTION AND USE OF BUILDINGS

Steve Curwell and Robert Lowe, and Chris March

Leeds Polytechnic, and University of Salford*

INTRODUCTION

The atmosphere is essential to life on earth. Constituent gases oxygen and carbon dioxide are of course necessary to animal and plant life, but equally important is the action of the atmosphere in retaining heat from the sun that would otherwise be reflected or re-radiated back into space. This process raises the temperature at the surface of the planet from what would otherwise be around −30°C to the present average of 15°C. This heat retention is known as the greenhouse effect and, without it, the earth would be uninhabitable. Carbon dioxide, together with methane and a number of other gases, which contribute most strongly to this effect, have come to be known as 'greenhouse gases'.

It has long been recognised that a number of the actions of man, particularly the combustion of fossil fuels, contribute to the quantity of greenhouse gases. The majority of scientific opinion is that this could upset the balance achieved in the atmosphere by increasing the effectiveness of the greenhouse process, causing a rise in temperature at the surface of the planet, known as global warming.

The industrialisation of the countries in the northern hemisphere has led to a vast increase in combustion for heating and in industrial processes, and in turn to increased release of carbon dioxide. When combined with the potential for industrialisation in the 'third' world, there is serious concern over global warming. Recent scientific evidence supports the view that global temperatures are rising, but it is still impossible to predict accurately the likely temperature rise and the effect this will have on the world's climate. Estimates vary from the

* The authors wish to acknowledge the invaluable assistance of David Oliver of the Open University.

inconvenient to the catastrophic. Another view is that the present changes are part of the long term temperature fluctuations experienced by the planet. This argument may however strengthen the case for the existence of global warming, as the earth ought to be cooling at the present stage in the long term temperature cycle, so the slight increase in average global temperature observed to date may in fact mask a much larger underlying man-made change.

The actions that need to be taken to minimise the effects of global warming require international cooperation and are currently a major global political issue.

Clearly the construction and use of buildings consumes energy and, because the vast majority of this energy is gained by burning fossil fuels, buildings contribute to global warming. The purpose of this chapter is to:

- identify the possible magnitude of global warming and the relative importance of carbon dioxide and other greenhouse gases;
- identify some of the possible climatic effects;
- assess the extent of the contribution of buildings to global warming;
- estimate the reduction in emissions that may be required and explore ways by which such reductions may be achieved using existing technology;
- identify a priority of action and discuss the role of each sector of the construction industry.

THE GREENHOUSE EFFECT AND GLOBAL WARMING

Short wave radiation from the sun penetrates the atmosphere relatively easily. About 80% of this energy reaches and warms the earth's surface, the remainder being absorbed by the atmosphere. The earth then radiates this heat back, primarily as long wavelength infra-red radiation. Much of this is absorbed by the so called greenhouse gases in the atmosphere, the most abundant of which are water vapour and carbon dioxide, but which also include methane, ozone, nitrogen oxides and chlorofluorocarbons (CFCs) – see Table D3.1. This process causes the atmosphere to heat up, and to radiate heat to space (illustrated in Figure D3.1).

A thermal balance is achieved resulting in the earth's surface remaining at a constant *average* temperature of around 15°C. The mechanisms that maintain this balance are not fully understood but include the length of time greenhouse gases persist in the atmosphere, the ability of the oceans to absorb carbon dioxide, and of vegetation, particularly the tropical rainforests, to fix carbon in the form of plant material or biomass.

The present concern over global warming arises from the observation that the concentrations of all the major greenhouse gases have been

Table D3.1 (Adapted from *The Heat Trap*, Friends of the Earth (FoE), Sept. 1988)	
GREENHOUSE GAS	TYPICAL SOURCE
Carbon Dioxide	Fossil fuel combustion, deforestation and other forms of changing land use, biomass burning, erosion
CFCs	Refrigeration, air-conditioning, plastic foam, solvents, food freezants and sterilants
Methane	Biological decay in water-logged areas (such as rice paddies) and animal waste, enteric fermentation in cattle and termites, biomass burning, oil and gas exploitation
Nitrous Oxide	Fertilizer use, fossil fuel combustion, biomass burning, changing land use
Ozone (low level)	Reactions involving other pollutants (carbon monoxide, methane and other hydrocarbons and nitrogen oxides) and sunshine

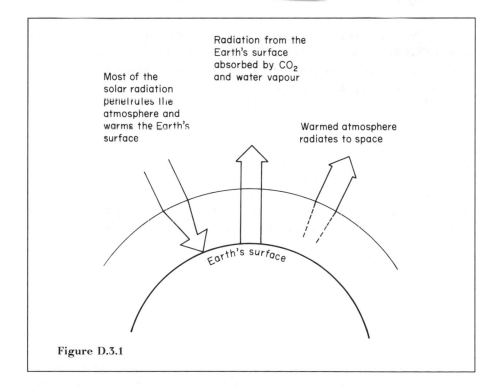

Figure D.3.1

increasing, at an accelerating rate, for the last 200 years. Figure D3.2 (Keeling, 1990) shows a 12% increase in CO_2 since measurements started in 1957. Subsequent analysis of bubbles of air trapped in arctic and

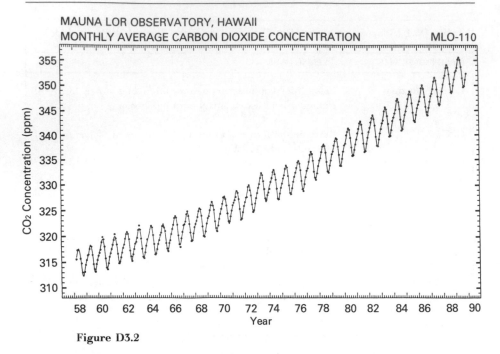

Figure D3.2

antarctic ice has enabled this graph to be extended backward, which has shown that the present levels of CO_2 are higher than at any time for the last 160,000 years (Gribben 1990). Similar measurements have been made for other greenhouse gases.

The behaviour of the global climatic system is complex, and its precise response to an enhanced greenhouse effect cannot be predicted with certainty. Changes in cloud cover and extent of polar ice cover may serve to mitigate and increase respectively any initial warming, but the magnitude of these effects is not accurately known. However the consensus of scientific opinion (Bolin et al 1986) is that increased greenhouse gas concentrations will produce global warming and the debate is now more on defining the severity of the problem, and the nature of regional and local climatic effects which result from a general increase in global temperatures. Observational evidence taken over the last 100 years is consistent with the increases in global average temperature that computer models predict should have occurred to date (Kaas et al, 1988). However it will be perhaps another 10 years before direct measurements of global temperature will prove absolutely that global warming has occurred.

Projections indicate that doubling of effective carbon dioxide might occur by the year 2030. At this level of effective CO_2* it is estimated that

---

* The term effective CO_2 takes account of the CFCs and other gases which molecule for molecule are more potent greenhouse gases than CO_2 (see Table D3.2).

there will be an overall global warming of between 1.5°C and 5.5°C with an increase of up to 8°C in the Arctic (Bolin et al 1986). Precipitation will probably increase by between 7 and 15% in the higher latitudes, but may well decline in the tropics and subtropics. It is estimated that sea levels will rise by between 25 and 165 mm (Bolin et al 1986).

The increase in fossil fuel consumption, which is the major cause of the increase in atmospheric concentration of CO_2, is coincident with the clearance of the tropical rainforest. Some 140,000 square kilometres of the forest is being cleared each year (just under 2% of the total), which, as well as contributing to CO_2 emissions, is having a further unbalancing effect on the climate system (Myers 1989).

Table D3.2 indicates the relative concentrations of greenhouse gases in 1985. The concentration figure is insufficient to indicate the overall contribution to the greenhouse effect; the length of time the gas remains in the atmosphere before being broken down, ie. the residence time *together with* the greenhouse potency must also be considered.

It can be seen from Table D3.2, that although the concentration of CFCs in the atmosphere relative to other greenhouse gases is low, if predicted growth rates, the residence time, and relative greenhouse potency are taken into account, they are a major cause for concern. This is especially important as the construction industry is a major user of CFCs, particularly in insulation materials, refrigeration and air-conditioning. CFCs are also implicated in depletion of the stratospheric

Table D3.2 Relative concentrations of greenhouse gases in 1985 (Derived from Cousins et al 1989, The Heat Trap FoE 1988, and Bolin et al 1986.)

Gas	Concentration in Atmosphere[a]	Growth Rate	Residence Time	Greenhouse Potency relative to CO_2	Contribution to enhancement of greenhouse effect relative to CO_2
CO_2	346 ppmv[b] (275)	0.5	7 yrs	1	1
CFC-11	0.22 ppbv[c] (0)	6.1	75 yrs	17,500	0.05
CFC-12	0.37 ppbv (0)	6.2	111 yrs	20,000	0.1
Methane	1650 ppbv (700)	1.0	10 yrs	25	0.33
Nitrous Oxide	309 ppbv (280)	0.4	170 yrs	250	0.1

[a] pre-industrial concentrations in brackets
[b] ppmv = parts per million by volume   [c] ppbv = parts per billion by volume

ozone layer, which provides protection from ultra violet radiation from the sun for living organisms on the planet. They are the subject of international agreements to reduce manufacture and use (Montreal 1987, Helsinki 1989), and the subject of a separate chapter (D2).

Whilst carbon dioxide is of lower greenhouse potency and residence time compared with CFCs, its vast concentration in the atmosphere makes it the most significant contributor to the greenhouse effect. Since buildings consume large quantities of energy in the manufacture of building components, in heating and air-conditioning, and since CO_2 is a by-product of energy production, it can be seen that the main contribution of buildings to global warming is via this route. Although this chapter concentrates on the problem of CO_2, the CFCs issue is also very important and should not be neglected.

SETTING LIMITS ON FOSSIL FUEL COMBUSTION

The first high level international meeting to consider the need for international action to limit global warming was the 1988 Toronto World Conference on the Changing Atmosphere. This conference proposed a long term goal of reducing CO_2 emissions from combustion of fossil fuels by 50%, with an initial global goal of a 20% reduction by the year 2005, taking 1988 as the base year (Anon 1988). Similar but more detailed conclusions were reached by the IPSEP project (Krause et al 1989), funded by the Dutch Government. This concluded that world average consumption of fossil carbon over the next 110 years must be less than one half of the current rate of consumption.

These proposed or recommended reductions must be seen in the context of UN projections of world population in the year 2000 of between 1.5 and 3 times the current population. Accounting for population growth, the Toronto Conference and IPSEP targets imply that per capita rates of consumption will need to be cut by somewhere between 75 and 90% respectively. If the world acts on these limits, the fossil fuel era will essentially be over by the middle of the next century. Most of the buildings currently being erected will still be in use at that time.

Given these global targets, what limits on CO_2 should apply in the industrialised countries? In 1985, the industrialised countries accounted for some 74% of the total. The UK population is about 1.1% of the world's total, whereas it has been estimated that, in 1987, the UK's emission of CO_2 from all sources into the atmosphere was 151 million metric tonnes (FOE, 1989) and represented 2.9% of the world total fossil carbon emissions of about 5 billion tonnes (5 Gte). Interests of equity and geopolitical stability suggest strongly that the fraction of fossil fuels consumed by the developing countries should rise. Whatever targets for global output of fossil CO_2 are set in the future, the industrialised countries will have to bear the brunt of reductions in output that are demanded. Assuming a modest 50% increase in developing country fossil carbon consumption by 2005 would mean that the industrialised countries would have to make reductions of the order of 40%, if the Toronto short term target (20% by 2005) is to be met by the world as a whole. The arguments presented here are not meant to preempt the results of the international political discourse that has already begun, but to emphasise the magnitude of the task that faces the industrialised countries if the problem of global warming is to be taken seriously.

The contribution to the enhancement of the greenhouse effect in the final column of the Table D3.2 is estimated by multiplying the difference between the present concentration and the pre-industrial concentration as quoted by Bolin et al, by the greenhouse potency quoted by Cousins et al. This process is necessarily approximate, but gives a rough guide to anthropogenic changes to date.

The atmospheric residence time can give a misleading impression of the relative importance or anthropogenic release of the various greenhouse gases, depending on whether a particular gas is entirely man-made or is part of a natural cycle. If emission of CFC 11, a man-made gas, is abruptly stopped, the concentration in the atmosphere will decay to zero with a time constant equal to the atmospheric residence time. For gases which are part of the natural cycle, such as CO_2, the residence time may be significantly shorter than the time constant for decay of excess concentration on cessation of emissions. This is of the order of 80 years for CO_2 (see Krause et al 1990), comparable with CFC 11.

It is necessary to explore the feasibility of such reductions in CO_2 output. To put these figures into perspective, the most rapid reductions in carbon dependency to date in the industrialised countries occurred between 1979 and 1983. To reduce their carbon dioxide output by 20% by 2005, without stifling economic growth, would require these countries to sustain or exceed this previous best *short term* performance, for the next 15 years. Much higher rates of improvement have been achieved through strong regulatory pressure in *some* sectors of *some* OECD countries (notably domestic space heating in Sweden and Denmark), but to achieve a 40% reduction by 2005 in all industrialised countries would be more problematical. A number of low energy or low CO_2 scenarios have been constructed for industrialised countries (see for example Olivier et al 1983) which establish the *technical* feasibility of reductions of the order of 50–80%. These scenarios are however predicated upon a revolution in society's approach to energy decision making. The possibility of a 50% reduction in the CO_2 output of the UK over the 30 years to 2020 has been examined by the Department of Energy's Energy Technology Support Unit, who considered it to be 'just about feasible, but by no means easy to achieve' (Dale 1989).

Reductions in CO_2 emissions and by inference in fossil fuel consumption of this magnitude can be achieved by actions on the demand side to reduce energy consumption, and actions on the supply side involving switching from coal and oil to natural gas (which contains proportionately less carbon, see Table D3.3), or from fossil fuels to nuclear and renewables. There is clearly some choice available to policy makers as to the balance of demand side and supply side action, and the extent of the commitment to renewable energy versus nuclear power. The extent of the choice is however less than many people think, owing to the size of the reductions that are needed.

There is general agreement among energy analysts and policy makers that energy conservation will be a major part of any global warming control strategy. The main reasons for this are very short pay back times, usually less than 5 years, and low environmental impact. *All* energy supply options, nuclear power, wind power, tidal power, solar power, biomass, are environmentally contentious. Energy conservation results in reduced environmental impact regardless of the supply strategy that is chosen.

One of the most important consequences of the short financial payback times of many energy conservation investments is that a very large amount of carbon can be saved at negative financial cost, in other words the total cost of energy services, including the cost of energy conservation, can be reduced if such measures are taken. Expansion of renewable or nuclear energy on the other hand tends to be very much more expensive, and would lead to higher energy costs overall. Most analyses of the technical implications of large reductions in CO_2 output show half or more of total reductions coming from energy conservation (see eg. Dale, 1989). A rational approach to reducing CO_2 output would therefore appear to consist of:

- making those energy conservation investments that are economically justified;

Table D3.3: Relationship Between Primary Fuel and Carbon Dioxide Emission in the UK (after Baldwin et al 1990)

FUEL	CARBON DIOXIDE EMISSION kg / kwh delivered
Electricity	0.832
Gas	0.198
Coal	0.331
Petroleum	0.302

- making investments in energy supply on the assumption that energy conservation will be successful and that energy consumption will fall by a large fraction.

In other words, rational global warming strategies will be *conservation led*. Most of what follows will therefore concentrate on energy conservation in the buildings sector.

BUILDINGS AND ENERGY CONSERVATION

Figure D3.3 shows the estimated CO_2 emission by end-use (Friends of the Earth 1987) and clearly demonstrates that buildings are major consumers of energy and contribute greatly to the greenhouse effect. It has been more recently estimated that the emission of carbon dioxide as a result of energy consumed by water and space heating, cooking, lighting and other appliances is of the order of 80 million tonnes per annum (Millbank, 1989). This does not include the amount emitted as a result of energy consumption for manufacture and transport of construction materials and in the construction process.

Energy use in buildings may be divided into two main categories:

direct   – energy consumed in operating the building;
indirect – energy consumed in materials manufacture and
              construction.

The targets identified above have assumed savings in direct consumption only. The possible role of conservation in indirect consumption is explored later.

The location of the building is also an important factor. For example

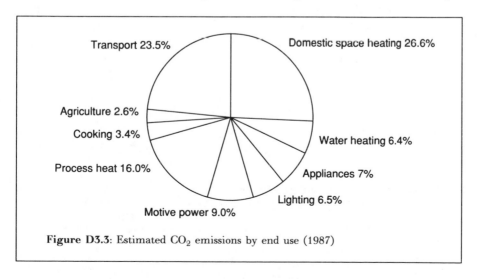

Transport 23.5%

Domestic space heating 26.6%

Agriculture 2.6%

Cooking 3.4%

Water heating 6.4%

Process heat 16.0%

Appliances 7%

Lighting 6.5%

Motive power 9.0%

Figure D3.3: Estimated CO_2 emissions by end use (1987)

the distance from home to work or from home to the out of town shopping centre will influence transport fuel consumption, particularly if these journeys are made by private car. In fact transport has been described as the 'neglected sector' of CO_2 emission. Total CO_2 output from road transport in the UK in 1987 was around 27 million tonnes, and is the fastest growing sector in the UK (EERU 1989). Thus transport and planning policies have a part to play and, although it is extremely difficult to quantify the cost in CO_2 emissions of decisions on the location of individual buildings at present, it is important to consider this issue at the inception and environmental impact analysis stages of any project.

In developing a conservation strategy it is important to note that the buildings sector differs from other end use sectors in two important ways:

- except in pathological cases, buildings are very long lived artifacts;
- it is usually cheaper to construct a new building to a high standard of energy efficiency than to retrofit the same building to the same standard at a later stage.

DIRECT ENERGY CONSERVATION – MEETING THE TARGET

In the case of new buildings, with an expected life extending up to or beyond the middle of the next century, the targets in CO_2 reductions identified above suggest a target of 50% reduction in delivered energy consumption compared with the current building regulations (as amended in 1990). This figure should be seen as applying to space and water heating, space cooling, and lighting, which are strongly influenced by the form and fabric of the building, and its main energy systems. It does *not* apply to end use systems such as domestic appliances, whose efficiency is not determined by strategic building design decisions.*

A reduction of 50% assumes that the buildings sector will have to make at least as large a reduction in carbon dioxide output by 2050 as the rest of the economy - as much as 75% or more compared to current levels. Assuming that the widespread use of technologies such as combined heat and power, and the introduction of renewables will produce significant reductions in the carbon intensity of delivered energy by 2050. Taken together, these improvements *approach* the required overall reduction in CO_2 output.

---

* The technical scope for greater appliance efficiency is however enormous (see eg Norgård 1989), and it would be inconsistent to say the least to ignore this area. In the authors' view the most effective measure which can be taken here is for government to set minimum appliance efficiency standards. There are however building design issues here too. More efficient domestic refrigerators are larger than the inefficient refrigerators they replace and may require redesign of kitchens or kitchen furniture.

Housing

For a wide range of dwellings, 50% reductions in gas consumption for the combined total of space and water heating, with respect to dwellings built to the current building regulations (as amended in 1990) can be achieved by a combination of 200 – 300 mm of insulation in walls, floors and roofs, the use of high performance glazing, thorough insulation of the domestic hot water system, and by replacing conventional boilers by a condensing boilers. Figure D3.4 shows the effects on low temperature heat requirements in three dwelling types of these and other measures. Lighting energy in the domestic sector can be reduced by some 75% by replacing incandescent lamps with equivalent compact fluorescent lamps. The practical problem here is that many light fittings currently on the market do not always accept the slightly larger replacement lamps. These proposals, taken together will produce the 50% cuts in delivered energy consumption proposed.

The levels of fabric insulation discussed here, together with minimum air tightness and ventilation standards, have been mandatory in Sweden since 1980 (Anon 1983), but have not hitherto been contemplated in the UK. It is worth noting that similar levels were adopted by Salford City Council from the late 1970s onwards for council housing (Anon 1987). For

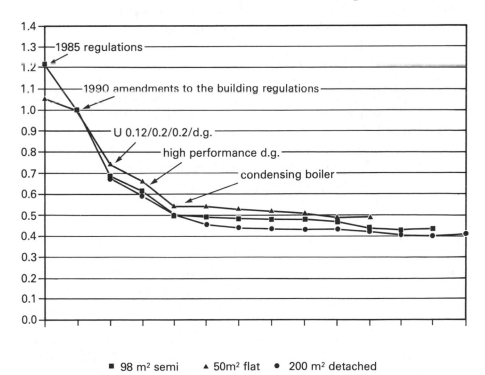

■ 98 m² semi   ▲ 50m² flat   ● 200 m² detached

Figure D3.4: Domestic space and water heat as a fraction of 1990 consumption other practical UK examples, see Ashley 1988, Evans 1990, Ruyssevelt 1987, and Olivier 1989. Note that these examples illustrate that the proposals do not rely on technologies which have not yet reached the UK market or which require further development, such as ventilation heat recovery, low flow or aspirated hot water taps and waste water heat recovery systems. Some or all of these are expected to be introduced in the second half of the 1990s, and to produce further savings.

The relationship between orientation and plan form, i.e. with living rooms facing south, bathrooms and kitchens to the north, to maximize solar gains is well understood. Whilst insulation benefits are of an order of magnitude greater than those of orientation (Everett, 1980) it will be desirable to place more emphasis on this factor when the layout of estates is considered.

Commercial Buildings

Deep plan office buildings clad in glazed curtain walling make air-conditioning a necessity. In fact many offices built in the 1970s and even some contemporary examples appear to pay scant regard to overall energy conservation measures, possessing poor thermal performance characteristics in both winter and summer. However, a number of commercial and technical factors involving the need to maximise the development potential of expensive city centre sites, where external traffic noise is a major problem, have been major influences upon modern office design. Recent studies (Bordass 1990) for the Energy Efficiency Office (EEO) call into question the standard recipe for the air-conditioned office 'box'. Annual space heating consumptions vary considerably (Figure D3.5) which indicates the potential for energy savings without recourse to 'unusual' design solutions simply by following good practice. The EEO's 'Best Practice Programme' aims to disseminate this experience; however additional measures will be necessary to achieve the targets identified above.

For the sector as a whole, space heating constitutes about one half of total primary energy consumption. The next component of energy consumption in order of importance is lighting. Large reductions in lighting energy can be made by increased use of daylight, together with use of improved control of artificial lighting systems (photoelectric or equivalent).

The complexities of office design make it difficult to give simple advice. The layout and orientation obviously affect the heating and cooling requirements as well as the need for artificial lighting and ventilation, so that the control strategies for the heating, ventilation and lighting are of vital importance to energy efficiency. However savings could be made by better fabric insulation, minimisation of the need for

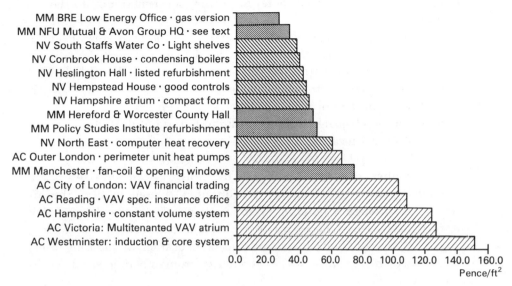

Figure D3.5: Typical annual energy costs of building services only (1987/88 prices), excluding computer rooms. (Bordass 1990)

'active' cooling and design for daylighting. Chillers in air-conditioning systems utilize CFCs and so efforts to reduce the need for cooling can have the double advantage of reduced CFC and energy consumption (see chapter D2). In most air-conditioned buildings in the UK, electricity use for the movement of air exceeds by a considerable margin the use in chillers. Large reductions in fan power are possible by a combination of larger ducts, better fan motors, and better motor control systems. Norgård et al 1983 suggest a factor of 25 may be technically possible in commercial and institutional buildings.

Studies indicate that, in temperate climatic zones, significant energy savings can be made in what have been described as 'mixed-mode' designs (Bordass 1990). Such buildings maximise the passive heating and cooling opportunities that are available so reducing the length of time during the heating and cooling seasons, when direct heating and cooling must be applied.

The main design factors related to a more passive energy and ventilation strategy and to reduce dependence on air conditioning may be summarized as follows:

- narrow plan forms or deep plans employing atria that permit daylighting and natural ventilation or a combination of natural ventilation assisted by simple mechanical ventilation;

- shading by louvres or balconies to prevent sun penetration to the interior in summer;
- appropriate percentage of external glazing to the total area of external wall and use of low emissivity double glazing;
- high thermal mass within an insulated fabric of low U value (0.3 Watts per square metre per °C or less);
- ventilation heat recovery;
- provision of adequate levels of daylight and use of daylight control for artificial lighting.

The importance of ventilation control must be emphasised, as a considerable percentage of energy consumption is used to heat the air which passes through a building. With mechanical systems the use of a heat reclaim system is necessary to realise the full potential of energy savings. Appropriate control systems and/or education of building users are necessary to minimise waste of energy from opening windows in multi mode buildings.

The air tightness of the outer fabric of the building also needs particular attention to detail, in order to reduce infiltration which can unbalance both passive and active ventilation arrangements. Windows must have good quality draught seals so that they are truly air tight when closed. Ventilation losses through external doors can be minimised by effective draught-stripping as well as the use of revolving doors or lobbies. Some cladding systems are far from air tight, particularly unplastered masonry walls, and designers should consider this problem both in the design and in workmanship.

Adoption of these design standards can show savings of up to 40% over the minimum standards of current practice and regulations (Ferraro 1990).

Plant and Equipment

Combined with the simple matter of improved insulation to pipework and cylinders, energy consumption can be reduced by the most efficient heat sources. Condensing gas boilers have annual average efficiencies of some 10% percentage points higher than the best non-condensing boilers, and pay back times of the order of 5 years in new buildings, or where an existing boiler is to be replaced for other reasons. The good part load efficiency of condensing boilers (in some cases the part load efficiency may be higher than the full load efficiency) reduces or eliminates the energy penalty from boiler oversizing. The question of rating of heat emitters (radiators or equivalent) within the building assumes more importance when condensing boilers are used. Generously sized heat emitters, with low flow and return temperatures, allow boilers to operate in fully condensing mode for more or all of the time, with a small increase in annual efficiency. Similar improvements may be achieved by use of an external temperature compensated primary boiler circuit.

There have been major improvements in energy-efficient lighting bulbs and the new compact fluorescent lamps use only about one-fifth of the energy of the usual incandescent lamps on sale and provide the same amount of light. They also last considerably longer, giving advantages in the area of maintenance.

There are of course further approaches, such as recycling waste heat generated in one part of the building to another part for heating. For example the excess heat produced in factory processes could be used for heating offices. Combined heat and power (CHP) takes this approach to a logical conclusion. UK energy policies since the second world war have resulted in very large power stations remote from centres of population. In the short term, therefore, it would be difficult to utilize the waste heat from these power stations to heat buildings directly. However, small-scale CHP (sometimes referred to as micro-CHP), is feasible for individual housing schemes or blocks of flats, either newly built or retrofitted. Carbon dioxide savings approaching 50% over conventional gas central heating are possible with this technology (EERU 1989, Evans 1990).

INDIRECT ENERGY CONSUMPTION – SELECTION OF MATERIALS

In order to place in perspective the possible savings from selecting materials of lower direct or embodied energy, the primary issue to be identified is the relative significance of energy consumed in the manufacture of buildings compared with that used directly in heating and lighting, etc. There has been very little recent research into this problem. The main sources of data are Chapman 1975 in the UK and Stein et al 1981 in the USA. Both are based on data collected in the late 1960s, although the latter was updated in the 1970s.

Chapman calculated that the total energy required to manufacture the building materials and to construct a three-bedroom semi-detached house, 100 square metres in floor area, is equivalent to the energy consumed over 3 years for heating and lighting the same property. The building used in the calculation was of masonry construction. So, if the nominal life expectancy of the building is 60 years, then the 'construction' energy needs are only one-twentieth of the total energy requirements to heat and light the building throughout its life. Figure D3.6 clearly indicates that conservation resulting from higher levels of insulation has greater influence on the total energy consumption, compared with that used in making the materials. On the basis of these calculations, even though they are some years old, it could be argued that in terms of energy conservation the 'construction' energy costs are insignificant and the effort should be concentrated on reducing direct energy consumption.

However, Figure D3.6 also shows that as the energy efficiency is improved the indirect energy consumption assumes a bigger proportion of the total. Further, with our rapidly changing society and needs, it could be that the lifespan of buildings (particularly industrial and commercial) could decrease, which will also increase the significance of the indirect component. These points are demonstrated in Figure D3.7. For simplicity it is assumed in each case that the 'construction' energy costs are constant, although it is appreciated that this is not strictly true as different construction and insulation solutions will also affect the total indirect energy used. The first line, based on Chapman's figures, shows that after 3 years the direct energy consumption in a typical house equates to the 'construction' energy. The second line, 1990, indicates that with improved insulation this point occurs later in the life of the building. Finally, the last line shows a hypothetical superinsulated low energy house. Here the indirect energy may become a much more significant fraction of the total energy consumption, especially if the building's lifespan is short. So, as the industry moves to well insulated energy efficient design standards, it becomes increasingly worthwhile for designers to consider the energy consumed in the manufacture of buildings.

Lack of recent data together with the complexities of the analysis make realistic decision-making in routine design impossible at present. For example a complete analysis should consider the energy used in winning raw materials, processing, all transport operations, that used on site, together with the life expectancy of components and the energy costs in maintenance and repair. However, although Chapman and Stein's data is out of date, the relative energy costs between components may still be valid. Table D3.4 compares the fuel cost of a number of common building materials (after Chapman).

The points above indicate that designers must resist the temptation to make the simple assumption that energy expensive materials must be avoided in pursuit of energy saving. A complete analysis must consider the full cost-in-use implications of various constructional alternatives (Stein et al 1981, Connaughton 1990). Given this caveat, the evidence that is available appears to show that timber can offer energy savings over other energy intensive materials, such as brickwork and aluminium. However this raises the issues of deforestation and of sustainability of timber resources. The promotion of timber as a 'cheap energy' construction option can only be justified where timber is obtained from sustainably managed sources. It is interesting to speculate whether the world could pursue the political and agricultural changes necessary to produce most of its building materials on this basis.

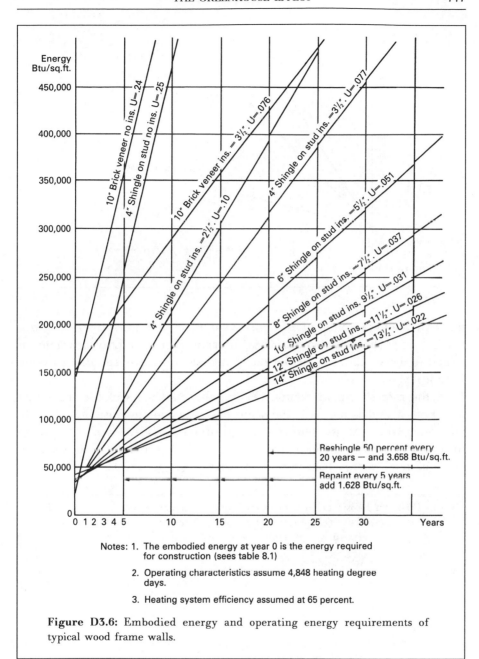

Figure D3.6: Embodied energy and operating energy requirements of typical wood frame walls.

An obvious point is that material from a local source will reduce transport costs, especially if it is necessary to import an alternative from another country.

The question of the relative, indirect energy costs of various insulation material alternatives has also been raised recently. For example, expanded polystyrene consumes almost ten times more energy in manufacture than

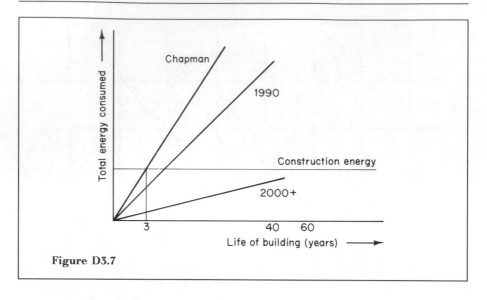

Figure D3.7

the equivalent amount of mineral wool (Connaughton 1990). Figures D3.8(a) and (b) demonstrate two different aspects of the problem in selecting between two insulation materials that are equally suitable technically.

In the case shown in Figure. D3.8(a) the *thicknesses* of the insulation materials A and B are both the same but A is a better insulator than B. However, the energy required to produce and transport the same thickness of each material is different, A requiring more. The break even point of total energy consumed is X years after which A, in spite of its

Table D3.4: Fuel costs of building commodities (Adapted from Table 10 in *Fuels paradise – energy options for Britain,* Peter Chapman, 1975. Reproduced by permission of Penguin Books Ltd.)

Item	Fuel cost (kWht)*
House (three-bedroom semi-detached)	100,000
Brick (common)	1.6 each
Wooden door	1.7 each
Glass for windows (per sq. metre)	86
Plastic (1 ton)	45,000
Cement (1 ton)	2,200
Copper (1 ton)	12,800
Aluminium (1 ton)	27,000
Finished steel (1 ton)	13,200
Plaster (1 ton)	900

* Unit = kilowatt hours thermal (kWht)

higher energy needs in manufacturing and transport, becomes more energy efficient. If the building is not expected to last more than X years, then B would be the better solution.

In the second case shown in Figure D3.8(b), it is assumed that the *standard* of insulation needs to be the same. It can be seen that irrespective of the life expectancy of the building, because insulation

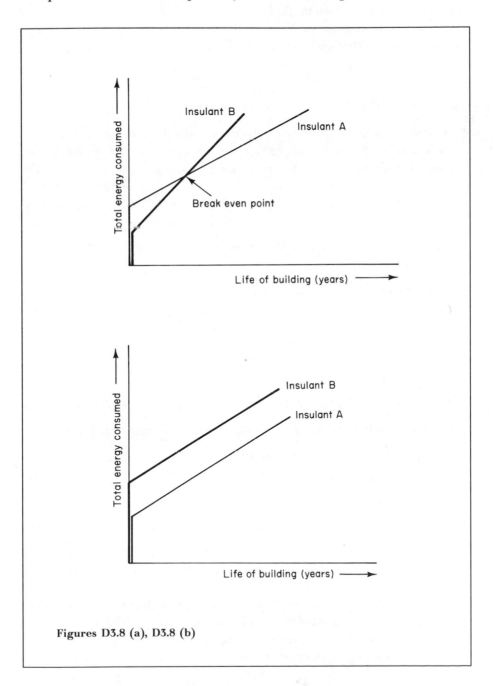

Figures D3.8 (a), D3.8 (b)

material B now needs to be of greater thickness, it requires more energy to produce and transport, making it overall a higher energy option. This indicates the potential importance of the relative thermal transmittance and building life in a complete analysis.

This review underlines the difficulties, with the present level of knowledge, of making selection between materials and construction alternatives. A clear system that could be applied in design in order to carry out full energy audits, of both direct and indirect energy consumption, will become increasingly important in the future.

CONCLUSIONS

✻ If global warming is to be effectively arrested, reductions in CO_2 emissions of the order of 75% must be made in the industrialised countries. Conservation of direct energy in buildings will make the most significant contribution in the construction sector. Savings of around 50% over current design standards (1990 Building Regulations) will be necessary, are feasible, and should be made in the short term.

✻ The conservation measures that need to be taken into account can be summarised as:

- superinsulation of the building fabric;

- layout and orientation of the building to maximise passive heating, ie solar and other incidental gains, as well as 'passive' cooling opportunities, to minimise the need for 'active' cooling;

- ventilation control and heat recovery;

- the selection of plant and equipment of high energy efficiency;

- efficient use of daylight in the commercial and institutional sector.

✻ The detailed application of these principles will vary between building types. Selection of building materials and construction methods of lower energy intensity can make a contribution. However, this contribution is more than an order of magnitude less significant than the contribution from conservation of direct energy consumed in buildings.

✻ The building design professions will be key players in the conservation strategy. However, if these savings are to be achieved sufficiently quickly, a major change in approach must be brought about in all sections of the industry. Developers should insist that higher insulation and equipment efficiency standards are met now. Building users and estate surveyors must realise that it is possible to create habitable office accommodation that is not fully air-conditioned. Designers should advise clients of the implications of the greenhouse effect on future energy use in buildings and encourage the adoption of effective energy conservation measures.

* In the industrial free market economies, it is difficult to see a sufficiently swift change being brought about without recourse to regulation for new build and for financial incentives for retro-fit and upgrading of the existing building stock. Measures such as a carbon tax on energy derived from fossil fuels would also ease the transition by giving a stronger financial incentive to building owners and occupiers to reduce consumption. Large reductions in energy consumption in all sectors of the industry will be significantly easier to bring about if a compulsory scheme for energy labelling is introduced. Similarly, regulations setting upper limits on annual energy consumption per square metre of floor area in the commercial and industrial sectors would also be valuable. An alternative approach, that of CO_2 labelling of buildings, will form part of the Building Research Establishments Environmental Assessment Method (BREEAM) (Baldwin et al 1990). Whilst such a voluntary code is to be applauded, it is difficult to see a non-compulsory scheme having sufficient impact.

* An effective strategy will involve both market mechanisms and direct government intervention. This strategy will be a vital ingredient in establishing the framework for the provision of the building stock in the post-fossil-fuel age.

REFERENCES

Anon (1983), *SBN 1980 Svensk Byggnorm (2nd Edition)*, Statens Planverks Författningssamling, 1983.

Anon (1987), *The Salford Low Energy House*, Energy Efficiency Office, Energy Efficiency Demonstration Scheme, Expanded Project Profile 59, HM Stationery Office, February 1987.

Anon (1988), *The Changing Atmosphere – Implications for Global Security*, Conference held in Toronto under the auspices of the Canadian Government, 27–30 June 1988. The Conference Statement is reproduced in 'Energy Policy Implications of the Greenhouse Effect – Volume 1', 6th Report of the House of Commons Energy Committee, HM Stationery Office, 1989.

Ashley, S. (1988), *What the Doctor Ordered*, Building Services, April 1988.

Baldwin, R. et al. (1990), *The Building Research Establishment Environmental Assessment Method (BREEAM) Version 1/90 – New Office Design*, Building Research Establishment, Watford 1990.

Bolin, B and others, editors (1986), *The Greenhouse Effect, Climatic change and Eco systems*, Scope 29. Wiley, Chichester, 1986.

Chapman, P.F., and Mortimer, N.D. (1975), *Research Report ERG006*, Open University, Milton Keynes.

Chapman, P.F. (1975), *Fuel's Paradise, Energy Options for Britain*, Harmondsworth, Penguin.

Connaughton, J. (1990), *Real Low Energy Buildings: a Life Cycle Energy Costings Approach to Energy Efficient Design.* Paper presented to the RIBA/EEO Conference, The Architect and Global Responsibility, RIBA, January 1990.

Cousins et al (1989), *The Greenhouse Effect and Energy Policy*, evidence prepared for the House of Commons Energy Select Committee Inquiry into the Greenhouse Effect, by Energy and Environment Research Unit, The Open University, Milton Keynes, 1989.

Dale, B.W. (1989), *Abatement of Greenhouse Gases in the UK*, Paper presented at the IEA/OECD Expert Seminar on Energy Technologies for Reducing Emissions of Greenhouse Gases, Paris, April 1989. Reproduced in Energy Policy Implications of the Greenhouse Effect. Volume III. 6th Report of the House of Commons Energy Committee, HMSO, 1989.

Evans, B. (1990), *Build it Green: Superinsulation*, Architects Journal, 7 March 1990.

Everett, R. (1980), *Passive solar in Milton Keynes*, ERG. Report 031. Open University.

Friends of the Earth, *Proof of evidence for Hinkley Point Public Enquiry*, June 1989.

Gribben, J. (1990), *Hothouse Earth: The Greenhouse Effect and Gaia*, Bantam Press.

Kaas, J.H.W., & Kelly, P. M. (1988), *The Heat Trap*, University of East Anglia, September 1988.

Keeling C.D. et al (1990), *A Three Dimensional Model of Atmospheric CO_2 Transport Based on Observed Winds: Observational Data and Preliminary Analysis*, Appendix A in Aspects of Climate Variability in the Pacific and Western Americas, Geophysical Monograph, American Geophysical Union, 55, November 1989.

Kellogg, W.W. (1978), *Is mankind warming the earth?*, Bulletin of the Atomic Scientists, February 1978, pp. 10–19.

Krause, F. et al. (1989), *Energy Policy in the Greenhouse*, Final report of the International Project for Sustainable Energy Paths (IPSEP), El Cerrito, California, USA, 1989.

Lovins, A.B. (1988), *A Preliminary Estimate of the Full Practical potential for Retrofit Savings of US Electricity*, Rocky Mountain Institute.

Millbank, N. (1989), *Building design and use – response to climate change*, Archit. J., 2, August 1989.

Myers, N. (1989), *Deforestation Rates in Tropical Forests and their Climatic Implications*, Friends of the Earth, 1989.

Olivier, D. (1986), *Experiences of superinsulation in Scandinavia and North America*, Proc. ISES Conf. on Superinsulation, Polytechnic of Central London, March 1986.

Olivier, D. (1989), *Beyond the Building Regulations*, Building Services, May 1989.

Institute for Energy Analysis, Oak Ridge Associated Universities, as presented in World Resources 1986, Basic Booke, New York.

Norgård et al (1983), *Lansigtede Tekniske Muligheder for El-Besparelse*, DEMO Projektet, Technical University of Denmark, Lyngby, Denmark.

Stein, R.G., et al (1981), *Handbook of Energy Use for Construction*, U.S. Dept. of Energy. Washington DC., 1981.

Section E

Overall Conclusions and Practical Implications

OVERALL CONCLUSIONS AND PRACTICAL IMPLICATIONS

Steve Curwell, Chris March and Roger Venables

Leeds Polytechnic, University of Salford and
Venables Consultancy Services Ltd

INTRODUCTION

Most of the chapters in this guide are concerned with health risks to individual users of buildings, construction workers and tradespeople. Many of the health risks to these groups are the subject of detailed regulation and codes of practice which, if followed, will minimise the majority of risks to health in buildings. However, a number of chapters, such as those on legionella, asbestos, contaminated land and pesticides in amenity areas, also relate to the quality of the local environment around any development project, and highlight the extended responsibilities of development teams beyond immediate users, construction workers and tradespeople to the local community.

The chapters on CFCs and global warming deal with wider environmental issues which, from the perspective of individual projects, do not appear to impose an immediate threat to the health of individuals. Nevertheless they are of vital concern to the world as a whole. It is often difficult for developers and design teams to see that they can make any significant contribution to solving the wider environmental problems because concerted international action is necessary to make a real impact. The complementary role of voluntary codes of practice and of government intervention through regulation or tax incentives will form an important topic of wider international and national political debate in the immediate future. However the need for consideration of, and action upon global environmental issues in every project must be underlined.

The chapters on risk assessment and environmental impact analysis provide different methods by which the range of risks, to individuals and to the local, national and global environment may be reconciled with all the other issues that must be considered in design and development, especially cost.

This last section is aimed at assisting with this complex analysis in anticipation that it will become a necessary part of every development project. In E1, the conclusions and essential points from each preceding chapter are drawn together within the framework of the stages in the development cycle identified in the Introduction to the Guide. This is supported by E2 – a checklist for benign building design. Together they provide an executive summary of the majority of points at issue.

In E3, some overall conclusions are drawn out, the role of the interested parties considered, and a number of issues and questions raised for the continuing debate on buildings, health and sustainable development.

E1: SUMMARY OF CONCLUSIONS RELATED TO STAGES IN THE DEVELOPMENT CYCLE

Overall project design

- Consideration of building orientation in relation to energy use can be extended to maximise the chances that factors leading to sick building syndrome will not develop.
- An overall strategy for the selection of materials based on the guidance in this book could significantly reduce risks of exposure to hazards from materials to a minimum.
- Development of an appropriate overall ventilation strategy and compatible overall energy strategy is feasible using the guidance given in this book, although the optimisation of both strategies at the same time cannot be achieved.
- Provision of atria and other amenity areas in buildings is shown to be beneficial to the well-being of occupants, but great care is needed in the use of pesticides and horticultural chemicals if occupants are not to be exposed to an unacceptable risk of exposure to such chemicals.
- As indicated above, guidance is available on the successful and cost-effective treatment of contaminated land and for design to take account of any remaining contamination.
- Environmental assessment is a required tool for many projects, but also very useful even if not required by the authorities. However, in the past, environmental assessment has tended to focus upon the external physical environmental effects of projects, with little attention being devoted to the building materials and internal

environmental issues primarily related to health. Consequently, many of the methods and predictive techniques developed for environmental assessment are not specifically directed to the needs of the building industry. The introduction of environmental awareness into the construction industry will stimulate the need for greater dissemination of information regarding the environmental performance of building materials. This could result in a paperchase unless attempts are made to focus upon only the significant environmental issues. The lack of knowledge is a fundamental constraint to many aspects of the environmental assessment process, which introduces uncertainty into the decision-making process. In this regard there is a need for research into the effects of low level exposure to pollutants within buildings.

Planning and land use

- Guidance is available on the identification of contaminated land and on the approach to be adopted in its development.
- Techniques are available for the identification and cost-effective treatment of contaminants, but a key concern remains the avoidance of contaminating groundwater when on-site treatment and/or encapsulation is used.
- Consideration must be given to the health and safety of those working on a contaminated land site during investigation, treatment and construction.
- Consideration must be made at the planning stage of energy use in the construction and use of buildings. Savings of about 50% over current design standards are feasible, involving such techniques as superinsulation of the building, orientation to maximise passive heating and use of natural light, maximising opportunities for passive cooling, ventilation control and heat recovery, and the selection of high-efficiency plant.
- Techniques and guidance are available for dealing with naturally-occurring hazards such as radon and pests.

Demolition

- Guidance is available on the identification of contaminants and their safe treatment or disposal.
- Controlled and comparatively safe disposal of asbestos and other fibrous materials is feasible using specialist contractors.
- Measures are available to control pests which may inhabit a building to be demolished to prevent them remaining on site to affect the new development.

Detailed building design

- The guidance in this book will help in the development of a detailed strategy for selection of materials for a project or organisation, and assist in reducing risks to health from building materials to a minimum.
- The guidance in the book will also help in the development of detailed ventilation strategies, and the identification of action plans to ensure risks are kept to a minimum.
- Guidance is provided on a number of aspects of energy strategy for buildings, and on interaction between energy and ventilation strategies, where some of the most important compromises have to be made in building design.
- Guidance is given on specific actions that can be taken to reduce the likelihood of sick building syndrome occurring.
- Guidance is provided and references given for the detailed design actions needed to take account of natural hazards such as radon and pests.

Construction phase

- Appropriate and cost-effective protective measures for handling hazardous materials are available.
- Control of noise, dusts, fumes, solvents and gases, and of site drainage to avoid nuisance, or possible contamination of groundwater, remain key problems on and around constructions sites.
- If specifications are to take account of the guidance given in this book, it is of crucial importance that there is satisfactory control of materials purchasing to ensure unspecified substitute materials are not used.
- Adherence to the Control of Substances Hazardous to Health Regulations will help to reduce health hazards to construction workers, and to occupiers of offices and public buildings.
- Because of the ever-increasing complexity of the composition of some construction materials, secure storage of materials *before* use is as important as safe procedures *during* their use.
- Questions need to be asked as to why there is waste on site. Could this be reduced by more sensible buying procedures or careful materials control on site? Amonst many other changes, the introduction of Quality Assurance to more construction sites will lead to better control of materials and less waste.
- Methods of disposal materials need to be considered, for example in terms of hazardous waste, burning of timber (which releases

CO_2) or disposal of any material and its effect on the local environment.

Building occupancy and maintenance

- Lingering odours and/or contaminants from the construction phase can cause nuisance and even health risks to occupants, and may require a building to be 'baked out' before first occupancy.
- The odour absorption characteristics of interior fixtures, fittings and furniture, and their influence on ventilation system operation must be considered in developing the interior design and operational procedures.
- Guidance is provided in this book on measures that can be taken to reduce the risk of sick building syndrome occurring, and to ameliorate it if it does occur.
- Guidance is provided in this book and elsewhere on how to avoid outbreaks of Legionnaires' Disease through good management and maintenance of air-conditioning and other water-bearing systems.
- Allergic responses to building material components cannot be eradicated but careful selection of materials and effective ventilation can reduce their occurrence.
- The importance of timely and effective maintenance of the building fabric and systems is demonstrated and cannot be over-emphasised.
- Selection of materials for maintenance work is even more important than for new construction in view of their proximity to occupants who may be unaware of their inherent dangers.
- Hazards to health from pests and the consequent importance of adequate pest control are underrated. Designers and specifiers, surveyors, facilities managers and building services engineers need to have a greater appreciation of the need to eliminate pests.

Refurbishment

- Identification of contaminants and their safe treatment or disposal, for which guidance and safe procedures are available, is doubly important in refurbishment if undertaken while some residents remain in the building during the work.
- Controlled disposal of asbestos and other fibrous materials are at least as important as in demolition, but consideration must be given to balancing risks from continued exposure to undisturbed asbestos and the increased risks to occupiers and a contractor's workforce associated with removal.
- Control of noise, dusts, fumes, solvents and gases remain as much

key problems on and around refurbishment contracts as sites of
new construction.
- As with new construction, issues of waste control and disposal
  need to be carefully and adequately addressed.

Wider environmental issues

- Construction professionals, clients, and owners must increasingly
  recognise that their selection and efficient use of materials can
  make a significant contribution to the solution of the world's
  environmental concerns. These issues are not 'someone else's
  problems'.
- Reduction of use of CFC-containing materials can be achieved
  without loss of building performance in the great majority of
  building applications.
- Specifiers should satisfy themselves that timber for their projects
  is procured from sustainable supplies.
- Energy conservation and energy use strategies for building
  design, construction and operation that take account of current
  concerns about global warming need to be developed.
- The balances to be struck between competing demands, for
  example the interaction between energy and ventilation
  strategies, remain the most difficult issue to resolve satisfactorily.
- Little is known about exposure to extremely low levels of some
  contaminants since it is very difficult to establish the *absence* of
  any effects.

E2: A CHECKLIST FOR BENIGN BUILDING DESIGN

Overall Project Design

- Use building forms, layouts and orientation that maximise
  passive solar gains and ventilation opportunities and minimise
  the need for cooling and artificial lighting.
- Provide superinsulated fabric (U Value: 0.2 $W/m^2/°C$ or less)
  together with massive construction of high thermal capacity and
  double or triple glazed windows.
- Consider the use of micro-combined heat and power.
- Provide for a minimum ventilation rate appropriate to the
  provision of adequate indoor air quality (0.7 air changes per hour
  for dwellings, 8 litres per second per person elsewhere)
- Provide separate smoking rooms with their own non-recirculating

ventilation systems.

- Consider the use of heat-reclaim equipment in mechanically ventilated buildings.
- Use air-conditioning only for spaces that demand this provision such as in conference rooms, auditoria and computer suites.
- Provide adequate space for access and maintenance of services equipment.
- Where appropriate consider the provision of adequate storage space for waste paper in the building to facilitate recycling.

Planning and Land Use

- Consider re-using existing urban sites in preference to green-field locations.
- Consider the transport implications when deciding the location of new developments.
- Consider layout, orientation and the interrelationship of buildings and tree planting to slow wind speeds and maximise group effects and micro-climate modification
- In larger urban development schemes consider the provision of combined heat and power and district heating.
- Minimise the effects of the location of the building upon the locale in terms of pollution and effect on the local ecology.
- Consider the problems of contaminated land at site selection stage as unexpected surprises can be expensive to correct.
- Ensure that adequate remedial treatment is undertaken and that appropriate precautions are employed to protect workers when redeveloping contaminated sites.
- Be aware of the radon problem when developing in the West of England, the Peak District and in the Highlands of Scotland.
- Attempt to plant additional trees in the development or at least replace any that are lost.

Detailed Design

- Avoid insulation materials containing CFCs.
- If air-conditioning is to be provided, use CFC22 and consider designing the system so that it may be easily converted to CFC134a when this becomes available.
- Consider the provision of leak detection equipment and drain down tanks for large air-conditioning installations.
- If possible avoid the use of wet cooling towers.
- Select materials of lowest toxicity consistent with technical performance, buildability and cost.

- Pay attention to detailing to ensure airtight construction and elimination of cold bridges.
- Use timber only from sustainable managed sources.
- Consider carefully whether it is necessary to treat timber with preservatives and if so use systems employing pemethrin or boron as the active ingredients.
- Consider the energy used in the manufacture of materials and components.
- Select services equipment of maximum energy efficiency and consider the use of occupancy sensors to control artificial lighting.
- Provide shading to south facing windows to minimise summer sun penetration.
- Minimise access and harbourages for pests.
- Provide adequate access traps for cleaning and maintenance of concealed services and duct spaces.
- Whenever possible avoid halon fire control systems.
- Where appropriate adopt construction techniques that prevent radon contamination from the ground.
- Provide information to the construction team on hazardous contents and materials to be used in the building.

Commissioning, Maintenance and Use

- Provide a user manual to include:
  - complete list of materials employed together with hazard data available;
  - operating instructions and control systems;
  - energy targets and anticipated consumption;
  - recommended maintenance periods and procedures.
- Properly commission the entire services system and monitor to test compliance with ventilation and energy targets and adjust as necessary.
- Consider bake or flush out before occupation to remove excess organic solvents and similar gas and chemical vapours.
- Ensure that adequate maintenance is undertaken and that accurate records are kept in the user manual, particularly of the work required to control legionella in water systems and of the use of poisons to control pests.
- Ensure that the health of occupants is not put at risk when maintenance work is undertaken.

Refurbishment and Demolition

- Identify hazardous material and remove before the main work commences. If asbestos is present, inform the HSE and the local authority before removal takes place.

- Ensure that appropriate precautions are taken to protect workers and the general public from dust and other hazardous contents.
- Ensure hazardous waste is disposed of properly.
- Consider recycling or re-using materials and components. CFCs from existing air-conditioning and refrigeration equipment should be recycled.
- Consider the pros and cons of remedial timber treatment.
- Ensure that timber treatment is carried out with proper regard to the safety of operatives and decant occupants during treatment and for at least 24 hours after completion.

E3: OVERALL CONCLUSIONS AND THE CONTINUING DEBATE ON BUILDINGS AND HEALTH

Overall Conclusions

The preceding chapters show that the issues affecting the health of building users, construction workers and the wider public are complex and interact one with another. A balance has to be struck between a succession of conflicting pressures, for example:

- between risks to health and the costs and practicality of reducing the risks to a minimum;
- between the use of chemicals to control disease, pests or to protect timber and the exposure of humans to those chemicals;
- between the risks to occupants from leaving asbestos in place compared with the risks of increased short term exposure after removal and the risks to workers who remove it.

Thus many difficult choices face specifiers, designers, builders and contractors, owners, maintenance teams and demolition contractors, and we can no longer avoid addressing the issues raised. The book helps in providing an introduction to, and information on, many aspects of buildings and health and, wherever adequate data is available, detailed practical guidance is also given.

The size of the guide illustrates the burgeoning information on the topic and provides a positive indication of the development of medical and scientific enquiry in response to increased public concern. There is still much work to be done. Many of the authors refer to the lack or incompleteness of information. They have in many cases to resort to less than satisfactory process of risk estimation using hazard data pertaining to the basic chemical compounds from which a material is composed. In other cases even this approach is not possible as no data exists. This raises the issue of availability and the responsibilities for provision of information, which is returned to later.

Regrettably, therefore, the answers to some of the balanced decisions required from construction professionals and their clients are either unavailable or less than complete. For example, man made mineral fibre is heralded by some as *the* insulation and fire resisting board material, while others feel passionately that this material should not be used because of the slight suspicion of a carcinogenic hazard. We do not have clear, unequivocal answers to many similar arguments.

Reference was made in the Introduction to the Guide to the World Health Organisation definition of health as '... a state of complete physical, mental and social well being, not merely the absence of disease or infirmity'. To achieve this objective would, for example, mean consideration of every possible allergic reaction to the contents of building materials and furnishings. Study of the contents of the book will bring the realization that this ideal is impossible to achieve within sensible cost parameters, for all building users, all of the time. We need to achieve a consensus on what proportion of the population it is reasonable to accept some level of discomfort. Therefore the building industry, those working in and for it, together with owners and users of its products must gain a greater appreciation of the concepts of hazard, risk, and acceptable level of risk, all related to the consequences of taking or being exposed to a specific risk.

As mentioned earlier, concerns over the health of the users of buildings interact with other environmental issues such as transport provisions, waste disposal, local pollution and recycling of land and materials. Recognition of these concerns together with changes in planning regulations has brought about the need for the application of environmental impact assessment and management in the larger building and civil engineering projects. Here a structured approach is considered essential in order to avoid resources being expended on issues of marginal significance. Such techniques seem equally applicable to smaller projects.

The Agenda for Future Action

A number of current environmental concerns such as destruction of the tropical rainforest, ozone depletion and proper disposal of hazardous waste from industrial processes call into question the interaction between modern society and the natural processes of the planet. There is much speculation about the changes required in modern industrial societies to create a sustainable economic future where man lives in better balance or harmony with nature. However, the chapters relating to CFCs and global warming identify the primary influences for change on design and construction practice, together with the first steps that the construction sector can take in this direction, particularly in respect of energy savings and associated CO_2 reduction from buildings.

In relation to the form, size and location of urban areas, there are increasingly calls for decentralization and the greater deployment of information technology and electronic communication to reduce the need for transport. Equally there are arguments for greater centralization to reduce journey length, which if coupled with an apartment block approach to housing has great potential for energy efficiency.

The use of fossil fuels seem certain to be severely reduced, and buildings will be far more energy-efficient in future so that there is a possibility of maintaining the present high standard of living using sustainable energy sources. A energy conservation strategy offers the option of minimising future dependence on nuclear power.

Energy use in the manufacture of building materials, components and in the construction of buildings will become a much more significant factor in the selection of material. As timber is a low energy-intensive material, the possibility of developing agricultural practice towards growing more trees in a sustainable manner to make greater use of this material in buildings is worth examining.

Research and development of new materials will need to address the full environmental implications of those new materials in terms of manufacture, installation, use and ultimately of disposal - what has come to be known as a 'cradle-to-grave' philosophy. Should this be left to the manufacturers, or are stricter legislative controls required? Stringent testing of materials in the manner of the drugs industry would inevitably increase the costs of developing new construction materials, but perhaps this is the price to be paid for greater safety of individuals and the environment. Easier access to information on the composition of materials and on the possible health effects is required. The proposals embodied in the EEC Construction Products Directive will assist in this respect, when brought into effect by member states. In general terms, the requirements of the UK Health and Safety at Work etc Act ensure that the majority of hazardous construction materials is adequately labelled in the UK, but there is a need to supply this data, routinely, to designers with the normal product information supplied by manufacturers. This information is vital in establishing the risk to construction workers for the completion of COSHH assessments, but requires careful interpretation and extrapolation to establish the risk to the occupant.

Concern has been expressed about what is known as 'synergistic' or 'cocktail' effects in relation to the possible reaction between various contaminants of indoor air to produce a much more significant hazard than that which is merely additive. The specialist authors have reported two cases, both involved with smoking, where smokers were shown to be at much more serious risk from exposure to radon and asbestos. The problem of synergistic effects requires further investigation to identify more clearly the potential hazards and risks involved.

The 'cradle-to-grave' approach requires careful consideration of disposal of material at the end of its useful life; many materials can be recycled. In the case of materials such as bricks this is of obvious environmental benefit as they can be reused without reprocessing, and the 'embodied' energy used in manufacture is preserved. In the case of CFCs, the main chemical companies have established recycling schemes, but the incentive to recycle is dependent upon the supply and demand situation together with the prevailing economic climate. The EEC CITIES Programme has established urban waste management as a major parameter of future sustainable development. Essential to successful schemes (for example in cities like Ghent) is the creation of appropriate incentive schemes and public education programmes.

Roles and Responsibilities for Action

How are we to bring about a more sustainable future? Who has primary responsibility to push future building developments down a 'greener' road which is overtly less hazardous to the health of individuals and of the environment? The need for international cooperation and consensus was alluded to above. As the recent agreements restricting CFCs have shown, there are hopeful signs that such cooperation may become a reality. Political complexions tend to influence the national response to international directives by individual nations. Sweden illustrates the positive aspects of the interventionist approach on environmental matters. Even in the 'free market' economies, the use of tax incentives, such as lower taxation upon lead-free petrol in the UK and excise duty on CFCs in the USA, indicates that government can provide a clear lead.

Regular and improved training is called for by many of the contributors to this guide. Here there is a clear role for the professional bodies and trade associations in the construction industry. CIBSE and the RIBA have issued guidance to members on a number of environmental issues. Professional institutions can also lobby government to make regulatory or fiscal changes. The RIBA have published a green mandate which presses government to introduce a range of new measures including better insulation standards in new buildings, subsidies for retro-fitting of insulation to existing buildings, energy efficiency rating of buildings, and detailed user manuals or log books recording energy use and material content. The RIBA's new environmental policy also obliges its members to persuade clients to use environmentally friendly materials in building work. The RICS has identified the advantages of log books to record the detailed maintenance and alterations made to buildings in the owner occupied housing sector. The CIOB now also has a committee examining environmental problems in the industry.

If clear directives are not given by means of legislation or fiscal incentives, reliance falls on the use of voluntary codes of practice. Here developers and designers have important roles. They must work closely together and with contractors to encourage the best environmental analysis, energy and specification practice within reasonable cost limits. Many designers complain of being constrained by an unsympathetic client and *vice versa*. Experience of energy-saving design shows that major energy savings can be made without additional cost. Experience at Rosehaugh is that avoidance of hazardous materials does not necessarily result in unconventional design solutions and need not add significantly to costs.

The development of the Building Research Establishment's environmental assessment scheme, BREEAM, a voluntary 'green' labelling scheme for office buildings, is to be applauded. The effectiveness of voluntary schemes will depend on the cooperation of developers and professionals alike. However, history shows that the industry is slow to change without the additional impetus of revised building regulations. Whatever the future holds, there is an important responsibility upon each and every individual in the industry to take on board the issues raised and apply the methodology promoted in this book.

A few building contractors, including some major firms, are now developing environmental policies in terms of selection of materials and site procedures. This is encouraging, but needs to be taken up by the industry as a whole.

An Agenda for the Continuing Debate

Finally, some key questions about potential future action remain:

- How is the balance to be struck in future between the competing pressures such as
  - adequate ventilation,
  - the desire by many for offices and other workplace environments to be fully air-conditioned whilst retaining the ability to provide natural ventilation as well,
  - a desire to reduce total energy consumption and improve energy efficiency, and,
  - avoidance of factors leading to sick building syndrome?
- Can our analysis of new products be improved to avoid creating an equivalent in twenty years' time of the past discoveries of dangers from materials previously thought to be harmless? What material do we use now which will be the asbestos of the next century?

- Can we develop clear simple guidelines to help everyone involved in construction to become more hazard-conscious?
- Can we define 'acceptable level of risk' for construction workers, occupiers, owners? Can we then make use of the definition in our decision-making?
- Is labelling of products and materials used in construction satisfactory? Is the composition of everything entering a site known and its hazards identified? Even with full adherence to the Control of Substances Hazardous to Health Regulations, can we reduce health risks to construction workers to 'acceptable' levels?
- Can those with responsibility to push future building developments down a 'greener' road which is overtly less hazardous to health be persuaded to act? Can they be provided by governments with the framework in which to do so? Will the forthcoming Environmental Protection Act provided sufficient impetus for change in the UK?
- Can individuals and organisations be persuaded that their actions can influence community, national and world opinion of the importance of Buildings and Health, to provide a less hazardous, more comfortable built environment in a renewable or sustainable manner?

Appendices

APPENDIX 1

MEASUREMENT TECHNIQUES FOR ASSESSING HAZARDS

Eddie Salter

SKC Limited

INTRODUCTION

Measurement techniques for assessing hazards are important for several reasons:

- the health of workers;
- the health of other people associated with the construction;
- the health of people not associated with the construction but present in the immediate vicinity; and
- the cleanliness of the environment, whether land, water or air.

Measurement should be carried out when a hazard or potential hazard could affect any of the above, and this can occur at various stages. Toxic vapours and gases can be produced by burning rubbish, nuisance dusts can be caused by various construction activities, and other forms of hazard such as those found underground may be present.

Existing and forthcoming legislation requires the setting up of a monitoring programme which should encompass the following fundamental questions:

Who should we sample?   What should we sample?
Where should we sample?   How should we sample?
When should we sample?

MEASUREMENT OF HAZARDS

As demonstrated throughout this book, hazards and their effects vary considerably. Some hazards such as dust may cause more distress to people outside the construction area than to those working inside. Some such as asbestos may have particular significance to the individual and others may affect the total environment, being either a nuisance or a significant hazard to health. It will therefore be necessary to treat the hazards according to their general influence, whether environmental or personal, and use appropriate measurement techniques accordingly.

The limits applied to individual hazards are listed by the Health and Safety Executive in their publication Occupational Exposure Limits, Guidance Note EH40. This publication is updated each year, with the year identified after EH40, for example EH40/90. From this document it will be seen that certain chemicals are given occupational exposure standards (OESs) and other more hazardous materials are given maximum exposure limits (MELs). Methods associated with some hazards are identified and described in 'Methods for the determination of hazardous substances' (MDHS) which should be obtained from HMSO prior to sampling.

Maximum Exposure Limits

The MEL is the maximum concentration of an airborne substance averaged over a reference period to which workers may be exposed by inhalation under any circumstances. The employer must ensure that all reasonable precautions have been taken to minimise levels of exposure to these substances and, in any event, keep exposures below the MEL. Some MELs are designated 'long term' and refer to exposure over an 8 hour period. This is the 8 hour time-weighted average (TWA). Other MELs are designated 'short term' and refer to exposure over a 10 minute period. Examples are given in Table App1.1.

Table App 1.1		
SUBSTANCE	8 HOUR EXPOSURE, long term (mg m^{-3})	10 MIN EXPOSURE, short term (mg m^{-3})
Formaldehyde	2.5	2.5
Isocyanates	0.02	0.07
Man-made fibre	5	–
Hardwood dust	5	–

Occupational Exposure Standards

An OES is the concentration of an airborne substance averaged over a reference period which, according to current knowledge, does not have an injurious effect on workers experiencing a daily exposure at that level. If a substance has been assigned an OES, exposure by inhalation should be reduced to or less than that standard. If exposure by inhalation does not exceed the OES, then control may be seen to be adequate. An employer is obliged to reduce exposure to the OES by the most practical and effective means. Examples of OES values are given in Table App1.2.

Monitoring Strategy

A further document (HSE Guidance Note EH42, 1989) is also available which advises employers as to how they should conduct investigations into the nature, extent and control of exposure to substances hazardous to health which are present in the atmosphere. It provides practical guidance on monitoring such substances.

Table App 1.2

Substance	8 hour exposure, long term (mg m⁻³)	10 min exposure, short term (mg m⁻³)
Ammonia	18	27
Butane	1430	1780
Carbon monoxide	55	330
Inhalable dust, general[a]	10	–
Respirable dust general[a]	5	–
White spirit	575	720

[a] This is a general level; each dust source must be checked according to its chemical nature as levels can be much lower than this.

SAMPLING METHODS

Man-made Fibres, Asbestos, and Natural Dusts and Particulates

Any material that can occur as a fibre, a particulate, a dust or an aerosol is usually sampled using a filter paper assembly with a specific holder and a pump. Taking the sample is relatively simple – weigh the filter, pass through a known volume of air by choosing a known flow, e.g. 2 litres per minute, for a known length of time and finally re-weigh the filter.

The choice of equipment should be made by someone with specific knowledge in the area concerned as it will vary from problem to problem. A package of equipment to take the sample would cost about £350, although the measuring equipment could cost at least £3,500 and would include microscopes, high sensitivity balances and analytical chemical equipment. Such equipment would be suitable for metals (e.g. lead) in the atmosphere, brick dust or nuisance dust from cement, sand and wood.

There are also direct-reading instruments for dusts which are non-specific, i.e. they give a total figure and are generally used to indicate problem areas. These are fairly easy to use and cost about £2,000–3,000. The instrument must be calibrated using the filter weighing method described above.

Radon can be absorbed onto filters and measured using special radioactive sensors. As in most cases the sampling process is relatively inexpensive, but the measuring process tends to be very expensive.

Solvents, Gases, Vapours and Fumes

Before testing, some knowledge of the area or location must be obtained. Is it a confined space, above or below ground? What type of materials could be present? What harm are they likely to cause? Once this has been established by discussing the problem with experienced personnel, testing and measurement can proceed. Small monitors can generally be employed to test and measure atmospheres. These are extremely easy to operate: they just require switching on and the unit does the rest. Although they are quite small, they are relatively expensive (around £350 upwards). If the hazard involved cannot be measured in this way it may be necessary to use a pump of some type. The cheapest is the colour detector pump and tube system, which costs about £100 and gives immediate but limited information. Other pumps and trapping devices for taking samples will cost from about £400, and further capital equipment costs of £5,000–15,000 will be incurred, depending on the problem to be investigated.

Hazards Underground or in Confined Unventilated Spaces

The key issue here is measuring the oxygen content of the air. Normally, the atmosphere is about 21% oxygen: a drop to 17% will cause impaired judgement, and a further reduction to around 10% will cause nausea, complete lack of coordination and loss of consciousness.

There are several types of direct-reading instrument with audible alarms that can be used to warn a worker of danger. These devices are small enough to be worn on the lapel or in a pocket and have alarms that can be adjusted as appropriate. Most are based on the principle of electrochemical cells (a chemical reaction) or use the magnetic properties of oxygen (paramagnetism).

Associated with oxygen deficiency are gases such as methane and hydrogen sulphide. 'Three-in-one' monitors which simultaneously monitor oxygen deficiency, flammable gas and toxic gas are quite common. The normal procedure is to switch the unit on, check that it is working correctly and lower it into the confined space before entering. Any alarm should be a warning not to enter! Individual alarm units similar to that for oxygen deficiency are available for flammable gases and also for a range of toxic gases.

MONITORING

Monitoring the Environment

Monitoring the environment can and will cover all forms of air, solid and liquids in order to ascertain the level of hazard present.

Solids: Sampling solids is usually only required in relation to land and/or building contamination prior to the commencement of work. Samples of soil are taken at varying depths using a core-sampling probe and are sent to the laboratory for analysis. Analysis will depend very much on the nature and history of the site being used, but samples are usually treated with weak acids or water to dissolve the contamination and the resultant solution is analysed for damaging salts or heavy metals. Materials that have been left on a derelict site and may be suspect, such as asbestos sheets, may also be involved. In this case sampling is relatively simple but in all operations care must be exercised by the person taking the samples to avoid further contamination and personal injury.

Liquids: Sampling liquids may be required to identify the composition and quality of stagnant or running water or any other liquid that may have been left on site after vacation by previous occupants. The liquids can be contained quite easily in appropriate vessels and labelled and sent for analysis. The analytical work will vary according to regulations concerning the concentrations of heavy metals and damaging salts. Other liquids will require identification tests to ascertain their nature and ultimately the manner of their disposal.

No material that has not been properly identified should be disposed of on an open fire as this may lead to explosions or the release of extremely toxic compounds that have a wide-reaching effect. Proper procedures must be adhered to at all times in disposing of any material.

Air: The air around the site can be sampled at all stages during construction work. Sampling will usually involve a sample pump used in conjunction with adsorbents, filters or bubblers according to the nature of the hazard being sampled.

For nuisance dusts which can occur during demolition and construction stages the pump is used in conjunction with a filter paper. The pump is placed in an appropriate position relative to the wind direction. The analytical side is relatively simple, only requiring weighing of the filter before and after sampling. Asbestos, in particular, is sampled in this way using a special 'gridded' filter paper, and the filters are inspected using a microscope as well as by straightforward weighing. Pumps can be mains operated or work from rechargeable batteries, and can be described as portable although they weigh more than the personal samplers used to measure exposure on the workers.

Table App1.3 provides a general guide to which equipment is appropriate to monitor the different hazards likely to be encountered. Professional advice should be sought to ensure that the most satisfactory equipment is selected in each case.

Work Area Air Quality Monitoring

Instrumental Methods: Many different instrumental techniques are used in air monitoring. The most important examples are as follows.

Paper Tape Monitors use chemically treated tape on a reel-to-reel recorder basis. Air is drawn through the tape by a pump and the contaminants react with the chemicals to produce a coloured stain. The intensity of the stain is proportional to the concentration and is measured by optical techniques. The results are displayed on a meter. This method is usually quite sensitive and specific and is used in storage areas where large volumes of toxic material are stored.

Semiconductor Detectors are made of metal oxide films which respond to the presence of a gas by a change in the conductivity either into or away from the

Table App 1.3

EQUIPMENT	SB	P	WT	I	FC	DC	DM	CS	CM	WM	SM	M
The working area												
Paper tape monitors	√										√	
Semiconductor detectors					√	√	√	√			√	
Infrared analysers			√			√	√			√		
Portable gas chromatographs			√			√	√				√	
Photo-ionization analysers	√	√			√		√			√		
Indicator tubes	√				√	√	√			√	√	
Spot or grab sampling			√			√		√				
Adsorption techniques	√	√	√	√		√				√	√	
Filter collection	√	√	√	√					√	√		
The working person												
Long-term colour detector tubes		√		√	√	√	√			√		√
Adsorption techniques		√	√	√	√					√		√
Filter techniques	√	√	√	√					√	√		
Personal monitors						√	√	√		√		√
Diffusive samplers			√				√					
Direct-reading diffusive samplers		√			√	√		√		√		
Analytical diffusive samplers			√	√	√		√			√		

SB, sand blasting; P, Painting; WT, wood treatment; I, insulation; FC, floor coverings; DC, drain cleaning: DM, diesel motors; CS, confined spaces; CM, cutting of masonry; WM welding of metals; SM, storage of materials; M, maintenance.

oxide film. These detectors can be sensitive but are difficult to make very specific. They are ideally suited for multichannel operation to cover a wide area in a cost-effective manner.

Infrared Analysers emit infrared radiation which is absorbed by the contaminated air, resulting in a change in molecular structure and the formation of a spectrum or fingerprint over a range of wavelengths. Thus specific gases can be measured accurately to low levels. These devices are used in tunnels and underground car parks to measure the concentration of carbon monoxide from vehicle exhausts.

In *Portable Gas Chromatographs,* a sample of air is drawn into the device and passed through a column which acts as a sieve and separates mixtures into individual components which pass through at different rates. Various detectors (flame ionization, electron capture, thermal conductivity) are used to measure the individual components. This method is very good for organic materials at low concentrations, but the equipment is fairly large and cumbersome. Chromatographs can be used as leak detectors in certain applications.

In *Photo-ionization Analysers*, the compound(s) in the air drawn through it absorb ultraviolet light which causes the molecules to ionize and the ionization is measured electronically. This is a similar type of device to the portable gas chromatograph with the distinct advantage that it does not require specific gases for the process to work.

Manual Sampling

Indicator Tubes, commonly known as colour detector tubes. A hand pump draws a known volume of air through a tube containing reactive chemicals on an inert support material. The chemicals react with the contaminant and produce a coloured stain which spreads down the length of the tube according to its concentration. The tube has a graduated marked scale, and the reading is taken at the border between the stained and the non-stained section. These devices are inexpensive, easy to use and cover a wide range of gases and vapours.

In *Spot or Grab Sampling*, an air sample is drawn into a collection device either by vacuum or using a pump. The contents are sealed and the device is sent away for analysis. The collecting device can be a 'plastic' bag, or a metal or glass container.

In *Adsorption Techniques*, a sample of air is drawn through a solid sorbent, e.g. charcoal, or a liquid via a sample pump whereupon the contaminant is trapped. The sorbent is taken to the laboratory for analysis.

In *Filter Collection*, a sample of air is pulled through a filter paper using a pump. Particles in the air are trapped on the paper which is then weighed and possibly treated to determine the nature of the trapped material. This technique has been used to measure nuisance dusts at the perimeter boundaries of building sites during construction work to ensure that neighbouring properties are not subjected to excessive amounts of dust.

Personal Monitoring

Here, the primary concern is with the actual exposure of a worker or group of workers. The standard term is the time-weighted average (TWA) and this usually refers to an exposure over an 8 hour period.

Long-Term Colour Detector Tubes: In principle these are the same as those discussed in the previous section except that they are designed to be exposed for a period of time (up to 8 hours), whereas the others are single-shot 'instant' read-out instruments. The long-term tubes are connected via a protective tube to a low flow sampling pump capable of pulling 20 millilitres per minute for 8 hours through the whole assembly. As before, read-out is made directly from the calibrated scale on the tube itself.

Adsorption Techniques: Exactly the same equipment and procedures as described above are used except that the equipment is worn by the worker rather than left in the work area. These devices have to be sent to a laboratory for analysis, which involves a variety of techniques. The liquid samples are usually treated using other chemical reagents which ultimately produce a coloured solution. The intensity of the coloured solution is measured using optical techniques and is proportional to the concentration. Electrode-type systems can also be used to measure acidity (pH value) and other specific compounds. The solid sorbent (charcoal) materials can either be heated or chemically treated; each process releases the trapped contaminants into an analytical instrument such as a gas chromatograph.

Filter Techniques: As previously described a pump and filter paper are used to collect airborne particles. Generally the flow rate used is around 2 litres per minute, although 4 or 8 litres per minute can be used in certain circumstances. The measurement can be made simply by weighing (gravimetry) to establish the amount of particulate found. After weighing, the filter can be dissolved or washed in a specific solution and the solution chemically analysed by various techniques. One well-known technique is atomic absorption spectroscopy which is widely used for measuring heavy metals such as lead.

Another major hazard that is sampled using this technique is asbestos. Sampling and measurement follow specific patterns as laid down by the Health and Safety Executive (MDHS 39/3, 1990). Sampling is carried out via a pump on a specific filter paper, and after sampling the paper is treated and then viewed under a microscope where the number of individual fibres is counted.

Personal Monitors: Personal monitors can vary in shape, size and suitability. They consist of a device about the same size as a cigarette packet that can fit into the top pocket and give both an audible and a visual alarm when a significant increase in concentration of the contaminant has been reached. These devices do not use a pump but rely on the diffusion of the atmosphere into the reaction chamber.

Nearly all the sampling devices described above use pumps and are referred to as active sampling techniques. Other devices based on diffusion techniques are available. Diffusive samplers are small devices in the form of a badge or a tube. Air diffuses into the device and the contaminant is trapped until it is released by some form of chemical analysis or is read out. The device is small, light and easy to wear on a lapel or safety hat for long periods. There are two types of diffusive sampler, the direct-reading type and those requiring analysis:

- *Direct-reading diffusive samplers* take the form of a badge or tube and generally rely on a colour change to indicate the concentration of contaminant. The samplers are disposable and are only used once; each test requires a new tube or badge. They are extremely useful as they require no pump and no analysis and can thus be used and read by almost anyone.

- In *Analytical diffusive samplers*, a sorbent material traps the contaminant. The sorbent can be removed and chemically treated, and the resultant solution is analysed using a specific procedure to identify and quantify the contaminant. This technique is known as solvent desorption. The sorbent may take the form of a solid material (like charcoal), or a liquid (water or a weak acid solution). In each case the adsorbent is disposed of but the main housing is generally re-usable. Analysis involves expensive equipment and is time consuming but usually enables a wider range of contaminants to be sampled. In addition to this there are tubular devices containing a solid adsorbent that are heat treated rather than chemically treated. This process is known as thermal desorption, and here the contaminant is released by heating the analytical device. The technique has certain advantages over solvent desorption in that there is no dilution effect. Therefore a smaller sample or a lower concentration can be used, and the device is re-usable rather than disposable.

These diffusive samplers are used in sampling gases and vapours; they are not designed for sampling dusts, aerosols and particulates. Diffusive samplers have become very acceptable because of their low cost, small size, low weight and user acceptability. They suffer certain disadvantages because they are affected by external environmental changes in wind velocity, humidity etc. and they take a small volume of sample. Another significant factor is validation, whereby the accuracy of the badge has to be determined for the contaminants of interest in order to give effective quantitative results. Not all diffusive samplers have been validated, and therefore it is necessary to check with the supplier as to the integrity of the device.

CALCULATION AND PRESENTATION OF RESULTS

As we have previously noted, sampling must meet recognized standards: TWA (8 hour sample), threshold limit value (TLV), MEL and OES. These standards are set for a concentration either in parts per million (ppm) or milligrams per cubic metre (mg m^{-3}). The relationship between the two is

$$mg\ m^{-3}\ =\ ppm\ x\ \frac{molecular\ weight\ (mass)}{24}$$

The molecular weight can be obtained from appropriate tables. In general, samples are measured in millilitres per minute (ml min^{-1}) or litres per minute (l min^{-1}). By calculating the total sampling time in minutes, the total volume on litres can be calculated easily.

An 8 hr sampling at 2 l min^{-1} = 8 x 60 x 2 = 960 litres = 0.96 m^3

Or 8 hr sampling at 20 ml min^{-1} = 8 x 60 x 20/1000 = 9.6 litres = 0.0096 m^3

CONCLUSIONS

* Air sampling and monitoring at work sites can cover a wide variety of compounds using a wide variety of techniques. It is essential to obtain the correct advice for the specific requirement. It is also important to realize that seemingly innocuous gases, such as carbon monoxide and carbon dioxide, and oxygen deficiency, can be and often are killers. It cannot be stressed too highly that proper advice must be taken at all stages. Consultation should be made with qualified industrial or occupational hygienists who are trained to recommend sampling, ventilation and other forms of remedial action. They will also advise on where, when and how to sample and in most cases are able to offer full analytical services in order to identify and quantify results.

* Never assume that everything is satisfactory. Most accidental deaths occur because of complacency: many of the most deadly compounds are odourless.

* Take care when disposing of waste in any form. There are procedures that must and should be followed. If in doubt ask a consultant or a construction advice unit. There is almost always some form of sampling, monitoring and analytical procedure that is suitable for any type of contaminant that can occur; some will be expensive and some will act more rapidly than others, but ultimately there should always be an answer.

REFERENCES AND FURTHER READING

Control of Substances Hazardous to Health Regulations 1988, HM Stationery Office, London.

Health and Safety Executive (1988), *Asbestos – Control Limits, Measurement of Airborne Dust Concentrations and the Assessment of Control Measures*, Guidance Note EH10, Health and Safety Executive, Bootle.

Health and Safety Executive (1989), *Building Contracts Undertaken on Education Premises – Strategies for Health and Safety of Staff*, Health and Safety Executive, Bootle.

Health and Safety Executive (1988), *Entry into Confined Spaces*, Guidance Note GS5, Health and Safety Executive, Bootle.

Health and Safety Executive (1989), *Essentials of Health and Safety at Work*, Health and Safety Executive, Bootle.

Health and Safety Executive (1989), *In-situ Timber Treatment using Timber Preservatives*, Guidance Note GS6, Health and Safety Executive, Bootle.

Health and Safety Executive (1989), *Monitoring Strategies for Toxic Substances*, Guidance Note EH42, Health and Safety Executive, Bootle.

Health and Safety Executive (1990), *Occupational Exposure Limits*, Guidance Note EH40/90, Health and Safety Executive, Bootle.

Methods for the determination of hazardous sustances, 39/3, HM Stationery Office, 1990.

GUIDANCE ON THERMAL COMFORT, LIGHTING AND NOISE

This appendix brings together brief guidance on issues more concerned with *comfort* than *hazard to health*, in the areas of temperature of the workplace and heat hazards experienced there, lighting of workplaces, and noise. Some case studies of how unsatisfactory situations have been rectified are included to illustrate the principles outlined.

App 2.1 THERMAL ENVIRONMENT – LEGISLATION AND STANDARDS FOR THE CONSTRUCTION INDUSTRY

Andrew Nicholl

Institute of Occupational Medicine Ltd.

INTRODUCTION

The human body is equipped with a very powerful regulation mechanism to keep the body temperature to within a degree or so of its optimum. If the body temperature rises much above or falls much below this relatively narrow optimum range, the function of the brain may be impaired and life may be at risk.

REACTIONS OF THE BODY TO HEAT AND COLD

Long before these dangerous levels are reached, the body will react to heat or cold stress in a number of ways. These reactions are designed to help the body temperature to remain constant.

Maintaining Body Temperature

Heat is continuously being produced by the body. The body has to get rid of this heat in order to keep its temperature constant, and so the heat has to be removed at the same rate as it is produced. The heat is transported to the skin by means of the blood, and this blood flow to the skin increases as the skin becomes warmer. Heat can be removed from the skin either directly or through clothing (by convection to the outside air, or by conduction to liquids or solid objects) and through breathing by evaporation of moisture. If the heat cannot be removed quickly enough by these means the skin produces sweat, which may or may not be noticeable. The sweat evaporating from the skin will also cool it. Evaporation and convective heat loss from the skin are increased by higher wind speeds, but evaporation rate is reduced as the humidity in the air rises.

Heat may also be gained or lost from the body by radiation, another way in which the body exchanges heat with the environment. If the radiant temperature of the body is higher than the surroundings, heat will be lost; if a radiant heat source at a higher radiant temperature than the body is present, such as an electric bar fire, the body will gain heat.

The body temperature will tend to drop when heat is removed too quickly. If the body gets wet or the air temperature is low, a high wind speed may remove more heat than the body can replace. Excessive cooling in this way may affect the extremities, fingers and toes, sooner than the trunk, because an effect of cold is to close down the blood vessels in the cold parts. This allows them to cool down even more quickly, as the blood provides much of the heat that these parts normally require. Under these conditions the body may try to produce more heat by making the muscles shiver.

Thermal Comfort

Under less extreme conditions, the body may experience heat or cold discomfort. Comfort is defined as the state in which the body is thermally neutral, i.e. there is no net gain or loss of heat, and discomfort occurs outside this range. Given reasonably temperate conditions, the comfort of the body is usually maintained by the levels of clothing worn or by technical aids such as air-conditioning. Humidity levels have little effect in the comfort region, but should not be allowed to fall below 30% as this can lead to health problems.

Effects of Heat and Cold on Performance

Working temperatures that are warmer than comfortable tend to lead to weariness, sleepiness, loss of performance and increased liability to make errors. Cooler temperatures produce restlessness which reduces alertness and concentration, particularly on mental tasks, and affects people's judgement. It is therefore essential to maintain thermal comfort both in a building and during its construction/demolition etc. in order to maximize efficiency, well-being and safety. Research has shown that the following temperatures are optimum for indoor comfort during sedentary work involving little physical effort:

- The air temperature in winter should be 21°C, and in summer between 20 and 24°C.
- The surface temperatures of nearby objects (walls etc.) should not differ by more than 2–3°C from the air temperature. No single surface

should be more than 4°C colder than the room air.

- The relative humidity of the room air should not fall below 30% in winter. In summer, the relative humidity will vary naturally between 40% and 60%.
- Air speed at the head and knee levels should not exceed 0.2 metres per second.

LEGISLATION RELATING TO HEAT AND COLD

The United Kingdom has a long history of industrialization, and many attempts have been made to control the health and safety of workers since the beginning of the nineteenth century. The Factories Act 1961 was the culmination of these, although this Act excluded many people from its cover. A factory is defined in the Act as any place where persons are employed in manual labour for the purposes of gain to make, alter, repair etc. any article. It also includes a range of occupations and industries specified in Section 175 of the Act.

Currently Enforceable Legislation

Building sites are specifically included in the definition of a factory under the Factories Act (Section 127), even though they do not strictly fit the definition above. Municipal or other public authority premises, however, or open-air premises, for example, are not covered by the Act (Section 175, Subsection 9).

Section 3 of the Factories Act (which does *not* apply to building sites) specifies the working temperature which must be achieved in workrooms by the end of the first hour at work as being 16°C. This only applies to people doing seated work not involving serious physical effort. Apart from this, the Act has a general requirement for the provision of a reasonable temperature in all workrooms.

Section 68 of the Factories Act concerns the employer's duty, in factories where artificial humidity is produced, to notify the inspector, to provide two hygrometers in each room, to provide a humidity table, and to read and record temperatures and humidities at prescribed times.

The Offices, Shops and Railway Premises Act 1963 also has a general requirement for reasonable temperatures and a 16°C minimum for sedentary work; its structure is similar to that of the Factories Act 1961, Section 3.

Summary of Scope of Legislation

In UK legislation,

- a minimum working temperature is quoted for some but not all work situations;
- no maximum working temperatures are quoted except in certain specific regulations, eg for textiles and woodworking machines;
- only where artificial humidity is produced are there any laws relating to humidity, but these are not of general application;

- no legislation relates to temperatures at higher workloads, such as those involved in manual tasks;
- for some industries, e.g. mines and quarries, there is no mention of thermal environment in the legislation relating to them.

OTHER THERMAL STANDARDS

As no occupational hygiene standards on the thermal environment have been produced by the British Government, the *de facto* standards used are those from the American Conference of Governmental and Industrial Hygienists (ACGIH), or ISO Standard 7243. Both these standards use the wet bulb globe temperature (WBGT) in degrees Celsius.

The WBGT Index of Thermal Stress

The WBGT is defined in two ways:

- outdoors, with solar radiation, WBGT $= 0.7$ NWB $+ 0.2$ GT $+ 0.1$ DB
- indoors with no solar load, WBGT $= 0.7$ NWB $+ 0.3$ GT

where:
WBGT is the index value in degrees Celsius,
NWB is the natural wet bulb temperature (taken on a thermometer with its bulb covered with a close-fitting wet sock),
GT is the temperature inside a black-painted copper globe of 6 inch diameter, and
DB is the dry bulb temperature.

The ACGIH gives a table of permissible heat exposure threshold limit values (TLVs) based on the proportion of work to rest in the task (Table App 2.1.1). These criteria are designed to maintain the deep body temperature below 38°C. For example, men are digging a trench under the following conditions:

NWB : 24°C, DB : 30°C, GT : 31°C.

They work an 8 hour day with a single 45 minute break. Then,

WBGT $= (0.7$ x $24) + (0.2$ x $30) + (0.1$ x $31) = 25.9$°C

From App Table 2.1.1, the limit for 100% work with no special rest breaks is 25.0°C. It would therefore be recommended that a 75:25 work-to-rest regime on an hourly basis should be introduced, as 25.9°C is the limit for this pattern at a high work rate; the environment should therefore be controlled where possible and/or personal protection applied. Medical surveillance of fitness should be carried out, and water and salt supplements given.

   If the humidity is high, NWB is closer to DB. If men are carrying out the same trench-digging job in a more humid climate, where NWB is 28°C, DB is still 30°C and GT is still 31°C, the WBGT works out at 28.7°C. This would

Table App 2.1.1 Recommended maximum environmental temperatures for a range of work/rest regimes and workloads.

Work %	Rest %	Workload		
		Light	Moderate	Heavy
100	0	30.0	26.7	25.0
75	25	30.6	28.0	25.9
50	50	31.4	29.4	27.9
25	75	32.2	31.1	30.0

mean that the work-to-rest regime should be changed from 75:25 down to say 40:60; in other words, raising the relative humidity from 63% in the first example to 86% in the second example effectively halved the amount of work which should be done each hour.

Wind Chill Standards for Cold Exposure

Workers are particularly at risk from the cold when the air temperature around them is below 10°C. It is important to realize that at these temperatures the wind can dramatically increase the cooling effect of the air, producing an equivalent temperature much lower than the actual air temperature. Although we tend to think of hypothermia affecting only old people in winter, it can in fact occur in the healthiest individuals if they are exposed to the cold for too long.

As the body becomes colder and hypothermia sets in, the skin first becomes blue as the blood supply to it is reduced. Shivering starts, extending to the whole body. The person may become irrational. If not treated, the skin becomes pale, cold and dry, muscles become rigid and the person will stop shivering; they may become stupefied and then unconscious. Hypothermia is treated by taking the person to a warm place and allowing slow recovery. An affected person may be irrational and try to resist this. Once a person has become stupefied or unconscious, an ambulance must be called.

The ACGIH has also produced limits for cold exposure based on the cooling power of the wind at different air temperatures (Table App 2.1.2). Humidity is not an important factor at low temperatures, but wetness of the skin will increase heat loss. The aim of the ACGIH cold exposure criteria is to ensure that the deep body temperature does not fall below 36°C and to avoid injuries caused by the cold such as trench foot or immersion foot, frostbite etc. The criterion levels on the wind chill temperature scale are as follows.

Criterion levels on the Wind Chill Temperature scale

- *Higher than −31°C:* little danger of tissue damage in a 1 hour exposure if the skin is dry; maximum danger of a false sense of security, leading to possible hypothermia

Table App 2.1.2 Wind Chill Table

Wind Speed in ms⁻¹	Air Temperatures (degrees C)*					
	10	0	-10	−20	−30	−40
0	10	0	−10	−20	−30	−40
5	5	−9	−23	−36	−47	−59
10	0	−16	−32	−46	−59	−73
15	−3	−20	−36	−50	−63	−80

* These values have been estimated from the ACGIH values which are published in degrees Fahrenheit; they are therefore approximate. An air speed of 5 ms⁻¹ is just over 10 mph.

- *Between −31 and −58°C:* increasing danger; exposed flesh may freeze in 1 minute
- *Below −58°C:* great danger; flesh may freeze in 30 seconds

Avoiding Health Hazards due to Cold

The three main ways of fighting cold are to stay dry, to dress properly and to stay out of the wind. 'Immersion foot' is a problem which occurs when the feet are wet, e.g. when digging trenches or in heavy rain. The wet causes heat to be lost too quickly; this may sometimes not be noticed, as the cold stops the nerves working properly. The skin turns white, the blood circulation is interrupted and the skin may be damaged. Slow and gentle warming should be applied.

Alcohol should never be given to anyone who is suffering from the cold. Anyone who drinks alcohol in the cold is increasing their chances of being frost-bitten in the first place. Suitable protective clothing and gloves must be worn in the cold.

Protective clothing must be durable, light, flexible and made of material which is completely resistant to wind and rain. It should be loose enough to allow a certain amount of air flow inside, in order to evaporate the sweat which can build up even in the coldest conditions. Great care should be taken to use effective insulating gloves in order to prevent the hands touching cold metal in subzero temperatures. Exposed flesh can stick onto very cold metals, and it can be very difficult to remove.

Weather protection of open working sites has become cheaper and more feasible in recent years. This protection may consist of a temporary tent or screen of polyethylene. If men are working at heights on scaffolding, for example, where winds tend to be much stronger than at ground level and the air temperature is low, an effective wind shield should be erected around the work area. This may seem like time wasted, but it will improve output and safety far beyond the cost of the shelter. Due allowance must be made for the extra wind loading on the scaffolding structure when such a screen is in place.

Longer-term sites will also benefit by having suitably warmed rest areas where hot meals and drinks can be prepared, and where clothes can be dried and stored.

CONCLUSIONS

* Although we have little legislation specifically controlling thermal environments, the ACGIH guidelines are in common use in the United Kingdom. The Health and Safety Executive is aware of the problems of cold on building sites, and some of the information given here also appears in the Construction Health Hazard Information Sheet No. 2 (HSC Construction Industry Advisory Committee).

App 2.2 LIGHTING COMFORT

Alan Bradley and Andrew Nicholl

Institute of Occupational Medicine Ltd.

INTRODUCTION

Lighting is important in a construction programme for a number of reasons. During actual building or demolition phases, good lighting is essential to illuminate the work and provide safe working conditions. In practice a lighting plan is rarely drawn up for a site; general lighting is normally provided by semi-permanent arc lamps, and lighting for closer work is provided by temporary mains lighting or hand lamps. Much more attention is usually paid to the provision of good lighting for the tasks and visual comfort of the building occupant. Any person responsible for planning the lighting of the interior of a building should refer to the CIBSE Code for Interior Lighting, produced by the Chartered Institution of Building Service Engineers.

PRINCIPLES OF GOOD LIGHTING

The eye is a very adjustable mechanism and therefore, given time, it can adjust to dim or strong lighting. When the eye looks at a scene, it tends to adapt to the average brightness that it sees. However, if areas are excessively bright or dark compared with the average level, some discomfort can occur. Excessive brightness appears to glare and in excessively dim areas the definition will be limited.

Glare can be classified in three ways: disability glare; discomfort glare; reflected glare. Disability glare is caused by direct intense light into the eye, where the extraneous light level is much in excess of the useful light reflected from the object being viewed. The result is a partial loss of vision and definition. Discomfort glare is caused by long-term glare from windows or light fittings which are too bright compared with the task being viewed. The effects of this type of glare increase with time. Typical of this type of glare is the gradual discomfort when working for a full day on a desk surface with glare from direct sunlight through an undraped window. Light sources in the field of view should not be more than 20 times brighter than their immediate surroundings. Reflected glare can be seen in polished surfaces which reflect an image of a light fitting or window. Typical of this type of glare is the image of a badly sited light fitting on a VDU screen.

The eye is attracted to the brightest object in the field of vision; it is therefore of advantage if the task appears brighter than the immediate background and that the far background is darker still. The brightness or luminance of the surfaces immediately surrounding the object viewed should be between a half and one-third of that on the object itself. Disability glare will occur if these surrounding surfaces are less than one-fifth of the object's luminance. In the same way, the overall range of brightness in a room should not exceed 40:1. Extremes of brightness and darkness should be avoided. Therefore in, say, an office situation it is an advantage to use matt desk tops with soft grey or green colouring, and to use pastel colours for walls and other furniture and fittings. White ceilings are preferable (British Standard 5252: Framework for Colour Coordinates for Building Purposes).

Light direction is important as most objects are best seen if the light is predominant from one direction. The strength of directional light can be quantified by the ratio of the magnitude of the illumination vector to the scalar illuminance (vector-to-scalar ratio). This ratio can be calculated and the recommended acceptable levels for a given situation can be obtained from tables.

Selection of the light source can be important for two reasons. Firstly, the light emitted by a source has an apparent colour, and secondly the light affects the way that we see the colour of surfaces or objects. The latter effect is called colour rendering. Each type of lamp is classified according to its correlated colour temperature (CCT) and these have been grouped into three classes by the Commission International de l'Eclairage (CIE). The selection of the correct CCT depends on the use to which the room is to be put, e.g. whether it needs apparently 'warm' light or a 'hard' white light. The CIE also classify the ability of a lamp type to render colours of room surfaces in their general colour-rendering index.

A new EC Directive issued in May 1990 on minimum safety and health requirements for work with display screen equipment includes lighting provisions and requirements on reflections and glare. Its provisions are due to come into force on 31 December 1992.

LEGISLATION AND GUIDANCE

There are various references to lighting in legislation and standards; the most relevant is:

Legislation

The Factories Act 1961
The Offices, Shops and Railways Premises Act 1963
The Fire Precaution Act 1971
The Protection of Eyes Regulations 1974 (amended 1975)
The Health and Safety at Work etc. Act 1974
Council Directive of 29 May 1990 on the minimum safety and health requirements for work with display screen equipment (fifth individual Directive within the meaning of Article 16 (1) of Directive 87/391/EEC) OJ L 156/14–18 21 June 1990.

British Standards

BS 3677 High Pressure Mercury Vapour Lamps
BS 3767 Low Pressure Sodium Vapour Lamps
BS 4727 Part 4: Glossary of Terms Particular to Lighting and Colour
BS 4800 Paint Colours for Building Purposes
BS 4902 Sheet and Tile Flooring Colours for Building Purposes
BS DD67 Basic Data for the Design of Buildings: Sunlight
BS DD73 Basic Data for the Design of Buildings: Daylight

HSE Publications

Guidance Note HS (G) 38 Lighting at Work

CIBSE Publications

Lighting Guides – Building and civil engineering sites

CASE STUDIES OF LIGHTING IN BUILDINGS

Case Study 1

The following circumstances were discovered as part of a study of a sick building where workers had complained of headaches and tired eyes.

The building was a high security establishment with no outside windows. The only natural light was through a large central roof-mounted skylight. The designer had mistakenly decided to use bold colours, mainly greens and orange, to give an impression of brightness. The ceilings were dark in colour, contrasting strongly with the natural light from the central skylight. The furniture was metal and also had bright green or orange surfaces. Lighting was by unshaded fluorescent fittings.

The following actions were taken to ameliorate the problems: the luminaires were shaded to avoid glare from metal fittings and VDU screens; the room was redecorated in pastel colours and luminaires were selected and matched using reference to CIE tables; all office furniture was changed to pale grey semi-matt surfaces and even the paper was changed to an off-white recycled paper. The symptoms of the work-force disappeared.

Case Study 2

Discomfort had been experienced in a large open-plan office where multiple VDUs were used. The remit given was to advise on solutions without spending an excessive amount of money on the project. The problem with VDUs is that the lighting requirements for hard copy (white paper documents) and for screen text are incompatible. Increasing the illumination of the hard copy increases the legibility to an optimum level but, of course, the self-illuminating symbols on the VDU screen suffer from reduced contrast. A compromise level which could comfortably be handled by the operators had to be found. Secondly, increased illumination of the screen could cause formation of bright areas created by source reflection and reflections from lights, which were unshaded and parallel with the screens, and windows which were not draped. Advice was given to carry out the following:

- shade the light fittings to avoid direct reflections onto screens;
- provide window drapes;
- set the screen luminance to approximately half the level of the luminance in the office;
- provide grey matt covers for desk tops;
- turn VDUs into a plane at right angles to the windows.

Further recommendations for future reference included the following:

- on redecoration, follow CIE guidance on lamp CCT and colour-rendering index;
- buy VDUs with a dark green screen colour with lighter green or yellow characters;
- buy VDUs with contrast adjustment controls in addition to brightness controls;
- ensure that the flicker rate (frequency of image regeneration) is a minimum of 50 Hz and much higher if possible;
- follow the general standards described by Kakir et al (1979).

Case Study 3

Night work was projected for the construction of a pumping station. Permanent outside lighting was planned with temporary lighting inside the partly constructed building.

The first problem to be tackled with outside arc lighting is the careful siting of the lights so that deep shadows are not thrown by obstructions such as building columns, parked vehicles etc. It is therefore desirable to have high lamp standards throwing a near vertical beam towards the ground. A compromise is usually called for as numerous lamp columns create obstacles around the site. Having agreed on the column siting, the easiest single criterion to apply is standard service illuminance, which is the mean illuminance throughout the maintenance cycle of the lighting installation averaged over the area being illuminated. The standard service illumination assumes that the arc area with work being done is typical of its type. It can be modified for, say, application of a more difficult task into the design service illumination.

As no standard service illuminances could be traced especially suited for the type of construction site in question, the CIBSE 'Code for Interior Lighting' was referred to and standard service illuminances for similar situations extracted. It was then suggested that this figure be increased by one box in the flow chart to give a standard service illuminance slightly better than required, thereby producing a safety factor. The suggested figures for standard service luminance were then:

- exterior walkways, platforms, stairs and ladders, 100 lux;
- conveyors, gantries and hoppers, 150 lux;
- work stations near rotating machinery, 200 lux;
- cable tunnels and basements, 100 lux.

This was supported by temporary lighting for small detailed work areas.

It should be noted that the above figures were suggested for a specific situation and set of circumstances and should not be taken as a general recommendation for all situations whether apparently similar to the original or not.

REFERENCE

Kakir, A. et al (1979) *The VDT manual.* Inca-Fiej Research Association, Darmstadt, Federal Republic of Germany.

App 2.3 NOISE

Alan Bradley and Robin Howie

Institute of Occupational Medicine Ltd.

INTRODUCTION

Noise, when associated with the construction industry, can be of concern in two ways:

* noise which can actually cause permanent damage to the construction workers themselves;
* noise from the construction site which causes a nuisance to persons occupying nearby properties.

Noise can affect the ability of a person to hear. If a person is exposed to a loud noise for a short time them a small loss of hearing occurs. This is known as temporary threshold shift, which means that the lowest sound pressure which can be detected by the ear (the threshold) is raised. In lay terms the person suffers temporary deafness. If the person is then removed from the noise source he will, in time, recover. However, should that person be repeatedly exposed to loud noise with shorter recovery times, permanent threshold shift will eventually occur. There is good scientific evidence to show that the main criteria in producing permanent threshold shift are length of exposure, the loudness of noise and the frequency of the noise. Impulsive noise, such as that produced during construction by piling machines can also cause significant permanent threshold shift, if adequate precautions are not taken to protect operatives and workmen in the vicinity. Various criteria are important in causing the damage such as peak noise level, length of exposure, rise time and rate of repetition.

In everyday life we are surrounded by noise and at certain perceived levels we become 'comfortable' with that noise. However, should an extra noise source impose itself on our environment it is perceived as a nuisance. The intruding noise may not be sufficient to cause permanent or even temporary hearing loss, but there is evidence that it can cause such medical disorders as irritation. The criteria important in noise nuisance are complex, but for instance, impulse noise from piling on a nearby site can be intolerable as can the pure tones such as those produced by fans and air movers.

LEGISLATION

The Council of European Communities issued a Council Directive on 12 May 1986 on 'The Protection of Workers from the Risks Related to Exposure to Noise at Work'. Article 13 of this Directive states that Member States shall bring into force the laws, regulations and administrative provisions necessary to comply with the Directive by 1 January 1990. The United Kingdom has produced regulations to meet the Directive and they came into force on the due date (Noise at Work Regulations 1989, Statutory Instrument 1989 No.1790).

Nuisance noise, or noise pollution, is somewhat less well defined, yet it is mentioned in a variety of legislation. Various sets of Motor Vehicles (Type Approved) Regulations and Motor Vehicles (Construction and Use) Regulations seek to control the problems of noise from road vehicles. The Motor Vehicles (Construction and Use) Regulations limit excessive vehicle noise whilst the other legislation allows local authorities to limit the numbers and sizes of vehicles on roads, particularly by-roads. The Control of Pollution Act 1974, Section 57 provides for summary proceedings to be taken at the instance of a local authority in the case of noise or vibrations which amount to a legal nuisance. Under Section 58, proceedings for the abatement of a noise nuisance may be commenced by an individual occupier of premises who is aggrieved. Under Section 60, which relates specifically to noise on construction sites, the local authority takes the initiative and serves a notice specifying how the relevant works are to be carried out. Under Section 61, a person intending to carry out such works may apply in advance for a consent, inter alia, as to the times during which the works may be carried out. Section 63, permits designated noise abatement zones to be set up. British Standards Institution Codes of Practice have been approved by the Secretary of State as being applicable to the carrying out of construction work under the Control of Noise (Codes of Practice for Construction and Open Sites) Orders 1984 and 1987. In addition another important document, whilst not strictly legislation must be mentioned here. British Standard 4142 (1967) gives directions on the ways to assess whether a given noise level is likely to give rise to complaint.

In addition to the above legislation, a person who considers that he is exposed to unacceptable levels of noise from neighbouring premises may be able to bring a civil action for damages or for an injunction seeking cessation of the nuisance. Even when the noise levels are not in excess of current guidelines the plaintiff can still obtain remedies through the court and the court, in addition, can impose new noise level requirements on the defendant.

Finally, guidance is available from CIRIA on various aspects of construction site noise – Technical Note 115 (1984) on 'Exposure of construction workers to noise' and Special Publication 38 (1985) on 'Simple Noise Screens for Site Use'.

SOME CASE NOTES FROM CONSTRUCTION

Most hazardous noise problems met in the construction industry require some form of engineering control and therefore are best solved at the planning stage rather than when a problem occurs during the actual work. Typical cases of good early planning are highlighted below.

Case Study 1

During construction of a chemical plant a large sheet-steel-clad partition was to be constructed in an area of intense construction activity. In addition to the team building the partition, several hundred other workers were relatively near by. It was perceived that to use a rivetting system to fix the sheets would cause unacceptable noise exposure to many of the work-force. An alternative – the use of bolts which is a relatively very quiet operation – was considered. For a variety of technical construction reasons, however, the bolting was not acceptable. A solution was found by fixing temporary damping pads to the structure. This method had the effect of reducing the resonance in the structure and reducing the vibration travelling from the punch site through the sheets. With these reduced noise levels, use of ear defenders by the rivetting gang and marking of exclusion zones to limit entry of non-essential workers into the area the job was successfully concluded.

Case Study 2

A common problem in construction is complaints from neighbours during sheet piling operations. There is also, when impact piling using a diesel explosion is used, a local problem of hazardous noise exposure of the operator. Recently a site was being worked in a relatively quiet rural area on the edge of a busy town in Scotland. It was decided to use a hydraulic piling system which allows one pile at a time to be pressed into the ground whilst several partially inserted piles act as anchors. This system proved successful as, because it is relatively quiet in operation, extended hours of work, including Sundays, were allowed by the local authority. There was no requirement for ear defenders to be worn by any of the work-force.

Case Study 3

Several examples of local authorities objecting to noise from conveyors emptying into storage bins and hoppers have been recorded. The processes which create the noise are the height of fall of the material, the mass of the material and the resonant structure of the material of which the hopper is constructed. Our first course of action has always been to recommend the use of an adjustable height conveyor, thereby reducing the free-fall height. Similarly we recommend hoppers with sloping sides and a conveyor discharge at the lip rather than a central position; this again drastically reduces the free-fall height. The lining of the hopper with resilient damping material covered by an abrasion-resistant inner skin can reduce resonance.

Case Study 4

Pneumatic picks are notoriously noisy because of the high frequency compressed air exhaust and the impulse noise as the blade hits the material being worked. Many commercial noise attenuators are available to control the exhaust sounds. These are usually in the form of a jacket built around the drill body to act as an expansion chamber and a noise screen. Nothing can be done to control the impulse noise from the blade. However, if the job is large enough, then increased mechanization in the form of a vehicle-mounted hydraulically operated ram can have the effect of drastically reducing the impulse noise and of removing the operator into a cab which can be partially sound-proofed.

Noise Problems in Ventilation Systems

Problems with noise are best anticipated and dealt with at the early stage of project planning. Probably the best examples of 'planning out' noise nuisance problems are found in cases involving ventilation systems in buildings.

- Fan noise is usually a nuisance not because of the high noise level but because the frequency is at a particularly annoying level. The frequency of the noise is dependent on the number of blades on the fan; the more blades there are, the higher is the frequency produced for a given rotational speed. Careful specification of the number of blades can therefore avoid annoying frequencies.

- Noise travelling in ducts can be attenuated by changing the shape, cross-sectional area or wall material. This has the effect of reflecting part of the sound energy back towards the source. Of course, care must be taken not to use this method of attenuation to extremes if the duct is used to transfer contaminants as they will then deposit at these changes of section. Pure tones, which are particularly annoying, can be effectively attenuated by interference attenuators, i.e a branch line is placed in the duct which loops away from the main duct and rejoins it a little way downstream. This has the effect of putting the sound travelling down the branch out of phase with the frequency of the noise in the main duct. Therefore when it rejoins the main duct the sounds are out of phase and tend to cancel each other out. Many air-conditioning ducts are simply lined with sound absorbent materials such as man-made fibre. The noise here is attenuated by the absorbent material.

IONIZING AND NON-IONIZING RADIATION IN CONSTRUCTION

Peter Bodsworth and Alan Bradley

Institute of Occupational Medicine Ltd.

INTRODUCTION

Radiation can be considered as a continuous electromagnetic field propagating through a medium which, depending upon its energy, can interact with matter in a variety of different ways. Some of the properties of radiation can be explained as though it were wave form; with others the behaviour is more like a particulate emission from a body. Whichever way radiation is viewed, however, the net effect on the human body can often be quite severe if proper precautions are not taken against exposure.

Ionizing radiation is found in the construction industry either as a closed source introduced to carry out a process such as steel radiography or as a natural problem such as seepage of radon gas into basement areas. There are a number of processes in the construction industry that either produce or make use of non-ionizing radiations. For example, ultraviolet (UV) radiation is produced by arc welding in construction and flame-cutting processes in demolition, while lasers are used to obtain level floors in new buildings.

These and other processes or other equipment are associated with a number of hazards to which not only process operators and users of equipment may be exposed but also others working in the vicinity, or even members of the general public. Such hazards are particularly prevalent in the construction industry where many trades work together to produce a finished building which may itself be in a prominent position within a town centre.

IONIZING RADIATION

Radon and Thoron

Radon and thoron are naturally occurring gases which tend to seep from the ground and usually enter buildings through gaps in the floor structure. The immediate decay products of radon, known as daughters, have relatively short half-lives but they can attach themselves to dust particles and be inhaled, thereby irradiating the lung. Radon is best controlled by sealing the subfloor areas, increasing the ventilation of the basement or sub-basement areas or using air-cleaning devices. The subject is discussed in more detail in Chapter C4.

Sealed Sources for Site Radiography

The radioactive sources used in construction for on-site radiography are effectively controlled by the Ionising Radiations Regulations 1985 and the accompanying HSC Approved Code of Practice entitled 'The Protection of Persons against Ionizing Radiation arising from a Work Activity'. Although ionizing radiation is highly hazardous, it is so effectively controlled that the authors have not experienced any incidents which constitute a case study, and there is no need for further mention here.

NON-IONIZING RADIATIONS

Ultraviolet Radiation

UV radiation belongs to that part of the electromagnetic spectrum merging with long-wave X-rays at one end and the shortest wavelength of visible light at the other, i.e. about 10–400 nanometres, although there are no clear dividing lines at each end of the band. As well as being part of the natural radiation emanating from the sun, UV radiation is produced artificially from processes involving hot metals over 3000°C, welding arcs, metal vaporization, thermionic valves and some tungsten lamps, carbon arcs, mercury vapour lamps and lasers.

Visible Light Radiation

That part of the electromagnetic spectrum between about 380 and 750 nanometres produces the physiological response in humans called vision. The majority of processes discussed in this chapter produce visible radiation as well as non ionizing radiation of other types, especially UV and infrared (IR). Visible radiation in the form of lighting, of which there are many types, is often essential for safety and precision when used to accompany other processes involving the use or production of different sources of non-ionizing radiation. Natural daylight cannot always be utilized.

Lasers

The term 'laser' is an acronym for light amplification by stimulated emission of radiation and refers to any device which can produce a narrow beam of monochromatic coherent intense radiation. The wavelength of emission depends on the chemical composition of the material which is excited sufficiently to produce the laser effect. Some lasers such as helium-neon and argon lasers have characteristic wavelengths between 400 and 700 nanometres and the beams are visible; others such as gallium arsenide lasers with wavelengths between 900 and 1300 nanometres produce invisible beams.

Since their initial exploitation in the early 1960s, lasers have found widespread use in many industries, and lasers are to be found in communications, medicine, engineering and scientific instrumentation as well as in the construction industry and other more recognizable areas such as advertising, entertainment and supermarket bar-code readers.

Infrared Radiation

IR radiation occupies that part of the electromagnetic spectrum with a wavelength range from 700 nanometres to 1 millimetre, i.e. from the red end of the visible spectrum to microwave frequencies. IR radiation is given off by all hot surfaces, e.g. molten metals, especially in steel making and welding, and glass making, and is also generated by tungsten lamps and other high intensity lamps and by lasers. It is widely used in the industry for heating processes.

Radio-frequency and microwave radiation

Whilst other non-ionizing radiation types are characterized by wavelength, radio-frequency radiation is more normally referred to by frequency. The region of the electromagnetic spectrum covered is from the far IR (wavelength 1 millimetre and frequency 300 GHz) down to frequencies of the order of 10 kHz, although there is no strict 'end' to the lower frequency band. One band within radio-frequency radiation that deserves special mention is the region from 300 GHz to 300 Mhz which is normally referred to as microwave radiation. Radio-frequency radiation is used in many forms of communication and radar as well as in other industries in the microwave region. Consumer products such as veneered chipboard can make use of a microwave gluing process, and the microwave oven is now a commonplace item in both industrial and domestic situations.

PRINCIPAL EFFECTS OF NON-IONIZING RADIATION

Ultraviolet Radiation

General

A process such as electric arc welding produces considerable amounts of UV radiation. The effects of exposure to this are similar to sunburn (erythenia) and, since there is a measurable time between exposure and development of injury, serious burns may be endured without immediate discomfort. Exposure to UV radiation below about 310 nanometres produces photokeratitis which develops into conjunctivitis. Initial symptoms can occur from 2–24 hours after exposure and may last for several days. This complaint is known among welders as 'arc eye' or 'welder's flash'.

Biological Effects

Since the effects of UV radiation are wavelength dependent, the occurrence of biological effects can be considered within the wavelength bands 315/320–400 nanometres (as UV-A), 280–315 nanometres (as UV-B) and 200–280 nanometres (as UV-C). Wavelengths below 200 nanometres are of little practical significance as they are readily absorbed in air.

As noted above, the critical organs for UV exposure are the eye and the skin. The effects observed and the threshold values vary significantly with wavelength, and various action spectra have been developed to establish dose-response relationships. Erythema is the most commonly observed effect in skin which has been exposed to UV radiation. It is a photochemical response of the skin resulting from overexposure to wavelengths in the UV-C range and does not seem to induce skin changes although UV-A plus UV-B exposure does intensify the erythemal response. Maximum sensitivity of the skin occurs at 295 nanometres. Chronic exposure to sunlight, especially UV-B, accelerates skin ageing and increases the risk of developing skin cancer. However, relatively few studies have examined whether chronic occupational exposure to artificially produced UV-B radiation is capable of enhancing the risk of skin cancer.

Actinic UV radiation (UV-B and UV-C) is strongly absorbed by the cornea and conjunctiva. Overexposure of these tissues causes the keratoconjuctival effect referred to above. Although it develops at any time from 2 to 24 hours after exposure, the usual latent period is from 6 to 12 hours depending on the severity of exposure. There is often an accompanying erythema of facial skin around the eyelids. Acute symptoms last for up to 24 hours and discomfort usually disappears after about 48 hours, but the individual is visually incapacitated during this time. Exposure rarely results in permanent ocular injury.

Thresholds for photokeratitis have been established from 220 to 310 nanometres, with the maximum sensitivity of the eye occurring at 270 nanometres. Cataracts have been produced in animals (rabbits) by UV radiation in the range 295–320 nanometres.

Standards

The development of threshold limit values (TLVs) for occupational exposure to UV radiation has had to take into account the risk of acute and chronic effects to both eye and skin. The TLV recommended by the American Conference of Governmental and Industrial Hygienists (ACGIH) is usually accepted in the United Kingdom as being suitable for occupational exposure control.

For UV-A radiation, irradiance of the unprotected eye or skin should not exceed 1 milliwatt per square centimetre for periods greater than 16 minutes. For the actinic UV region (UV-C), radiant exposure incident on the unprotected eye or skin should not exceed a figure calculated from the 'effective irradiance' which is based on the wavelength of maximum biological effectiveness of 270 nanometres – the wavelength noted above which has the maximum effect in producing photokeratitis. Daily exposure durations range from 0.1 microwatts per square centimetre for 0.1 seconds to 1000 seconds (approximately 16 minutes).

Repeated exposure of the eye to potentially hazardous levels of UV radiation does not increase the protective capability of the cornea in the way that tanning and thickening protects the skin. Thus the threshold limits described are more readily applicable to the eye. Evaluation of skin hazards is more complex because of wide variations in threshold values and exposure history among individuals. The built-in safety factor for eye protection is thought likely to protect all but the most sensitive individuals from skin effects.

However, it should be remembered that occupational exposure to UV-B adds to an individual's non-occupational exposure to solar UV-B. In addition, other hazards also exist in the workplace as a result of UV radiation, i.e. ozone, oxides of nitrogen and, in the vicinity of a degreasing bath, the possibility of phosgene production.

Visible and Infrared Radiation

General

Although photochemical injuries predominate for UV radiation, they appear to be significant only at short wavelengths of visible radiation (blue light). Reflex action on the part of a person exposed to high levels of visible radiation tends to cause evasion. Thermal injury is the dominant effect at longer wavelengths associated with IR radiation. Consequently, but for different reasons than for UV radiation, both skin and eye effects must be taken into account with visible and IR radiation.

Biological Effects

When visible and near-IR radiation impinges on the eye it is focused on and absorbed by the retina. If this happens as a result of high intensity radiance from either an excessively bright light source or an electronic flash lamp, the blood circulation within the retina may not be effective in dissipating the energy. Light from 400 to 500 nanometres can also cause photochemical injury to the retina (blue light hazard). This differs from thermal injury and is caused by exposure to sources too weak to produce retinal thermal burns.

There is much evidence that IR radiation causes damage to the lens of the eye owing to the transparency of the cornea to radiation energies between 700 and 1300 nanometres. The effect is to produce cataracts – known widely as steel puddler's, glass blower's or furnaceman's cataract. The long-term levels of exposure required are believed to be of the order of 100 microwatts per square centimetre. Much higher acute levels (greater than 4 watts per square centimetre) have produced IR cataracts in animal experiments. There is also evidence that cataracts may be produced by a synergistic effect of UV, visible and IR radiation.

The eye does not possess the ability of the skin to detect the heat effect of IR radiation by the nerve endings and, since the heat threshold is below that of the burn threshold, reflex withdrawal can provide a useful warning mechanism. Consequently, thermal flash burns of the skin are rare; irradiance would exceed 1 watts per square centimetre for an acute skin injury.

Standards

The ACGIH have published a notice of intent to establish TLVs for the spectral region 400–1400 nanometres, i.e. for visible and near-IR radiation. The proposed TLVs for visible radiation include spectrally weighted functions to take account of blue light and retinal burn hazard, and a complex relationship has been established. A simpler and probably more practical approach is to limit source illuminance to a maximum of 1 candela per square centimetre. Most light sources such as unfiltered high pressure mercury, argon and xenon arc lamps, carbon arcs, and white fluorescent and incandescent lamps with a luminance below 1 candela per square centimetre will also be below the TLV for retinal burn and blue light hazard.

IR radiation at wavelengths greater than 1400 nanometres does not involve a retinal hazard, and acute injuries from this region can only occur at relatively high irradiances exceeding hundreds of milliwatts per square centimetre. For near-

IR radiation, exposure to the cornea should be limited to 10 milliwatts per square centimetre or below. It is uncommon to encounter IR irradiances of this level at viewing distances of 1–2 metres from welding areas, and so the major concern in this area is normally limited to the eyes of welders and their assistants.

As noted above, long-term exposure to IR radiation at high (uncomfortably warm) irradiance is believed to cause cataracts. A level of 10 milliwatts per square centimetre for broad-band IR radiation from 700 to 3000 nanometres is considered a guidance level for continuous exposure, although brief excursions above this level would not be considered hazardous. Hot process industries such as furnace work and glass blowing would exceed this level at close working quarters, but most exposures to such sources at close distances are brief.

Lasers

General

Exposure to a concentrated beam of radiation induced by the laser technique can cause burns. The target organs of concern are the eye and skin. The eye is once again the most sensitive organ, and damage can range from mild retinal burns to severe central blindness. Lasers can also cause cataracts, which may be large or small depending on the radiation energy and duration of exposure. An additional hazard from lasers is that *reflected* laser light can cause eye damage. This can lead to some difficulties in use without careful pre-planning since reflectance paths are not always preditable.

Biological Effects

The effects of lasers on the eye and skin are strongly dependent on wavelength, which makes the establishment of standards difficult and complex. Lasers operating in the UV-B and UV-C regions or in the IR region greater than 1400 nanometres will have little penetration and their effects are limited to surface burns (albeit to the cornea and conjunctiva). Lasers operating between 400 and 1400 nanometres will penetrate to various depths within the eye or skin depending on the operating wavelength of the laser.

Retinal damage is the most likely result of exposure of the eye, and both visible and near-IR laser sources focus onto the retina. Depending on the diameter of the pupil compared with that of the laser source, there may be considerable enhancement because of the focusing effect from cornea to retina which can be of the order of 2×10^5. For any given exposure in the visible region of the spectrum, retinal irradiance is always significantly higher than that of the cornea or skin. One of the characteristics of a laser beam is its monochromaticity. Therefore a very small image is produced on the retina. Any laser operating in the near IR is of particular concern in this respect, as the eye will not perceive its presence and damage can occur without immediate knowledge.

Standards

The ACGIH have published TLVs for exposure to laser sources at a wide range of wavelengths (UV through to IR) for direct ocular exposure, diffuse reflection of a laser beam and skin.

The United Kingdom has adopted an alternative approach as put forward in British Standard 4803: 1983: Parts 1, 2 and 3. This approach is a practical means of evaluation and control of laser radiation by classification of relative hazard potential and specification of appropriate controls for each class identified. The British Standard requires that lasers are grouped into one of five classes which are based on accessible emission levels (AELs), i.e. the level of radiation to which a person may possibly be exposed. These classes are as follows.

Class 1: lasers which are inherently safe either because they cannot deliver a beam of injuring power or because the design (e.g. total enclosure) is such that the beam is not hazardous to the operator or others. This ideal situation is, of course, to be preferred.

Class 2: low power lasers operating in the visible range 400–700 nanometres up to 1 milliwatt output, which are not inherently safe but afford eye protection by virtue of the natural reflex response of the eye to bright light.

Class 3A: as for Class 2, but operating up to 5mW output. The maximum irradiance, however, must not exceed 25 milliwatts per square metre which restricts the amount of radiation which would enter a pupil of diameter 7 millimetres to 1 milliwatt. Eye protection by reflex response is still afforded, but direct viewing with optical aids may be hazardous.

Class 3B: laser operation in the UV, visible and IR regions (200 nanometres to 1 millimetre). These radiations are safe only when viewed as extended sources at a minimum viewing distance or when viewed by diffuse reflection provided that the output cannot exceed the specified AEL. Direct intra-beam viewing is hazardous and optical aids should not be used.

Class 4: high powered lasers. Both beam and diffuse reflection are dangerous to the eye. Outputs exceed those of Class 3B and may be in any part of the spectrum from 200 nanometres to 1 millimetre.

Manufacturers are required to label the laser product and provide all additional safety and health guidance in accordance with Section 6 of the Health and Safety at Work etc Act 1974. It is considered that only users of Class 3B and Class 4 lasers should have pre-employment and regular medical eye examinations.

Radio-frequency and Microwave Radiation

General

The principal hazard associated with radio-frequency and microwave radiation is that of heat. Microwaves are capable of heating tissues in depth and, whilst the body as a whole has effective temperature regulatory systems through blood circulation, certain tissues such as the lens of the eye have no blood supply and are therefore particularly at risk. A relatively small rise in temperature can result in damage to cell proteins. Many other effects of radio-frequency and microwave radiation have been postulated and studied, such as effects on the central nervous system and ears. Other personality effects have been reported from animal experiments but there has been some difficulty in establishing the validity of some of these effects for humans. Many of the processes and areas of potential exposure remain controversial, e.g. VDU screens (which may also emit low level X-ray, UV, visible and IR radiation) and proximity to power lines and communications centres.

Biological Effects

It is generally considered that some reactions to radio-frequency and microwave radiation, which can be termed biological effects, remain within the range of normal bodily physiological compensation and are not therefore necessarily hazardous.

Most biological data are explained by thermal energy conversion, although non-uniform deep body irradiation of organs with complex temperature responses may act to alter normal functions in both the heated organ and other organs within the system. Symptoms involving changes in mental function and other disturbances of body physiology are difficult to assess. Many studies carried out to investigate these effects have, in fact, been poorly designed, and many of the effects could be explained alternatively, e.g. by personality problems.

Exposure to microwave radiation over 10 milliwatts per square centimetre produces body heating which must be dissipated through bodily thermo-regulatory mechanisms, including blood circulation and sweating. As noted above, these self-regulatory effects are absent in the eye, and microwave radiation can cause sufficient heating to produce irreversible effects such as lens opacity, cataract, corneal damage and retinal lesion.

Non-thermal effects were first postulated in Eastern Europe, and have to some extent been supported more recently in the West by animal experiments. As noted earlier, some difficulties have arisen in extrapolating to humans but, by normalizing on body weight, the concept of specific absorption rate (SAR) can be used to describe the energy absorption of an irradiated body in watts per kilogram. The most sensitive indications of biological effects in exposed animals appears to be within the range 4–8 watts per kilogram of body weight.

Standards

The UK exposure standard designed to protect both eyes and skin from thermal effects is 10 milliwatts per square centimetre. This applies for continuous exposure within the frequency range from 30 Mhz to 300 GHz. For short-term or intermittent exposure, the standard allows an exposure of up to 25 milliwatts per square centimetre within any 60 minute period. These standards are based on limits initially introduced in the United States. As noted earlier, the East European concept of biological effects has differed from that in the West, and the maximum permissible exposure level in the USSR is 10 microwatts per square centimetre.

The newer US (ANSI 95.1) and international exposure standards take account of the SAR of electromagnetic energy by the human body over the frequency range from 300 kHz to 100 GHz. These standards specify field strengths or power densities which vary with frequency but keep the mean absorption rate below 0.4 watts per kilogram i.e. a tenth of the threshold of observed biological response effects.

The above standards are exposure related. An alternative approach is to limit process emission, and the standard for microwave ovens adopted in the United Kingdom specifies an upper limit of 1 milliwatt per square centimetre at 5 centimetres when manufactured, with an allowance for degradation to no more than 5 milliwatts per square centimetre at 5 centimetres in use.

REQUIREMENTS FOR SAFE PRACTICE IN A CONSTRUCTION PROGRAMME

Planning

It is said with good reason that prevention is better than cure, and the planning stage of a construction programme is the ideal starting point for all aspects of health and safety throughout the active phases of a project. If engineering controls, contractual obligations, procedures for fulfilling statutory requirements, and cooperative liaisons with Health and Safety Executive Inspectors and local enforcement authorities are built in at this stage, the project will be relieved of an unnecessary crisis management approach to health and safety at a later time. Lack of exposure to any form of non-ionizing radiation in the early stages of a project does not preclude exposure later on, and the planning team must carefully compile all the potential sources of exposure that may occur during the various phases of the projected contract and take account of the control procedures available for reducing exposure among the contractor's or subcontractors' operatives appointed to develop the project. This will involve knowledge of working methods and procedures (e.g. welding), specialist instrumentation etc.

It is recommended that planning teams write into contracts the level of control that would be expected to protect workmen and others from radiation and other hazards emanating from operations such as flame cutting or welding. Safety policy and technical advice should be sought to ensure that no loopholes exist that could result in unnecessary or unknown exposure of site operatives or members of the general public to the hazards of non-ionizing radiation from welding.

As noted earlier, without detailed technical knowledge, it is not always possible to be aware in advance of all devices that are capable of emitting non-ionizing radiation. Again as part of contractual obligation it should be written in that a contractor or subcontractor requiring to use a device or instrument that emits any type of non-ionizing radiation (including lasers) should submit a full description of the instrument, its use, the type of radiation emitted, the precautions to be followed by the operator, and other controls and procedures to be followed in the case of acute exposure of any operative on site.

Demolition and Land Clearance

The most probable exposure to non-ionizing radiation to occur during demolition and land clearance processes will result from flame cutting of structural and other steelwork. Flame cutting aids the dismantling of the building and further cutting assists in the manageable removal of material in the clearance phase. As in arc welding, UV, visible and IR radiation is produced.

Protection against specific process hazards cannot be considered in isolation. The need to protect against non-ionizing radiation, toxic metal fumes and gases as well as the requirement for site safety needs a coordinated approach. The welder's visor is a familiar sight and in fact protects a welder from far more than exposure of the eyes to UV and intense visible radiation (see below). However, the normal protection worn by operatives carrying out flame cutting is often restricted to eye goggles or glasses and little thought is given to other than minimal skin protection. One of the most effective controls against exposure to hazardous materials is knowledge and understanding of the risks of the material and hazards of the process. The understanding that UV radiation can cause more than just eye damage is necessary to persuade operators to wear proper protective clothing that covers as much of the skin as possible. This task is more difficult in summer than winter. The wearing of respiratory protective equipment to protect against fumes (e.g. lead from painted steel, zinc from galvanized steel) should also be considered, and the correct type of respirator chosen as a result of the assessment of the activities and hazards of the process. An important part of this is compatibility of goggles (for protection against non-ionizing radiation) and respirators, and operators should always be given a choice to ensure both their working comfort and full protection.

Construction

Welding

The most likely source of exposure to non-ionizing radiation in a construction programme is from electric arc welding, which is a skilled trade. Training and refresher courses for welders should cover more than just technical ability. Instruction on hazards and control measures should form an important part of any such course.

One of the difficulties on a construction site is that, with different operations going on all the time, isolation of hazardous processes is not always possible. The importance of coordinated planning cannot be over-emphasized. However, whilst it is easy to state that unprotected workers or those not involved in a welding operation should not be in the direct path of the radiation generated, the reality of a building programme makes other control measures a necessity. It is important, therefore, that welding processes are enclosed as far as possible. Clearly the building of welding booths on a building site is not feasible, but it may be possible to engineer an enclosure system with welding curtains. Semitransparent UV-radiation-absorbing plastics have become available in recent years, and the best colours found for reducing dazzle are orange, yellow and green. It is also found that yellow attenuates hazardous blue light more effectively. This simple measure can be effective in providing adequate protection to passers-by. The use of warning signs to inform others of the activity should also be considered where appropriate.

Inside a temporary enclosure, the welders should be protected by a number of measures. Face visors may be hand held or head-mounted depending on preference. The visor filter plate must have the ability to attenuate UV, visible and IR radiation sufficiently but still allow enough visible radiation to pass to allow the welder to see the task being undertaken. In addition to face protection, welders should also wear dark clothing (to prevent reflection of radiation onto the face) over all parts of the body susceptible to UV and IR radiation. Wool is preferable to cotton as it has greater resistance to UV radiation. Synthetic materials (e.g. nylon) should not be worn. With the increasing understanding of the effects of UV radiation on the skin, many UV filter creams are now available.

The necessity of thorough training of welders was mentioned earlier. Induction courses devoted to health and safety of all trades operations (including courses for new starters) should be instituted by the main contractor for all operatives on a site. Similar induction and training courses are mandatory for contractors in the oil industry.

Other Processes

Other activities on a building site involving emission of non-ionizing radiation may include the use of lasers, radio-frequency and microwave radiation and arc floodlighting.

Use of lasers is confined to specialist applications. It has already been noted that control measures are largely governed by the classification of the laser in use. It is most unlikely that Class 3B or Class 4 lasers would be required on a building site, and with some of the difficulties of site supervision and control already mentioned it would be advisable if only Class 1 lasers were allowed. Justification for more powerful lasers should be provided. Since the development of lasers is relatively recent, engineering controls have been built in to a greater degree than with older traditional operations. Personal protection of the eyes and administrative controls such as warning signs are only required when engineering controls are not adequate.

It is conceivable that radio-frequency and microwave radiation (as well as UV and IR radiation) could be encouraged in specialist heating/curing processes. All these processes, which are normally found in enclosed industrial locations, should have an equivalent engineering control if used on a building site. Measurements should be taken where appropriate to guard against radiation leakage. This should also be carried out periodically on mess room microwave ovens, which are likely to be used (and possibly abused) by a large number of operatives.

The use of floodlighting is possible on construction sites and the choice of high intensity light sources should ensure that actinic UV radiation is adequately filtered.

Maintenance Requirements

The most important part of planning a maintenance programme is that all potential hazards for each of the required tasks are listed. By the very nature of their work, maintenance engineers find themselves in the kinds of location where very few others would normally work. As a result, the potential exposure to hazards can be minimal on some days and very high on others. The requirement for maintenance may take the engineer past the engineering controls of a process designed to protect the user. In the same way that an electrician isolates a switchboard or other machinery before commencing work, so must a similar range of activities be adopted by the maintenance engineer.

The protection of a maintenance engineer is easier to provide in a finished building than during the construction phase. The maintenance requirements of the building should have been drawn up as part of the planning team's overall responsibility, and precautions to be taken, protection required, etc. should form part of the maintenance manual.

Ad hoc repairs to equipment by fitters and electricians during the construction phase are more difficult to anticipate and supervise. Needless to say, good site supervision with the implementation of a system of permits to work in certain areas is of paramount importance. The responsibility of knowing what tasks are being performed, especially when maintenance or repair is required, should not be delegated to the subcontractor alone. The contractor's site supervisors must maintain an effective line of communication before tasks are carried out so that all aspects of health and safety can be taken into account. In the context of this chapter this would be particularly important if work needed to be undertaken in an area where welding was taking place. If there was no alternative but for both operations to proceed, the degree of protection required would depend on how near to the welders the maintenance task was required. Certainly at the very least any person not engaged in welding, but close to the process, should wear UV-absorbing eye protection.

Hazards of Occupancy

The majority of hazards discussed in this chapter are transient and, by the time a contractor hands over a building to the client or occupier, little should remain in terms of risk from construction processes. If the handover is phased there may be some risks from uncompleted work, but this should be taken care of by continued site management. Workers in the completed parts of the building should be protected in the same way as members of the general public, i.e. exposure to hazards from construction processes should be considered unacceptable and reduced to a minimal level.

Maintenance in the finished building has been discussed earlier, but where possible, and especially in an office environment, it should be carried out during evenings or weekends. This will minimize both potential exposure to hazards as a result of the maintenance and disruption of normal tasks being performed in the area.

Non-ionizing radiation hazards that are likely to be encountered in the finished building should normally be covered by the company's own control procedures for health and safety. One area that the design team should have taken into account is the possibility of solar gain in the form of IR radiation from windows. In most modern buildings, the heating and ventilation systems are designed so that windows should not be opened because of upsetting the balance of the system; the efficiency of such systems is of major importance to the thermal comfort of the occupant workers.

Although not part of the construction programme, the building's end user may well introduce further hazards which are difficult to quantify in terms of emitted radiation. The prime example of this is the VDU, which has found widespread application in industry and office work (not to mention personal computers in the domestic environment). These devices can produce a wide range of radiation from low level X-rays and UV through to radio-frequency and microwave emission. The majority of complaints from VDU users can normally be attributed to poor picture definition, bad lighting of the screen and bad ergonomic design of screen position relative to the posture of the operator. Many other effects have been postulated as being caused by exposure to the non-ionizing radiation emitted by VDUs. As well as addressing the conditions under which VDUs are used, regular rest periods prevent the build-up of tension and stress from long periods of concentration. Regular maintenance is essential to minimize radiation leakage from the screen.

A new EC Directive* was issued in May 1990 on minimum safety and health requirements for work with display screen equipment. It requires that 'all radiation with the exception of the visible part of the electromagnetic spectrum shall be reduced to negligible levels from the point of view of the protection of workers' safety and health'.

---

* Council Directive of 29 May 1990 on the minimum safety and health requirements for work with display screen equipment (fifth individual Directive within the meaning of Article 16 (1) of Directive 87/391/EEC) OJ L 156/14–18 21 June 1990.

APPENDIX 4

LIST OF USEFUL ADDRESSES

Aluminium Association
900 19th Street N W
Washington 20006
USA

Asbestos Cement Manufacturers
Association Ltd. *See Fibre Cement
Manufacturers Association Ltd*

Asbestos Information Centre
St Andrew's House
22–28 High Street
Epsom
Surrey KT19 8AH

Asbestos Removal Contractors' Association
1 High Street
Chelmsford
Essex CM1 1BE

ASHRAE, the American Society of
Heating, Refrigeration & Air-
Conditioning Engineers
1791 Tulley Circle NE
Atlanta
Georgia 30329/2305
USA

British Agrochemicals Association
4 Lincoln Court
Lincoln Road
Peterborough
Cambridgeshire PE1 2RP

British Pest Control Association
3 St James Court
Friar Gate
Derby DE1 1ZU

British Plastics Federation
5 Belgrave Square
London SW1X 8PH

British Standards Institution
Head Office
2 Park Street
London W1A 2BS

Building Research Establishment
Garston
Watford
Herts WD2 7JR

Building Services Research &
Information Association
Old Bracknell Lane West
Bracknell
Berkshire RG12 4AH

Chartered Institution of Building
Services Engineers
Delta House
222 Balham High Road
London SW12 9BS

CIRIA, the Construction Industry
Research & Information Association
6 Storey's Gate
Westminster
London SW1P 3AU

Construction Industry Advisory
Committee
1 Long Lane
London SE1 4PG

Department of Energy
1 Palace Street
London SW1E 5HE

Department of the Environment
2 Marsham Street
London SW1P 3EB

Department of Trade & Industry
1 Victoria Street
London SW1H 0ET

Energy & Environment Research Unit
Wimpey 3A
The Open University
Walton Hall
Milton Keynes MK7 6AA

Fibre Cement Manufacturers
Association
PO Box 92
Elmswell
Bury St Edmunds
Suffolk IP30 9HS

Fire Research Station
Melrose Avenue
Borehamwood
Hertfordshire WD6 2BL

Friends of the Earth
26/28 Underwood Street
London N1 7JQ

Health & Safety Executive
Regina House
259-269 Marylebone Road
London NW1 5RR

Health & Safety Commission
Regina House
259-256 Marylebone Road
London NW1 5RR

Heating & Ventilating Contractors
Association
ESCA House
34 Palace Court
London W2 4GJ

Her Majesty's Stationery Office
St Crispins
Duke Street
Norwich
Norfolk NR3 1PD

Her Majesty's Stationery Office
London Bookshop
49 High Holborn
London WC1V 6HB

Home Office
50 Queen Anne's Gate
London SW1

Institute of Aerosol Science
University of Essex
Wivenhoe Park
Colchester
Essex CO4 3SQ

Institute of Occupational Medicine Ltd
8 Roxburgh Place
Edinburgh EH8 9FU

Institute of Environmental Health
Officers
Chadwick House
Rushworth Street
London SE1 0QT

Institute of Refrigeration
Kelvin House
76 Mill Lane
Carshalton
Surrey SM5 2JR

Institute of Wastes Management
3 Albion Place
Derngate
Northampton NN1 1UD

Institution of Water & Environmental
Management
15 John Street
London WC1N 2EB

International Agency for Research on
Cancer
150 Cours Albert Thomas
Lyon 69372
Cedex 08
France

International Labour Organisation
Ch-1211
Geneva 22
Switzerland

Ministry of Agriculture, Fisheries and
Food Pesticide Advisory Service
Nobel House
17 Smith Square
London SW1P 3HX

National Radiological Protection Board
Chilton
Didcot
Oxfordshire OX11 ORQ

Organisation for Economic Cooperation & Development
2 Rue Andre Pascal
F-75775 Paris
France

Paintmakers Association of Great
Britain
Alembic House
93 Albert Embankment
London SE1 7TY

Royal Commission on Environmental
Pollution
Church House
Great Smith Street
London SW1P 3BL

Society of Chemical Industry
14 Belgrave Square
London SW1X 8PS

Swedish Council for Building Research
(BFR)
St Goransgatan 66
11233 Stockholm
Sweden

Warrington Fire Research Consultants
Holmesfield Road
Warrington WA1 2DS

Water Byelaws Advisory Service
660 Ajax Avenue
Slough
Buckinghamshire SL1 4BG

Water Research Centre
PO Box 16
Henley Road
Medmenham
Marlow
Buckinghamshire SL7 2HD

Welsh Office
Gwydr House
Whitehall
London SW1

World Health Organisation
Ch 1211
Geneva 27
Switzerland

World Resources Institute
1735 New York Avenue
Washington DC 2006
USA

INDEX